For Percentages
over 110%
see
The "Express" Profit Reckoner

or

The "Ideal" 1 to 200 Percent
Reckoner

A¹

(*For* 105% *to* 197½%, *see* '*Express*' *Profit Reckoner*.)

THE

'NEW EXPRESS'

PERCENTAGE

AND

DISCOUNT RECKONER

SHOWING

(*a*) *The value of* ⅟₁₆th% *to* 98¾%, 1*d. to* £5000.
(*b*) *The Net value of sums after deducting Discount*.

BY

J. GALL INGLIS, F.R.S.E.

*Compiler of '*The Long-range Reckoner,*' '*The Express Profit Reckoner,*' &c.*

The 'Express Series.' Vol. 2.

London:
GALL & INGLIS, 13 HENRIETTA ST., STRAND, W.C.
AND EDINBURGH

INDEX TO

USEFUL FRACTIONS.

For which there are Tables in this Book.

(See also last page)

Sixths, &c.

Fraction	No.	Percent
	1. =	$16\frac{2}{3}$%
$\frac{1}{3}$...	2.	$33\frac{1}{3}$
	3.	50
$\frac{2}{3}$...	4.	$66\frac{2}{3}$
	5. =	$83\frac{1}{3}$%

Sixteenths, &c.

Fraction	No.	Percent
	1. =	$6\frac{1}{4}$%
$\frac{1}{8}$..	2.	$12\frac{1}{2}$
	3.	$18\frac{3}{4}$
$\frac{1}{4}$...	4.	25
	5.	$31\frac{1}{4}$
$\frac{3}{8}$..	6.	$37\frac{1}{2}$
	7.	$43\frac{3}{4}$
$\frac{1}{2}$...	8. =	50%
	9.	$56\frac{1}{4}$
$\frac{5}{8}$..	10.	$62\frac{1}{2}$
	11.	$68\frac{3}{4}$
$\frac{3}{4}$...	12.	75
	13.	$81\frac{1}{4}$
$\frac{7}{8}$..	14.	$87\frac{1}{2}$
	15. =	$93\frac{3}{4}$%

Twentieths, &c.

Fraction	No.	Percent
	1. =	5%
	2.	10
	3.	15
$\frac{1}{5}$..	4.	20
$\frac{1}{4}$...	5. =	25%
	6.	30
	7.	35
$\frac{2}{5}$..	8.	40
	9.	45
$\frac{1}{2}$...	10. =	50%
	11.	55
$\frac{3}{5}$..	12.	60
	13.	65
	14.	70
$\frac{3}{4}$...	15. =	75%
$\frac{4}{5}$..	16.	80
	17.	85
	18.	90
	19. =	95%

Eightieths $=1\frac{1}{4}$%s.

Fortieths $=2\frac{1}{2}$%s.

One-Twelfth $=8\frac{1}{3}$%, **One-Twentyfourth** $=4\frac{1}{6}$%,

One-Seventh $=14\frac{2}{7}$%.

The complete range of **12ths** is given in the 'Ideal' Percentage Reckoner, which also gives $\frac{1}{4}$%s up to **110%**, and **$2\frac{1}{2}$%s** up to **$197\frac{1}{2}$%**

PREFACE.

Wartime restrictions and need for economy in paper have necessitated the omission of the Profit on Returns Tables that appeared in former editions of this book, but these can be found in the "Express" Profit Reckoner.

The Rates per cent in this present edition of the "Express" Percentage Reckoner are carried by 1% and 1¼% right on to 20%; then by 2½% to 97½%; 91¼%, 93¾%, 96¼%, 98¾%, are also included, and the equivalents of **6ths** (1 to 5), and **16ths** (1 to 15).

The "Off" sub-headings at the foot of the page will be found valuable time-savers for invoicing and costing, as they give at a glance the net cost, *i.e.*, the amount less the required discount.

The Resulting Percentage of two discounts in succession, or of Surcharges and Discount, will be found on pages 4 and 5.

Fractions are given to the nearest farthing, half-farthings (⅛ths) being reckoned farthings. Scrupulous care has been taken to ensure accuracy, and the proofs have been read three times to eradicate typographical errors.

R.G.I.

EDINBURGH, 1942.

ORDER OF CONTENTS.

Index to Useful Fractions: equivalent Percentages... *p. 2*

Discounting Bills. Actual rate per cent paid ... *p. 4*

Two Discounts in succession. Resulting Percentage Off *p. 4*

Surcharges & Discount. Resulting Perc't'ge, On or Off *p. 5*

Discount at 1d. to 5½d. per 1/- ... ... *p. 6*

Percentage, Discount, &c., Tables, 1/16th% to 98¾% *264 pp.*

On and Off Percentage Tables, 1% to 33⅓%, 1d. to 20/-. *16 pp.*

Fractional Percentages, 1/7th, 1/9th, 1/11th, 1/12th, 1/13th, 1/14th, 1/15th, 1/17th, 1/18th, 1/19th ...*last page*

1⅞%, 2⅜%, 2⅞%, 3⅜%, 3⅞%, 4⅜%, 4⅞%, are shown out of sequence, facing the corresponding ⅛ or ⅞.

"7½% off," &c. These sub-headings at the bottom corner of the page show at a glance the net amount after deducting the discount. Thus £93 less 17½% is opposite £93 on the page with "17½% off at the foot—*i.e.*, the page *headed* 82½% = £76 14s. 6d.

"(42½ on Gross Returns, &c.)" These notes at the foot of the pages show the corresponding rate per cent realised on the Selling Price or Gross Returns; *vice versa* for Sect. II. Thus Cost price *plus* 22½% gives 18$\frac{4}{10}$% Profit on the price charged. (Rates not exact marked *.)

DISCOUNT.

Percentages realised, on Cost, Gross Returns, &c. by adding to cost.—

Add	=On Cost ⅌ Cent	⅌ 1/-	⅌ £	⅌ £100	On Gr. Ret.	Add	=On Cost ⅌ Cent	⅌ 1/-	⅌ £	⅌ £100	On Gr. Ret.
Once	100%	1/-	20/-	£100	50%	1-9th	11 1/9%	1 5/16d	2/2 3/4	11 2 3	10%
Half	50	6d	10/-	50 0 0	33 1/3	1-10th	10	1 3/16d	2/-	10 0 0	9 1/11
1-3rd	33 1/3	4d	6/8	33 6 8	25	1-11th	9 1/11	1 1/16d	1/9 3/4	9 1 10	8 1/3
1-4th	25	3d	5/-	25 0 0	20	1-12th	8 1/3	1d	1/8	8 6 8	7 9/13
1-5th	20	2 3/8d	4/-	20 0 0	16 2/3	1-13th	7 9/13	15/16d	1/6 1/2	7 13 10	7 1/7
1-6th	16 2/3	2d	3/4	16 13 4	14 2/7	1-14th	7 1/7	7/8d	1/5 1/4	7 2 10	6 2/3
1-7th	14 2/7	1 11/16d	2/10 1/4	14 5 8 1/2	12 1/2	1-15th	6 2/3	13/16d	1/4	6 13 4	6 1/4
1-8th	12 1/2	1 1/2d	2/6	12 10 0	11 1/9	1-16th	6 1/4	3/4d	1/3	6 5 0	5 15/17

Actual rate per cent. paid in Discounting Bills.—Bankers deduct the discount at once from the sum advanced. The following table shows, to the nearest 1/16%, the *actual* rate per cent. charged, if calculated on same basis as ordinary interest, payable at the end of the period.

Disct.	*Actual*	Disct.	*Actual*	Disct.	*Actual*	Disct.	*Actual*	Disct.	*Actual*
1 1/4%	1 9/32%	2 1/4%	2 5/16%	3 1/4%	3 3/8%	4 1/4%	4 7/16%	5 1/4%	5 9/16%
1 1/2	1 17/32	2 1/2	2 9/16	3 1/2	3 5/8	4 1/2	4 11/16	5 1/2	5 13/16
1 3/4	1 25/32	2 3/4	2 13/16	3 3/4	3 7/8	4 3/4	5	5 3/4	6 1/8
2%	2 1/16%	3%	3 1/16%	4%	4 3/16%	5%	5 1/4%	6%	6 3/8%

Two Discounts deducted in succession.—The total discount thus obtained is not the same as the sum of the two discounts, but is *less*, and the following Table gives the equivalent *single* discount per cent. for any two of the ordinary rates. *Ex.*: An allowance of **40%**, and then of **5%** is not **45%**, but (see **40%** in left-hand column, and **5%** in top line) **43%** only.

1st Dist. ⅌Cnt	⅌1/-	Second Discount:— 1 1/4%	2 1/2%	3 3/4%	5%	6 1/4%	7 1/2%	10%	12 1/2	15%	17 1/2	20%	22 1/2	25%
2 1/2%	...	3 3/4	4 15/16	6 3/16	7 3/8	8 5/8	9 13/16	12 1/4	14 11/16	17 1/8	19 9/16	22	24 7/16	26 7/8
3 3/4	...	4 15/16	6 3/16	7 3/8	8 9/16	9 3/4	11	13 3/8	15 13/16	18 3/16	20 5/8	23	25 7/16	27 13/16
4 1/6	1/2d	5 3/8	6 9/16	7 3/4	8 15/16	10 3/16	11 3/8	13 3/4	16 1/8	18 9/16	20 15/16	23 1/3	25 3/4	28 1/8
5%	...	6 3/16	7 3/8	8 9/16	9 3/4	10 15/16	12 1/8	14 1/2	16 7/8	19 1/4	21 5/8	24	26 3/8	28 3/4
6 1/4	...	7 7/16	8 5/8	9 3/4	10 15/16	12 1/8	13 5/16	15 5/8	18	20 5/16	22 11/16	25	27 3/8	29 11/16
7 1/2	...	8 11/16	9 13/16	11	12 1/8	13 5/16	14 7/16	16 3/4	19 1/16	21 3/8	23 11/16	26	28 5/16	30 5/8
8 1/3	1d	9 1/2	10 5/8	11 3/4	12 15/16	14 1/16	15 3/16	17 1/2	19 13/16	22 1/16	24 3/8	26 2/3	28 15/16	31 1/4
10%	...	11 1/8	12 1/4	13 3/8	14 1/2	15 5/8	16 3/4	19	21 1/4	23 1/2	25 3/4	28	30 1/4	32 1/2
12 1/2	1 1/2d	13 5/8	14 11/16	15 13/16	16 7/8	18	19 1/16	21 1/4	23 7/16	25 5/8	27 13/16	30	32 3/16	34 3/8
15	...	16 1/16	17 1/8	18 3/16	19 1/4	20 5/16	21 3/8	23 1/2	25 5/8	27 3/4	29 7/8	32	34 1/8	36 1/4
16 2/3	2d	17 11/16	18 3/4	19 13/16	20 13/16	21 7/8	22 15/16	25	27 1/16	29 3/16	31 1/4	33 1/3	35 7/16	37 1/2
17 1/2	...	18 9/16	19 9/16	20 5/8	21 5/8	22 11/16	23 11/16	25 3/4	27 13/16	29 7/8	31 15/16	34	36 1/16	38 1/8
20%	...	21	22	23	24	25	26	28	30	32	34	36	38	40
20 5/6	2 1/2d	21 13/16	22 13/16	23 13/16	24 13/16	25 13/16	26 3/4	28 3/4	30 3/4	32 11/16	34 11/16	36 2/3	38 5/8	40 5/8
22 1/2	...	23 1/2	24 7/16	25 7/16	26 3/8	27 3/8	28 5/16	30 1/4	32 3/16	34 1/8	36 1/16	38	39 15/16	41 7/8
25	3d	25 15/16	26 7/8	27 13/16	28 3/4	29 11/16	30 5/8	32 1/2	34 3/8	36 1/4	38 1/8	40	41 7/8	43 3/4
29 1/6	3 1/2d	30 1/16	30 15/16	31 13/16	32 11/16	33 5/8	34 1/2	36 1/4	38	39 13/16	41 9/16	43 1/3	45 1/8	46 7/8
30%	...	30 7/8	31 3/4	32 5/8	33 1/2	34 3/8	35 1/4	37	38 3/4	40 1/2	42 1/4	44	45 3/4	47 1/2
33 1/3	4d	34 3/16	35	35 13/16	36 2/3	37 1/2	38 1/3	40	41 2/3	43 1/3	45	46 2/3	48 1/3	50
35	...	35 13/16	36 5/8	37 7/16	38 1/4	39 1/16	39 7/8	41 1/2	43 1/8	44 3/4	46 3/8	48	49 5/8	51 1/4
37 1/2	4 1/2d	38 5/16	39 1/16	39 7/8	40 5/8	41 7/16	42 3/16	43 3/4	45 5/16	46 7/8	48 7/16	50	51 9/16	53 1/8
40%	...	40 3/4	41 1/2	42 1/4	43	43 3/4	44 1/2	46	47 1/2	49	50 1/2	52	53 1/2	55
41 2/3	5d	42 3/8	43 1/8	43 7/8	44 9/16	45 5/16	46 1/16	47 1/2	48 15/16	50 7/16	50 7/8	53 1/3	54 13/16	56 1/4
45	...	45 11/16	46 3/8	47 1/16	47 3/4	48 7/16	49 1/8	50 1/2	51 7/8	53 1/4	54 5/8	56	57 3/8	58 3/4
45 5/6	5 1/2d	46 1/2	47 3/16	47 7/8	48 9/16	49 1/4	49 7/8	51 1/4	52 5/8	53 15/16	55 5/16	56 2/3	58	59 3/8
50%	6d	50 5/8	51 1/4	51 7/8	52 1/2	53 1/8	53 3/4	55	56 1/4	57 1/2	58 3/4	60	61 1/4	62 1/2

SURCHARGES, WITH DISCOUNT.

Resulting Net Percentage (Off or On), for invoices with discount and surcharge. Same result for the surcharge added first, and discount then deducted, or the discount first deducted and the surcharge added.

− **figures (above the line)** show resulting perc'tage **Off** List price.
\+ ,, **(below ,,)** ,, ,, ,, **Above** ,, ,,
= **sign** shows the surchge equals the disct.; + or −, it is greater or less.

Surcharges above 120%. For *each* **5%** extra, add to 120% value the percentage at foot of disct. column, as **5% & 150%** = $109 + 4\frac{3}{4} \times 6$, = **137½%.**

Sur-chge	Discount deducted (2^{7}, 2^{15}, are 16ths % —$2\frac{7}{16}$%, $2\frac{15}{16}$%, &c):— 2½%	3¾%	5%	6¼%	7½%	10	12½	15	17½	20	25	30	33⅓
2½%	-0^{1}	-1^{5}	−2⅝	−3⅞	-5^{3}	−7¾	-10^{5}	−12⅞	-15^{7}	−18	−23⅛	−28¼	−31⅔
5	+2⅜	$+1^{1}$	−0¼	-1^{9}	2⅞	5½	8⅛	10¾	13⅜	16	21¼	26½	30
7½	4^{13}	3^{7}	+2⅛	+0¾	-0^{9}	3¼	5^{15}	8⅝	11^{5}	14	19⅜	24¾	28⅓
10%	**7¼**	**5⅞**	**4½**	**3⅛**	**+1¾**	**−1**	**3¾**	**6½**	**9¼**	**12**	**17½**	**23**	**26⅔**
12½	9^{11}	8¼	6⅞	5^{7}	4^{1}	+1¼	-1^{9}	4⅜	7^{3}	10	15⅝	21¼	25
15	12⅛	10^{11}	9¼	7^{13}	6⅜	3½	+0⅝	2¼	5⅛	8	13¾	19½	23⅓
17½	14^{9}	13^{1}	11⅝	10⅛	8^{11}	5¾	2^{13}	−0⅛	3^{1}	6	11⅞	17¾	21⅔
20	**17**	**15½**	**14**	**12½**	**11**	**8**	**5**	**+2**	**−1**	**4**	**10**	**16**	**20**
22½	19^{7}	17⅞	16⅜	14^{13}	13^{5}	10¼	7^{3}	4⅛	$+1^{1}$	−2	8⅛	14¼	18⅓
25	21⅞	20^{5}	18¾	17^{3}	15⅝	12½	9⅜	6¼	3⅛	=	6¼	12½	16⅔
27½	24^{5}	22^{11}	21⅛	19½	17^{15}	14¾	11^{9}	8⅜	5^{3}	+2	4⅜	10¾	15
30%	**26¾**	**25⅛**	**23½**	**21⅞**	**20¼**	**17**	**13¾**	**10½**	**7¼**	**4**	**2½**	**9**	**13⅓**
32½	29^{3}	27½	25⅞	24^{3}	22^{9}	19¼	15^{15}	12⅝	9^{5}	6	−0⅝	7¼	11⅔
33⅓	30	28⅓	26⅔	25	23⅓	20	16⅔	13⅓	10	6⅔	=	6⅔	11⅑
35	31⅝	29^{15}	28¼	26^{9}	24⅞	21½	18⅛	14¾	11⅜	8	+1¼	5½	10
37½	34^{1}	32^{5}	30⅝	28⅞	27^{3}	23¾	20^{5}	16⅞	13^{7}	10	3⅛	3¾	8⅓
40	**36½**	**34¾**	**33**	**31¼**	**29½**	**26**	**22½**	**19**	**15½**	**12**	**5**	**2**	**6⅔**
42½	38^{15}	37⅛	35⅜	33^{9}	31^{13}	28¼	24^{11}	21⅛	17^{9}	14	6⅞	−0¼	5
45	41⅜	39^{9}	37¾	35^{15}	34⅛	30½	26⅞	23¼	19⅝	16	8¾	+1½	3⅓
47½	43^{13}	41^{15}	40⅛	38¼	36^{7}	32¾	29^{1}	25⅜	21^{11}	18	10⅝	3¼	−1⅔
50%	**46¼**	**44⅜**	**42½**	**40⅝**	**38¾**	**35**	**31¼**	**27½**	**23¾**	**20**	**12½**	**5**	**=**
52½	48^{11}	46¾	44⅞	42^{15}	41^{1}	37¼	33^{7}	29⅝	25^{13}	22	14⅜	6¾	+1⅔
55	51⅛	49^{3}	47¼	45^{5}	43⅜	39½	35⅝	31¾	27⅞	24	16¼	8½	3⅓
57½	53^{9}	51^{9}	49⅝	47⅝	45^{11}	41¾	37^{13}	33⅞	29^{15}	26	18⅛	10¼	5
60	**56**	**54**	**52**	**50**	**48**	**44**	**40**	**36**	**32**	**28**	**20**	**12**	**6⅔**
62½	58^{7}	56⅜	54⅜	52^{5}	50^{5}	46¼	42^{3}	38⅛	34^{1}	30	21⅞	13¾	8⅓
65	60⅞	58^{13}	56¾	54^{11}	52⅝	48½	44⅜	40¼	36⅛	32	23¾	15½	10
67½	63^{5}	61^{3}	59⅛	57	54^{15}	50¾	46^{9}	42⅜	38^{3}	34	25⅝	17¼	11⅔
70%	**65¾**	**63⅝**	**61½**	**59⅜**	**57¼**	**53**	**48¾**	**44½**	**40¼**	**36**	**27½**	**19**	**13⅓**
72½	68^{3}	66	63⅞	61^{11}	59^{9}	55¼	50^{15}	46⅝	42^{5}	38	29⅜	20¾	15
75	70⅝	68^{7}	66¼	64^{1}	61⅞	57½	53⅛	48¾	44⅜	40	31¼	22½	16⅔
77½	73^{1}	70^{13}	68⅝	66⅜	64^{3}	59¾	55^{5}	50⅞	46^{7}	42	33⅛	24¼	18⅓
80	**75½**	**73¼**	**71**	**68¾**	**66½**	**62**	**57½**	**53**	**48½**	**44**	**35**	**26**	**20**
82½	77^{15}	75⅝	73⅜	71^{1}	68^{13}	64¼	59^{11}	55⅛	50^{9}	46	36⅞	27¾	21⅔
85	80⅜	78^{1}	75¾	73^{7}	71⅛	66½	61⅞	57¼	52⅝	48	38¾	29½	23⅓
87½	82^{13}	80^{7}	78⅛	75¾	73^{7}	68¾	64^{1}	59⅜	54^{11}	50	40⅝	31¼	25
90%	**85¼**	**82⅞**	**80½**	**78⅛**	**75¾**	**71**	**66¼**	**61½**	**56¾**	**52**	**42½**	**33**	**26⅔**
92½	87^{11}	85¼	82⅞	80^{7}	78^{1}	73¼	68^{7}	63⅝	58^{13}	54	44⅜	34¾	28⅓
95	90⅛.	87^{11}	85¼	82^{13}	80⅜	75½	70⅝	65¾	60⅞	56	46¼	36½	30
97½	92^{9}	90^{1}	87⅝	85⅛	82^{11}	77¾	72^{13}	67⅞	62^{15}	58	48⅛	38¼	31⅔
100	**95**	**92½**	**90**	**87½**	**85**	**80**	**75**	**70**	**65**	**60**	**50**	**40**	**33⅓**
105	99⅞	97^{5}	94¾	92^{3}	89⅝	84½	79⅜	74¼	69⅛	64	53¾	43½	36⅔
110	104¾	102⅛	99½	96⅞	94¼	89	83¾	78½	73¼	68	57½	47	40
120	**114½**	**111¾**	**109**	**106¼**	**103½**	**98**	**92½**	**87**	**81½**	**76**	**65**	**54**	**46⅔**
℞ 5%	4⅞%	$4\frac{13}{16}$	4¾	$4\frac{11}{16}$	4⅝	4½	4⅜	4¼	4⅛	4%	3¾	3½	3⅓

Discount at 1d., 2d., &c., per 1/-.

The following table gives the net result after discount at the rate of 1d., 1½d., 2d., &c., per 1/-, has been deducted off the price (Pr.). The equivalent rates per cent. are shown at the foot of the page.

Per 1/-, Pr.	1d Off	1½d Off	2d Off	2½d Off	3d Off	3½d Off	4d Off	4½d Off	5d Off	5½d Off
1d	0s 1d	0s 0¾	0s 0¾	0s 0¾	0s 0¾	0s 0¾	0s 0¾	0s 0½	0s 0½	0s 0½
2d	0 1¾	0 1¾	0 1¾	0 1½	0 1½	0 1½	0 1¼	0 1¼	0 1¼	0 1
3d	0 2¾	0 2½	0 2½	0 2¼	0 2¼	0 2	0 2	0 1¾	0 1¾	0 1½
4d	0 3¾	0 3½	0 3¼	0 3¼	0 3	0 2¾	0 2¾	0 2½	0 2¼	0 2¼
5d	0 4½	0 4¼	0 4¼	0 4	0 3¾	0 3½	0 3¼	0 3	0 3	0 2¾
6d	0 5½	0 5¼	0 5	0 4¾	0 4½	0 4¼	0 4	0 3¾	0 3½	0 3¼
7d	0 6½	0 6	0 5¾	0 5½	0 5¼	0 5	0 4¾	0 4½	0 4	0 3¾
8d	0 7¼	0 7	0 6¾	0 6¼	0 6	0 5¾	0 5¼	0 5	0 4¾	0 4¼
9d	0 8¼	0 7¾	0 7½	0 7	0 6¾	0 6¼	0 6	0 5½	0 5¼	0 4¾
10d	0 9¼	0 8¾	0 8¼	0 8	0 7½	0 7	0 6¾	0 6¼	0 5¾	0 5½
11d	0 10	0 9½	0 9¼	0 8¾	0 8¼	0 7¾	0 7¼	0 6¾	0 6½	0 6
1/-	**0s 11d**	**0s 10½**	**0s 10d**	**0s 9½**	**0s 9d**	**0s 8½**	**0s 8d**	**0s 7½**	**0s 7d**	**0s 6½**
1	1s 0d	0s 11¼	0s 10¾	0s 10¼	0s 9¾	0s 9¼	0s 8¾	0s 8d	0s 7½	0s 7d
2	1 0¾	1 0¼	0 11¾	0 11	0 10½	0 10	0 9¼	0 8¾	0 8¼	0 7½
3	1 1¾	1 1	1 0½	0 11¾	0 11¼	0 10½	0 10	0 9½	0 8¾	0 8
4	1 2¾	1 2	1 1¼	1 0¾	1 0	0 11¼	0 10¾	0 10	0 9¼	0 8¾
5	1 3½	1 2¾	1 2¼	1 1½	1 0¾	1 0	0 11¼	0 10½	0 10	0 9¼
6	1 4½	1 3¾	1 3	1 2¼	1 1½	1 0¾	1 0	0 11¼	0 10½	0 9¾
7	1 5½	1 4½	1 3¾	1 3	1 2¼	1 1½	1 0¾	0 11¾	0 11	0 10¼
8	1 6¼	1 5½	1 4¾	1 3¾	1 3	1 2¼	1 1¼	1 0½	0 11¾	0 10¾
9	1 7¼	1 6¼	1 5½	1 4½	1 3¾	1 2¾	1 2	1 1	1 0¼	0 11¼
10	1 8¼	1 7¼	1 6¼	1 5½	1 4½	1 3½	1 2¾	1 1¾	1 0¾	1 0
11	1 9	1 8	1 7¼	1 6¼	1 5¼	1 4¼	1 3¼	1 2½	1 1½	1 0½
2/-	**1s 10d**	**1s 9d**	**1s 8d**	**1s 7d**	**1s 6d**	**1s 5d**	**1s 4d**	**1s 3d**	**1s 2d**	**1s 1d**
1	1s 11d	1s 9¾	1s 8¾	1s 7¾	1s 6¾	1s 5¾	1s 4¾	1s 3½	1s 2½	1s 1½
2	1 11¾	1 10¾	1 9¾	1 8½	1 7½	1 6½	1 5¼	1 4¼	1 3¼	1 2
3	2 0¾	1 11½	1 10½	1 9¼	1 8¼	1 7	1 6	1 4¾	1 3¾	1 2½
4	2 1¾	2 0½	1 11¼	1 10¼	1 9	1 7¾	1 6¾	1 5½	1 4¼	1 3¼
5	2 2½	2 1¼	2 0¼	1 11	1 9¾	1 8½	1 7¼	1 6	1 5	1 3¾
6	2 3½	2 2¼	2 1	1 11¾	1 10½	1 9¼	1 8	1 6¾	1 5½	1 4¼
7	2 4½	2 3	2 1¾	2 0½	1 11¼	1 10	1 8¾	1 7½	1 6	1 4¾
8	2 5¼	2 4	2 2¾	2 1¼	2 0	1 10¾	1 9¼	1 8	1 6¾	1 5¼
9	2 6¼	2 4¾	2 3½	2 2	2 0¾	1 11¼	1 10	1 8½	1 7¼	1 5¾
10	2 7¼	2 5¾	2 4¼	2 3	2 1½	2 0	1 10¾	1 9¼	1 7¾	1 6½
11	2 8	2 6½	2 5¼	2 3¾	2 2¼	2 0¾	1 11¼	1 9¾	1 8½	1 7
3/-	**2s 9d**	**2s 7½**	**2s 6d**	**2s 4½**	**2s 3d**	**2s 1½**	**2s 0d**	**1s 10½**	**1s 9d**	**1s 7½**
1	2s 10d	2s 8¼	2s 6¾	2s 5¼	2s 3¾	2s 2¼	2s 0¾	1s 11d	1s 9½	1s 8d
2	2 10¾	2 9¼	2 7¾	2 6	2 4½	2 3	2 1¼	1 11¾	1 10¼	1 8½
3	2 11¾	2 10	2 8½	2 6¾	2 5¼	2 3½	2 2	2 0½	1 10¾	1 9
4	3 0¾	2 11	2 9¼	2 7¾	2 6	2 4¼	2 2¾	2 1	1 11¼	1 9¾
5	3 1½	2 11¾	2 10¼	2 8½	2 6¾	2 5	2 3¼	2 1½	2 0	1 10¼
6	3 2½	3 0¾	2 11	2 9¼	2 7½	2 5¾	2 4	2 2¼	2 0½	1 10¾
7	3 3½	3 1½	2 11¾	2 10	2 8¼	2 6½	2 4¾	2 2¾	2 1	1 11¼
8	3 4¼	3 2½	3 0¾	2 10¾	2 9	2 7¼	2 5¼	2 3½	2 1¾	1 11¾
9	3 5¼	3 3¼	3 1½	2 11½	2 9¾	2 7¾	2 6	2 4	2 2¼	2 0¼
10	3 6¼	3 4¼	3 2¼	3 0½	2 10½	2 8½	2 6¾	2 4¾	2 2¾	2 1
11	3 7	3 5	3 3¼	3 1¼	2 11¼	2 9¼	2 7¼	2 5½	2 3½	2 1½
4/-	**3s 8d**	**3s 6d**	**3s 4d**	**3s 2d**	**3s 0d**	**2s 10d**	**2s 8d**	**2s 6d**	**2s 4d**	**2s 2d**
3	3 10¾	3 8½	3 6½	3 4¼	3 2¼	3 0	2 10	2 7¾	2 5¾	2 3½
4/6	4s 1½	3s 11¼	3s 9d	3s 6¾	3s 4½	3s 2¼	3s 0d	2s 9¾	2s 7½	2s 5¼
off Cost,	8⅓%	12½%	16⅔%	20⅚%	25%	29⅙%	33⅓%	37½%	41⅔%	45⅚%

CONTENTS

'EXPRESS' PERCENT RECKONER

(145 Rates Percent)

℔ Cent	℔ Cent	℔ Cent	℔ Cent
...	4⅛	15	43⅓
...	4⅙ (1/24)	16	43¾ (7/16)
1/16	¼	16¼	45
1/10	⅜	16½	47
⅛	4½	16⅔ (⅙)	47½
¼	⅝	17	50 (½)
⅜	¾	17½	52½
½	⅞	18	55
⅝	5 (1/20)	18½	56¼ (9/16)
¾	5¼	18¾ (3/16)	57½
⅞	5½	19	60
1	5¾	19½	62½ (⅝)
⅛	6	20	65
¼	6¼ (1/16)	21	66⅔ (⅔)
⅜	6½	22	67½
1½	7	22½	68¾ (11/16)
⅝	7½	23	70
¾	8	24	72½
⅞	8⅓ (1/12)	25 (¼)	75 (¾)
2 (1/50)	8½	26	77½
⅛	8¾	27	80
¼	9	27½	81¼ (13/16)
⅜	9½	28	82½
2½ (1/40)	10	29	83⅓
⅝	10½	30	85
¾	11	31¼ (5/16)	87½ (⅞)
⅞	11¼	32	90
3	11½	32½	91¼
⅛ (1/32)	12	33	92½
¼	12½ (⅛)	33⅓ (⅓)	93¾ (15/16)
⅜	13	34	95
3½	13½	35	96¼
⅝	13¾	36⅔	97½
¾	14	37½ (⅜)	98¾
⅞	14²⁄₇ (⅐)	40	
4	14½	42½	

[above 100% use "Express" Profit Reckoner with 101% to 197½%]

On & Off Percentage Rates

1% to 33⅓%

1d. to 20/-

FOR CLOSER INTERVALS.

The "Ideal" Percent & Per Hundred Reckoner,
Gives every 1¼% to 98¾%, and 6d% to 42/-%.

The "Long-range" Per Cent Reckoner gives:—
Quarter per Cents to 10%; Half per Cents to 99½%;
every £1 to £100, in £ s. d., also in decimals of £1.

1/16th Per Cent.

£1	0s.	0¼	£51	£0	0s.	7¾
2	0	0¼	52	0	0	7¾
3	0	0½	53	0	0	8
4	0	0½	54	0	0	8
5	0	0¾	55	0	0	8¼
6	0	1	56	0	0	8½
7	0	1	57	0	0	8½
8	0	1¼	58	0	0	8¾
9	0	1¼	59	0	0	8¾
10	0s.	1½	**60**	£0	0s.	9
11	0s.	1¾	61	£0	0s.	9¼
12	0	1¾	62	0	0	9¼
13	0	2	63	0	0	9½
14	0	2	64	0	0	9½
15	0	2¼	65	0	0	9¾
16	0	2½	66	0	0	10
17	0	2½	67	0	0	10
18	0	2¾	68	0	0	10¼
19	0	2¾	69	0	0	10¼
20	0s.	3	**70**	£0	0s.	10½
21	0s.	3¼	71	£0	0s.	10¾
22	0	3¼	72	0	0	10¾
23	0	3½	73	0	0	11
24	0	3½	74	0	0	11
25	0	3¾	75	0	0	11¼
26	0	4	76	0	0	11½
27	0	4	77	0	0	11½
28	0	4¼	78	0	0	11¾
29	0	4¼	79	0	0	11¾
30	0s.	4½	**80**	£0	1s.	0
31	0s.	4¾	81	£0	1s.	0¼
32	0	4¾	82	0	1	0¼
33	0	5	83	0	1	0½
34	0	5	84	0	1	0½
35	0	5¼	85	0	1	0¾
36	0	5½	86	0	1	1
37	0	5½	87	0	1	1
38	0	5¾	88	0	1	1¼
39	0	5¾	89	0	1	1¼
40	0s.	6	**90**	£0	1s.	1½
41	0s.	6¼	91	£0	1s.	1¾
42	0	6¼	92	0	1	1¾
43	0	6½	93	0	1	2
44	0	6½	94	0	1	2
45	0	6¾	95	0	1	2¼
46	0	7	96	0	1	2½
47	0	7	97	0	1	2½
48	0	7¼	98	0	1	2¾
49	0	7¼	99	0	1	2¾
50	0s.	7½	**100**	£0	1s.	3

200	£0	2s.	6d	700	£0	8s.	9d
300	0	3	9	750	0	9	4½
400	0	5	0	800	0	10	0
500	0	6	3	900	0	11	3
600	£0	7s.	6d	1000	£0	12s.	6d

1/10th Per Cent.

£1	0s.	0¼	£51	£0	1s.	0¼
2	0	0½	52	0	1	0½
3	0	0¾	53	0	1	0¾
4	0	1	54	0	1	1
5	0	1¼	55	0	1	1¼
6	0	1½	56	0	1	1½
7	0	1¾	57	0	1	1¾
8	0	2	58	0	1	2
9	0	2¼	59	0	1	2¼
10	0s.	2½	**60**	£0	1s.	2½
11	0s.	2¾	61	£0	1s.	2¾
12	0	3	62	0	1	3
13	0	3	63	0	1	3
14	0	3¼	64	0	1	3¼
15	0	3½	65	0	1	3½
16	0	3¾	66	0	1	3¾
17	0	4	67	0	1	4
18	0	4¼	68	0	1	4¼
19	0	4½	69	0	1	4½
20	0s.	4¾	**70**	£0	1s.	4¾
21	0s.	5	71	£0	1s.	5
22	0	5¼	72	0	1	5¼
23	0	5½	73	0	1	5½
24	0	5¾	74	0	1	5¾
25	0	6	75	0	1	6
26	0	6¼	76	0	1	6¼
27	0	6½	77	0	1	6½
28	0	6¾	78	0	1	6¾
29	0	7	79	0	1	7
30	0s.	7¼	**80**	£0	1s.	7¼
31	0s.	7½	81	£0	1s.	7½
32	0	7¾	82	0	1	7¾
33	0	8	83	0	1	8
34	0	8¼	84	0	1	8¼
35	0	8½	85	0	1	8½
36	0	8¾	86	0	1	8¾
37	0	9	87	0	1	9
38	0	9	88	0	1	9
39	0	9¼	89	0	1	9¼
40	0s.	9½	**90**	£0	1s.	9½
41	0s.	9¾	91	£0	1s.	9¾
42	0	10	92	0	1	10
43	0	10¼	93	0	1	10¼
44	0	10½	94	0	1	10½
45	0	10¾	95	0	1	10¾
46	0	11	96	0	1	11
47	0	11¼	97	0	1	11¼
48	0	11½	98	0	1	11½
49	0	11¾	99	0	1	11¾
50	1s.	0	**100**	£0	2s.	0

200	0	4s.	0d	700	0	14s.	0d
300	0	6	0	750	0	15	0
400	0	8	0	800	0	16	0
500	0	10	0	900	0	18	0
600	0	12s.	0d	1000	£1	0s.	0d

⅛% ⅛%

One-Eighth Per Cent.

£1	0s.	0¼	£51	£0	1s.	3¼	£101	£0	2s.	6¼	£151	£0	3s.	9¼
2	0	0½	52	0	1	3½	102	0	2	6½	152	0	3	9½
3	0	1	53	0	1	4	103	0	2	7	153	0	3	10
4	0	1¼	54	0	1	4¼	104	0	2	7¼	154	0	3	10¼
5	0	1½	55	0	1	4½	105	0	2	7½	155	0	3	10½
6	0	1¾	56	0	1	4¾	106	0	2	7¾	156	0	3	10¾
7	0	2	57	0	1	5	107	0	2	8	157	0	3	11
8	0	2½	58	0	1	5½	108	0	2	8½	158	0	3	11½
9	0	2¾	59	0	1	5¾	109	0	2	8¾	159	0	3	11¾
10	0s.	3	**60**	£0	1s.	6	**110**	£0	2s.	9	**160**	£0	4s.	0
11	0s.	3¼	61	£0	1s.	6¼	111	£0	2s.	9¼	161	£0	4s.	0¼
12	0	3½	62	0	1	6½	112	0	2	9½	162	0	4	0½
13	0	4	63	0	1	7	113	0	2	10	163	0	4	1
14	0	4¼	64	0	1	7¼	114	0	2	10¼	164	0	4	1¼
15	0	4½	65	0	1	7½	115	0	2	10½	165	0	4	1½
16	0	4¾	66	0	1	7¾	116	0	2	10¾	166	0	4	1¾
17	0	5	67	0	1	8	117	0	2	11	167	0	4	2
18	0	5½	68	0	1	8½	118	0	2	11½	168	0	4	2½
19	0	5¾	69	0	1	8¾	119	0	2	11¾	169	0	4	2¾
20	0s.	6	**70**	£0	1s.	9	**120**	£0	3s.	0	**170**	£0	4s.	3
21	0s.	6¼	71	£0	1s.	9¼	121	£0	3s.	0¼	171	£0	4s.	3¼
22	0	6½	72	0	1	9½	122	0	3	0½	172	0	4	3½
23	0	7	73	0	1	10	123	0	3	1	173	0	4	4
24	0	7¼	74	0	1	10¼	124	0	3	1¼	174	0	4	4¼
25	0	7½	75	0	1	10½	125	0	3	1½	175	0	4	4½
26	0	7¾	76	0	1	10¾	126	0	3	1¾	176	0	4	4¾
27	0	8	77	0	1	11	127	0	3	2	177	0	4	5
28	0	8½	78	0	1	11½	128	0	3	2½	178	0	4	5½
29	0	8¾	79	0	1	11¾	129	0	3	2¾	179	0	4	5¾
30	0s.	9	**80**	£0	2s.	0	**130**	£0	3s.	3	**180**	£0	4s.	6
31	0s.	9¼	81	£0	2s.	0¼	131	£0	3s.	3¼	181	£0	4s.	6¼
32	0	9½	82	0	2	0½	132	0	3	3½	182	0	4	6½
33	0	10	83	0	2	1	133	0	3	4	183	0	4	7
34	0	10¼	84	0	2	1¼	134	0	3	4¼	184	0	4	7¼
35	0	10½	85	0	2	1½	135	0	3	4½	185	0	4	7½
36	0	10¾	86	0	2	1¾	136	0	3	4¾	186	0	4	7¾
37	0	11	87	0	2	2	137	0	3	5	187	0	4	8
38	0	11½	88	0	2	2½	138	0	3	5½	188	0	4	8½
39	0	11¾	89	0	2	2¾	139	0	3	5¾	189	0	4	8¾
40	1s.	0	**90**	£0	2s.	3	**140**	£0	3s.	6	**190**	£0	4s.	9
41	1s.	0¼	91	£0	2s.	3¼	141	£0	3s.	6¼	191	£0	4s.	9¼
42	1	0½	92	0	2	3½	142	0	3	6½	192	0	4	9½
43	1	1	93	0	2	4	143	0	3	7	193	0	4	10
44	1	1¼	94	0	2	4¼	144	0	3	7¼	194	0	4	10¼
45	1	1½	95	0	2	4½	145	0	3	7½	195	0	4	10½
46	1	1¾	96	0	2	4¾	146	0	3	7¾	196	0	4	10¾
47	1	2	97	0	2	5	147	0	3	8	197	0	4	11
48	1	2½	98	0	2	5½	148	0	3	8½	198	0	4	11½
49	1	2¾	99	0	2	5¾	149	0	3	8¾	199	0	4	11¾
50	1s.	3	**100**	£0	2s.	6	**150**	£0	3s.	9	**200**	£0	5s.	0

250	0	6s.	3d	700	£0	17s.	6d	1200	£1	10s.	0d	2000	£2	10s.	0
300	0	7	6	750	0	18	9	1400	1	15	0	2500	3	2	6
400	0	10	0	800	1	0	0	1500	1	17	6	3000	3	15	0
500	0	12	6	900	1	2	6	1600	2	0	0	4000	5	0	0
600	0	15s.	0d	1000	£1	5s.	0d	1800	£2	5s.	0d	5000	£6	5s.	0

99⅞% off.

¼% ONE-QUARTER PER CENT. ¼%

£1	0s. 0½	£51	£0 2s. 6½	£101	£0 5s. 0½	£151	£0 7s. 6½
2	0 1¼	52	0 2 7¼	102	0 5 1¼	152	0 7 7¼
3	0 1¾	53	0 2 7¾	103	0 5 1¾	153	0 7 7¾
4	0 2½	54	0 2 8½	104	0 5 2½	154	0 7 8½
5	0 3	55	0 2 9	105	0 5 3	155	0 7 9
6	0 3½	56	0 2 9½	106	0 5 3½	156	0 7 9½
7	0 4¼	57	0 2 10¼	107	0 5 4¼	157	0 7 10¼
8	0 4¾	58	0 2 10¾	108	0 5 4¾	158	0 7 10¾
9	0 5½	59	0 2 11½	109	0 5 5½	159	0 7 11½
10	0s. 6	**60**	£0 3s. 0	**110**	£0 5s. 6	**160**	£0 8s. 0
11	0s. 6½	61	£0 3s. 0½	111	£0 5s 6½	161	£0 8s. 0½
12	0 7¼	62	0 3 1¼	112	0 5 7¼	162	0 8 1¼
13	0 7¾	63	0 3 1¾	113	0 5 7¾	163	0 8 1¾
14	0 8½	64	0 3 2½	114	0 5 8½	164	0 8 2½
15	0 9	65	0 3 3	115	0 5 9	165	0 8 3
16	0 9½	66	0 3 3½	116	0 5 9½	166	0 8 3½
17	0 10¼	67	0 3 4¼	117	0 5 10¼	167	0 8 4¼
18	0 10¾	68	0 3 4¾	118	0 5 10¾	168	0 8 4¾
19	0 11½	69	0 3 5½	119	0 5 11½	169	0 8 5½
20	1s. 0	**70**	£0 3s. 6	**120**	£0 6s. 0	**170**	£0 8s. 6
21	1s. 0½	71	£0 3s. 6½	121	£0 6s. 0½	171	£0 8s. 6½
22	1 1¼	72	0 3 7¼	122	0 6 1¼	172	0 8 7¼
23	1 1¾	73	0 3 7¾	123	0 6 1¾	173	0 8 7¾
24	1 2½	74	0 3 8½	124	0 6 2½	174	0 8 8½
25	1 3	75	0 3 9	125	0 6 3	175	0 8 9
26	1 3½	76	0 3 9½	126	0 6 3½	176	0 8 9½
27	1 4¼	77	0 3 10¼	127	0 6 4¼	177	0 8 10¼
28	1 4¾	78	0 3 10¾	128	0 6 4¾	178	0 8 10¾
29	1 5½	79	0 3 11½	129	0 6 5½	179	0 8 11½
30	1s. 6	**80**	£0 4s. 0	**130**	£0 6s. 6	**180**	£0 9s. 0
31	1s. 6½	81	£0 4s. 0½	131	£0 6s. 6½	181	£0 9s. 0½
32	1 7¼	82	0 4 1¼	132	0 6 7¼	182	0 9 1¼
33	1 7¾	83	0 4 1¾	133	0 6 7¾	183	0 9 1¾
34	1 8½	84	0 4 2½	134	0 6 8½	184	0 9 2½
35	1 9	85	0 4 3	135	0 6 9	185	0 9 3
36	1 9½	86	0 4 3½	136	0 6 9½	186	0 9 3½
37	1 10¼	87	0 4 4¼	137	0 6 10¼	187	0 9 4¼
38	1 10¾	88	0 4 4¾	138	0 6 10¾	188	0 9 4¾
39	1 11½	89	0 4 5½	139	0 6 11½	189	0 9 5½
40	2s. 0	**90**	£0 4s. 6	**140**	£0 7s. 0	**190**	£0 9s. 6
41	2s. 0½	91	£0 4s. 6½	141	£0 7s. 0½	191	£0 9s. 6½
42	2 1¼	92	0 4 7¼	142	0 7 1¼	192	0 9 7¼
43	2 1¾	93	0 4 7¾	143	0 7 1¾	193	0 9 7¾
44	2 2½	94	0 4 8½	144	0 7 2½	194	0 9 8½
45	2 3	95	0 4 9	145	0 7 3	195	0 9 9
46	2 3½	96	0 4 9½	146	0 7 3½	196	0 9 9½
47	2 4¼	97	0 4 10¼	147	0 7 4¼	197	0 9 10¼
48	2 4¾	98	0 4 10¾	148	0 7 4¾	198	0 9 10¾
49	2 5½	99	0 4 11½	149	0 7 5½	199	0 9 11½
50	2s. 6	**100**	£0 5s. 0	**150**	£0 7s. 6	**200**	£0 10s. 0
250	0 12s. 6d	700	£1 15s. 0d	1200	£3 0s. 0d	2000	£5 0s. 0
300	0 15 0	750	1 17 6	1400	3 10 0	2500	6 5 0
400	1 0 0	800	2 0 0	1500	3 15 0	3000	7 10 0
500	1 5 0	900	2 5 0	1600	4 0 0	4000	10 0 0
600	1 10s. 0d	1000	£2 10s. 0d	1800	£4 10s. 0d	5000	£12 10s. 0

99¾% off.

£1	0s. 1	£51	£0 3s.10	£101	£0 7s. 7	£151	£0 11s. 4
2	0 1¾	52	0 3 10¾	102	0 7 7¾	152	0 11 4¾
3	0 2¾	53	0 3 11¾	103	0 7 8¾	153	0 11 5¾
4	0 3½	54	0 4 0½	104	0 7 9½	154	0 11 6½
5	0 4½	55	0 4 1½	105	0 7 10½	155	0 11 7½
6	0 5½	56	0 4 2½	106	0 7 11½	156	0 11 8½
7	0 6¼	57	0 4 3¼	107	0 8 0¼	157	0 11 9¼
8	0 7¼	58	0 4 4¼	108	0 8 1¼	158	0 11 10¼
9	0 8	59	0 4 5	109	0 8 2	159	0 11 11
10	0s. 9	**60**	£0 4s. 6	**110**	£0 8s. 3	**160**	£0 12s. 0
11	0s.10	61	£0 4s. 7	111	£0 8s 4	161	£0 12s. 1
12	0 10¾	62	0 4 7¾	112	0 8 4¾	162	0 12 1¾
13	0 11¾	63	0 4 8¾	113	0 8 5¾	163	0 12 2¾
14	1 0½	64	0 4 9½	114	0 8 6½	164	0 12 3½
15	1 1½	65	0 4 10½	115	0 8 7½	165	0 12 4½
16	1 2½	66	0 4 11½	116	0 8 8½	166	0 12 5½
17	1 3¼	67	0 5 0¼	117	0 8 9¼	167	0 12 6¼
18	1 4¼	68	0 5 1¼	118	0 8 10¼	168	0 12 7¼
19	1 5	69	0 5 2	119	0 8 11	169	0 12 8
20	1s. 6	**70**	£0 5s. 3	**120**	£0 9s. 0	**170**	£0 12s. 9
21	1s. 7	71	£0 5s. 4	121	£0 9s. 1	171	£0 12s.10
22	1 7¾	72	0 5 4¾	122	0 9 1¾	172	0 12 10¾
23	1 8¾	73	0 5 5¾	123	0 9 2¾	173	0 12 11¾
24	1 9½	74	0 5 6½	124	0 9 3½	174	0 13 0½
25	1 10½	75	0 5 7½	125	0 9 4½	175	0 13 1½
26	1 11½	76	0 5 8½	126	0 9 5½	176	0 13 2½
27	2 0¼	77	0 5 9¼	127	0 9 6¼	177	0 13 3¼
28	2 1¼	78	0 5 10¼	128	0 9 7¼	178	0 13 4¼
29	2 2	79	0 5 11	129	0 9 8	179	0 13 5
30	2s. 3	**80**	£0 6s. 0	**130**	£0 9s. 9	**180**	£0 13s. 6
31	2s. 4	81	£0 6s. 1	131	£0 9s.10	181	£0 13s. 7
32	2 4¾	82	0 6 1¾	132	0 9 10¾	182	0 13 7¾
33	2 5¾	83	0 6 2¾	133	0 9 11¾	183	0 13 8¾
34	2 6½	84	0 6 3½	134	0 10 0½	184	0 13 9½
35	2 7½	85	0 6 4½	135	0 10 1½	185	0 13 10½
36	2 8½	86	0 6 5½	136	0 10 2½	186	0 13 11½
37	2 9¼	87	0 6 6¼	137	0 10 3¼	187	0 14 0¼
38	2 10¼	88	0 6 7¼	138	0 10 4¼	188	0 14 1¼
39	2 11	89	0 6 8	139	0 10 5	189	0 14 2
40	3s. 0	**90**	£0 6s. 9	**140**	£0 10s. 6	**190**	£0 14s. 3
41	3s. 1	91	£0 6s.10	141	£0 10s. 7	191	£0 14s. 4
42	3 1¾	92	0 6 10¾	142	0 10 7¾	192	0 14 4¾
43	3 2¾	93	0 6 11¾	143	0 10 8¾	193	0 14 5¾
44	3 3½	94	0 7 0½	144	0 10 9½	194	0 14 6½
45	3 4½	95	0 7 1½	145	0 10 10½	195	0 14 7½
46	3 5½	96	0 7 2½	146	0 10 11½	196	0 14 8½
47	3 6¼	97	0 7 3¼	147	0 11 0¼	197	0 14 9¼
48	3 7¼	98	0 7 4¼	148	0 11 1¼	198	0 14 10¼
49	3 8	99	0 7 5	149	0 11 2	199	0 14 11
50	3s. 9	**100**	£0 7s. 6	**150**	£0 11s. 3	**200**	£0 15s. 0

250	0 18s. 9d	700	£2 12s. 6d	1200	£4 10s. 0d	2000	£7 10s. 0
300	1 2 6	750	2 16 3	1400	5 5 0	2500	9 7 6
400	1 10 0	800	3 0 0	1500	5 12 6	3000	11 5 0
500	1 17 6	900	3 7 6	1600	6 0 0	4000	15 0 0
600	2 5s. 0d	1000	£3 15s. 0d	1800	£6 15s. 0d	5000	£18 15s. 0

99⅝% off.

Amt		Amt		Amt		Amt	
£1	0s. 1¼	£51	£0 5s. 1¼	£101	£0 10s. 1¼	£151	£0 15s. 1¼
2	0 2½	52	0 5 2½	102	0 10 2½	152	0 15 2½
3	0 3½	53	0 5 3½	103	0 10 3½	153	0 15 3½
4	0 4¾	54	0 5 4¾	104	0 10 4¾	154	0 15 4¾
5	0 6	55	0 5 6	105	0 10 6	155	0 15 6
6	0 7¼	56	0 5 7¼	106	0 10 7¼	156	0 15 7¼
7	0 8½	57	0 5 8½	107	0 10 8½	157	0 15 8½
8	0 9½	58	0 5 9½	108	0 10 9½	158	0 15 9½
9	0 10¾	59	0 5 10¾	109	0 10 10¾	159	0 15 10¾
10	1s. 0	60	£0 6s. 0	110	£0 11s. 0	160	£0 16s. 0
11	1s. 1¼	61	£0 6s. 1¼	111	£0 11s 1¼	161	£0 16s. 1¼
12	1 2½	62	0 6 2½	112	0 11 2½	162	0 16 2½
13	1 3½	63	0 6 3½	113	0 11 3½	163	0 16 3½
14	1 4¾	64	0 6 4¾	114	0 11 4¾	164	0 16 4¾
15	1 6	65	0 6 6	115	0 11 6	165	0 16 6
16	1 7¼	66	0 6 7¼	116	0 11 7¼	166	0 16 7¼
17	1 8½	67	0 6 8½	117	0 11 8½	167	0 16 8½
18	1 9½	68	0 6 9½	118	0 11 9½	168	0 16 9½
19	1 10¾	69	0 6 10¾	119	0 11 10¾	169	0 16 10¾
20	2s. 0	70	£0 7s. 0	120	£0 12s. 0	170	£0 17s. 0
21	2s. 1¼	71	£0 7s. 1¼	121	£0 12s. 1¼	171	£0 17s. 1¼
22	2 2½	72	0 7 2½	122	0 12 2½	172	0 17 2½
23	2 3½	73	0 7 3½	123	0 12 3½	173	0 17 3½
24	2 4¾	74	0 7 4¾	124	0 12 4¾	174	0 17 4¾
25	2 6	75	0 7 6	125	0 12 6	175	0 17 6
26	2 7¼	76	0 7 7¼	126	0 12 7¼	176	0 17 7¼
27	2 8½	77	0 7 8½	127	0 12 8½	177	0 17 8½
28	2 9½	78	0 7 9½	128	0 12 9½	178	0 17 9½
29	2 10¾	79	0 7 10¾	129	0 12 10¾	179	0 17 10¾
30	3s. 0	80	£0 8s. 0	130	£0 13s. 0	180	£0 18s. 0
31	3s. 1¼	81	£0 8s. 1¼	131	£0 13s. 1¼	181	£0 18s. 1¼
32	3 2½	82	0 8 2½	132	0 13 2½	182	0 18 2½
33	3 3½	83	0 8 3½	133	0 13 3½	183	0 18 3½
34	3 4¾	84	0 8 4¾	134	0 13 4¾	184	0 18 4¾
35	3 6	85	0 8 6	135	0 13 6	185	0 18 6
36	3 7¼	86	0 8 7¼	136	0 13 7¼	186	0 18 7¼
37	3 8½	87	0 8 8½	137	0 13 8½	187	0 18 8½
38	3 9½	88	0 8 9½	138	0 13 9½	188	0 18 9½
39	3 10¾	89	0 8 10¾	139	0 13 10¾	189	0 18 10¾
40	4s. 0	90	£0 9s. 0	140	£0 14s. 0	190	£0 19s. 0
41	4s. 1¼	91	£0 9s. 1¼	141	£0 14s. 1¼	191	£0 19s. 1¼
42	4 2½	92	0 9 2½	142	0 14 2½	192	0 19 2½
43	4 3½	93	0 9 3½	143	0 14 3½	193	0 19 3½
44	4 4¾	94	0 9 4¾	144	0 14 4¾	194	0 19 4¾
45	4 6	95	0 9 6	145	0 14 6	195	0 19 6
46	4 7¼	96	0 9 7¼	146	0 14 7¼	196	0 19 7¼
47	4 8½	97	0 9 8½	147	0 14 8½	197	0 19 8½
48	4 9½	98	0 9 9½	148	0 14 9½	198	0 19 9½
49	4 10¾	99	0 9 10¾	149	0 14 10¾	199	0 19 10¾
50	5s. 0	100	£0 10s. 0	150	£0 15s. 0	200	£1 0s. 0

Amt		Amt		Amt		Amt	
250	1 5s. 0d	700	£3 10s. 0d	1200	£6 0s. 0d	2000	£10 0s. 0
300	1 10 0	750	3 15 0	1400	7 0 0	2500	12 10 0
400	2 0 0	800	4 0 0	1500	7 10 0	3000	15 0 0
500	2 10 0	900	4 10 0	1600	8 0 0	4000	20 0 0
600	3 0s. 0d	1000	£5 0s. 0d	1800	£9 0s. 0d	5000	£25 0s. 0

1⅛% ONE & ONE-EIGHTH PER CENT. 1⅛%

£1	0s. 2¾	£51	£0 11s. 5¾	£101	£1 2s. 8¾	£151	£1 13s.11¾
2	0 5½	52	0 11 8½	102	1 2 11½	152	1 14 2½
3	0 8	53	0 11 11	103	1 3 2	153	1 14 5
4	0 10¾	54	0 12 1¾	104	1 3 4¾	154	1 14 7¾
5	1 1½	55	0 12 4½	105	1 3 7½	155	1 14 10½
6	1 4¼	56	0 12 7¼	106	1 3 10¼	156	1 15 1¼
7	1 7	57	0 12 10	107	1 4 1	157	1 15 4
8	1 9½	58	0 13 0½	108	1 4 3½	158	1 15 6½
9	2 0¼	59	0 13 3¼	109	1 4 6¼	159	1 15 9¼
10	**2s. 3**	**60**	**£0 13s. 6**	**110**	**£1 4s. 9**	**160**	**£1 16s. 0**
11	2s. 5¾	61	£0 13s. 8¾	111	£1 4s.11¾	161	£1 16s. 2¾
12	2 8½	62	0 13 11½	112	1 5 2½	162	1 16 5½
13	2 11	63	0 14 2	113	1 5 5	163	1 16 8
14	3 1¾	64	0 14 4¾	114	1 5 7¾	164	1 16 10¾
15	3 4½	65	0 14 7½	115	1 5 10½	165	1 17 1½
16	3 7¼	66	0 14 10¼	116	1 6 1¼	166	1 17 4¼
17	3 10	67	0 15 1	117	1 6 4	167	1 17 7
18	4 0½	68	0 15 3½	118	1 6 6½	168	1 17 9½
19	4 3¼	69	0 15 6¼	119	1 6 9¼	169	1 18 0¼
20	**4s. 6**	**70**	**£0 15s. 9**	**120**	**£1 7s. 0**	**170**	**£1 18s. 3**
21	4s. 8¾	71	£0 15s.11¾	121	£1 7s. 2¾	171	£1 18s. 5¾
22	4 11½	72	0 16 2½	122	1 7 5½	172	1 18 8½
23	5 2	73	0 16 5	123	1 7 8	173	1 18 11
24	5 4¾	74	0 16 7¾	124	1 7 10¾	174	1 19 1¾
25	5 7½	75	0 16 10½	125	1 8 1½	175	1 19 4½
26	5 10¼	76	0 17 1¼	126	1 8 4¼	176	1 19 7¼
27	6 1	77	0 17 4	127	1 8 7	177	1 19 10
28	6 3½	78	0 17 6½	128	1 8 9½	178	2 0 0½
29	6 6¼	79	0 17 9¼	129	1 9 0¼	179	2 0 3¼
30	**6s. 9**	**80**	**£0 18s. 0**	**130**	**£1 9s. 3**	**180**	**£2 0s. 6**
31	6s.11¾	81	£0 18s. 2¾	131	£1 9s. 5¾	181	£2 0s. 8¾
32	7 2½	82	0 18 5½	132	1 9 8½	182	2 0 11½
33	7 5	83	0 18 8	133	1 9 11	183	2 1 2
34	7 7¾	84	0 18 10¾	134	1 10 1¾	184	2 1 4¾
35	7 10½	85	0 19 1½	135	1 10 4½	185	2 1 7½
36	8 1¼	86	0 19 4¼	136	1 10 7¼	186	2 1 10¼
37	8 4	87	0 19 7	137	1 10 10	187	2 2 1
38	8 6½	88	0 19 9½	138	1 11 0½	188	2 2 3½
39	8 9¼	89	1 0 0¼	139	1 11 3¼	189	2 2 6¼
40	**9s. 0**	**90**	**£1 0s. 3**	**140**	**£1 11s. 6**	**190**	**£2 2s. 9**
41	9s. 2¾	91	£1 0s. 5¾	141	£1 11s. 8¾	191	£2 2s.11¾
42	9 5½	92	1 0 8½	142	1 11 11½	192	2 3 2½
43	9 8	93	1 0 11	143	1 12 2	193	2 3 5
44	9 10¾	94	1 1 1¾	144	1 12 4¾	194	2 3 7¾
45	10 1½	95	1 1 4½	145	1 12 7½	195	2 3 10½
46	10 4¼	96	1 1 7¼	146	1 12 10¼	196	2 4 1¼
47	10 7	97	1 1 10	147	1 13 1	197	2 4 4
48	10 9½	98	1 2 0½	148	1 13 3½	198	2 4 6½
49	11 0¼	99	1 2 3¼	149	1 13 6¼	199	2 4 9¼
50	**11s. 3**	**100**	**£1 2s. 6**	**150**	**£1 13s. 9**	**200**	**£2 5s. 0**
250	2 16s. 3d	700	£7 17s. 6d	1200	£13 10s. 0d	2000	£22 10s. 0
300	3 7 6	750	8 8 9	1400	15 15 0	2500	28 2 6
400	4 10 0	800	9 0 0	1500	16 17 6	3000	33 15 0
500	5 12 6	900	10 2 6	1600	18 0 0	4000	45 0 0
600	6 15s. 0d	1000	£11 5s. 0d	1800	£20 5s. 0d	5000	£56 5s. 0

98⅞% off.

$1\frac{1}{4}\%$ **1¼ PER CENT.** $1\frac{1}{4}\%$

£1		0s	3	£51	£0	12s	9	£101	£1	5s	3	£151	£1	17s	9	6d	..
2		0	6	52	0	13	0	102	1	5	6	152	1	18	0	1/-	¼d
3		0	9	53	0	13	3	103	1	5	9	153	1	18	3	6	,,
4		1	0	54	0	13	6	104	1	6	0	154	1	18	6	2/-	,,
5		1	3	55	0	13	9	105	1	6	3	155	1	18	9	6	½d
6		1	6	56	0	14	0	106	1	6	6	156	1	19	0	3/-	,,
7		1	9	57	0	14	3	107	1	6	9	157	1	19	3	6	,,
8		2	0	58	0	14	6	108	1	7	0	158	1	19	6	4/-	,,
9		2	3	59	0	14	9	109	1	7	3	159	1	19	9	6	¾d
10		2	6	**60**	0	15	0	**110**	1	7	6	**160**	2	0	0	**5/-**	,,
11		2	9	61	0	15	3	111	1	7	9	161	2	0	3	6	,,
12		3	0	62	0	15	6	112	1	8	0	162	2	0	6	6/-	1d
13		3	3	63	0	15	9	113	1	8	3	163	2	0	9	6	,,
14		3	6	64	0	16	0	114	1	8	6	164	2	1	0	7/-	,,
15		3	9	65	0	16	3	115	1	8	9	165	2	1	3	6	1¼
16		4	0	66	0	16	6	116	1	9	0	166	2	1	6	8/-	,,
17		4	3	67	0	16	9	117	1	9	3	167	2	1	9	6	,,
18		4	6	68	0	17	0	118	1	9	6	168	2	2	0	9/-	,,
19		4	9	69	0	17	3	119	1	9	9	169	2	2	3	6	1½
20		5	0	**70**	0	17	6	**120**	1	10	0	**170**	2	2	6	**10/-**	,,
21		5	3	71	0	17	9	121	1	10	3	171	2	2	9	6	,,
22		5	6	72	0	18	0	122	1	10	6	172	2	3	0	11/-	1¾
23		5	9	73	0	18	3	123	1	10	9	173	2	3	3	6	,,
24		6	0	74	0	18	6	124	1	11	0	174	2	3	6	12/-	,,
25		6	3	75	0	18	9	125	1	11	3	175	2	3	9	6	2d
26		6	6	76	0	19	0	126	1	11	6	176	2	4	0	13/-	,,
27		6	9	77	0	19	3	127	1	11	9	177	2	4	3	6	,,
28		7	0	78	0	19	6	128	1	12	0	178	2	4	6	14/-	,,
29		7	3	79	0	19	9	129	1	12	3	179	2	4	9	6	2¼
30		7	6	**80**	1	0	0	**130**	1	12	6	**180**	2	5	0	**15/-**	,,
31		7	9	81	1	0	3	131	1	12	9	181	2	5	3	6	,,
32		8	0	82	1	0	6	132	1	13	0	182	2	5	6	16/-	2½
33		8	3	83	1	0	9	133	1	13	3	183	2	5	9	6	,,
34		8	6	84	1	1	0	134	1	13	6	184	2	6	0	17/-	,,
35		8	9	85	1	1	3	135	1	13	9	185	2	6	3	6	2¾
36		9	0	86	1	1	6	136	1	14	0	186	2	6	6	18/-	,,
37		9	3	87	1	1	9	137	1	14	3	187	2	6	9	6	,,
38		9	6	88	1	2	0	138	1	14	6	188	2	7	0	19/-	,,
39		9	9	89	1	2	3	139	1	14	9	189	2	7	3	6	3d
40		10	0	**90**	1	2	6	**140**	1	15	0	**190**	2	7	6	**20/-**	,,
41		10	3	91	1	2	9	141	1	15	3	191	2	7	9	21/-	3¼
42		10	6	92	1	3	0	142	1	15	6	192	2	8	0	22/-	3¼
43		10	9	93	1	3	3	143	1	15	9	193	2	8	3	23/-	3½
44		11	0	94	1	3	6	144	1	16	0	194	2	8	6	24/-	3½
45		11	3	95	1	3	9	145	1	16	3	195	2	8	9	25/-	3¾
46		11	6	96	1	4	0	146	1	16	6	196	2	9	0	26/-	4d
47		11	9	97	1	4	3	147	1	16	9	197	2	9	3	27/-	4d
48		12	0	98	1	4	6	148	1	17	0	198	2	9	6	28/-	4¼
49		12	3	99	1	4	9	149	1	17	3	199	2	9	9	29/-	4¼
50		12s	6	**100**	1	5	0	**150**	1	17	6	**200**	2	10	0	**30/-**	4½
250	3	2s	6	700	8	15s	0d	1200	15	0s	0d	2000	25	0s	0d	31/-	4¾
300	3	15	0	750	9	7	6	1400	17	10	0	2500	31	5	0	32/-	4¾
400	5	0	0	800	10	0	0	1500	18	15	0	3000	37	10	0	33/-	5d
500	6	5	0	900	11	5	0	1600	20	0	0	4000	50	0	0	34/-	5d
600	7	10s	0	1000	12	10s	0d	1800	22	10s	0d	5000	62	10s	0d	35/-	5¼

98¾% off.

1⅜% ONE & THREE-EIGHTHS PER CENT. 1⅜%

£1	0s. 3¼	£51	£0 14s. 0¼	£101	£1 7s. 9¼	£151	£2 1s. 6¼
2	0 6½	52	0 14 3½	102	1 8 0½	152	2 1 9½
3	0 10	53	0 14 7	103	1 8 4	153	2 2 1
4	1 1¼	54	0 14 10¼	104	1 8 7¼	154	2 2 4¼
5	1 4½	55	0 15 1½	105	1 8 10½	155	2 2 7½
6	1 7¾	56	0 15 4¾	106	1 9 1¾	156	2 2 10¾
7	1 11	57	0 15 8	107	1 9 5	157	2 3 2
8	2 2½	58	0 15 11½	108	1 9 8½	158	2 3 5½
9	2 5¾	59	0 16 2¾	109	1 9 11¾	159	2 3 8¾
10	2s. 9	**60**	£0 16s. 6	**110**	£1 10s. 3	**160**	£2 4s. 0
11	3s. 0¼	61	£0 16s. 9¼	111	£1 10s. 6¼	161	£2 4s. 3¼
12	3 3½	62	0 17 0½	112	1 10 9½	162	2 4 6½
13	3 7	63	0 17 4	113	1 11 1	163	2 4 10
14	3 10¼	64	0 17 7¼	114	1 11 4¼	164	2 5 1¼
15	4 1½	65	0 17 10½	115	1 11 7½	165	2 5 4½
16	4 4¾	66	0 18 1¾	116	1 11 10¾	166	2 5 7¾
17	4 8	67	0 18 5	117	1 12 2	167	2 5 11
18	4 11½	68	0 18 8½	118	1 12 5½	168	2 6 2½
19	5 2¾	69	0 18 11¾	119	1 12 8¾	169	2 6 5¾
20	5s. 6	**70**	£0 19s. 3	**120**	£1 13s. 0	**170**	£2 6s. 9
21	5s. 9¼	71	£0 19s. 6¼	121	£1 13s. 3¼	171	£2 7s. 0¼
22	6 0½	72	0 19 9½	122	1 13 6½	172	2 7 3½
23	6 4	73	1 0 1	123	1 13 10	173	2 7 7
24	6 7¼	74	1 0 4¼	124	1 14 1¼	174	2 7 10¼
25	6 10½	75	1 0 7½	125	1 14 4½	175	2 8 1½
26	7 1¾	76	1 0 10¾	126	1 14 7¾	176	2 8 4¾
27	7 5	77	1 1 2	127	1 14 11	177	2 8 8
28	7 8½	78	1 1 5½	128	1 15 2½	178	2 8 11½
29	7 11¾	79	1 1 8¾	129	1 15 5¾	179	2 9 2¾
30	8s. 3	**80**	£1 2s. 0	**130**	£1 15s. 9	**180**	£2 9s. 6
31	8s. 6¼	81	£1 2s. 3¼	131	£1 16s. 0¼	181	£2 9s. 9¼
32	8 9½	82	1 2 6½	132	1 16 3½	182	2 10 0½
33	9 1	83	1 2 10	133	1 16 7	183	2 10 4
34	9 4¼	84	1 3 1¼	134	1 16 10¼	184	2 10 7¼
35	9 7½	85	1 3 4½	135	1 17 1½	185	2 10 10½
36	9 10¾	86	1 3 7¾	136	1 17 4¾	186	2 11 1¾
37	10 2	87	1 3 11	137	1 17 8	187	2 11 5
38	10 5½	88	1 4 2½	138	1 17 11½	188	2 11 8½
39	10 8¾	89	1 4 5¾	139	1 18 2¾	189	2 11 11¾
40	11s. 0	**90**	£1 4s. 9	**140**	£1 18s. 6	**190**	£2 12s. 3
41	11s. 3¼	91	£1 5s. 0¼	141	£1 18s. 9¼	191	£2 12s. 6¼
42	11 6½	92	1 5 3½	142	1 19 0½	192	2 12 9½
43	11 10	93	1 5 7	143	1 19 4	193	2 13 1
44	12 1¼	94	1 5 10¼	144	1 19 7¼	194	2 13 4¼
45	12 4½	95	1 6 1½	145	1 19 10½	195	2 13 7½
46	12 7¾	96	1 6 4¾	146	2 0 1¾	196	2 13 10¾
47	12 11	97	1 6 8	147	2 0 5	197	2 14 2
48	13 2½	98	1 6 11½	148	2 0 8½	198	2 14 5½
49	13 5¾	99	1 7 2¾	149	2 0 11¾	199	2 14 8¾
50	13s. 9	**100**	£1 7s. 6	**150**	£2 1s. 3	**200**	£2 15s. 0
250	3 8s. 9d	700	£9 12s. 6d	1200	£16 10s. 0d	2000	£27 10s. 0
300	4 2 6	750	10 6 3	1400	19 5 0	2500	34 7 6
400	5 10 0	800	11 0 0	1500	20 12 6	3000	41 5 0
500	6 17 6	900	12 7 6	1600	22 0 0	4000	55 0 0
600	8 5s. 0d	1000	£13 15s. 0d	1800	£24 15s. 0d	5000	£68 15s. 0

98⅝% off.

1½ Per Cent.

£1	0s. 3½	£51	£0 15s. 3½	£101	£1 10s. 3½	£151	£2 5s. 3½
2	0 7¼	52	0 15 7¼	102	1 10 7¼	152	2 5 7¼
3	0 10¾	53	0 15 10¾	103	1 10 10¾	153	2 5 10¾
4	1 2½	54	0 16 2½	104	1 11 2½	154	2 6 2½
5	1 6	55	0 16 6	105	1 11 6	155	2 6 6
6	1 9½	56	0 16 9½	106	1 11 9½	156	2 6 9½
7	2 1¼	57	0 17 1¼	107	1 12 1¼	157	2 7 1¼
8	2 4¾	58	0 17 4¾	108	1 12 4¾	158	2 7 4¾
9	2 8½	59	0 17 8½	109	1 12 8½	159	2 7 8½
10	**3s. 0**	**60**	**£0 18s. 0**	**110**	**£1 13s. 0**	**160**	**£2 8s. 0**
11	3s. 3½	61	£0 18s. 3½	111	£1 13s. 3½	161	£2 8s. 3½
12	3 7¼	62	0 18 7¼	112	1 13 7¼	162	2 8 7¼
13	3 10¾	63	0 18 10¾	113	1 13 10¾	163	2 8 10¾
14	4 2½	64	0 19 2½	114	1 14 2½	164	2 9 2½
15	4 6	65	0 19 6	115	1 14 6	165	2 9 6
16	4 9½	66	0 19 9½	116	1 14 9½	166	2 9 9½
17	5 1¼	67	1 0 1¼	117	1 15 1¼	167	2 10 1¼
18	5 4¾	68	1 0 4¾	118	1 15 4¾	168	2 10 4¾
19	5 8½	69	1 0 8½	119	1 15 8½	169	2 10 8½
20	**6s. 0**	**70**	**£1 1s. 0**	**120**	**£1 16s. 0**	**170**	**£2 11s. 0**
21	6s. 3½	71	£1 1s. 3½	121	£1 16s. 3½	171	£2 11s. 3½
22	6 7¼	72	1 1 7¼	122	1 16 7¼	172	2 11 7¼
23	6 10¾	73	1 1 10¾	123	1 16 10¾	173	2 11 10¾
24	7 2½	74	1 2 2½	124	1 17 2½	174	2 12 2½
25	7 6	75	1 2 6	125	1 17 6	175	2 12 6
26	7 9½	76	1 2 9½	126	1 17 9½	176	2 12 9½
27	8 1¼	77	1 3 1¼	127	1 18 1¼	177	2 13 1¼
28	8 4¾	78	1 3 4¾	128	1 18 4¾	178	2 13 4¾
29	8 8½	79	1 3 8½	129	1 18 8½	179	2 13 8½
30	**9s. 0**	**80**	**£1 4s. 0**	**130**	**£1 19s. 0**	**180**	**£2 14s. 0**
31	9s. 3½	81	£1 4s. 3½	131	£1 19s. 3½	181	£2 14s. 3½
32	9 7¼	82	1 4 7¼	132	1 19 7¼	182	2 14 7¼
33	9 10¾	83	1 4 10¾	133	1 19 10¾	183	2 14 10¾
34	10 2½	84	1 5 2½	134	2 0 2½	184	2 15 2½
35	10 6	85	1 5 6	135	2 0 6	185	2 15 6
36	10 9½	86	1 5 9½	136	2 0 9½	186	2 15 9½
37	11 1¼	87	1 6 1¼	137	2 1 1¼	187	2 16 1¼
38	11 4¾	88	1 6 4¾	138	2 1 4¾	188	2 16 4¾
39	11 8½	89	1 6 8½	139	2 1 8½	189	2 16 8½
40	**12s 0**	**90**	**£1 7s. 0**	**140**	**£2 2s. 0**	**190**	**£2 17s 0**
41	12s. 3½	91	£1 7s. 3½	141	£2 2s. 3½	191	£2 17s. 3½
42	12 7¼	92	1 7 7¼	142	2 2 7¼	192	2 17 7¼
43	12 10¾	93	1 7 10¾	143	2 2 10¾	193	2 17 10¾
44	13 2½	94	1 8 2½	144	2 3 2½	194	2 18 2½
45	13 6	95	1 8 6	145	2 3 6	195	2 18 6
46	13 9½	96	1 8 9½	146	2 3 9½	196	2 18 9½
47	14 1¼	97	1 9 1¼	147	2 4 1¼	197	2 19 1¼
48	14 4¾	98	1 9 4¾	148	2 4 4¾	198	2 19 4¾
49	14 8½	99	1 9 8½	149	2 4 8½	199	2 19 8½
50	**15s. 0**	**100**	**£1 10s. 0**	**150**	**£2 5s. 0**	**200**	**£3 0s. 0**
250	3 15 0d	700	£10 10s. 0d	1200	£18 0s.0d	2000	£30 0s. 0
300	4 10 0	750	11 5 0	1400	21 0 0	2500	37 10 0
400	6 0 0	800	12 0 0	1500	22 10 0	3000	45 0 0
500	7 10 0	900	13 10 0	1600	24 0 0	4000	60 0 0
600	9 0 0d	1000	£15 0s. 0d	1800	£27 0s.0d	5000	£75 0s. 0

98½% off.

1½ Per Cent.

1d	0s.	0d	4/1	0s.	0¾	8/1	0s.	1½	12/1	0s.	2¼	16/1	0s.	3
2d	0	0	2	0	0¾	2	0	1½	2	0	2¼	2	0	3
3d	0	0	3	0	0¾	3	0	1½	3	0	2¼	3	0	3
4d	0	0	4	0	0¾	4	0	1½	4	0	2¼	4	0	3
5d	0	0	5	0	0¾	5	0	1½	5	0	2¼	5	0	3
6d	0	0	4/6	0	0¾	8/6	0	1½	12/6	0	2¼	16/6	0	3
7d	0	0	7	0	0¾	7	0	1½	7	0	2¼	7	0	3
8d	0	0	8	0	0¾	8	0	1½	8	0	2¼	8	0	3
9d	0	0¼	9	0	0¾	9	0	1½	9	0	2¼	9	0	3
10d	0	0¼	10	0	0¾	10	0	1½	10	0	2¼	10	0	3
11d	0	0¼	11	0	1	11	0	1½	11	0	2¼	11	0	3
1/-	0s.	0¼	**5/-**	0s.	1	**9/-**	0s.	1½	**13/-**	0s.	2¼	**17/-**	0s.	3
1/1	0s.	0¼	5/1	0s.	1	9/1	0s.	1¾	13/1	0s.	2¼	17/1	0s.	3
2	0	0¼	2	0	1	2	0	1¾	2	0	2¼	2	0	3
3	0	0¼	3	0	1	3	0	1¾	3	0	2½	3	0	3
4	0	0¼	4	0	1	4	0	1¾	4	0	2½	4	0	3
5	0	0¼	5	0	1	5	0	1¾	5	0	2½	5	0	3¼
1/6	0	0¼	5/6	0	1	9/6	0	1¾	13/6	0	2½	17/6	0	3¼
7	0	0¼	7	0	1	7	0	1¾	7	0	2½	7	0	3¼
8	0	0¼	8	0	1	8	0	1¾	8	0	2½	8	0	3¼
9	0	0¼	9	0	1	9	0	1¾	9	0	2½	9	0	3¼
10	0	0¼	10	0	1	10	0	1¾	10	0	2½	10	0	3¼
11	0	0¼	11	0	1	11	0	1¾	11	0	2½	11	0	3¼
2/-	0s.	0¼	**6/-**	0s.	1	**10/-**	0s.	1¾	**14/-**	0s.	2½	**18/-**	0s.	3¼
2/1	0s.	0½	6/1	0s.	1	10/1	0s.	1¾	14/1	0s.	2½	18/1	0s.	3¼
2	0	0½	2	0	1	2	0	1¾	2	0	2½	2	0	3¼
3	0	0½	3	0	1¼	3	0	1¾	3	0	2½	3	0	3¼
4	0	0½	4	0	1¼	4	0	1¾	4	0	2½	4	0	3¼
5	0	0½	5	0	1¼	5	0	2	5	0	2½	5	0	3¼
2/6	0	0½	6/6	0	1¼	10/6	0	2	14/6	0	2½	18/6	0	3¼
7	0	0½	7	0	1¼	7	0	2	7	0	2¾	7	0	3¼
8	0	0½	8	0	1¼	8	0	2	8	0	2¾	8	0	3¼
9	0	0½	9	0	1¼	9	0	2	9	0	2¾	9	0	3½
10	0	0½	10	0	1¼	10	0	2	10	0	2¾	10	0	3½
11	0	0½	11	0	1¼	11	0	2	11	0	2¾	11	0	3½
3/-	0s.	0½	**7/-**	0s.	1¼	**11/-**	0s.	2	**15/-**	0s.	2¾	**19/-**	0s.	3½
3/1	0s.	0½	7/1	0s.	1¼	11/1	0s.	2	15/1	0s.	2¾	19/1	0s.	3½
2	0	0½	2	0	1¼	2	0	2	2	0	2¾	2	0	3½
3	0	0½	3	0	1¼	3	0	2	3	0	2¾	3	0	3½
4	0	0½	4	0	1¼	4	0	2	4	0	2¾	4	0	3½
5	0	0½	5	0	1¼	5	0	2	5	0	2¾	5	0	3½
3/6	0	0¾	7/6	0	1¼	11/6	0	2	15/6	0	2¾	19/6	0	3½
7	0	0¾	7	0	1½	7	0	2	7	0	2¾	7	0	3½
8	0	0¾	8	0	1½	8	0	2	8	0	2¾	8	0	3½
9	0	0¾	9	0	1½	9	0	2	9	0	2¾	9	0	3½
10	0	0¾	10	0	1½	10	0	2¼	10	0	2¾	10	0	3½
11	0	0¾	11	0	1½	11	0	2¼	11	0	2¾	11	0	3½
4/-	0s.	0¾	**8/-**	0s.	1½	**12/-**	0s.	2¼	**16/-**	0s.	3	**20/-**	0s.	3½

20/6	0s.	3¾	25/6	0s.	4½	31/-	0s.	5½	35/6	0s.	6½	Guineas.		
21/-	0	3¾	26/-	0	4¾	31/6	0	5¾	36/-	0	6½	1.	0s.	3¾
22/-	0	4	27/-	0	4¾	32/-	0	5¾	37/-	0	6¾	2.	0	7½
22/6	0	4	27/6	0	5	32/6	0	5¾	37/6	0	6¾	3.	0	11¼
23/-	0	4¼	28/-	0	5	33/-	0	6	38/-	0	6¾	4.	1	3
24/-	0	4¼	29/-	0	5¼	34/-	0	6	39/-	0	7	5.	1	7
25/-	0s.	4½	**30/-**	0s.	5½	**35/-**	0s.	6¼	**40/-**	0s.	7¼	6.	1s.	10¾

1⅝% ONE & FIVE-EIGHTHS PER CENT. 1⅝%

£1	0s. 4	£51	£0 16s. 7	£101	£1 12s.10	£151	£2 9s. 1
2	0 7¾	52	0 16 10¾	102	1 13 1¾	152	2 9 4¾
3	0 11¾	53	0 17 2¾	103	1 13 5¾	153	2 9 8¾
4	1 3½	54	0 17 6½	104	1 13 9½	154	2 10 0½
5	1 7½	55	0 17 10½	105	1 14 1½	155	2 10 4½
6	1 11½	56	0 18 2½	106	1 14 5½	156	2 10 8½
7	2 3¼	57	0 18 6¼	107	1 14 9¼	157	2 11 0¼
8	2 7¼	58	0 18 10¼	108	1 15 1¼	158	2 11 4¼
9	2 11	59	0 19 2	109	1 15 5	159	2 11 8
10	3s. 3	**60**	£0 19s. 6	**110**	£1 15s. 9	**160**	£2 12s. 0
11	3s. 7	61	£0 19s.10	111	£1 16s. 1	161	£2 12s. 4
12	3 10¾	62	1 0 1¾	112	1 16 4¾	162	2 12 7¾
13	4 2¾	63	1 0 5¾	113	1 16 8¾	163	2 12 11¾
14	4 6½	64	1 0 9½	114	1 17 0½	164	2 13 3½
15	4 10½	65	1 1 1½	115	1 17 4½	165	2 13 7½
16	5 2½	66	1 1 5½	116	1 17 8½	166	2 13 11½
17	5 6¼	67	1 1 9¼	117	1 18 0¼	167	2 14 3¼
18	5 10¼	68	1 2 1¼	118	1 18 4¼	168	2 14 7¼
19	6 2	69	1 2 5	119	1 18 8	169	2 14 11
20	6s. 6	**70**	£1 2s. 9	**120**	£1 19s. 0	**170**	£2 15s. 3
21	6s.10	71	£1 3s. 1	121	£1 19s. 4	171	£2 15s. 7
22	7 1¾	72	1 3 4¾	122	1 19 7¾	172	2 15 10¾
23	7 5¾	73	1 3 8¾	123	1 19 11¾	173	2 16 2¾
24	7 9½	74	1 4 0½	124	2 0 3½	174	2 16 6½
25	8 1½	75	1 4 4½	125	2 0 7½	175	2 16 10½
26	8 5½	76	1 4 8½	126	2 0 11½	176	2 17 2½
27	8 9¼	77	1 5 0¼	127	2 1 3¼	177	2 17 6¼
28	9 1¼	78	1 5 4¼	128	2 1 7¼	178	2 17 10¼
29	9 5	79	1 5 8	129	2 1 11	179	2 18 2
30	9s. 9	**80**	£1 6s. 0	**130**	£2 2s. 3	**180**	£2 18s. 6
31	10s. 1	81	£1 6s. 4	131	£2 2s. 7	181	£2 18s.10
32	10 4¾	82	1 6 7¾	132	2 2 10¾	182	2 19 1¾
33	10 8¾	83	1 6 11¾	133	2 3 2¾	183	2 19 5¾
34	11 0½	84	1 7 3½	134	2 3 6½	184	2 19 9½
35	11 4½	85	1 7 7½	135	2 3 10½	185	3 0 1½
36	11 8½	86	1 7 11½	136	2 4 2½	186	3 0 5½
37	12 0¼	87	1 8 3¼	137	2 4 6¼	187	3 0 9¼
38	12 4¼	88	1 8 7¼	138	2 4 10¼	188	3 1 1¼
39	12 8	89	1 8 11	139	2 5 2	189	3 1 5
40	13s. 0	**90**	£1 9s. 3	**140**	£2 5s. 6	**190**	£3 1s. 9
41	13s. 4	91	£1 9s. 7	141	£2 5s.10	191	£3 2s. 1
42	13 7¾	92	1 9 10¾	142	2 6 1¾	192	3 2 4¾
43	13 11¾	93	1 10 2¾	143	2 6 5¾	193	3 2 8¾
44	14 3½	94	1 10 6½	144	2 6 9½	194	3 3 0½
45	14 7½	95	1 10 10½	145	2 7 1½	195	3 3 4½
46	14 11½	96	1 11 2½	146	2 7 5½	196	3 3 8½
47	15 3¼	97	1 11 6¼	147	2 7 9¼	197	3 4 0¼
48	15 7¼	98	1 11 10¼	148	2 8 1¼	198	3 4 4¼
49	15 11	99	1 12 2	149	2 8 5	199	3 4 8
50	16s. 3	**100**	£1 12s. 6	**150**	£2 8s. 9	**200**	£3 5s. 0
250	4 1s. 3d	700	11 7s. 6d	1200	£19 10s. 0d	2000	£32 10s. 0
300	4 17 6	750	12 3 9	1400	22 15 0	2500	40 12 6
400	6 10 0	800	13 0 0	1500	24 7 6	3000	48 15 0
500	8 2 6	900	14 12 6	1600	26 0 0	4000	65 0 0
600	9 15s. 0d	1000	£16 5s. 0d	1800	£29 5s. 0d	5000	£81 5s. 0

98⅜% off.

1⅞% ONE & SEVEN-EIGHTHS PER CENT. 1⅞%

	£ s. d.		£ s. d.		£ s. d.		£ s. d.
£1	0s. 4½	£51	£0 19s. 1½	£101	£1 17s.10½	£151	£2 16s. 7½
2	0 9	52	0 19 6	102	1 18 3	152	2 17 0
3	1 1½	53	0 19 10½	103	1 18 7½	153	2 17 4½
4	1 6	54	1 0 3	104	1 19 0	154	2 17 9
5	1 10½	55	1 0 7½	105	1 19 4½	155	2 18 1½
6	2 3	56	1 1 0	106	1 19 9	156	2 18 6
7	2 7½	57	1 1 4½	107	2 0 1½	157	2 18 10½
8	3 0	58	1 1 9	108	2 0 6	158	2 19 3
9	3 4½	59	1 2 1½	109	2 0 10½	159	2 19 7½
10	3s. 9	60	£1 2s. 6	110	£2 1s. 3	160	£3 0 0
11	4s. 1½	61	£1 2s.10½	111	£2 1s. 7½	161	£3 0s. 4½
12	4 6	62	1 3 3	112	2 2 0	162	3 0 9
13	4 10½	63	1 3 7½	113	2 2 4½	163	3 1 1½
14	5 3	64	1 4 0	114	2 2 9	164	3 1 6
15	5 7½	65	1 4 4½	115	2 3 1½	165	3 1 10½
16	6 0	66	1 4 9	116	2 3 6	166	3 2 3
17	6 4½	67	1 5 1½	117	2 3 10½	167	3 2 7½
18	6 9	68	1 5 6	118	2 4 3	168	3 3 0
19	7 1½	69	1 5 10½	119	2 4 7½	169	3 3 4½
20	7s. 6	70	£1 6s. 3	120	£2 5s. 0	170	£3 3s. 9
21	7s.10½	71	£1 6s. 7½	121	£2 5s. 4½	171	£3 4s. 1½
22	8 3	72	1 7 0	122	2 5 9	172	3 4 6
23	8 7½	73	1 7 4½	123	2 6 1½	173	3 4 10½
24	9 0	74	1 7 9	124	2 6 6	174	3 5 3
25	9 4½	75	1 8 1½	125	2 6 10½	175	3 5 7½
26	9 9	76	1 8 6	126	2 7 3	176	3 6 0
27	10 1½	77	1 8 10½	127	2 7 7½	177	3 6 4½
28	10 6	78	1 9 3	128	2 8 0	178	3 6 9
29	10 10½	79	1 9 7½	129	2 8 4½	179	3 7 1½
30	11s. 3	80	£1 10s. 0	130	£2 8s. 9	180	£3 7s. 6
31	11s. 7½	81	£1 10s. 4½	131	£2 9s. 1½	181	£3 7s.10½
32	12 0	82	1 10 9	132	2 9 6	182	3 8 3
33	12 4½	83	1 11 1½	133	2 9 10½	183	3 8 7½
34	12 9	84	1 11 6	134	2 10 3	184	3 9 0
35	13 1½	85	1 11 10½	135	2 10 7½	185	3 9 4½
36	13 6	86	1 12 3	136	2 11 0	186	3 9 9
37	13 10½	87	1 12 7½	137	2 11 4½	187	3 10 1½
38	14 3	88	1 13 0	138	2 11 9	188	3 10 6
39	14 7½	89	1 13 4½	139	2 12 1½	189	3 10 10½
40	15s. 0	90	£1 13s. 9	140	£2 12s. 6	190	£3 11s. 3
41	15s. 4½	91	£1 14s. 1½	141	£2 12s.10½	191	£3 11s. 7½
42	15 9	92	1 14 6	142	2 13 3	192	3 12 0
43	16 1½	93	1 14 10½	143	2 13 7½	193	3 12 4½
44	16 6	94	1 15 3	144	2 14 0	194	3 12 9
45	16 10½	95	1 15 7½	145	2 14 4½	195	3 13 1½
46	17 3	96	1 16 0	146	2 14 9	196	3 13 6
47	17 7½	97	1 16 4½	147	2 15 1½	197	3 13 10½
48	18 0	98	1 16 9	148	2 15 6	198	3 14 3
49	18 4½	99	1 17 1½	149	2 15 10½	199	3 14 7½
50	18s. 9	100	£1 17s. 6	150	£2 16s. 3	200	£3 15s. 0

250	4 13s. 9d	700	13 2s. 6d	1200	£22 10s. 0d	2000	£37 10s. 0
300	5 12 6	750	14 1 3	1400	26 5 0	2500	46 17 6
400	7 10 0	800	15 0 0	1500	28 2 6	3000	56 5 0
500	9 7 6	900	16 17 6	1600	30 0 0	4000	75 0 0
600	11 5s. 0d	1000	£18 15s. 0d	1800	£33 15s. 0d	5000	£93 15s. 0

98⅛% off.

1¾ PER CENT.

1¾%

£1	0s. 4¼	£51	£0 17s.10¼	£101	£1 15s. 4¼	£151	£2 12s.10¼
2	0 8½	52	0 18 2½	102	1 15 8½	152	2 13 2½
3	1 0½	53	0 18 6½	103	1 16 0½	153	2 13 6½
4	1 4¾	54	0 18 10¾	104	1 16 4¾	154	2 13 10¾
5	1 9	55	0 19 3	105	1 16 9	155	2 14 3
6	2 1¼	56	0 19 7¼	106	1 17 1¼	156	2 14 7¼
7	2 5½	57	0 19 11½	107	1 17 5½	157	2 14 11½
8	2 9½	58	1 0 3½	108	1 17 9½	158	2 15 3½
9	3 1¾	59	1 0 7¾	109	1 18 1¾	159	2 15 7¾
10	3s. 6	**60**	£1 1s. 0	**110**	£1 18s. 6	**160**	£2 16s. 0
11	3s.10¼	61	£1 1s. 4¼	111	£1 18s.10¼	161	£2 16s. 4¼
12	4 2½	62	1 1 8½	112	1 19 2½	162	2 16 8½
13	4 6½	63	1 2 0½	113	1 19 6½	163	2 17 0½
14	4 10¾	64	1 2 4¾	114	1 19 10¾	164	2 17 4¾
15	5 3	65	1 2 9	115	2 0 3	165	2 17 9
16	5 7¼	66	1 3 1¼	116	2 0 7¼	166	2 18 1¼
17	5 11½	67	1 3 5½	117	2 0 11½	167	2 18 5½
18	6 3½	68	1 3 9½	118	2 1 3½	168	2 18 9½
19	6 7¾	69	1 4 1¾	119	2 1 7¾	169	2 19 1¾
20	7s. 0	**70**	£1 4s. 6	**120**	£2 2s. 0	**170**	£2 19s. 6
21	7s. 4¼	71	£1 4s.10¼	121	£2 2s. 4¼	171	£2 19s.10¼
22	7 8½	72	1 5 2½	122	2 2 8½	172	3 0 2½
23	8 0½	73	1 5 6½	123	2 3 0½	173	3 0 6½
24	8 4¾	74	1 5 10¾	124	2 3 4¾	174	3 0 10¾
25	8 9	75	1 6 3	125	2 3 9	175	3 1 3
26	9 1¼	76	1 6 7¼	126	2 4 1¼	176	3 1 7¼
27	9 5½	77	1 6 11½	127	2 4 5½	177	3 1 11½
28	9 9½	78	1 7 3½	128	2 4 9½	178	3 2 3½
29	10 1¾	79	1 7 7¾	129	2 5 1¾	179	3 2 7¾
30	10s. 6	**80**	£1 8s. 0	**130**	£2 5s. 6	**180**	£3 3s. 0
31	10s.10¼	81	£1 8s. 4¼	131	£2 5s.10¼	181	£3 3s. 4¼
32	11 2½	82	1 8 8½	132	2 6 2½	182	3 3 8½
33	11 6½	83	1 9 0½	133	2 6 6½	183	3 4 0½
34	11 10¾	84	1 9 4¾	134	2 6 10¾	184	3 4 4¾
35	12 3	85	1 9 9	135	2 7 3	185	3 4 9
36	12 7¼	86	1 10 1¼	136	2 7 7¼	186	3 5 1¼
37	12 11½	87	1 10 5½	137	2 7 11½	187	3 5 5½
38	13 3½	88	1 10 9½	138	2 8 3½	188	3 5 9½
39	13 7¾	89	1 11 1¾	139	2 8 7¾	189	3 6 1¾
40	14s 0	**90**	£1 11s. 6	**140**	£2 9s. 0	**190**	£3 6s 6
41	14s. 4¼	91	£1 11s.10¼	141	£2 9s. 4¼	191	£3 6s.10¼
42	14 8½	92	1 12 2½	142	2 9 8½	192	3 7 2½
43	15 0½	93	1 12 6½	143	2 10 0½	193	3 7 6½
44	15 4¾	94	1 12 10¾	144	2 10 4¾	194	3 7 10¾
45	15 9	95	1 13 3	145	2 10 9	195	3 8 3
46	16 1¼	96	1 13 7¼	146	2 11 1¼	196	3 8 7¼
47	16 5½	97	1 13 11½	147	2 11 5½	197	3 8 11½
48	16 9½	98	1 14 3½	148	2 11 9½	198	3 9 3½
49	17 1¾	99	1 14 7¾	149	2 12 1¾	199	3 9 7¾
50	17s. 6	**100**	£1 15s. 0	**150**	£2 12s. 6	**200**	£3 10s. 0
250	4 7 6d	700	£12 5s. 0d	1200	£21 0s.0d	2000	£35 0s. 0
300	5 5 0	750	13 2 6	1400	24 10 0	2500	43 15 0
400	7 0 0	800	14 0 0	1500	26 5 0	3000	52 10 0
500	8 15 0	900	15 15 0	1600	28 0 0	4000	70 0 0
600	10 10 0d	1000	£17 10s. 0d	1800	£31 10s.0d	5000	£87 10s. 0

98½% off.

1¾ Per Cent.

1d	0s.	0d	4/1	0s.	0¾	8/1	0s.	1¾	12/1	0s.	2½	16/1	0s.	3½
2d	0	0	2	0	1	2	0	1¾	2	0	2½	2	0	3½
3d	0	0	3	0	1	3	0	1¾	3	0	2½	3	0	3½
4d	0	0	4	0	1	4	0	1¾	4	0	2½	4	0	3½
5d	0	0	5	0	1	5	0	1¾	5	0	2½	5	0	3½
6d	0	0	4/6	0	1	8/6	0	1¾	12/6	0	2¾	16/6	0	3½
7d	0	0	7	0	1	7	0	1¾	7	0	2¾	7	0	3½
8d	0	0¼	8	0	1	8	0	1¾	8	0	2¾	8	0	3½
9d	0	0¼	9	0	1	9	0	1¾	9	0	2¾	9	0	3½
10d	0	0¼	10	0	1	10	0	1¾	10	0	2¾	10	0	3½
11d	0	0¼	11	0	1	11	0	1¾	11	0	2¾	11	0	3½
1/-	0s.	0¼	**5/-**	0s.	1	**9/-**	0s.	2	**13/-**	0s.	2¾	**17/-**	0s.	3½
1/1	0s.	0¼	5/1	0s.	1	9/1	0s.	2	13/1	0s.	2¾	17/1	0s.	3½
2	0	0¼	2	0	1	2	0	2	2	0	2¾	2	0	3½
3	0	0½	3	0	1	3	0	2	3	0	2¾	3	0	3½
4	0	0¼	4	0	1	4	0	2	4	0	2¾	4	0	3¾
5	0	0¼	5	0	1¼	5	0	2	5	0	2¾	5	0	3¾
1/6	0	0¼	5/6	0	1¼	9/6	0	2	13/6	0	2¾	17/6	0	3¾
7	0	0¼	7	0	1¼	7	0	2	7	0	2¾	7	0	3¾
8	0	0¼	8	0	1¼	8	0	2	8	0	2¾	8	0	3¾
9	0	0¼	9	0	1¼	9	0	2	9	0	3	9	0	3¾
10	0	0½	10	0	1¼	10	0	2	10	0	3	10	0	3¾
11	0	0½	11	0	1¼	11	0	2	11	0	3	11	0	3¾
2/-	0s.	0½	**6/-**	0s.	1¼	**10/-**	0s.	2	**14/-**	0s.	3	**18/-**	0s.	3¾
2/1	0s.	0½	6/1	0s.	1¼	10/1	0s.	2	14/1	0s.	3	18/1	0s.	3¾
2	0	0½	2	0	1¼	2	0	2¼	2	0	3	2	0	3¾
3	0	0½	3	0	1¼	3	0	2¼	3	0	3	3	0	3¾
4	0	0½	4	0	1¼	4	0	2¼	4	0	3	4	0	3¾
5	0	0½	5	0	1¼	5	0	2¼	5	0	3	5	0	3¾
2/6	0	0½	6/6	0	1½	10/6	0	2¼	14/6	0	3	18/6	0	4
7	0	0½	7	0	1½	7	0	2¼	7	0	3	7	0	4
8	0	0½	8	0	1½	8	0	2¼	8	0	3	8	0	4
9	0	0½	9	0	1½	9	0	2¼	9	0	3	9	0	4
10	0	0½	10	0	1½	10	0	2¼	10	0	3	10	0	4
11	0	0½	11	0	1½	11	0	2¼	11	0	3¼	11	0	4
3/-	0s.	0¾	**7/-**	0s.	1½	**11/-**	0s.	2¼	**15/-**	0s.	3¼	**19/-**	0s.	4
3/1	0s.	0¾	7/1	0s.	1½	11/1	0s.	2¼	15/1	0s.	3¼	19/1	0s.	4
2	0	0¾	2	0	1½	2	0	2¼	2	0	3¼	2	0	4
3	0	0¾	3	0	1½	3	0	2¼	3	0	3¼	3	0	4
4	0	0¾	4	0	1½	4	0	2½	4	0	3¼	4	0	4
5	0	0¾	5	0	1½	5	0	2½	5	0	3¼	5	0	4
3/6	0	0¾	7/6	0	1½	11/6	0	2½	15/6	0	3¼	19/6	0	4
7	0	0¾	7	0	1½	7	0	2½	7	0	3¼	7	0	4
8	0	0¾	8	0	1½	8	0	2½	8	0	3¼	8	0	4¼
9	0	0¾	9	0	1¾	9	0	2½	9	0	3¼	9	0	4¼
10	0	0¾	10	0	1¾	10	0	2½	10	0	3¼	10	0	4¼
11	0	0¾	11	0	1¾	11	0	2½	11	0	3¼	11	0	4¼
4/-	0s.	0¾	**8/-**	0s.	1¾	**12/-**	0s.	2½	**16/-**	0s.	3¼	**20/-**	0s.	4¼

20/6	0s.	4¼	25/6	0s.	5¼	31/-	0s.	6½	35/6	0s.	7½	Guineas.		
21/-	0	4½	26/-	0	5½	31/6	0	6½	36/-	0	7½	1.	0s.	4½
22/-	0	4½	27/-	0	5¾	32/-	0	6¾	37/-	0	7¾	2.	0	8¾
22/6	0	4¾	27/6	0	5¾	32/6	0	6¾	37/6	0	8	3.	1	1¼
23/-	0	4¾	28/-	0	6	33/-	0	7	38/-	0	8	4.	1	5¾
24/-	0	5	29/-	0	6	34/-	0	7¼	39/-	0	8¼	5.	1	10
25/-	0s.	5¼	**30/-**	0s.	6¼	**35/-**	0s.	7¼	**40/-**	0s.	8½	6.	2s.	2½

£	s. d.	£	s. d.	£	s. d.	£	s. d.
£1	0s. 4¾	£51	0s. 4¾	£101 £2	0s. 4¾	£151 £3	0s. 4¾
2	0 9½	52	1 0 9½	102	2 0 9½	152	3 0 9½
3	1 2½	53	1 1 2½	103	2 1 2½	153	3 1 2½
4	1 7¼	54	1 1 7¼	104	2 1 7¼	154	3 1 7¼
5	2 0	55	1 2 0	105	2 2 0	155	3 2 0
6	2 4¾	56	1 2 4¾	106	2 2 4¾	156	3 2 4¾
7	2 9½	57	1 2 9½	107	2 2 9½	157	3 2 9½
8	3 2½	58	1 3 2½	108	2 3 2½	158	3 3 2½
9	3 7¼	59	1 3 7¼	109	2 3 7¼	159	3 3 7¼
10	4s. 0	60	£1 4s. 0	110	£2 4s. 0	160	£3 4s. 0
11	4s. 4¾	61	£1 4s. 4¾	111	£2 4s. 4¾	161	£3 4s. 4¾
12	4 9½	62	1 4 9½	112	2 4 9½	162	3 4 9½
13	5 2½	63	1 5 2½	113	2 5 2½	163	3 5 2½
14	5 7¼	64	1 5 7¼	114	2 5 7¼	164	3 5 7¼
15	6 0	65	1 6 0	115	2 6 0	165	3 6 0
16	6 4¾	66	1 6 4¾	116	2 6 4¾	166	3 6 4¾
17	6 9½	67	1 6 9½	117	2 6 9½	167	3 6 9½
18	7 2½	68	1 7 2½	118	2 7 2½	168	3 7 2½
19	7 7¼	69	1 7 7¼	119	2 7 7¼	169	3 7 7¼
20	8s. 0	70	£1 8s. 0	120	£2 8s. 0	170	£3 8s. 0
21	8s. 4¾	71	£1 8s. 4¾	121	£2 8s. 4¾	171	£3 8s. 4¾
22	8 9½	72	1 8 9½	122	2 8 9½	172	3 8 9½
23	9 2½	73	1 9 2½	123	2 9 2½	173	3 9 2½
24	9 7¼	74	1 9 7¼	124	2 9 7¼	174	3 9 7¼
25	10 0	75	1 10 0	125	2 10 0	175	3 10 0
26	10 4¾	76	1 10 4¾	126	2 10 4¾	176	3 10 4¾
27	10 9½	77	1 10 9½	127	2 10 9½	177	3 10 9½
28	11 2½	78	1 11 2½	128	2 11 2½	178	3 11 2½
29	11 7¼	79	1 11 7¼	129	2 11 7¼	179	3 11 7¼
30	12s. 0	80	£1 12s. 0	130	£2 12s. 0	180	£3 12s. 0
31	12s. 4¾	81	£1 12s. 4¾	131	£2 12s. 4¾	181	£3 12s. 4¾
32	12 9½	82	1 12 9½	132	2 12 9½	182	3 12 9½
33	13 2½	83	1 13 2½	133	2 13 2½	183	3 13 2½
34	13 7¼	84	1 13 7¼	134	2 13 7¼	184	3 13 7¼
35	14 0	85	1 14 0	135	2 14 0	185	3 14 0
36	14 4¾	86	1 14 4¾	136	2 14 4¾	186	3 14 4¾
37	14 9½	87	1 14 9½	137	2 14 9½	187	3 14 9½
38	15 2½	88	1 15 2½	138	2 15 2½	188	3 15 2½
39	15 7¼	89	1 15 7¼	139	2 15 7¼	189	3 15 7¼
40	16s 0	90	£1 16s. 0	140	£2 16s. 0	190	£3 16s 0
41	16s. 4¾	91	£1 16s. 4¾	141	£2 16s. 4¾	191	£3 16s. 4¾
42	16 9½	92	1 16 9½	142	2 16 9½	192	3 16 9½
43	17 2½	93	1 17 2½	143	2 17 2½	193	3 17 2½
44	17 7¼	94	1 17 7¼	144	2 17 7¼	194	3 17 7¼
45	18 0	95	1 18 0	145	2 18 0	195	3 18 0
46	18 4¾	96	1 18 4¾	146	2 18 4¾	196	3 18 4¾
47	18 9½	97	1 18 9½	147	2 18 9½	197	3 18 9½
48	19 2½	98	1 19 2½	148	2 19 2½	198	3 19 2½
49	19 7¼	99	1 19 7¼	149	2 19 7¼	199	3 19 7¼
50	20s. 0	100	£2 0s. 0	150	£3 0s. 0	200	£4 0s. 0
250	5 0 0d	700	£14 0s. 0d	1200	£24 0s.0d	2000	£40 0s. 0
300	6 0 0	750	15 0 0	1400	28 0 0	2500	50 0 0
400	8 0 0	800	16 0 0	1500	30 0 0	3000	60 0 0
500	10 0 0	900	18 0 0	1600	32 0 0	4000	80 0 0
600	12 0 0d	1000	£20 0s. 0d	1800	£36 0s.0d	5000	£100 0s. 0

98% off.

2% Two Per Cent. 2%

1d	0s.	0d	4/1	0s.	1	8/1	0s.	2	12/1	0s.	3	16/1	0s.	3¾
2d	0	0	2	0	1	2	0	2	2	0	3	2	0	4
3d	0	0	3	0	1	3	0	2	3	0	3	3	0	4
4d	0	0	4	0	1	4	0	2	4	0	3	4	0	4
5d	0	0	5	0	1	5	0	2	5	0	3	5	0	4
6d	0	0	4/6	0	1	8/6	0	2	12/6	0	3	16/6	0	4
7d	0	0½	7	0	1	7	0	2	7	0	3	7	0	4
8d	0	0¼	8	0	1	8	0	2	8	0	3	8	0	4
9d	0	0¼	9	0	1¼	9	0	2	9	0	3	9	0	4
10d	0	0¼	10	0	1¼	10	0	2	10	0	3	10	0	4
11d	0	0¼	11	0	1¼	11	0	2¼	11	0	3	11	0	4
1/-	0s.	0¼	**5/-**	0s.	1¼	**9/-**	0s.	2¼	**13/-**	0s.	3	**17/-**	0s.	4
1/1	0s.	0¼	5/1	0s.	1¼	9/1	0s.	2¼	13/1	0s.	3¼	17/1	0s.	4
2	0	0¼	2	0	1¼	2	0	2¼	2	0	3¼	2	0	4
3	0	0½	3	0	1¼	3	0	2¼	3	0	3¼	3	0	4¼
4	0	0¼	4	0	1¼	4	0	2¼	4	0	3¼	4	0	4¼
5	0	0¼	5	0	1¼	5	0	2¼	5	0	3¼	5	0	4¼
1/6	0	0¼	5/6	0	1¼	9/6	0	2¼	13/6	0	3¼	17/6	0	4¼
7	0	0½	7	0	1¼	7	0	2¼	7	0	3¼	7	0	4¼
8	0	0½	8	0	1¼	8	0	2¼	8	0	3¼	8	0	4¼
9	0	0½	9	0	1½	9	0	2¼	9	0	3¼	9	0	4¼
10	0	0½	10	0	1½	10	0	2¼	10	0	3¼	10	0	4¼
11	0	0½	11	0	1½	11	0	2½	11	0	3¼	11	0	4¼
2/-	0s.	0½	**6/-**	0s.	1½	**10/-**	0s.	2½	**14/-**	0s.	3¼	**18/-**	0s.	4¼
2/1	0s.	0½	6/1	0s.	1½	10/1	0s.	2½	14/1	0s.	3½	18/1	0s.	4¼
2	0	0½	2	0	1½	2	0	2½	2	0	3½	2	0	4¼
3	0	0½	3	0	1½	3	0	2½	3	0	3½	3	0	4½
4	0	0½	4	0	1½	4	0	2½	4	0	3½	4	0	4½
5	0	0½	5	0	1½	5	0	2½	5	0	3½	5	0	4½
2/6	0	0½	6/6	0	1½	10/6	0	2½	14/6	0	3½	18/6	0	4½
7	0	0½	7	0	1½	7	0	2½	7	0	3½	7	0	4½
8	0	0¾	8	0	1½	8	0	2½	8	0	3½	8	0	4½
9	0	0¾	9	0	1½	9	0	2½	9	0	3½	9	0	4½
10	0	0¾	10	0	1¾	10	0	2½	10	0	3½	10	0	4½
11	0	0¾	11	0	1¾	11	0	2½	11	0	3½	11	0	4½
3/-	0s.	0¾	**7/-**	0s.	1¾	**11/-**	0s.	2¾	**15/-**	0s.	3½	**19/-**	0s.	4½
3/1	0s.	0¾	7/1	0s.	1¾	11/1	0s.	2¾	15/1	0s.	3½	19/1	0s.	4½
2	0	0¾	2	0	1¾	2	0	2¾	2	0	3¾	2	0	4½
3	0	0¾	3	0	1¾	3	0	2¾	3	0	3¾	3	0	4½
4	0	0¾	4	0	1¾	4	0	2¾	4	0	3¾	4	0	4¾
5	0	0¾	5	0	1¾	5	0	2¾	5	0	3¾	5	0	4¾
3/6	0	0¾	7/6	0	1¾	11/6	0	2¾	15/6	0	3¾	19/6	0	4¾
7	0	0¾	7	0	1¾	7	0	2¾	7	0	3¾	7	0	4¾
8	0	1	8	0	1¾	8	0	2¾	8	0	3¾	8	0	4¾
9	0	1	9	0	1¾	9	0	2¾	9	0	3¾	9	0	4¾
10	0	1	10	0	2	10	0	2¾	10	0	3¾	10	0	4¾
11	0	1	11	0	2	11	0	2¾	11	0	3¾	11	0	4¾
4/-	0s.	1	**8/-**	0s.	2	**12/-**	0s.	3	**16/-**	0s.	3¾	**20/-**	0s.	4¾

20/6	0s.	5	25/6	0s.	6	31/-	0s.	7½	35/6	0s.	8½	Guineas.		
21/-	0	5	26/-	0	6¼	31/6	0	7½	36/-	0	8¾	1.	0s.	5
22/-	0	5¼	27/-	0	6½	32/-	0	7¾	37/-	0	9	2.	0	10
22/6	0	5½	27/6	0	6½	32/6	0	7¾	37/6	0	9	3.	1	3
23/-	0	5½	28/-	0	6¾	33/-	0	8	38/-	0	9	4.	1	8¼
24/-	0	5¾	29/-	0	7	34/-	0	8¼	39/-	0	9¼	5.	2	1¼
25/-	0s.	6	**30/-**	0s.	7¼	**35/-**	0s.	8½	**40/-**	0s.	9½	6.	2s.	6¼

2⅛% TWO & ONE-EIGHTH PER CENT. 2⅛%

£1	0s 5	£51	£1 1s. 8	£101	£2 2s.11	£151	£3 4s. 2
2	0 10¼	52	1 2 1¼	102	2 3 4¼	152	3 4 7¼
3	1 3¼	53	1 2 6¼	103	2 3 9¼	153	3 5 0¼
4	1 8½	54	1 2 11½	104	2 4 2½	154	3 5 5½
5	2 1½	55	1 3 4½	105	2 4 7½	155	3 5 10½
6	2 6½	56	1 3 9½	106	2 5 0½	156	3 6 3½
7	2 11¾	57	1 4 2¾	107	2 5 5¾	157	3 6 8¾
8	3 4¾	58	1 4 7¾	108	2 5 10¾	158	3 7 1¾
9	3 10	59	1 5 1	109	2 6 4	159	3 7 7
10	**4s. 3**	**60**	**£1 5s. 6**	**110**	**£2 6s. 9**	**160**	**£3 8s. 0**
11	4s. 8	61	£1 5s.11	111	£2 7s. 2	161	£3 8s. 5
12	5 1¼	62	1 6 4¼	112	2 7 7¼	162	3 8 10¼
13	5 6¼	63	1 6 9¼	113	2 8 0¼	163	3 9 3¼
14	5 11½	64	1 7 2½	114	2 8 5½	164	3 9 8½
15	6 4½	65	1 7 7½	115	2 8 10½	165	3 10 1½
16	6 9½	66	1 8 0½	116	2 9 3½	166	3 10 6½
17	7 2¾	67	1 8 5¾	117	2 9 8¾	167	3 10 11¾
18	7 7¾	68	1 8 10¾	118	2 10 1¾	168	3 11 4¾
19	8 1	69	1 9 4	119	2 10 7	169	3 11 10
20	**8s. 6**	**70**	**£1 9s. 9**	**120**	**£2 11s. 0**	**170**	**£3 12s. 3**
21	8s.11	71	£1 10s. 2	121	£2 11s. 5	171	£3 12s. 8
22	9 4¼	72	1 10 7¼	122	2 11 10¼	172	3 13 1¼
23	9 9¼	73	1 11 0¼	123	2 12 3¼	173	3 13 6¼
24	10 2½	74	1 11 5½	124	2 12 8½	174	3 13 11½
25	10 7½	75	1 11 10½	125	2 13 1½	175	3 14 4½
26	11 0½	76	1 12 3½	126	2 13 6½	176	3 14 9½
27	11 5¾	77	1 12 8¾	127	2 13 11¾	177	3 15 2¾
28	11 10¾	78	1 13 1¾	128	2 14 4¾	178	3 15 7¾
29	12 4	79	1 13 7	129	2 14 10	179	3 16 1
30	**12s. 9**	**80**	**£1 14s. 0**	**130**	**£2 15s. 3**	**180**	**£3 16s. 6**
31	13s. 2	81	£1 14s. 5	131	£2 15s. 8	181	£3 16s.11
32	13 7¼	82	1 14 10¼	132	2 16 1¼	182	3 17 4¼
33	14 0¼	83	1 15 3¼	133	2 16 6¼	183	3 17 9¼
34	14 5½	84	1 15 8½	134	2 16 11½	184	3 18 2½
35	14 10½	85	1 16 1½	135	2 17 4½	185	3 18 7½
36	15 3½	86	1 16 6½	136	2 17 9½	186	3 19 0½
37	15 8¾	87	1 16 11¾	137	2 18 2¾	187	3 19 5¾
38	16 1¾	88	1 17 4¾	138	2 18 7¾	188	3 19 10¾
39	16 7	89	1 17 10	139	2 19 1	189	4 0 4
40	**17s. 0**	**90**	**£1 18s. 3**	**140**	**£2 19s. 6**	**190**	**£4 0s. 9**
41	17s. 5	91	£1 18s. 8	141	£2 19s.11	191	£4 1s. 2
42	17 10¼	92	1 19 1¼	142	3 0 4¼	192	4 1 7¼
43	18 3¼	93	1 19 6¼	143	3 0 9¼	193	4 2 0¼
44	18 8½	94	1 19 11½	144	3 1 2½	194	4 2 5½
45	19 1½	95	2 0 4½	145	3 1 7½	195	4 2 10½
46	19 6½	96	2 0 9½	146	3 2 0½	196	4 3 3½
47	19 11¾	97	2 1 2¾	147	3 2 5¾	197	4 3 8¾
48	20 4¾	98	2 1 7¾	148	3 2 10¾	198	4 4 1¾
49	20 10	99	2 2 1	149	3 3 4	199	4 4 7
50	**21s. 3**	**100**	**£2 2s. 6**	**150**	**£3 3s. 9**	**200**	**£4 5s. 0**

250	5 6s.3d	700	14 17s. 6d	1200	£25 10s. 0d	2000	£42 10s. 0
300	6 7 6	750	15 18 9	1400	29 15 0	2500	53 2 6
400	8 10 0	800	17 0 0	1500	31 17 6	3000	63 15 0
500	10 12 6	900	19 2 6	1600	34 0 0	4000	85 0 0
600	12 15s.0d	1000	£21 5s. 0d	1800	£38 5s. 0d	5000	£106 5s. 0

97⅞% off.

2⅜% TWO & THREE-EIGHTHS PER CENT. 2⅜%

£1	0s. 5¾	£51	£1 4s. 2¾	£101	£2 7s.11¾	£151	£3 11s. 8¾
2	0 11½	52	1 4 8½	102	2 8 5½	152	3 12 2½
3	1 5	53	1 5 2	103	2 8 11	153	3 12 8
4	1 10¾	54	1 5 7¾	104	2 9 4¾	154	3 13 1¾
5	2 4½	55	1 6 1½	105	2 9 10½	155	3 13 7½
6	2 10¼	56	1 6 7¼	106	2 10 4¼	156	3 14 1¼
7	3 4	57	1 7 1	107	2 10 10	157	3 14 7
8	3 9½	58	1 7 6½	108	2 11 3½	158	3 15 0½
9	4 3¼	59	1 8 0¼	109	2 11 9¼	159	3 15 6¼
10	**4s. 9**	**60**	**£1 8s. 6**	**110**	**£2 12s. 3**	**160**	**£3 16s. 0**
11	5s. 2¾	61	£1 8s.11¾	111	£2 12s. 8¾	161	£3 16s. 5¾
12	5 8½	62	1 9 5½	112	2 13 2½	162	3 16 11½
13	6 2	63	1 9 11	113	2 13 8	163	3 17 5
14	6 7¾	64	1 10 4¾	114	2 14 1¾	164	3 17 10¾
15	7 1½	65	1 10 10½	115	2 14 7½	165	3 18 4½
16	7 7¼	66	1 11 4¼	116	2 15 1¼	166	3 18 10¼
17	8 1	67	1 11 10	117	2 15 7	167	3 19 4
18	8 6½	68	1 12 3½	118	2 16 0½	168	3 19 9½
19	9 0¼	69	1 12 9¼	119	2 16 6¼	169	4 0 3¼
20	**9s. 6**	**70**	**£1 13s. 3**	**120**	**£2 17s. 0**	**170**	**£4 0s. 9**
21	9s.11¾	71	£1 13s. 8¾	121	£2 17s. 5¾	171	£4 1s. 2¾
22	10 5½	72	1 14 2½	122	2 17 11½	172	4 1 8½
23	10 11	73	1 14 8	123	2 18 5	173	4 2 2
24	11 4¾	74	1 15 1¾	124	2 18 10¾	174	4 2 7¾
25	11 10½	75	1 15 7½	125	2 19 4½	175	4 3 1½
26	12 4¼	76	1 16 1¼	126	2 19 10¼	176	4 3 7¼
27	12 10	77	1 16 7	127	3 0 4	177	4 4 1
28	13 3½	78	1 17 0½	128	3 0 9½	178	4 4 6½
29	13 9¼	79	1 17 6¼	129	3 1 3¼	179	4 5 0¼
30	**14s. 3**	**80**	**£1 18s. 0**	**130**	**£3 1s. 9**	**180**	**£4 5s. 6**
31	14s. 8¾	81	£1 18s. 5¾	131	£3 2s. 2¾	181	£4 5s.11¾
32	15 2½	82	1 18 11½	132	3 2 8½	182	4 6 5½
33	15 8	83	1 19 5	133	3 3 2	183	4 6 11
34	16 1¾	84	1 19 10¾	134	3 3 7¾	184	4 7 4¾
35	16 7½	85	2 0 4½	135	3 4 1½	185	4 7 10½
36	17 1¼	86	2 0 10¼	136	3 4 7¼	186	4 8 4¼
37	17 7	87	2 1 4	137	3 5 1	187	4 8 10
38	18 0½	88	2 1 9½	138	3 5 6½	188	4 9 3½
39	18 6¼	89	2 2 3¼	139	3 6 0¼	189	4 9 9¼
40	**19s. 0**	**90**	**£2 2s. 9**	**140**	**£3 6s. 6**	**190**	**£4 10s. 3**
41	19s. 5¾	91	£2 3s. 2¾	141	£3 6s.11¾	191	£4 10s. 8¾
42	19 11½	92	2 3 8½	142	3 7 5½	192	4 11 2½
43	20 5	93	2 4 2	143	3 7 11	193	4 11 8
44	20 10¾	94	2 4 7¾	144	3 8 4¾	194	4 12 1¾
45	21 4½	95	2 5 1½	145	3 8 10½	195	4 12 7½
46	21 10¼	96	2 5 7¼	146	3 9 4¼	196	4 13 1¼
47	22 4	97	2 6 1	147	3 9 10	197	4 13 7
48	22 9½	98	2 6 6½	148	3 10 3½	198	4 14 0½
49	23 3¼	99	2 7 0¼	149	3 10 9¼	199	4 14 6¼
50	**23s. 9**	**100**	**£2 7s. 6**	**150**	**£3 11s. 3**	**200**	**£4 15s. 0**
250	5 18s.9d	700	16 12s. 6d	1200	£28 10s. 0d	2000	£47 10s. 0
300	7 2 6	750	17 16 3	1400	33 5 0	2500	59 7 6
400	9 10 0	800	19 0 0	1500	35 12 6	3000	71 5 0
500	11 17 6	900	21 7 6	1600	38 0 0	4000	95 0 0
600	14 5s.0d	1000	£23 15s. 0d	1800	£42 15s. 0d	5000	£118 15s. 0

97⅝% off.

£1	£0	0s	5½	£51	£1	2s	11½	£101	£2	5s	5½	£151	£3	7s	11½
2	0	0	10¾	52	1	3	4¾	102	2	5	10¾	152	3	8	4¾
3	0	1	4¼	53	1	3	10¼	103	2	6	4¼	153	3	8	10¼
4	0	1	9½	54	1	4	3½	104	2	6	9½	154	3	9	3½
5	0	2	3	55	1	4	9	105	2	7	3	155	3	9	9
6	0	2	8½	56	1	5	2½	106	2	7	8½	156	3	10	2½
7	0	3	1¾	57	1	5	7¾	107	2	8	1¾	157	3	10	7¾
8	0	3	7¼	58	1	6	1¼	108	2	8	7¼	158	3	11	1¼
9	0	4	0½	59	1	6	6½	109	2	9	0½	159	3	11	6½
10	**0**	**4**	**6**	**60**	**1**	**7**	**0**	**110**	**2**	**9**	**6**	**160**	**3**	**12**	**0**
11	0	4	11½	61	1	7	5½	111	2	9	11½	161	3	12	5½
12	0	5	4¾	62	1	7	10¾	112	2	10	4¾	162	3	12	10¾
13	0	5	10¼	63	1	8	4¼	113	2	10	10¼	163	3	13	4¼
14	0	6	3½	64	1	8	9½	114	2	11	3½	164	3	13	9½
15	0	6	9	65	1	9	3	115	2	11	9	165	3	14	3
16	0	7	2½	66	1	9	8½	116	2	12	2½	166	3	14	8½
17	0	7	7¾	67	1	10	1¾	117	2	12	7¾	167	3	15	1¾
18	0	8	1¼	68	1	10	7¼	118	2	13	1¼	168	3	15	7¼
19	0	8	6½	69	1	11	0½	119	2	13	6½	169	3	16	0½
20	**0**	**9**	**0**	**70**	**1**	**11**	**6**	**120**	**2**	**14**	**0**	**170**	**3**	**16**	**6**
21	0	9	5½	71	1	11	11½	121	2	14	5½	171	3	16	11½
22	0	9	10¾	72	1	12	4¾	122	2	14	10¾	172	3	17	4¾
23	0	10	4¼	73	1	12	10¼	123	2	15	4¼	173	3	17	10¼
24	0	10	9½	74	1	13	3½	124	2	15	9½	174	3	18	3½
25	0	11	3	75	1	13	9	125	2	16	3	175	3	18	9
26	0	11	8½	76	1	14	2½	126	2	16	8½	176	3	19	2½
27	0	12	1¾	77	1	14	7¾	127	2	17	1¾	177	3	19	7¾
28	0	12	7¼	78	1	15	1¼	128	2	17	7¼	178	4	0	1¼
29	0	13	0½	79	1	15	6½	129	2	18	0½	179	4	0	6½
30	**0**	**13**	**6**	**80**	**1**	**16**	**0**	**130**	**2**	**18**	**6**	**180**	**4**	**1**	**0**
31	0	13	11½	81	1	16	5½	131	2	18	11½	181	4	1	5½
32	0	14	4¾	82	1	16	10¾	132	2	19	4¾	182	4	1	10¾
33	0	14	10¼	83	1	17	4¼	133	2	19	10¼	183	4	2	4¼
34	0	15	3½	84	1	17	9½	134	3	0	3½	184	4	2	9½
35	0	15	9	85	1	18	3	135	3	0	9	185	4	3	3
36	0	16	2½	86	1	18	8½	136	3	1	2½	186	4	3	8½
37	0	16	7¾	87	1	19	1¾	137	3	1	7¾	187	4	4	1¾
38	0	17	1¼	88	1	19	7¼	138	3	2	1¼	188	4	4	7¼
39	0	17	6½	89	2	0	0½	139	3	2	6½	189	4	5	0½
40	**0**	**18**	**0**	**90**	**2**	**0**	**6**	**140**	**3**	**3**	**0**	**190**	**4**	**5**	**6**
41	0	18	5½	91	2	0	11½	141	3	3	5½	191	4	5	11½
42	0	18	10¾	92	2	1	4¾	142	3	3	10¾	192	4	6	4¾
43	0	19	4¼	93	2	1	10¼	143	3	4	4¼	193	4	6	10¼
44	0	19	9½	94	2	2	3½	144	3	4	9½	194	4	7	3½
45	1	0	3	95	2	2	9	145	3	5	3	195	4	7	9
46	1	0	8½	96	2	3	2½	146	3	5	8½	196	4	8	2½
47	1	1	1¾	97	2	3	7¾	147	3	6	1¾	197	4	8	7¾
48	1	1	7¼	98	2	4	1¼	148	3	6	7¼	198	4	9	1¼
49	1	2	0½	99	2	4	6½	149	3	7	0½	199	4	9	6½
50	**1**	**2**	**6**	**100**	**2**	**5**	**0**	**150**	**3**	**7**	**6**	**200**	**4**	**10**	**0**
250	5	12s	6d	700	15	15s	0d	1200	27	0s	0d	2000	45	0s	0d
300	6	15	0	750	16	17	6	1400	31	10	0	2500	56	5	0
400	9	0	0	800	18	0	0	1500	33	15	0	3000	67	10	0
500	11	5	0	900	20	5	0	1600	36	0	0	4000	90	0	0
600	13	10s	0d	1000	22	10s	0d	1800	40	10s	0d	5000	112	10s	0d

97¾% off.

1d	0s.	0d	4/1	0s.	1	8/1	0s.	2¼	12/1	0s.	3¼	16/1	0s.	4¼
2d	0	0	2	0	1¼	2	0	2¼	2	0	3¼	2	0	4¼
3d	0	0	3	0	1¼	3	0	2¼	3	0	3¼	3	0	4½
4d	0	0	4	0	1¼	4	0	2¼	4	0	3¼	4	0	4½
5d	0	0	5	0	1¼	5	0	2¼	5	0	3¼	5	0	4½
6d	0	0¼	4/6	0	1¼	8/6	0	2¼	12/6	0	3½	16/6	0	4½
7d	0	0¼	7	0	1¼	7	0	2¼	7	0	3½	7	0	4½
8d	0	0¼	8	0	1¼	8	0	2¼	8	0	3½	8	0	4½
9d	0	0¼	9	0	1¼	9	0	2¼	9	0	3½	9	0	4½
10d	0	0¼	10	0	1¼	10	0	2½	10	0	3½	10	0	4½
11d	0	0¼	11	0	1¼	11	0	2½	11	0	3½	11	0	4½
1/-	0s.	0¼	**5/-**	0s.	1¼	**9/-**	0s.	2½	**13/-**	0s.	3½	**17/-**	0s.	4½
1/1	0s.	0¼	5/1	0s.	1¼	9/1	0s.	2½	13/1	0s.	3½	17/1	0s.	4½
2	0	0¼	2	0	1½	2	0	2½	2	0	3½	2	0	4¾
3	0	0½	3	0	1½	3	0	2½	3	0	3½	3	0	4¾
4	0	0¼	4	0	1½	4	0	2½	4	0	3½	4	0	4¾
5	0	0½	5	0	1½	5	0	2½	5	0	3½	5	0	4¾
1/6	0	0½	5/6	0	1½	9/6	0	2½	13/6	0	3¾	17/6	0	4¾
7	0	0½	7	0	1½	7	0	2½	7	0	3¾	7	0	4¾
8	0	0½	8	0	1½	8	0	2½	8	0	3¾	8	0	4¾
9	0	0½	9	0	1½	9	0	2¾	9	0	3¾	9	0	4¾
10	0	0½	10	0	1½	10	0	2¾	10	0	3¾	10	0	4¾
11	0	0½	11	0	1½	11	0	2¾	11	0	3¾	11	0	4¾
2/-	0s.	0½	**6/-**	0s.	1½	**10/-**	0s.	2¾	**14/-**	0s.	3¾	**18/-**	0s.	4¾
2/1	0s.	0½	6/1	0s.	1¾	10/1	0s.	2¾	14/1	0s.	3¾	18/1	0s.	5
2	0	0½	2	0	1¾	2	0	2¾	2	0	3¾	2	0	5
3	0	0½	3	0	1¾	3	0	2¾	3	0	3¾	3	0	5
4	0	0¾	4	0	1¾	4	0	2¾	4	0	3¾	4	0	5
5	0	0¾	5	0	1¾	5	0	2¾	5	0	4	5	0	5
2/6	0	0¾	6/6	0	1¾	10/6	0	2¾	14/6	0	4	18/6	0	5
7	0	0¾	7	0	1¾	7	0	2¾	7	0	4	7	0	5
8	0	0¾	8	0	1¾	8	0	3	8	0	4	8	0	5
9	0	0¾	9	0	1¾	9	0	3	9	0	4	9	0	5
10	0	0¾	10	0	1¾	10	0	3	10	0	4	10	0	5
11	0	0¾	11	0	1¾	11	0	3	11	0	4	11	0	5
3/-	0s.	0¾	**7/-**	0s.	2	**11/-**	0s.	3	**15/-**	0s.	4	**19/-**	0s.	5¼
3/1	0s.	0¾	7/1	0s.	2	11/1	0s.	3	15/1	0s.	4	19/1	0s.	5¼
2	0	0¾	2	0	2	2	0	3	2	0	4	2	0	5¼
3	0	1	3	0	2	3	0	3	3	0	4	3	0	5¼
4	0	1	4	0	2	4	0	3	4	0	4¼	4	0	5¼
5	0	1	5	0	2	5	0	3	5	0	4¼	5	0	5¼
3/6	0	1	7/6	0	2	11/6	0	3	15/6	0	4¼	19/6	0	5¼
7	0	1	7	0	2	7	0	3¼	7	0	4¼	7	0	5¼
8	0	1	8	0	2	8	0	3¼	8	0	4¼	8	0	5¼
9	0	1	9	0	2	9	0	3¼	9	0	4¼	9	0	5¼
10	0	1	10	0	2	10	0	3¼	10	0	4¼	10	0	5¼
11	0	1	11	0	2¼	11	0	3¼	11	0	4¼	11	0	5½
4/-	0s.	1	**8/-**	0s.	2¼	**12/-**	0s.	3¼	**16/-**	0s.	4¼	**20/-**	0s.	5½

20/6	0s.	5½	25/6	0s.	7	31/-	0s.	8¼	35/6	0s.	9½	Guineas.		
21/-	0	5¾	26/-	0	7	31/6	0	8½	36/-	0	9¾	1.	0s.	5¾
22/-	0	6	27/-	0	7¼	32/-	0	8¾	37/-	0	10	2.	0	11¼
22/6	0	6	27/6	0	7½	32/6	0	8¾	37/6	0	10¼	3.	1	5
23/-	0	6¼	28/-	0	7½	33/-	0	9	38/-	0	10¼	4.	1	10¾
24/-	0	6½	29/-	0	7¾	34/-	0	9¼	39/-	0	10½	5.	2	4¼
25/-	0s.	6¾	**30/-**	0s.	8	**35/-**	0s.	9½	**40/-**	0s.	10¾	6.	2s.	10

2½%   2½ PER CENT.   2½%

£1	£0	0s 6	£51	£1	5s 6	£101	£2	10s 6	£151	£3	15s 6
2	0	1 0	52	1	6 0	102	2	11 0	152	3	16 0
3	0	1 6	53	1	6 6	103	2	11 6	153	3	16 0
4	0	2 0	54	1	7 0	104	2	12 0	154	3	17 0
5	0	2 6	55	1	7 6	105	2	12 6	155	3	17 6
6	0	3 0	56	1	8 0	106	2	13 0	156	3	18 0
7	0	3 6	57	1	8 6	107	2	13 6	157	3	18 6
8	0	4 0	58	1	9 0	108	2	14 0	158	3	19 0
9	0	4 6	59	1	9 6	109	2	14 6	159	3	19 6
10	0	5 0	60	1	10 0	110	2	15 0	160	4	0 0
11	0	5 6	61	1	10 6	111	2	15 6	161	4	0 6
12	0	6 0	62	1	11 0	112	2	16 0	162	4	1 0
13	0	6 6	63	1	11 6	113	2	16 6	163	4	1 6
14	0	7 0	64	1	12 0	114	2	17 0	164	4	2 0
15	0	7 6	65	1	12 6	115	2	17 6	165	4	2 6
16	0	8 0	66	1	13 0	116	2	18 0	166	4	3 0
17	0	8 6	67	1	13 6	117	2	18 6	167	4	3 6
18	0	9 0	68	1	14 0	118	2	19 0	168	4	4 0
19	0	9 6	69	1	14 6	119	2	19 6	169	4	4 6
20	0	10 0	70	1	15 0	120	3	0 0	170	4	5 0
21	0	10 6	71	1	15 6	121	3	0 6	171	4	5 6
22	0	11 0	72	1	16 0	122	3	1 0	172	4	6 0
23	0	11 6	73	1	16 6	123	3	1 6	173	4	6 6
24	0	12 0	74	1	17 0	124	3	2 0	174	4	7 0
25	0	12 6	75	1	17 6	125	3	2 6	175	4	7 6
26	0	13 0	76	1	18 0	126	3	3 0	176	4	8 0
27	0	13 6	77	1	18 6	127	3	3 6	177	4	8 6
28	0	14 0	78	1	19 0	128	3	4 0	178	4	9 0
29	0	14 6	79	1	19 6	129	3	4 6	179	4	9 6
30	0	15 0	80	2	0 0	130	3	5 0	180	4	10 0
31	0	15 6	81	2	0 6	131	3	5 6	181	4	10 6
32	0	16 0	82	2	1 0	132	3	6 0	182	4	11 0
33	0	16 6	83	2	1 6	133	3	6 6	183	4	11 6
34	0	17 0	84	2	2 0	134	3	7 0	184	4	12 0
35	0	17 6	85	2	2 6	135	3	7 6	185	4	12 6
36	0	18 0	86	2	3 0	136	3	8 0	186	4	13 0
37	0	18 6	87	2	3 6	137	3	8 6	187	4	13 6
38	0	19 0	88	2	4 0	138	3	9 0	188	4	14 0
39	0	19 6	89	2	4 6	139	3	9 6	189	4	14 6
40	1	0 0	90	2	5 0	140	3	10 0	190	4	15 0
41	1	0 6	91	2	5 6	141	3	10 6	191	4	15 6
42	1	1 0	92	2	6 0	142	3	11 0	192	4	16 0
43	1	1 6	93	2	6 6	143	3	11 6	193	4	16 6
44	1	2 0	94	2	7 0	144	3	12 0	194	4	17 0
45	1	2 6	95	2	7 6	145	3	12 6	195	4	17 6
46	1	3 0	96	2	8 0	146	3	13 0	196	4	18 0
47	1	3 6	97	2	8 6	147	3	13 6	197	4	18 6
48	1	4 0	98	2	9 0	148	3	14 0	198	4	19 0
49	1	4 6	99	2	9 6	149	3	14 6	199	4	19 6
50	1	5 0	100	2	10 0	150	3	15 0	200	5	0 0

250	6	5s 0d	700	17	10s 0d	1200	30	0s 0d	2000	50	0s 0d
300	7	10 0	750	18	15 0	1400	35	0 0	2500	62	10 0
400	10	0 0	800	20	0 0	1500	37	10 0	3000	75	0 0
500	12	10 0	900	22	10 0	1600	40	0 0	4000	100	0 0
600	15	0s 0d	1000	25	0s 0d	1800	45	0s 0d	5000	125	0s 0d

97½% off.

1d	0s.	0d	4/1	0s.	1¼	8/1	0s.	2½	12/1	0s.	3¾	16/1	0s.	4¾
2d	0	0	2	0	1¼	2	0	2½	2	0	3¾	2	0	4¾
3d	0	0	3	0	1¼	3	0	2½	3	0	3¾	3	0	5
4d	0	0	4	0	1¼	4	0	2½	4	0	3¾	4	0	5
5d	0	0¼	5	0	1¼	5	0	2½	5	0	3¾	5	0	5
6d	0	0¼	4/6	0	1¼	8/6	0	2½	12/6	0	3¾	16/6	0	5
7d	0	0¼	7	0	1½	7	0	2½	7	0	3¾	7	0	5
8d	0	0¼	8	0	1½	8	0	2½	8	0	3¾	8	0	5
9d	0	0¼	9	0	1½	9	0	2¾	9	0	3¾	9	0	5
10d	0	0¼	10	0	1½	10	0	2¾	10	0	3¾	10	0	5
11d	0	0¼	11	0	1½	11	0	2¾	11	0	4	11	0	5
1/-	0s.	0¼	**5/-**	0s.	1½	**9/-**	0s.	2¾	**13/-**	0s.	4	**17/-**	0s.	5
1/1	0s.	0¼	5/1	0s.	1½	9/1	0s.	2¾	13/1	0s.	4	17/1	0s.	5¼
2	0	0¼	2	0	1½	2	0	2¾	2	0	4	2	0	5¼
3	0	0½	3	0	1½	3	0	2¾	3	0	4	3	0	5¼
4	0	0½	4	0	1½	4	0	2¾	4	0	4	4	0	5¼
5	0	0½	5	0	1¾	5	0	2¾	5	0	4	5	0	5¼
1/6	0	0½	5/6	0	1¾	9/6	0	2¾	13/6	0	4	17/6	0	5¼
7	0	0½	7	0	1¾	7	0	3	7	0	4	7	0	5¼
8	0	0½	8	0	1¾	8	0	3	8	0	4	8	0	5¼
9	0	0½	9	0	1¾	9	0	3	9	0	4¼	9	0	5¼
10	0	0½	10	0	1¾	10	0	3	10	0	4¼	10	0	5¼
11	0	0½	11	0	1¾	11	0	3	11	0	4¼	11	0	5½
2/-	0s.	0½	**6/-**	0s.	1¾	**10/-**	0s.	3	**14/-**	0s.	4¼	**18/-**	0s.	5½
2/1	0s.	0¾	6/1	0s.	1¾	10/1	0s.	3	14/1	0s.	4¼	18/1	0s.	5½
2	0	0¾	2	0	1¾	2	0	3	2	0	4¼	2	0	5½
3	0	0¾	3	0	2	3	0	3	3	0	4¼	3	0	5½
4	0	0¾	4	0	2	4	0	3	4	0	4¼	4	0	5½
5	0	0¾	5	0	2	5	0	3¼	5	0	4¼	5	0	5½
2/6	0	0¾	6/6	0	2	10/6	0	3¼	14/6	0	4¼	18/6	0	5½
7	0	0¾	7	0	2	7	0	3¼	7	0	4½	7	0	5½
8	0	0¾	8	0	2	8	0	3¼	8	0	4½	8	0	5½
9	0	0¾	9	0	2	9	0	3¼	9	0	4½	9	0	5¾
10	0	0¾	10	0	2	10	0	3¼	10	0	4½	10	0	5¾
11	0	1	11	0	2	11	0	3¼	11	0	4½	11	0	5¾
3/-	0s.	1	**7/-**	0s.	2	**11/-**	0s.	3¼	**15/-**	0s.	4½	**19/-**	0s.	5¾
3/1	0s.	1	7/1	0s.	2¼	11/1	0s.	3¼	15/1	0s.	4½	19/1	0s.	5¾
2	0	1	2	0	2¼	2	0	3¼	2	0	4½	2	0	5¾
3	0	1	3	0	2¼	3	0	3½	3	0	4½	3	0	5¾
4	0	1	4	0	2¼	4	0	3½	4	0	4½	4	0	5¾
5	0	1	5	0	2¼	5	0	3½	5	0	4¾	5	0	5¾
3/6	0	1	7/6	0	2¼	11/6	0	3½	15/6	0	4¾	19/6	0	5¾
7	0	1	7	0	2¼	7	0	3½	7	0	4¾	7	0	6
8	0	1	8	0	2¼	8	0	3½	8	0	4¾	8	0	6
9	0	1¼	9	0	2¼	9	0	3½	9	0	4¾	9	0	6
10	0	1¼	10	0	2¼	10	0	3½	10	0	4¾	10	0	6
11	0	1¼	11	0	2½	11	0	3½	11	0	4¾	11	0	6
4/-	0s.	1¼	**8/-**	0s.	2½	**12/-**	0s.	3½	**16/-**	0s.	4¾	**20/-**	0s.	6

20/6	0s.	6¼	25/6	0s.	7¾	31/-	0s.	9¼	35/6	0s.	10¾	Guineas.		
21/-	0	6¼	26/-	0	7¾	31/6	0	9½	36/-	0	10¾	1.	0s.	6¼
22/-	0	6½	27/-	0	8	32/-	0	9½	37/-	0	11	2.	1	0½
22/6	0	6¾	27/6	0	8¼	32/6	0	9¾	37/6	0	11¼	3.	1	7
23/-	0	7	28/-	0	8½	33/-	0	10	38/-	0	11½	4.	2	1¼
24/-	0	7¼	29/-	0	8¾	34/-	0	10¼	39/-	0	11¾	5.	2	7½
25/-	0s.	7½	**30/-**	0s.	9	**35/-**	0s.	10½	**40/-**	1s.	0	6.	3s.	1¾

(=2$\frac{4}{10}$%* on Gross Returns).

2⅝% £2. 12. 6 PER CENT OR PER 100. 2⅝%

£1	0s. 6¼	£51	£1 6s. 9¼	£101	£2 13s. 0¼	£151	£3 19s. 3¼
2	1 0½	52	1 7 3½	102	2 13 6½	152	3 19 9½
3	1 7	53	1 7 10	103	2 14 1	153	4 0 4
4	2 1¼	54	1 8 4¼	104	2 14 7¼	154	4 0 10¼
5	2 7½	55	1 8 10½	105	2 15 1½	155	4 1 4½
6	3 1¾	56	1 9 4¾	106	2 15 7¾	156	4 1 10¾
7	3 8	57	1 9 11	107	2 16 2	157	4 2 5
8	4 2½	58	1 10 5½	108	2 16 8½	158	4 2 11½
9	4 8¾	59	1 10 11¾	109	2 17 2¾	159	4 3 5¾
10	5s. 3	**60**	£1 11s. 6	**110**	£2 17s. 9	**160**	£4 4s. 0
11	5s. 9¼	61	£1 12s. 0¼	111	£2 18s. 3¼	161	£4 4s. 6¼
12	6 3½	62	1 12 6½	112	2 18 9½	162	4 5 0½
13	6 10	63	1 13 1	113	2 19 4	163	4 5 7
14	7 4¼	64	1 13 7¼	114	2 19 10¼	164	4 6 1¼
15	7 10½	65	1 14 1½	115	3 0 4½	165	4 6 7½
16	8 4¾	66	1 14 7¾	116	3 0 10¾	166	4 7 1¾
17	8 11	67	1 15 2	117	3 1 5	167	4 7 8
18	9 5½	68	1 15 8½	118	3 1 11½	168	4 8 2½
19	9 11¾	69	1 16 2¾	119	3 2 5¾	169	4 8 8¾
20	10s. 6	**70**	£1 16s. 9	**120**	£3 3s. 0	**170**	£4 9s. 3
21	11s. 0¼	71	£1 17s. 3¼	121	£3 3s. 6¼	171	£4 9s. 9¼
22	11 6½	72	1 17 9½	122	3 4 0½	172	4 10 3½
23	12 1	73	1 18 4	123	3 4 7	173	4 10 10
24	12 7¼	74	1 18 10¼	124	3 5 1¼	174	4 11 4¼
25	13 1½	75	1 19 4½	125	3 5 7½	175	4 11 10½
26	13 7¾	76	1 19 10¾	126	3 6 1¾	176	4 12 4¾
27	14 2	77	2 0 5	127	3 6 8	177	4 12 11
28	14 8½	78	2 0 11½	128	3 7 2½	178	4 13 5½
29	15 2¾	79	2 1 5¾	129	3 7 8¾	179	4 13 11¾
30	15s. 9	**80**	£2 2s. 0	**130**	£3 8s. 3	**180**	£4 14s. 6
31	16s. 3¼	81	£2 2s. 6¼	131	£3 8s. 9¼	181	£4 15s. 0¼
32	16 9½	82	2 3 0½	132	3 9 3½	182	4 15 6½
33	17 4	83	2 3 7	133	3 9 10	183	4 16 1
34	17 10¼	84	2 4 1¼	134	3 10 4¼	184	4 16 7¼
35	18 4½	85	2 4 7½	135	3 10 10½	185	4 17 1½
36	18 10¾	86	2 5 1¾	136	3 11 4¾	186	4 17 7¾
37	19 5	87	2 5 8	137	3 11 11	187	4 18 2
38	19 11½	88	2 6 2½	138	3 12 5½	188	4 18 8½
39	20 5¾	89	2 6 8¾	139	3 12 11¾	189	4 19 2¾
40	21s. 0	**90**	£2 7s. 3	**140**	£3 13s. 6	**190**	£4 19s. 9
41	21s. 6¼	91	£2 7s. 9¼	141	£3 14s. 0¼	191	£5 0s. 3¼
42	22 0½	92	2 8 3½	142	3 14 6½	192	5 0 9½
43	22 7	93	2 8 10	143	3 15 1	193	5 1 4
44	23 1¼	94	2 9 4¼	144	3 15 7¼	194	5 1 10¼
45	23 7½	95	2 9 10½	145	3 16 1½	195	5 2 4½
46	24 1¾	96	2 10 4¾	146	3 16 7¾	196	5 2 10¾
47	24 8	97	2 10 11	147	3 17 2	197	5 3 5
48	25 2½	98	2 11 5½	148	3 17 8½	198	5 3 11½
49	25 8¾	99	2 11 11¾	149	3 18 2¾	199	5 4 5¾
50	26s. 3	**100**	£2 12s. 6	**150**	£3 18s. 9	**200**	£5 5s. 0
250	6 11s.3d	700	18 7s. 6d	1200	£31 10s. 0d	2000	£52 10s. 0
300	7 17 6	750	19 13 9	1400	36 15 0	2500	65 12 6
400	10 10 0	800	21 0 0	1500	39 7 6	3000	78 15 0
500	13 2 6	900	23 12 6	1600	42 0 0	4000	105 0 0
600	15 15s.0d	1000	£26 5s. 0d	1800	£47 5s. 0d	5000	£131 5s. 0

97⅜% off. (=2 6/10%* on Gross Returns).

2⅞% £2. 17. 6 PER CENT OR PER 100. 2⅞%

£1	0s. 7	£51	£1 9s. 4	£101	£2 18s. 1	£151	£4 6s.10
2	1 1¾	52	1 9 10¾	102	2 18 7¾	152	4 7 4¾
3	1 8¾	53	1 10 5¾	103	2 19 2¾	153	4 7 11¾
4	2 3½	54	1 11 0½	104	2 19 9½	154	4 8 6½
5	2 10½	55	1 11 7½	105	3 0 4½	155	4 9 1½
6	3 5½	56	1 12 2½	106	3 0 11½	156	4 9 8½
7	4 0¼	57	1 12 9¼	107	3 1 6¼	157	4 10 3¼
8	4 7¼	58	1 13 4¼	108	3 2 1¼	158	4 10 10¼
9	5 2	59	1 13 11	109	3 2 8	159	4 11 5
10	**5s. 9**	**60**	**£1 14s. 6**	**110**	**£3 3s. 3**	**160**	**£4 12s. 0**
11	6s. 4	61	£1 15s. 1	111	£3 3s.10	161	£4 12s. 7
12	6 10¾	62	1 15 7¾	112	3 4 4¾	162	4 13 1¾
13	7 5¾	63	1 16 2¾	113	3 4 11¾	163	4 13 8¾
14	8 0½	64	1 16 9½	114	3 5 6½	164	4 14 3½
15	8 7½	65	1 17 4½	115	3 6 1½	165	4 14 10½
16	9 2½	66	1 17 11½	116	3 6 8½	166	4 15 5½
17	9 9¼	67	1 18 6¼	117	3 7 3¼	167	4 16 0¼
18	10 4¼	68	1 19 1¼	118	3 7 10¼	168	4 16 7¼
19	10 11	69	1 19 8	119	3 8 5	169	4 17 2
20	**11s. 6**	**70**	**£2 0s. 3**	**120**	**£3 9s. 0**	**170**	**£4 17s. 9**
21	12s. 1	71	£2 0s.10	121	£3 9s. 7	171	£4 18s. 4
22	12 7¾	72	2 1 4¾	122	3 10 1¾	172	4 18 10¾
23	13 2¾	73	2 1 11¾	123	3 10 8¾	173	4 19 5¾
24	13 9½	74	2 2 6½	124	3 11 3½	174	5 0 0½
25	14 4½	75	2 3 1½	125	3 11 10½	175	5 0 7½
26	14 11½	76	2 3 8½	126	3 12 5½	176	5 1 2½
27	15 6¼	77	2 4 3¼	127	3 13 0¼	177	5 1 9¼
28	16 1¼	78	2 4 10¼	128	3 13 7¼	178	5 2 4¼
29	16 8	79	2 5 5	129	3 14 2	179	5 2 11
30	**17s. 3**	**80**	**£2 6s. 0**	**130**	**£3 14s. 9**	**180**	**£5 3s. 6**
31	17s.10	81	£2 6s. 7	131	£3 15s. 4	181	£5 4s. 1
32	18 4¾	82	2 7 1¾	132	3 15 10¾	182	5 4 7¾
33	18 11¾	83	2 7 8¾	133	3 16 5¾	183	5 5 2¾
34	19 6½	84	2 8 3½	134	3 17 0½	184	5 5 9½
35	20 1½	85	2 8 10½	135	3 17 7½	185	5 6 4½
36	20 8½	86	2 9 5½	136	3 18 2½	186	5 6 11½
37	21 3¼	87	2 10 0¼	137	3 18 9¼	187	5 7 6¼
38	21 10¼	88	2 10 7¼	138	3 19 4¼	188	5 8 1¼
39	22 5	89	2 11 2	139	3 19 11	189	5 8 8
40	**23s. 0**	**90**	**£2 11s. 9**	**140**	**£4 0s. 6**	**190**	**£5 9s. 3**
41	23s. 7	91	£2 12s. 4	141	£4 1s. 1	191	£5 9s.10
42	24 1¾	92	2 12 10¾	142	4 1 7¾	192	5 10 4¾
43	24 8¾	93	2 13 5¾	143	4 2 2¾	193	5 10 11¾
44	25 3½	94	2 14 0½	144	4 2 9½	194	5 11 6½
45	25 10½	95	2 14 7½	145	4 3 4½	195	5 12 1½
46	26 5½	96	2 15 2½	146	4 3 11½	196	5 12 8½
47	27 0¼	97	2 15 9¼	147	4 4 6¼	197	5 13 3¼
48	27 7¼	98	2 16 4¼	148	4 5 1¼	198	5 13 10¼
49	28 2	99	2 16 11	149	4 5 8	199	5 14 5
50	**28s. 9**	**100**	**£2 17s. 6**	**150**	**£4 6s. 3**	**200**	**£5 15s. 0**
250	7 3s.9d	700	20 2s. 6d	1200	£34 10s. 0d	2000	£57 10s. 0
300	8 12 6	750	21 11 3	1400	40 5 0	2500	71 17 6
400	11 10 0	800	23 0 0	1500	43 2 6	3000	86 5 0
500	14 7 6	900	25 17 6	1600	46 0 0	4000	115 0 0
600	17 5s.0d	1000	£28 15s. 0d	1800	£51 15s. 0d	5000	£143 15s. 0

97⅛% off. (=2$\frac{8}{10}$%* on Gross Returns).

£1	£0	0s	6½	£51	£1	8s	0½	£101	£2	15s	6½	£151	£4	3s	0½
2	0	1	1¼	52	1	8	7¼	102	2	16	1¼	152	4	3	7¼
3	0	1	7¾	53	1	9	1¾	103	2	16	7¾	153	4	4	1¾
4	0	2	2½	54	1	9	8½	104	2	17	2½	154	4	4	8½
5	0	2	9	55	1	10	3	105	2	17	9	155	4	5	3
6	0	3	3½	56	1	10	9½	106	2	18	3½	156	4	5	9½
7	0	3	10¼	57	1	11	4¼	107	2	18	10¼	157	4	6	4¼
8	0	4	4¾	58	1	11	10¾	108	2	19	4¾	158	4	6	10¾
9	0	4	11½	59	1	12	5½	109	2	19	11½	159	4	7	5½
10	**0**	**5**	**6**	**60**	**1**	**13**	**0**	**110**	**3**	**0**	**6**	**160**	**4**	**8**	**0**
11	0	6	0½	61	1	13	6½	111	3	1	0½	161	4	8	6½
12	0	6	7¼	62	1	14	1¼	112	3	1	7¼	162	4	9	1¼
13	0	7	1¾	63	1	14	7¾	113	3	2	1¾	163	4	9	7¾
14	0	7	8½	64	1	15	2½	114	3	2	8½	164	4	10	2½
15	0	8	3	65	1	15	9	115	3	3	3	165	4	10	9
16	0	8	9½	66	1	16	3½	116	3	3	9½	166	4	11	3½
17	0	9	4¼	67	1	16	10¼	117	3	4	4¼	167	4	11	10¼
18	0	9	10¾	68	1	17	4¾	118	3	4	10¾	168	4	12	4¾
19	0	10	5½	69	1	17	11½	119	3	5	5½	169	4	12	11½
20	**0**	**11**	**0**	**70**	**1**	**18**	**6**	**120**	**3**	**6**	**0**	**170**	**4**	**13**	**6**
21	0	11	6½	71	1	19	0½	121	3	6	6½	171	4	14	0½
22	0	12	1¼	72	1	19	7¼	122	3	7	1¼	172	4	14	7¼
23	0	12	7¾	73	2	0	1¾	123	3	7	7¾	173	4	15	1¾
24	0	13	2½	74	2	0	8½	124	3	8	2½	174	4	15	8½
25	0	13	9	75	2	1	3	125	3	8	9	175	4	16	3
26	0	14	3½	76	2	1	9½	126	3	9	3½	176	4	16	9½
27	0	14	10¼	77	2	2	4¼	127	3	9	10¼	177	4	17	4¼
28	0	15	4¾	78	2	2	10¾	128	3	10	4¾	178	4	17	10¾
29	0	15	11½	79	2	3	5½	129	3	10	11½	179	4	18	5½
30	**0**	**16**	**6**	**80**	**2**	**4**	**0**	**130**	**3**	**11**	**6**	**180**	**4**	**19**	**0**
31	0	17	0½	81	2	4	6½	131	3	12	0½	181	4	19	6½
32	0	17	7¼	82	2	5	1¼	132	3	12	7¼	182	5	0	1¼
33	0	18	1¾	83	2	5	7¾	133	3	13	1¾	183	5	0	7¾
34	0	18	8½	84	2	6	2½	134	3	13	8½	184	5	1	2½
35	0	19	3	85	2	6	9	135	3	14	3	185	5	1	9
36	0	19	9½	86	2	7	3½	136	3	14	9½	186	5	2	3½
37	1	0	4¼	87	2	7	10¼	137	3	15	4¼	187	5	2	10¼
38	1	0	10¾	88	2	8	4¾	138	3	15	10¾	188	5	3	4¾
39	1	1	5½	89	2	8	11½	139	3	16	5½	189	5	3	11½
40	**1**	**2**	**0**	**90**	**2**	**9**	**6**	**140**	**3**	**17**	**0**	**190**	**5**	**4**	**6**
41	1	2	6½	91	2	10	0½	141	3	17	6½	191	5	5	0½
42	1	3	1¼	92	2	10	7¼	142	3	18	1¼	192	5	5	7¼
43	1	3	7¾	93	2	11	1¾	143	3	18	7¾	193	5	6	1¾
44	1	4	2½	94	2	11	8½	144	3	19	2½	194	5	6	8½
45	1	4	9	95	2	12	3	145	3	19	9	195	5	7	3
46	1	5	3½	96	2	12	9½	146	4	0	3½	196	5	7	9½
47	1	5	10¼	97	2	13	4¼	147	4	0	10¼	197	5	8	4¼
48	1	6	4¾	98	2	13	10¾	148	4	1	4¾	198	5	8	10¾
49	1	6	11½	99	2	14	5½	149	4	1	11½	199	5	9	5½
50	**1**	**7**	**6**	**100**	**2**	**15**	**0**	**150**	**4**	**2**	**6**	**200**	**5**	**10**	**0**

250	6	17s	6d	700	19	5s	0d	1200	33	0s	0d	2000	55	0s	0d
300	8	5	0	750	20	12	6	1400	38	10	0	2500	68	15	0
400	11	0	0	800	22	0	0	1500	41	5	0	3000	82	10	0
500	13	15	0	900	24	15	0	1600	44	0	0	4000	110	0	0
600	16	10s	0d	1000	27	10s	0d	1800	49	10s	0d	5000	137	10s	0d

97¼% off.

1d	0s.	0d	4/1	0s.	1¼	8/1	0s.	2¾	12/1	0s.	4	16/1	0s.	5¼
2d	0	0	2	0	1½	2	0	2¾	2	0	4	2	0	5¼
3d	0	0	3	0	1½	3	0	2¾	3	0	4	3	0	5¼
4d	0	0	4	0	1½	4	0	2¾	4	0	4	4	0	5½
5d	0	0¼	5	0	1½	5	0	2¾	5	0	4	5	0	5½
6d	0	0¼	4/6	0	1½	8/6	0	2¾	12/6	0	4¼	16/6	0	5½
7d	0	0¼	7	0	1½	7	0	2¾	7	0	4¼	7	0	5½
8d	0	0¼	8	0	1½	8	0	2¾	8	0	4¼	8	0	5½
9d	0	0¼	9	0	1½	9	0	3	9	0	4¼	9	0	5½
10d	0	0¼	10	0	1½	10	0	3	10	0	4¼	10	0	5½
11d	0	0¼	11	0	1½	11	0	3	11	0	4¼	11	0	5½
1/-	0s.	0¼	**5/-**	0s.	1¾	**9/-**	0s.	3	**13/-**	0s.	4¼	**17/-**	0s.	5½
1/1	0s.	0¼	5/1	0s.	1¾	9/1	0s.	3	13/1	0s.	4¼	17/1	0s.	5¾
2	0	0½	2	0	1¾	2	0	3	2	0	4¼	2	0	5¾
3	0	0½	3	0	1¾	3	0	3	3	0	4¼	3	0	5¾
4	0	0½	4	0	1¾	4	0	3	4	0	4½	4	0	5¾
5	0	0½	5	0	1¾	5	0	3	5	0	4½	5	0	5¾
1/6	0	0½	5/6	0	1¾	9/6	0	3¼	13/6	0	4½	17/6	0	5¾
7	0	0½	7	0	1¾	7	0	3¼	7	0	4½	7	0	5¾
8	0	0½	8	0	1¾	8	0	3¼	8	0	4½	8	0	5¾
9	0	0½	9	0	2	9	0	3¼	9	0	4½	9	0	5¾
10	0	0½	10	0	2	10	0	3¼	10	0	4½	10	0	6
11	0	0¾	11	0	2	11	0	3¼	11	0	4½	11	0	6
2/-	0s.	0¾	**6/-**	0s.	2	**10/-**	0s.	3¼	**14/-**	0s.	4½	**18/-**	0s.	6
2/1	0s.	0¾	6/1	0s.	2	10/1	0s.	3¼	14/1	0s.	4¾	18/1	0s.	6
2	0	0¾	2	0	2	2	0	3¼	2	0	4¾	2	0	6
3	0	0¾	3	0	2	3	0	3½	3	0	4¾	3	0	6
4	0	0¾	4	0	2	4	0	3½	4	0	4¾	4	0	6
5	0	0¾	5	0	2	5	0	3½	5	0	4¾	5	0	6
2/6	0	0¾	6/6	0	2¼	10/6	0	3½	14/6	0	4¾	18/6	0	6
7	0	0¾	7	0	2¼	7	0	3½	7	0	4¾	7	0	6¼
8	0	1	8	0	2¼	8	0	3½	8	0	4¾	8	0	6¼
9	0	1	9	0	2¼	9	0	3½	9	0	4¾	9	0	6¼
10	0	1	10	0	2¼	10	0	3½	10	0	5	10	0	6¼
11	0	1	11	0	2¼	11	0	3½	11	0	5	11	0	6¼
3/-	0s.	1	**7/-**	0s.	2¼	**11/-**	0s.	3¾	**15/-**	0s.	5	**19/-**	0s.	6¼
3/1	0s.	1	7/1	0s.	2¼	11/1	0s.	3¾	15/1	0s.	5	19/1	0s.	6¼
2	0	1	2	0	2¼	2	0	3¾	2	0	5	2	0	6¼
3	0	1	3	0	2½	3	0	3¾	3	0	5	3	0	6¼
4	0	1	4	0	2½	4	0	3¾	4	0	5	4	0	6½
5	0	1¼	5	0	2½	5	0	3¾	5	0	5	5	0	6½
3/6	0	1¼	7/6	0	2½	11/6	0	3¾	15/6	0	5	19/6	0	6½
7	0	1¼	7	0	2½	7	0	3¾	7	0	5¼	7	0	6½
8	0	1¼	8	0	2½	8	0	3¾	8	0	5¼	8	0	6½
9	0	1¼	9	0	2½	9	0	4	9	0	5¼	9	0	6½
10	0	1¼	10	0	2½	10	0	4	10	0	5¼	10	0	6½
11	0	1¼	11	0	2½	11	0	4	11	0	5¼	11	0	6½
4/-	0s.	1¼	**8/-**	0s.	2¾	**12/-**	0s.	4	**16/-**	0s.	5¼	**20/-**	0s.	6½

20/6	0s.	6¾	25/6	0s.	8½	31/-	0s.	10¼	35/6	0s.	11¾	Guineas.		
21/-	0	7	26/-	0	8½	31/6	0	10½	36/-	1	0	1.	0s.	7
22/-	0	7¼	27/-	0	9	32/-	0	10½	37/-	1	0¼	2.	1	1¾
22/6	0	7½	27/6	0	9	32/6	0	10¾	37/6	1	0½	3.	1	8¾
23/-	0	7½	28/-	0	9¼	33/-	0	11	38/-	1	0½	4.	2	3¾
24/-	0	8	29/-	0	9½	34/-	0	11¼	39/-	1	0¾	5.	2	10¾
25/-	0s.	8¼	**30/-**	0s.	10	**35/-**	0s.	11½	**40/-**	1s.	1¼	6.	3s.	5½

(=2$\frac{1}{16}$%* on Gross Returns).

No.	£	s	d	No.	£	s	d	No.	£	s	d	No.	£	s	d
£1	£0	0s	7¼	£51	£1	10s	7¼	£101	£3	0s	7¼	£151	£4	10s	7¼
2	0	1	2½	52	1	11	2½	102	3	1	2½	152	4	11	2½
3	0	1	9½	53	1	11	9½	103	3	1	9½	153	4	11	9½
4	0	2	4¾	54	1	12	4¾	104	3	2	4¾	154	4	12	4¾
5	0	3	0	55	1	13	0	105	3	3	0	155	4	13	0
6	0	3	7¼	56	1	13	7¼	106	3	3	7¼	156	4	13	7¼
7	0	4	2½	57	1	14	2½	107	3	4	2½	157	4	14	2½
8	0	4	9½	58	1	14	9½	108	3	4	9½	158	4	14	9½
9	0	5	4¾	59	1	15	4¾	109	3	5	4¾	159	4	15	4¾
10	0	6	0	60	1	16	0	110	3	6	0	160	4	16	0
11	0	6	7¼	61	1	16	7¼	111	3	6	7¼	161	4	16	7¼
12	0	7	2½	62	1	17	2½	112	3	7	2½	162	4	17	2½
13	0	7	9½	63	1	17	9½	113	3	7	9½	163	4	17	9½
14	0	8	4¾	64	1	18	4¾	114	3	8	4¾	164	4	18	4¾
15	0	9	0	65	1	19	0	115	3	9	0	165	4	19	0
16	0	9	7¼	66	1	19	7¼	116	3	9	7¼	166	4	19	7¼
17	0	10	2½	67	2	0	2½	117	3	10	2½	167	5	0	2½
18	0	10	9½	68	2	0	9½	118	3	10	9½	168	5	0	9½
19	0	11	4¾	69	2	1	4¾	119	3	11	4¾	169	5	1	4¾
20	0	12	0	70	2	2	0	120	3	12	0	170	5	2	0
21	0	12	7¼	71	2	2	7¼	121	3	12	7¼	171	5	2	7¼
22	0	13	2½	72	2	3	2½	122	3	13	2½	172	5	3	2½
23	0	13	9½	73	2	3	9½	123	3	13	9½	173	5	3	9½
24	0	14	4¾	74	2	4	4¾	124	3	14	4¾	174	5	4	4¾
25	0	15	0	75	2	5	0	125	3	15	0	175	5	5	0
26	0	15	7¼	76	2	5	7¼	126	3	15	7¼	176	5	5	7¼
27	0	16	2½	77	2	6	2½	127	3	16	2½	177	5	6	2½
28	0	16	9½	78	2	6	9½	128	3	16	9½	178	5	6	9½
29	0	17	4¾	79	2	7	4¾	129	3	17	4¾	179	5	7	4¾
30	0	18	0	80	2	8	0	130	3	18	0	180	5	8	0
31	0	18	7¼	81	2	8	7¼	131	3	18	7¼	181	5	8	7¼
32	0	19	2½	82	2	9	2½	132	3	19	2½	182	5	9	2½
33	0	19	9½	83	2	9	9½	133	3	19	9½	183	5	9	9½
34	1	0	4¾	84	2	10	4¾	134	4	0	4¾	184	5	10	4¾
35	1	1	0	85	2	11	0	135	4	1	0	185	5	11	0
36	1	1	7¼	86	2	11	7¼	136	4	1	7¼	186	5	11	7¼
37	1	2	2½	87	2	12	2½	137	4	2	2½	187	5	12	2½
38	1	2	9½	88	2	12	9½	138	4	2	9½	188	5	12	9½
39	1	3	4¾	89	2	13	4¾	139	4	3	4¾	189	5	13	4¾
40	1	4	0	90	2	14	0	140	4	4	0	190	5	14	0
41	1	4	7¼	91	2	14	7¼	141	4	4	7¼	191	5	14	7¼
42	1	5	2½	92	2	15	2½	142	4	5	2½	192	5	15	2½
43	1	5	9½	93	2	15	9½	143	4	5	9½	193	5	15	9½
44	1	6	4¾	94	2	16	4¾	144	4	6	4¾	194	5	16	4¾
45	1	7	0	95	2	17	0	145	4	7	0	195	5	17	0
46	1	7	7¼	96	2	17	7¼	146	4	7	7¼	196	5	17	7¼
47	1	8	2½	97	2	18	2½	147	4	8	2½	197	5	18	2½
48	1	8	9½	98	2	18	9½	148	4	8	9½	198	5	18	9½
49	1	9	4¾	99	2	19	4¾	149	4	9	4¾	199	5	19	4¾
50	1	10	0	100	3	0	0	150	4	10	0	200	6	0	0

No.	£	s	d	No.	£	s	d	No.	£	s	d	No.	£	s	d
250	7	10s	0d	700	21	0s	0d	1200	36	0s	0d	2000	60	0s	0d
300	9	0	0	750	22	10	0	1400	42	0	0	2500	75	0	0
400	12	0	0	800	24	0	0	1500	45	0	0	3000	90	0	0
500	15	0	0	900	27	0	0	1600	48	0	0	4000	120	0	0
600	18	0s	0d	1000	30	0s	0d	1800	54	0s	0d	5000	150	0s	0d

97% off.

1d	0s.	0d	4/1	0s.	1½	8/1	0s.	3	12/1	0s.	4½	16/1	0s.	5¾
2d	0	0	2	0	1½	2	0	3	2	0	4½	2	0	5¾
3d	0	0	3	0	1½	3	0	3	3	0	4½	3	0	5¾
4d	0	0	4	0	1½	4	0	3	4	0	4½	4	0	6
5d	0	0¼	5	0	1½	5	0	3	5	0	4½	5	0	6
6d	0	0¼	4/6	0	1½	8/6	0	3	12/6	0	4½	16/6	0	6
7d	0	0¼	7	0	1¾	7	0	3	7	0	4½	7	0	6
8d	0	0¼	8	0	1¾	8	0	3	8	0	4½	8	0	6
9d	0	0¼	9	0	1¾	9	0	3¼	9	0	4½	9	0	6
10d	0	0¼	10	0	1¾	10	0	3¼	10	0	4½	10	0	6
11d	0	0¼	11	0	1¾	11	0	3¼	11	0	4¾	11	0	6
1/-	0s.	0¼	**5/-**	0s.	1¾	**9/-**	0s.	3¼	**13/-**	0s.	4¾	**17/-**	0s.	6
1/1	0s.	0½	5/1	0s.	1¾	9/1	0s.	3¼	13/1	0s.	4¾	17/1	0s.	6¼
2	0	0½	2	0	1¾	2	0	3¼	2	0	4¾	2	0	6¼
3	0	0½	3	0	2	3	0	3¼	3	0	4¾	3	0	6¼
4	0	0½	4	0	2	4	0	3¼	4	0	4¾	4	0	6¼
5	0	0½	5	0	2	5	0	3½	5	0	4¾	5	0	6¼
1/6	0	0½	5/6	0	2	9/6	0	3½	13/6	0	4¾	17/6	0	6¼
7	0	0½	7	0	2	7	0	3½	7	0	5	7	0	6¼
8	0	0½	8	0	2	8	0	3½	8	0	5	8	0	6¼
9	0	0¾	9	0	2	9	0	3½	9	0	5	9	0	6½
10	0	0¾	10	0	2	10	0	3½	10	0	5	10	0	6½
11	0	0¾	11	0	2¼	11	0	3½	11	0	5	11	0	6½
2/-	0s.	0¾	**6/-**	0s.	2¼	**10/-**	0s.	3½	**14/-**	0s.	5	**18/-**	0s.	6½
2/1	0s.	0¾	6/1	0s.	2¼	10/1	0s.	3¾	14/1	0s.	5	18/1	0s.	6½
2	0	0¾	2	0	2¼	2	0	3¾	2	0	5	2	0	6½
3	0	0¾	3	0	2¼	3	0	3¾	3	0	5¼	3	0	6½
4	0	0¾	4	0	2¼	4	0	3¾	4	0	5¼	4	0	6½
5	0	0¾	5	0	2¼	5	0	3¾	5	0	5¼	5	0	6¾
2/6	0	1	6/6	0	2¼	10/6	0	3¾	14/6	0	5¼	18/6	0	6¾
7	0	1	7	0	2¼	7	0	3¾	7	0	5¼	7	0	6¾
8	0	1	8	0	2½	8	0	3¾	8	0	5¼	8	0	6¾
9	0	1	9	0	2½	9	0	3¾	9	0	5¼	9	0	6¾
10	0	1	10	0	2½	10	0	4	10	0	5¼	10	0	6¾
11	0	1	11	0	2½	11	0	4	11	0	5¼	11	0	6¾
3/-	0s.	1	**7/-**	0s.	2½	**11/-**	0s.	4	**15/-**	0s.	5½	**19/-**	0s.	6¾
3/1	0s.	1	7/1	0s.	2½	11/1	0s.	4	15/1	0s.	5½	19/1	0s.	6¾
2	0	1¼	2	0	2½	2	0	4	2	0	5½	2	0	7
3	0	1¼	3	0	2½	3	0	4	3	0	5½	3	0	7
4	0	1¼	4	0	2¾	4	0	4	4	0	5½	4	0	7
5	0	1¼	5	0	2¾	5	0	4	5	0	5½	5	0	7
3/6	0	1¼	7/6	0	2¾	11/6	0	4¼	15/6	0	5½	19/6	0	7
7	0	1¼	7	0	2¾	7	0	4¼	7	0	5½	7	0	7
8	0	1¼	8	0	2¾	8	0	4¼	8	0	5¾	8	0	7
9	0	1¼	9	0	2¾	9	0	4¼	9	0	5¾	9	0	7
10	0	1½	10	0	2¾	10	0	4¼	10	0	5¾	10	0	7¼
11	0	1½	11	0	2¾	11	0	4¼	11	0	5¾	11	0	7¼
4/-	0s.	1½	**8/-**	0s.	3	**12/-**	0s.	4¼	**16/-**	0s.	5¾	**20/-**	0s.	7¼

20/6	0s.	7½	25/6	0s.	9¼	31/-	0s.	11¼	35/6	1s.	0¾	Guineas.		
21/-	0	7½	26/-	0	9¼	31/6	0	11¼	36/-	1	1	1.	0s.	7½
22/-	0	8	27/-	0	9¾	32/-	0	11½	37/-	1	1¼	2.	1	3
22/6	0	8	27/6	0	10	32/6	0	11¾	37/6	1	1½	3.	1	10¾
23/-	0	8¼	28/-	0	10	33/-	1	0	38/-	1	1¾	4.	2	6¼
24/-	0	8¾	29/-	0	10½	34/-	1	0¼	39/-	1	2	5.	3	1¾
25/-	0s.	9	**30/-**	0s.	10¾	**35/-**	1s.	0½	**40/-**	1s.	2½	6.	3s.	9¼

(=2[illegible]%* or Gross Returns).

£	Value	£	Value	£	Value	£	Value
£1	0s. 7½	£51	£1 11s.10½	£101	£3 3s. 1½	£151	£4 14s. 4½
2	1 3	52	1 12 6	102	3 3 9	152	4 15 0
3	1 10½	53	1 13 1½	103	3 4 4½	153	4 15 7½
4	2 6	54	1 13 9	104	3 5 0	154	4 16 3
5	3 1½	55	1 14 4½	105	3 5 7½	155	4 16 10½
6	3 9	56	1 15 0	106	3 6 3	156	4 17 6
7	4 4½	57	1 15 7½	107	3 6 10½	157	4 18 1½
8	5 0	58	1 16 3	108	3 7 6	158	4 18 9
9	5 7½	59	1 16 10½	109	3 8 1½	159	4 19 4½
10	6s. 3	60	£1.17s. 6	110	£3 8s. 9	160	£5 0s. 0
11	6s.10½	61	1 18s. 1½	111	£3 9s. 4½	161	£5 0s. 7½
12	7 6	62	1 18 9	112	3 10 0	162	5 1 3
13	8 1½	63	1 19 4½	113	3 10 7½	163	5 1 10½
14	8 9	64	2 0 0	114	3 11 3	164	5 2 6
15	9 4½	65	2 0 7½	115	3 11 10½	165	5 3 1½
16	10 0	66	2 1 3	116	3 12 6	166	5 3 9
17	10 7½	67	2 1 10½	117	3 13 1½	167	5 4 4½
18	11 3	68	2 2 6	118	3 13 9	168	5 5 0
19	11 10½	69	2 3 1½	119	3 14 4½	169	5 5 7½
20	12s. 6	70	£2 3s. 9	120	£3 15s. 0	170	£5 6s. 3
21	13s. 1½	71	£2 4s. 4½	121	£3 15s. 7½	171	£5 6s.10½
22	13 9	72	2 5 0	122	3 16 3	172	5 7 6
23	14 4½	73	2 5 7½	123	3 16 10½	173	5 8 1½
24	15 0	74	2 6 3	124	3 17 6	174	5 8 9
25	15 7½	75	2 6 10½	125	3 18 1½	175	5 9 4½
26	16 3	76	2 7 6	126	3 18 9	176	5 10 0
27	16 10½	77	2 8 1½	127	3 19 4½	177	5 10 7½
28	17 6	78	2 8 9	128	4 0 0	178	5 11 3
29	18 1½	79	2 9 4½	129	4 0 7½	179	5 11 10½
30	18s. 9	80	£2 10s. 0	130	£4 1s. 3	180	£5 12s. 6
31	19s. 4½	81	£2 10s. 7½	131	£4 1s.10½	181	£5 13s. 1½
32	20 0	82	2 11 3	132	4 2 6	182	5 13 9
33	20 7½	83	2 11 10½	133	4 3 1½	183	5 14 4½
34	21 3	84	2 12 6	134	4 3 9	184	5 15 0
35	21 10½	85	2 13 1½	135	4 4 4½	185	5 15 7½
36	22 6	86	2 13 9	136	4 5 0	186	5 16 3
37	23 1½	87	2 14 4½	137	4 5 7½	187	5 16 10½
38	23 9	88	2 15 0	138	4 6 3	188	5 17 6
39	24 4½	89	2 15 7½	139	4 6 10½	189	5 18 1½
40	25s. 0	90	£2 16s. 3	140	£4 7s. 6	190	£5 18s. 9
41	25s. 7½	91	£2 16s.10½	141	£4 8s. 1½	191	£5 19s. 4½
42	26 3	92	2 17 6	142	4 8 9	192	6 0 0
43	26 10½	93	2 18 1½	143	4 9 4½	193	6 0 7½
44	27 6	94	2 18 9	144	4 10 0	194	6 1 3
45	28 1½	95	2 19 4½	145	4 10 7½	195	6 1 10½
46	28 9	96	3 0 0	146	4 11 3	196	6 2 6
47	29 4½	97	3 0 7½	147	4 11 10½	197	6 3 1½
48	30 0	98	3 1 3	148	4 12 6	198	6 3 9
49	30 7½	99	3 1 10½	149	4 13 1½	199	6 4 4½
50	31s. 3	100	£3 2s. 6	150	£4 13s. 9	200	£6 5s. 0

£	Value	£	Value	£	Value	£	Value
250	7 16s.3d	700	21 17s. 6d	1200	£37 10s. 0d	2000	£62 10s. 0
300	9 7 6	750	23 8 9	1400	43 15 0	2500	78 2 6
400	12 10 0	800	25 0 0	1500	46 17 6	3000	93 15 0
500	15 12 6	900	28 2 6	1600	50 0 0	4000	125 0 0
600	18 15s.0d	1000	£31 5s. 0d	1800	£56 5s. 0d	5000	£156 5s. 0

96⅞% off.   (3%* on Gross Returns).

3⅜% £3. 7. 6 PER CENT OR PER 100. 3⅜%

£1	0s. 8	£51	£1 14s. 5	£101	£3 8s. 2	£151	£5 1s.11
2	1 4¼	52	1 15 1¼	102	3 8 10¼	152	5 2 7¼
3	2 0¼	53	1 15 9¼	103	3 9 6¼	153	5 3 3¼
4	2 8½	54	1 16 5½	104	3 10 2½	154	5 3 11½
5	3 4½	55	1 17 1½	105	3 10 10½	155	5 4 7½
6	4 0½	56	1 17 9½	106	3 11 6½	156	5 5 3½
7	4 8¾	57	1 18 5¾	107	3 12 2¾	157	5 5 11¾
8	5 4¾	58	1 19 1¾	108	3 12 10¾	158	5 6 7¾
9	6 1	59	1 19 10	109	3 13 7	159	5 7 4
10	**6s. 9**	**60**	**£2 0s. 6**	**110**	**£3 14s. 3**	**160**	**£5 8s. 0**
11	7s. 5	61	£2 1s. 2	111	£3 14s.11	161	£5 8s. 8
12	8 1¼	62	2 1 10¼	112	3 15 7¼	162	5 9 4¼
13	8 9¼	63	2 2 6¼	113	3 16 3¼	163	5 10 0¼
14	9 5½	64	2 3 2½	114	3 16 11½	164	5 10 8½
15	10 1½	65	2 3 10½	115	3 17 7½	165	5 11 4½
16	10 9½	66	2 4 6½	116	3 18 3½	166	5 12 0½
17	11 5¾	67	2 5 2¾	117	3 18 11¾	167	5 12 8¾
18	12 1¾	68	2 5 10¾	118	3 19 7¾	168	5 13 4¾
19	12 10	69	2 6 7	119	4 0 4	169	5 14 1
20	**13s. 6**	**70**	**£2 7s. 3**	**120**	**£4 1s. 0**	**170**	**£5 14s. 9**
21	14s. 2	71	£2 7s.11	121	£4 1s. 8	171	£5 15s. 5
22	14 10¼	72	2 8 7¼	122	4 2 4¼	172	5 16 1¼
23	15 6¼	73	2 9 3¼	123	4 3 0¼	173	5 16 9¼
24	16 2½	74	2 9 11½	124	4 3 8½	174	5 17 5½
25	16 10½	75	2 10 7½	125	4 4 4½	175	5 18 1½
26	17 6½	76	2 11 3½	126	4 5 0½	176	5 18 9½
27	18 2¾	77	2 11 11¾	127	4 5 8¾	177	5 19 5¾
28	18 10¾	78	2 12 7¾	128	4 6 4¾	178	6 0 1¾
29	19 7	79	2 13 4	129	4 7 1	179	6 0 10
30	**20s. 3**	**80**	**£2 14s. 0**	**130**	**£4 7s. 9**	**180**	**£6 1s. 6**
31	20s.11	81	£2 14s. 8	131	£4 8s. 5	181	£6 2s. 2
32	21 7¼	82	2 15 4¼	132	4 9 1¼	182	6 2 10¼
33	22 3¼	83	2 16 0¼	133	4 9 9¼	183	6 3 6¼
34	22 11½	84	2 16 8½	134	4 10 5½	184	6 4 2½
35	23 7½	85	2 17 4½	135	4 11 1½	185	6 4 10½
36	24 3½	86	2 18 0½	136	4 11 9½	186	6 5 6½
37	24 11¾	87	2 18 8¾	137	4 12 5¾	187	6 6 2¾
38	25 7¾	88	2 19 4¾	138	4 13 1¾	188	6 6 10¾
39	26 4	89	3 0 1	139	4 13 10	189	6 7 7
40	**27s. 0**	**90**	**£3 0s. 9**	**140**	**£4 14s. 6**	**190**	**£6 8s. 3**
41	27s. 8	91	£3 1s. 5	141	£4 15s. 2	191	£6 8s.11
42	28 4¼	92	3 2 1¼	142	4 15 10¼	192	6 9 7¼
43	29 0¼	93	3 2 9¼	143	4 16 6¼	193	6 10 3¼
44	29 8½	94	3 3 5½	144	4 17 2½	194	6 10 11½
45	30 4½	95	3 4 1½	145	4 17 10½	195	6 11 7½
46	31 0½	96	3 4 9½	146	4 18 6½	196	6 12 3½
47	31 8¾	97	3 5 5¾	147	4 19 2¾	197	6 12 11¾
48	32 4¾	98	3 6 1¾	148	4 19 10¾	198	6 13 7¾
49	33 1	99	3 6 10	149	5 0 7	199	6 14 4
50	**33s. 9**	**100**	**£3 7s. 6**	**150**	**£5 1s. 3**	**200**	**£6 15s. 0**
250	8 8s.9d	700	23 12s. 6d	1200	£40 10s. 0d	2000	£67 10s. 0
300	10 2 6	750	25 6 3	1400	47 5 0	2500	84 7 6
400	13 10 0	800	27 0 0	1500	50 12 6	3000	101 5 0
500	16 17 6	900	30 7 6	1600	54 0 0	4000	135 0 0
600	20 5s.0d	1000	£33 15s. 0d	1800	£60 15s. 0d	5000	£168 15s. 0

96⅝% off. (=3 3/16%* on Gross Returns).

£1	£0	0s	7¾	£51	£1	13s	1¾	£101	£3	5s	7¾	£151	£4	18s	1¾
2	0	1	3½	52	1	13	9½	102	3	6	3½	152	4	18	9½
3	0	1	11½	53	1	14	5½	103	3	6	11½	153	4	19	5½
4	0	2	7¼	54	1	15	1¼	104	3	7	7¼	154	5	0	1¼
5	0	3	3	55	1	15	9	105	3	8	3	155	5	0	9
6	0	3	10¾	56	1	16	4¾	106	3	8	10¾	156	5	1	4¾
7	0	4	6½	57	1	17	0½	107	3	9	6½	157	5	2	0½
8	0	5	2½	58	1	17	8½	108	3	10	2½	158	5	2	8½
9	0	5	10¼	59	1	18	4¼	109	3	10	10¼	159	5	3	4¼
10	**0**	**6**	**6**	**60**	**1**	**19**	**0**	**110**	**3**	**11**	**6**	**160**	**5**	**4**	**0**
11	0	7	1¾	61	1	19	7¾	111	3	12	1¾	161	5	4	7¾
12	0	7	9½	62	2	0	3½	112	3	12	9½	162	5	5	3½
13	0	8	5½	63	2	0	11½	113	3	13	5½	163	5	5	11½
14	0	9	1¼	64	2	1	7¼	114	3	14	1¼	164	5	6	7¼
15	0	9	9	65	2	2	3	115	3	14	9	165	5	7	3
16	0	10	4¾	66	2	2	10¾	116	3	15	4¾	166	5	7	10¾
17	0	11	0½	67	2	3	6½	117	3	16	0½	167	5	8	6½
18	0	11	8½	68	2	4	2½	118	3	16	8½	168	5	9	2½
19	0	12	4¼	69	2	4	10¼	119	3	17	4¼	169	5	9	10¼
20	**0**	**13**	**0**	**70**	**2**	**5**	**6**	**120**	**3**	**18**	**0**	**170**	**5**	**10**	**6**
21	0	13	7¾	71	2	6	1¾	121	3	18	7¾	171	5	11	1¾
22	0	14	3½	72	2	6	9½	122	3	19	3½	172	5	11	9½
23	0	14	11½	73	2	7	5½	123	3	19	11½	173	5	12	5½
24	0	15	7¼	74	2	8	1¼	124	4	0	7¼	174	5	13	1¼
25	0	16	3	75	2	8	9	125	4	1	3	175	5	13	9
26	0	16	10¾	76	2	9	4¾	126	4	1	10¾	176	5	14	4¾
27	0	17	6½	77	2	10	0½	127	4	2	6½	177	5	15	0½
28	0	18	2½	78	2	10	8½	128	4	3	2½	178	5	15	8½
29	0	18	10¼	79	2	11	4¼	129	4	3	10¼	179	5	16	4¼
30	**0**	**19**	**6**	**80**	**2**	**12**	**0**	**130**	**4**	**4**	**6**	**180**	**5**	**17**	**0**
31	1	0	1¾	81	2	12	7¾	131	4	5	1¾	181	5	17	7¾
32	1	0	9½	82	2	13	3½	132	4	5	9½	182	5	18	3½
33	1	1	5½	83	2	13	11½	133	4	6	5½	183	5	18	11½
34	1	2	1¼	84	2	14	7¼	134	4	7	1¼	184	5	19	7¼
35	1	2	9	85	2	15	3	135	4	7	9	185	6	0	3
36	1	3	4¾	86	2	15	10¾	136	4	8	4¾	186	6	0	10¾
37	1	4	0½	87	2	16	6½	137	4	9	0½	187	6	1	6½
38	1	4	8½	88	2	17	2½	138	4	9	8½	188	6	2	2½
39	1	5	4¼	89	2	17	10¼	139	4	10	4¼	189	6	2	10¼
40	**1**	**6**	**0**	**90**	**2**	**18**	**6**	**140**	**4**	**11**	**0**	**190**	**6**	**3**	**6**
41	1	6	7¾	91	2	19	1¾	141	4	11	7¾	191	6	4	1¾
42	1	7	3½	92	2	19	9½	142	4	12	3½	192	6	4	9½
43	1	7	11½	93	3	0	5½	143	4	12	11½	193	6	5	5½
44	1	8	7¼	94	3	1	1¼	144	4	13	7¼	194	6	6	1¼
45	1	9	3	95	3	1	9	145	4	14	3	195	6	6	9
46	1	9	10¾	96	3	2	4¾	146	4	14	10¾	196	6	7	4¾
47	1	10	6½	97	3	3	0½	147	4	15	6½	197	6	8	0½
48	1	11	2½	98	3	3	8½	148	4	16	2½	198	6	8	8½
49	1	11	10¼	99	3	4	4¼	149	4	16	10¼	199	6	9	4¼
50	**1**	**12**	**6**	**100**	**3**	**5**	**0**	**150**	**4**	**17**	**6**	**200**	**6**	**10**	**0**
250	8	2s	6d	700	22	15s	0d	1200	39	0s	0d	2000	65	0s	0d
300	9	15	0	750	24	7	6	1400	45	10	0	2500	81	5	0
400	13	0	0	800	26	0	0	1500	48	15	0	3000	97	10	0
500	16	5	0	900	29	5	0	1600	52	0	0	4000	130	0	0
600	19	10s	0d	1000	32	10s	0d	1800	58	10s	0d	5000	162	10s	0d

96¾% off.

3¼% 3¼ PER CENT. 3¼%

1d	0s.	0d	4/1	0s.	1½	8/1	0s.	3¼	12/1	0s.	4¾	16/1	0s.	6¼
2d	0	0	2	0	1¾	2	0	3¼	2	0	4¾	2	0	6¼
3d	0	0	3	0	1¾	3	0	3¼	3	0	4¾	3	0	6¼
4d	0	0¼	4	0	1¾	4	0	3¼	4	0	4¾	4	0	6¼
5d	0	0¼	5	0	1¾	5	0	3¼	5	0	4¾	5	0	6½
6d	0	0¼	4/6	0	1¾	8/6	0	3¼	12/6	0	5	16/6	0	6½
7d	0	0¼	7	0	1¾	7	0	3¼	7	0	5	7	0	6½
8d	0	0¼	8	0	1¾	8	0	3½	8	0	5	8	0	6½
9d	0	0¼	9	0	1¾	9	0	3½	9	0	5	9	0	6½
10d	0	0¼	10	0	2	10	0	3½	10	0	5	10	0	6½
11d	0	0¼	11	0	2	11	0	3½	11	0	5	11	0	6½
1/-	0s.	0½	**5/-**	0s.	2	**9/-**	0s.	3½	**13/-**	0s.	5	**17/-**	0s.	6¾
1/1	0s.	0½	5/1	0s.	2	9/1	0s.	3½	13/1	0s.	5	17/1	0s.	6¾
2	0	0½	2	0	2	2	0	3½	2	0	5¼	2	0	6¾
3	0	0½	3	0	2	3	0	3½	3	0	5¼	3	0	6¾
4	0	0½	4	0	2	4	0	3¾	4	0	5¼	4	0	6¾
5	0	0½	5	0	2	5	0	3¾	5	0	5¼	5	0	6¾
1/6	0	0½	5/6	0	2¼	9/6	0	3¾	13/6	0	5¼	17/6	0	6¾
7	0	0½	7	0	2¼	7	0	3¾	7	0	5¼	7	0	6¾
8	0	0¾	8	0	2¼	8	0	3¾	8	0	5¼	8	0	7
9	0	0¾	9	0	2¼	9	0	3¾	9	0	5¼	9	0	7
10	0	0¾	10	0	2¼	10	0	3¾	10	0	5½	10	0	7
11	0	0¾	11	0	2¼	11	0	3¾	11	0	5½	11	0	7
2/-	0s.	0¾	**6/-**	0s.	2¼	**10/-**	0s.	4	**14/-**	0s.	5½	**18/-**	0s.	7
2/1	0s.	0¾	6/1	0s.	2¼	10/1	0s.	4	14/1	0s.	5½	18/1	0s.	7
2	0	0¾	2	0	2½	2	0	4	2	0	5½	2	0	7
3	0	1	3	0	2½	3	0	4	3	0	5½	3	0	7
4	0	1	4	0	2½	4	0	4	4	0	5½	4	0	7¼
5	0	1	5	0	2½	5	0	4	5	0	5½	5	0	7¼
2/6	0	1	6/6	0	2½	10/6	0	4	14/6	0	5¾	18/6	0	7¼
7	0	1	7	0	2½	7	0	4¼	7	0	5¾	7	0	7¼
8	0	1	8	0	2½	8	0	4¼	8	0	5¾	8	0	7¼
9	0	1	9	0	2¾	9	0	4¼	9	0	5¾	9	0	7¼
10	0	1	10	0	2¾	10	0	4¼	10	0	5¾	10	0	7¼
11	0	1¼	11	0	2¾	11	0	4¼	11	0	5¾	11	0	7½
3/-	0s.	1¼	**7/-**	0s.	2¾	**11/-**	0s.	4¼	**15/-**	0s.	5¾	**19/-**	0s.	7½
3/1	0s.	1¼	7/1	0s.	2¾	11/1	0s.	4¼	15/1	0s.	6	19/1	0s.	7½
2	0	1¼	2	0	2¾	2	0	4¼	2	0	6	2	0	7½
3	0	1¼	3	0	2¾	3	0	4½	3	0	6	3	0	7½
4	0	1¼	4	0	2¾	4	0	4½	4	0	6	4	0	7½
5	0	1¼	5	0	3	5	0	4½	5	0	6	5	0	7½
3/6	0	1¼	7/6	0	3	11/6	0	4½	15/6	0	6	19/6	0	7½
7	0	1½	7	0	3	7	0	4½	7	0	6	7	0	7¾
8	0	1½	8	0	3	8	0	4½	8	0	6	8	0	7¾
9	0	1½	9	0	3	9	0	4½	9	0	6¼	9	0	7¾
10	0	1½	10	0	3	10	0	4½	10	0	6¼	10	0	7¾
11	0	1½	11	0	3	11	0	4¾	11	0	6¼	11	0	7¾
4/-	0s.	1½	**8/-**	0s.	3	**12/-**	0s.	4¾	**16/-**	0s.	6¼	**20/-**	0s.	7¾

20/6	0s.	8	25/6	0s.	10	31/-	1s.	0	35/6	1s.	1¾	Guineas.		
21/-	0	8¼	26/-	0	10¼	31/6	1	0¼	36/-	1	2	1.	0s.	8¼
22/-	0	8½	27/-	0	10½	32/-	1	0½	37/-	1	2½	2.	1	4½
22/6	0	8¾	27/6	0	10¾	32/6	1	0¾	37/6	1	2¾	3.	2	0½
23/-	0	9	28/-	0	11	33/-	1	0¾	38/-	1	2¾	4.	2	8¾
24/-	0	9¼	29/-	0	11¼	34/-	1	1¼	39/-	1	3¼	5.	3	5
25/-	0s.	9¾	**30/-**	0s.	11¾	**35/-**	1s.	1¾	**40/-**	1s.	3½	6.	4s.	1¼

(=3 1/10 %* on Gross Returns).

£1	£0	0s	8½	£51	£1	15s	8½	£101	£3	10s	8½	£151	£5	5s	8½
2	0	1	4¾	52	1	16	4¾	102	3	11	4¾	152	5	6	4¾
3	0	2	1¼	53	1	17	1¼	103	3	12	1¼	153	5	7	1¼
4	0	2	9½	54	1	17	9½	104	3	12	9½	154	5	7	9½
5	0	3	6	55	1	18	6	105	3	13	6	155	5	8	6
6	0	4	2½	56	1	19	2½	106	3	14	2½	156	5	9	2½
7	0	4	10¾	57	1	19	10¾	107	3	14	10¾	157	5	9	10¾
8	0	5	7¼	58	2	0	7¼	108	3	15	7¼	158	5	10	7¼
9	0	6	3½	59	2	1	3½	109	3	16	3½	159	5	11	3½
10	**0**	**7**	**0**	**60**	**2**	**2**	**0**	**110**	**3**	**17**	**0**	**160**	**5**	**12**	**0**
11	0	7	8½	61	2	2	8½	111	3	17	8½	161	5	12	8½
12	0	8	4¾	62	2	3	4¾	112	3	18	4¾	162	5	13	4¾
13	0	9	1¼	63	2	4	1¼	113	3	19	1¼	163	5	14	1¼
14	0	9	9½	64	2	4	9½	114	3	19	9½	164	5	14	9½
15	0	10	6	65	2	5	6	115	4	0	6	165	5	15	6
16	0	11	2½	66	2	6	2½	116	4	1	2½	166	5	16	2½
17	0	11	10¾	67	2	6	10¾	117	4	1	10¾	167	5	16	10¾
18	0	12	7¼	68	2	7	7¼	118	4	2	7¼	168	5	17	7¼
19	0	13	3½	69	2	8	3½	119	4	3	3½	169	5	18	3½
20	**0**	**14**	**0**	**70**	**2**	**9**	**0**	**120**	**4**	**4**	**0**	**170**	**5**	**19**	**0**
21	0	14	8½	71	2	9	8½	121	4	4	8½	171	5	19	8½
22	0	15	4¾	72	2	10	4¾	122	4	5	4¾	172	6	0	4¾
23	0	16	1¼	73	2	11	1¼	123	4	6	1¼	173	6	1	1¼
24	0	16	9½	74	2	11	9½	124	4	6	9½	174	6	1	9½
25	0	17	6	75	2	12	6	125	4	7	6	175	6	2	6
26	0	18	2½	76	2	13	2½	126	4	8	2½	176	6	3	2½
27	0	18	10¾	77	2	13	10¾	127	4	8	10¾	177	6	3	10¾
28	0	19	7¼	78	2	14	7¼	128	4	9	7¼	178	6	4	7¼
29	1	0	3½	79	2	15	3½	129	4	10	3½	179	6	5	3½
30	**1**	**1**	**0**	**80**	**2**	**16**	**0**	**130**	**4**	**11**	**0**	**180**	**6**	**6**	**0**
31	1	1	8½	81	2	16	8½	131	4	11	8½	181	6	6	8½
32	1	2	4¾	82	2	17	4¾	132	4	12	4¾	182	6	7	4¾
33	1	3	1¼	83	2	18	1¼	133	4	13	1¼	183	6	8	1¼
34	1	3	9½	84	2	18	9½	134	4	13	9½	184	6	8	9½
35	1	4	6	85	2	19	6	135	4	14	6	185	6	9	6
36	1	5	2½	86	3	0	2½	136	4	15	2½	186	6	10	2½
37	1	5	10¾	87	3	0	10¾	137	4	15	10¾	187	6	10	10¾
38	1	6	7¼	88	3	1	7¼	138	4	16	7¼	188	6	11	7¼
39	1	7	3½	89	3	2	3½	139	4	17	3½	189	6	12	3½
40	**1**	**8**	**0**	**90**	**3**	**3**	**0**	**140**	**4**	**18**	**0**	**190**	**6**	**13**	**0**
41	1	8	8½	91	3	3	8½	141	4	18	8½	191	6	13	8½
42	1	9	4¾	92	3	4	4¾	142	4	19	4¾	192	6	14	4¾
43	1	10	1¼	93	3	5	1¼	143	5	0	1¼	193	6	15	1¼
44	1	10	9½	94	3	5	9½	144	5	0	9½	194	6	15	9½
45	1	11	6	95	3	6	6	145	5	1	6	195	6	16	6
46	1	12	2½	96	3	7	2½	146	5	2	2½	196	6	17	2½
47	1	12	10¾	97	3	7	10¾	147	5	2	10¾	197	6	17	10¾
48	1	13	7¼	98	3	8	7¼	148	5	3	7¼	198	6	18	7¼
49	1	14	3½	99	3	9	3½	149	5	4	3½	199	6	19	3½
50	**1**	**15**	**0**	**100**	**3**	**10**	**0**	**150**	**5**	**5**	**0**	**200**	**7**	**0**	**0**

250	8	15s	0d	700	24	10s	0d	1200	42	0s	0d	2000	70	0s	0d
300	10	10	0	750	26	5	0	1400	49	0	0	2500	87	10	0
400	14	0	0	800	28	0	0	1500	52	10	0	3000	105	0	0
500	17	10	0	900	31	10	0	1600	56	0	0	4000	140	0	0
600	21	0s	0d	1000	35	0s	0d	1800	63	0s	0d	5000	175	0s	0d

96½% off.

1d	0s.	0d	4/1	0s.	1¾	8/1	0s.	3½	12/1	0s.	5	16/1	0s.	6¾
2d	0	0	2	0	1¾	2	0	3½	2	0	5	2	0	6¾
3d	0	0	3	0	1¾	3	0	3½	3	0	5¼	3	0	6¾
4d	0	0¼	4	0	1¾	4	0	3½	4	0	5¼	4	0	6¾
5d	0	0¼	5	0	1¾	5	0	3½	5	0	5¼	5	0	7
6d	0	0¼	4/6	0	2	8/6	0	3½	12/6	0	5¼	16/6	0	7
7d	0	0¼	7	0	2	7	0	3½	7	0	5¼	7	0	7
8d	0	0¼	8	0	2	8	0	3¾	8	0	5¼	8	0	7
9d	0	0¼	9	0	2	9	0	3¾	9	0	5¼	9	0	7
10d	0	0¼	10	0	2	10	0	3¾	10	0	5½	10	0	7
11d	0	0½	11	0	2	11	0	3¾	11	0	5½	11	0	7
1/-	0s.	0½	**5/-**	0s.	2	**9/-**	0s.	3¾	**13/-**	0s.	5½	**17/-**	0s.	7¼
1/1	0s.	0½	5/1	0s.	2¼	9/1	0s.	3¾	13/1	0s.	5½	17/1	0s.	7¼
2	0	0½	2	0	2¼	2	0	3¾	2	0	5½	2	0	7¼
3	0	0½	3	0	2¼	3	0	4	3	0	5½	3	0	7¼
4	0	0½	4	0	2¼	4	0	4	4	0	5½	4	0	7¼
5	0	0½	5	0	2¼	5	0	4	5	0	5¾	5	0	7¼
1/6	0	0¾	5/6	0	2¼	9/6	0	4	13/6	0	5¾	17/6	0	7¼
7	0	0¾	7	0	2¼	7	0	4	7	0	5¾	7	0	7½
8	0	0¾	8	0	2½	8	0	4	8	0	5¾	8	0	7½
9	0	0¾	9	0	2½	9	0	4	9	0	5¾	9	0	7½
10	0	0¾	10	0	2½	10	0	4¼	10	0	5¾	10	0	7½
11	0	0¾	11	0	2½	11	0	4¼	11	0	5¾	11	0	7½
2/-	0s.	0¾	**6/-**	0s.	2½	**10/-**	0s.	4¼	**14/-**	0s.	6	**18/-**	0s.	7½
2/1	0s.	1	6/1	0s.	2½	10/1	0s.	4¼	14/1	0s.	6	18/1	0s.	7½
2	0	1	2	0	2½	2	0	4¼	2	0	6	2	0	7¾
3	0	1	3	0	2¾	3	0	4¼	3	0	6	3	0	7¾
4	0	1	4	0	2¾	4	0	4¼	4	0	6	4	0	7¾
5	0	1	5	0	2¾	5	0	4½	5	0	6	5	0	7¾
2/6	0	1	6/6	0	2¾	10/6	0	4½	14/6	0	6	18/6	0	7¾
7	0	1	7	0	2¾	7	0	4½	7	0	6¼	7	0	7¾
8	0	1	8	0	2¾	8	0	4½	8	0	6¼	8	0	7¾
9	0	1¼	9	0	2¾	9	0	4½	9	0	6¼	9	0	8
10	0	1¼	10	0	2¾	10	0	4½	10	0	6¼	10	0	8
11	0	1¼	11	0	3	11	0	4½	11	0	6¼	11	0	8
3/-	0s.	1¼	**7/-**	0s.	3	**11/-**	0s.	4½	**15/-**	0s.	6¼	**19/-**	0s.	8
3/1	0s.	1¼	7/1	0s.	3	11/1	0s.	4¾	15/1	0s.	6¼	19/1	0s.	8
2	0	1¼	2	0	3	2	0	4¾	2	0	6¼	2	0	8
3	0	1¼	3	0	3	3	0	4¾	3	0	6½	3	0	8
4	0	1½	4	0	3	4	0	4¾	4	0	6½	4	0	8
5	0	1½	5	0	3	5	0	4¾	5	0	6½	5	0	8¼
3/6	0	1½	7/6	0	3¼	11/6	0	4¾	15/6	0	6½	19/6	0	8¼
7	0	1½	7	0	3¼	7	0	4¾	7	0	6½	7	0	8¼
8	0	1½	8	0	3¼	8	0	5	8	0	6½	8	0	8¼
9	0	1½	9	0	3¼	9	0	5	9	0	6½	9	0	8¼
10	0	1½	10	0	3¼	10	0	5	10	0	6¾	10	0	8¼
11	0	1¾	11	0	3¼	11	0	5	11	0	6¾	11	0	8¼
4/-	0s.	1¾	**8/-**	0s.	3¼	**12/-**	0s.	5	**16/-**	0s.	6¾	**20/-**	0s.	8½

												Guineas.		
20/6	0s.	8½	25/6	0s.	10¾	31/-	1s.	1	35/6	1s.	3			
21/-	0	8¾	26/-	0	11	31/6	1	1¼	36/-	1	3	1.	0s.	8¾
22/-	0	9¼	27/-	0	11¼	32/-	1	1½	37/-	1	3½	2.	1	5¾
22/6	0	9½	27/6	0	11½	32/6	1	1¾	37/6	1	3¾	3.	2	2½
23/-	0	9¾	28/-	0	11¾	33/-	1	1¾	38/-	1	4	4.	2	11¼
24/-	0	10	29/-	1	0¼	34/-	1	2¼	39/-	1	4½	5.	3	8
25/-	0s.	10½	**30/-**	1s.	0½	**35/-**	1s.	2¾	**40/-**	1s.	4¾	6.	4s.	5

(=3$\frac{4}{10}$%* on Gross Returns).

3⅝% £3. 12. 6 PER CENT OR PER 100. 3⅝%

£1	0s. 8¾	£51	£1 16s. 11¾	£101	£3 13s. 2¾	£151	£5 9s. 5¾
2	1 5½	52	1 17 8½	102	3 13 11½	152	5 10 2½
3	2 2	53	1 18 5	103	3 14 8	153	5 10 11
4	2 10¾	54	1 19 1¾	104	3 15 4¾	154	5 11 7¾
5	3 7½	55	1 19 10½	105	3 16 1½	155	5 12 4½
6	4 4¼	56	2 0 7¼	106	3 16 10¼	156	5 13 1¼
7	5 1	57	2 1 4	107	3 17 7	157	5 13 10
8	5 9½	58	2 2 0½	108	3 18 3½	158	5 14 6½
9	6 6¼	59	2 2 9¼	109	3 19 0¼	159	5 15 3¼
10	**7s. 3**	**60**	**£2 3s. 6**	**110**	**£3 19s. 9**	**160**	**£5 16s. 0**
11	7s. 11¾	61	£2 4s. 2¾	111	£4 0s. 5¾	161	£5 16s. 8¾
12	8 8½	62	2 4 11½	112	4 1 2½	162	5 17 5½
13	9 5	63	2 5 8	113	4 1 11	163	5 18 2
14	10 1¾	64	2 6 4¾	114	4 2 7¾	164	5 18 10¾
15	10 10½	65	2 7 1½	115	4 3 4½	165	5 19 7½
16	11 7¼	66	2 7 10¼	116	4 4 1¼	166	6 0 4¼
17	12 4	67	2 8 7	117	4 4 10	167	6 1 1
18	13 0½	68	2 9 3½	118	4 5 6½	168	6 1 9½
19	13 9¼	69	2 10 0¼	119	4 6 3¼	169	6 2 6¼
20	**14s. 6**	**70**	**£2 10s. 9**	**120**	**£4 7s. 0**	**170**	**£6 3s. 3**
21	15s. 2¾	71	£2 11s. 5¾	121	£4 7s. 8¾	171	£6 3s. 11¾
22	15 11½	72	2 12 2½	122	4 8 5½	172	6 4 8½
23	16 8	73	2 12 11	123	4 9 2	173	6 5 5
24	17 4¾	74	2 13 7¾	124	4 9 10¾	174	6 6 1¾
25	18 1½	75	2 14 4½	125	4 10 7½	175	6 6 10½
26	18 10¼	76	2 15 1¼	126	4 11 4¼	176	6 7 7¼
27	19 7	77	2 15 10	127	4 12 1	177	6 8 4
28	20 3½	78	2 16 6½	128	4 12 9½	178	6 9 0½
29	21 0¼	79	2 17 3¼	129	4 13 6¼	179	6 9 9¼
30	**21s. 9**	**80**	**£2 18s. 0**	**130**	**£4 14s. 3**	**180**	**£6 10s. 6**
31	22s. 5¾	81	£2 18s. 8¾	131	£4 14s. 11¾	181	£6 11s. 2¾
32	23 2½	82	2 19 5½	132	4 15 8½	182	6 11 11½
33	23 11	83	3 0 2	133	4 16 5	183	6 12 8
34	24 7¾	84	3 0 10¾	134	4 17 1¾	184	6 13 4¾
35	25 4½	85	3 1 7½	135	4 17 10½	185	6 14 1½
36	26 1¼	86	3 2 4¼	136	4 18 7¼	186	6 14 10¼
37	26 10	87	3 3 1	137	4 19 4	187	6 15 7
38	27 6½	88	3 3 9½	138	5 0 0½	188	6 16 3½
39	28 3¼	89	3 4 6¼	139	5 0 9¼	189	6 17 0¼
40	**29s. 0**	**90**	**£3 5s. 3**	**140**	**£5 1s. 6**	**190**	**£6 17s. 9**
41	29s. 8¾	91	£3 5s. 11¾	141	£5 2s. 2¾	191	£6 18s. 5¾
42	30 5½	92	3 6 8½	142	5 2 11½	192	6 19 2½
43	31 2	93	3 7 5	143	5 3 8	193	6 19 11
44	31 10¾	94	3 8 1¾	144	5 4 4¾	194	7 0 7¾
45	32 7½	95	3 8 10½	145	5 5 1½	195	7 1 4½
46	33 4¼	96	3 9 7¼	146	5 5 10¼	196	7 2 1¼
47	34 1	97	3 10 4	147	5 6 7	197	7 2 10
48	34 9½	98	3 11 0½	148	5 7 3½	198	7 3 6½
49	35 6¼	99	3 11 9¼	149	5 8 0¼	199	7 4 3¼
50	**36s. 3**	**100**	**£3 12s. 6**	**150**	**£5 8s. 9**	**200**	**£7 5s. 0**
250	9 1s. 3d	700	25 7s. 6d	1200	£43 10s. 0d	2000	£72 10s. 0
300	10 17 6	750	27 3 9	1400	50 15 0	2500	90 12 6
400	14 10 0	800	29 0 0	1500	54 7 6	3000	108 15 0
500	18 2 6	900	32 12 6	1600	58 0 0	4000	145 0 0
600	21 15s. 0d	1000	£36 5s. 0d	1800	£65 5s. 0d	5000	£181 5s. 0

96⅜% off. (=3½%* on Gross Returns).

3⅞% £3. 17. 6 PER CENT OR PER 100. 3⅞%

£1	0s. 9¼	£51	£1 19s. 6¼	£101	£3 18s. 3¼	£151	£5 17s. 0¼
2	1 6½	52	2 0 3½	102	3 19 0½	152	5 17 9½
3	2 4	53	2 1 1	103	3 19 10	153	5 18 7
4	3 1¼	54	2 1 10¼	104	4 0 7¼	154	5 19 4¼
5	3 10½	55	2 2 7½	105	4 1 4½	155	6 0 1½
6	4 7¾	56	2 3 4¾	106	4 2 1¾	156	6 0 10¾
7	5 5	57	2 4 2	107	4 2 11	157	6 1 8
8	6 2½	58	2 4 11½	108	4 3 8½	158	6 2 5½
9	6 11¾	59	2 5 8¾	109	4 4 5¾	159	6 3 2¾
10	**7s. 9**	**60**	**£2 6s. 6**	**110**	**£4 5s. 3**	**160**	**£6 4s. 0**
11	8s. 6¼	61	£2 7s. 3¼	111	£4 6s. 0¼	161	£6 4s. 9¼
12	9 3½	62	2 8 0½	112	4 6 9½	162	6 5 6½
13	10 1	63	2 8 10	113	4 7 7	163	6 6 4
14	10 10¼	64	2 9 7¼	114	4 8 4¼	164	6 7 1¼
15	11 7½	65	2 10 4½	115	4 9 1½	165	6 7 10½
16	12 4¾	66	2 11 1¾	116	4 9 10¾	166	6 8 7¾
17	13 2	67	2 11 11	117	4 10 8	167	6 9 5
18	13 11½	68	2 12 8½	118	4 11 5½	168	6 10 2½
19	14 8¾	69	2 13 5¾	119	4 12 2¾	169	6 10 11¾
20	**15s. 6**	**70**	**£2 14s. 3**	**120**	**£4 13s. 0**	**170**	**£6 11s. 9**
21	16s. 3¼	71	£2 15s. 0¼	121	£4 13s. 9¼	171	£6 12s. 6¼
22	17 0½	72	2 15 9½	122	4 14 6½	172	6 13 3½
23	17 10	73	2 16 7	123	4 15 4	173	6 14 1
24	18 7¼	74	2 17 4¼	124	4 16 1¼	174	6 14 10¼
25	19 4½	75	2 18 1½	125	4 16 10½	175	6 15 7½
26	20 1¾	76	2 18 10¾	126	4 17 7¾	176	6 16 4¾
27	20 11	77	2 19 8	127	4 18 5	177	6 17 2
28	21 8½	78	3 0 5½	128	4 19 2½	178	6 17 11½
29	22 5¾	79	3 1 2¾	129	4 19 11¾	179	6 18 8¾
30	**23s. 3**	**80**	**£3 2s. 0**	**130**	**£5 0s. 9**	**180**	**£6 19s. 6**
31	24s. 0¼	81	£3 2s. 9¼	131	£5 1s. 6¼	181	£7 0s. 3¼
32	24 9½	82	3 3 6½	132	5 2 3½	182	7 1 0½
33	25 7	83	3 4 4	133	5 3 1	183	7 1 10
34	26 4¼	84	3 5 1¼	134	5 3 10¼	184	7 2 7¼
35	27 1½	85	3 5 10½	135	5 4 7½	185	7 3 4½
36	27 10¾	86	3 6 7¾	136	5 5 4¾	186	7 4 1¾
37	28 8	87	3 7 5	137	5 6 2	187	7 4 11
38	29 5½	88	3 8 2½	138	5 6 11½	188	7 5 8½
39	30 2¾	89	3 8 11¾	139	5 7 8¾	189	7 6 5¾
40	**31s. 0**	**90**	**£3 9s. 9**	**140**	**£5 8s. 6**	**190**	**£7 7s. 3**
41	31s. 9¼	91	£3 10s. 6¼	141	£5 9s. 3¼	191	£7 8s. 0¼
42	32 6½	92	3 11 3½	142	5 10 0½	192	7 8 9½
43	33 4	93	3 12 1	143	5 10 10	193	7 9 7
44	34 1¼	94	3 12 10¼	144	5 11 7¼	194	7 10 4¼
45	34 10½	95	3 13 7½	145	5 12 4½	195	7 11 1½
46	35 7¾	96	3 14 4¾	146	5 13 1¾	196	7 11 10¾
47	36 5	97	3 15 2	147	5 13 11	197	7 12 8
48	37 2½	98	3 15 11½	148	5 14 8½	198	7 13 5½
49	37 11¾	99	3 16 8¾	149	5 15 5¾	199	7 14 2¾
50	**38s. 9**	**100**	**£3 17s. 6**	**150**	**£5 16s. 3**	**200**	**£7 15s. 0**

250	9 13s. 9d	700	27 2s. 6d	1200	£46 10s. 0d	2000	£77 10s. 0
300	11 12 6	750	29 1 3	1400	54 5 0	2500	96 17 6
400	15 10 0	800	31 0 0	1500	58 2 6	3000	116 5 0
500	19 7 6	900	34 17 6	1600	62 0 0	4000	155 0 0
600	23 5s. 0d	1000	£38 15s. 0d	1800	£69 15s. 0d	5000	£193 15s. 0

96⅛% off. (= $3\frac{1}{10}$%* on Gross Returns).

£	£ s d	£	£ s d	£	£ s d	£	£ s d
£1	£0 0s 9	£51	£1 18s 3	£101	£3 15s 9	£151	£5 13s 3
2	0 1 6	52	1 19 0	102	3 16 6	152	5 14 0
3	0 2 3	53	1 19 9	103	3 17 3	153	5 14 9
4	0 3 0	54	2 0 6	104	3 18 0	154	5 15 6
5	0 3 9	55	2 1 3	105	3 18 9	155	5 16 3
6	0 4 6	56	2 2 0	106	3 19 6	156	5 17 0
7	0 5 3	57	2 2 9	107	4 0 3	157	5 17 9
8	0 6 0	58	2 3 6	108	4 1 0	158	5 18 6
9	0 6 9	59	2 4 3	109	4 1 9	159	5 19 3
10	0 7 6	60	2 5 0	110	4 2 6	160	6 0 0
11	0 8 3	61	2 5 9	111	4 3 3	161	6 0 9
12	0 9 0	62	2 6 6	112	4 4 0	162	6 1 6
13	0 9 9	63	2 7 3	113	4 4 9	163	6 2 3
14	0 10 6	64	2 8 0	114	4 5 6	164	6 3 0
15	0 11 3	65	2 8 9	115	4 6 3	165	6 3 9
16	0 12 0	66	2 9 6	116	4 7 0	166	6 4 6
17	0 12 9	67	2 10 3	117	4 7 9	167	6 5 3
18	0 13 6	68	2 11 0	118	4 8 6	168	6 6 0
19	0 14 3	69	2 11 9	119	4 9 3	169	6 6 9
20	0 15 0	70	2 12 6	120	4 10 0	170	6 7 6
21	0 15 9	71	2 13 3	121	4 10 9	171	6 8 3
22	0 16 6	72	2 14 0	122	4 11 6	172	6 9 0
23	0 17 3	73	2 14 9	123	4 12 3	173	6 9 9
24	0 18 0	74	2 15 6	124	4 13 0	174	6 10 6
25	0 18 9	75	2 16 3	125	4 13 9	175	6 11 3
26	0 19 6	76	2 17 0	126	4 14 6	176	6 12 0
27	1 0 3	77	2 17 9	127	4 15 3	177	6 12 9
28	1 1 0	78	2 18 6	128	4 16 0	178	6 13 6
29	1 1 9	79	2 19 3	129	4 16 9	179	6 14 3
30	1 2 6	80	3 0 0	130	4 17 6	180	6 15 0
31	1 3 3	81	3 0 9	131	4 18 3	181	6 15 9
32	1 4 0	82	3 1 6	132	4 19 0	182	6 16 6
33	1 4 9	83	3 2 3	133	4 19 9	183	6 17 3
34	1 5 6	84	3 3 0	134	5 0 6	184	6 18 0
35	1 6 3	85	3 3 9	135	5 1 3	185	6 18 9
36	1 7 0	86	3 4 6	136	5 2 0	186	6 19 6
37	1 7 9	87	3 5 3	137	5 2 9	187	7 0 3
38	1 8 6	88	3 6 0	138	5 3 6	188	7 1 0
39	1 9 3	89	3 6 9	139	5 4 3	189	7 1 9
40	1 10 0	90	3 7 6	140	5 5 0	190	7 2 6
41	1 10 9	91	3 8 3	141	5 5 9	191	7 3 3
42	1 11 6	92	3 9 0	142	5 6 6	192	7 4 0
43	1 12 3	93	3 9 9	143	5 7 3	193	7 4 9
44	1 13 0	94	3 10 6	144	5 8 0	194	7 5 6
45	1 13 9	95	3 11 3	145	5 8 9	195	7 6 3
46	1 14 6	96	3 12 0	146	5 9 6	196	7 7 0
47	1 15 3	97	3 12 9	147	5 10 3	197	7 7 9
48	1 16 0	98	3 13 6	148	5 11 0	198	7 8 6
49	1 16 9	99	3 14 3	149	5 11 9	199	7 9 3
50	1 17 6	100	3 15 0	150	5 12 6	200	7 10 0

£	£ s d	£	£ s d	£	£ s d	£	£ s d
250	9 7s 6d	700	26 5s 0d	1200	45 0s 0d	2000	75 0s 0d
300	11 5 0	750	28 2 6	1400	52 10 0	2500	93 15 0
400	15 0 0	800	30 0 0	1500	56 5 0	3000	112 10 0
500	18 15 0	900	33 15 0	1600	60 0 0	4000	150 0 0
600	22 10s 0d	1000	37 10s 0d	1800	67 10s 0d	5000	187 10s 0d

96¼% off.

1d	0s.	0d	4/1	0s.	1¾	8/1	0s.	3¾	12/1	0s.	5½	16/1	0s.	7¼
2d	0	0	2	0	2	2	0	3¾	2	0	5½	2	0	7¼
3d	0	0	3	0	2	3	0	3¾	3	0	5½	3	0	7¼
4d	0	0¼	4	0	2	4	0	3¾	4	0	5½	4	0	7¼
5d	0	0¼	5	0	2	5	0	3¾	5	0	5½	5	0	7½
6d	0	0¼	4/6	0	2	8/6	0	3¾	12/6	0	5¾	16/6	0	7½
7d	0	0¼	7	0	2	7	0	3¾	7	0	5¾	7	0	7½
8d	0	0¼	8	0	2	8	0	4	8	0	5¾	8	0	7½
9d	0	0¼	9	0	2¼	9	0	4	9	0	5¾	9	0	7½
10d	0	0½	10	0	2¼	10	0	4	10	0	5¾	10	0	7½
11d	0	0½	11	0	2¼	11	0	4	11	0	5¾	11	0	7½
1/-	0s.	0½	**5/-**	0s.	2¼	**9/-**	0s.	4	**13/-**	0s.	5¾	**17/-**	0s.	7¾
1/1	0s.	0½	5/1	0s.	2¼	9/1	0s.	4	13/1	0s.	6	17/1	0s.	7¾
2	0	0½	2	0	2¼	2	0	4¼	2	0	6	2	0	7¾
3	0	0½	3	0	2¼	3	0	4¼	3	0	6	3	0	7¾
4	0	0½	4	0	2½	4	0	4¼	4	0	6	4	0	7¾
5	0	0¾	5	0	2½	5	0	4¼	5	0	6	5	0	7¾
1/6	0	0¾	5/6	0	2½	9/6	0	4¼	13/6	0	6	17/6	0	8
7	0	0¾	7	0	2½	7	0	4¼	7	0	6	7	0	8
8	0	0¾	8	0	2½	8	0	4¼	8	0	6¼	8	0	8
9	0	0¾	9	0	2½	9	0	4½	9	0	6¼	9	0	8
10	0	0¾	10	0	2¾	10	0	4½	10	0	6¼	10	0	8
11	0	0¾	11	0	2¾	11	0	4½	11	0	6¼	11	0	8
2/-	0s.	1	**6/-**	0s.	2¾	**10/-**	0s.	4½	**14/-**	0s.	6¼	**18/-**	0s.	8
2/1	0s.	1	6/1	0s.	2¾	10/1	0s.	4½	14/1	0s.	6¼	18/1	0s.	8¼
2	0	1	2	0	2¾	2	0	4½	2	0	6½	2	0	8¼
3	0	1	3	0	2¾	3	0	4½	3	0	6½	3	0	8¼
4	0	1	4	0	2¾	4	0	4¾	4	0	6½	4	0	8¼
5	0	1	5	0	3	5	0	4¾	5	0	6½	5	0	8¼
2/6	0	1¼	6/6	0	3	10/6	0	4¾	14/6	0	6½	18/6	0	8¼
7	0	1¼	7	0	3	7	0	4¾	7	0	6½	7	0	8¼
8	0	1¼	8	0	3	8	0	4¾	8	0	6½	8	0	8½
9	0	1¼	9	0	3	9	0	4¾	9	0	6¾	9	0	8½
10	0	1¼	10	0	3	10	0	5	10	0	6¾	10	0	8½
11	0	1¼	11	0	3	11	0	5	11	0	6¾	11	0	8½
3/-	0s.	1¼	**7/-**	0s.	3¼	**11/-**	0s.	5	**15/-**	0s.	6¾	**19/-**	0s.	8½
3/1	0s.	1½	7/1	0s.	3¼	11/1	0s.	5	15/1	0s.	6¾	19/1	0s.	8½
2	0	1½	2	0	3¼	2	0	5	2	0	6¾	2	0	8¾
3	0	1½	3	0	3¼	3	0	5	3	0	6¾	3	0	8¾
4	0	1½	4	0	3¼	4	0	5	4	0	7	4	0	8¾
5	0	1½	5	0	3¼	5	0	5¼	5	0	7	5	0	8¾
3/6	0	1½	7/6	0	3½	11/6	0	5¼	15/6	0	7	19/6	0	8¾
7	0	1½	7	0	3½	7	0	5¼	7	0	7	7	0	8¾
8	0	1¾	8	0	3½	8	0	5¼	8	0	7	8	0	8¾
9	0	1¾	9	0	3½	9	0	5¼	9	0	7	9	0	9
10	0	1¾	10	0	3½	10	0	5¼	10	0	7¼	10	0	9
11	0	1¾	11	0	3½	11	0	5¼	11	0	7¼	11	0	9
4/-	0s.	1¾	**8/-**	0s.	3½	**12/-**	0s.	5½	**16/-**	0s.	7¼	**20/-**	0s.	9

20/6	0s.	9¼	25/6	0s.	11½	31/-	1s.	2	35/6	1s.	4	Guineas.		
21/-	0	9½	26/-	0	11¾	31/6	1	2¼	36/-	1	4¼	1.	0s.	9½
22/-	0	10	27/-	1	0¼	32/-	1	2½	37/-	1	4¾	2.	1	7
22/6	0	10¼	27/6	1	0½	32/6	1	2¾	37/6	1	5	3.	2	4¼
23/-	0	10½	28/-	1	0½	33/-	1	2¾	38/-	1	5	4.	3	1¾
24/-	0	10¾	29/-	1	1	34/-	1	3¼	39/-	1	5½	5.	3	11¼
25/-	0s.	11¼	**30/-**	1s.	1½	**35/-**	1s.	3¾	**40/-**	1s.	6	6.	4s.	8¾

(= $3\frac{6}{10}$%* on Gross Returns).

£1	£0	0s	9½	£51	£2	0s	9½	£101	£4	0s	9½	£151	£6	0s	9½
2	0	1	7¼	52	2	1	7¼	102	4	1	7¼	152	6	1	7¼
3	0	2	4¾	53	2	2	4¾	103	4	2	4¾	153	6	2	4¾
4	0	3	2½	54	2	3	2½	104	4	3	2½	154	6	3	2½
5	0	4	0	55	2	4	0	105	4	4	0	155	6	4	0
6	0	4	9½	56	2	4	9½	106	4	4	9½	156	6	4	9½
7	0	5	7¼	57	2	5	7¼	107	4	5	7¼	157	6	5	7¼
8	0	6	4¾	58	2	6	4¾	108	4	6	4¾	158	6	6	4¾
9	0	7	2½	59	2	7	2½	109	4	7	2½	159	6	7	2½
10	**0**	**8**	**0**	**60**	**2**	**8**	**0**	**110**	**4**	**8**	**0**	**160**	**6**	**8**	**0**
11	0	8	9½	61	2	8	9½	111	4	8	9½	161	6	8	9½
12	0	9	7¼	62	2	9	7¼	112	4	9	7¼	162	6	9	7¼
13	0	10	4¾	63	2	10	4¾	113	4	10	4¾	163	6	10	4¾
14	0	11	2½	64	2	11	2½	114	4	11	2½	164	6	11	2½
15	0	12	0	65	2	12	0	115	4	12	0	165	6	12	0
16	0	12	9½	66	2	12	9½	116	4	12	9½	166	6	12	9½
17	0	13	7¼	67	2	13	7¼	117	4	13	7¼	167	6	13	7¼
18	0	14	4¾	68	2	14	4¾	118	4	14	4¾	168	6	14	4¾
19	0	15	2½	69	2	15	2½	119	4	15	2½	169	6	15	2½
20	**0**	**16**	**0**	**70**	**2**	**16**	**0**	**120**	**4**	**16**	**0**	**170**	**6**	**16**	**0**
21	0	16	9½	71	2	16	9½	121	4	16	9½	171	6	16	9½
22	0	17	7¼	72	2	17	7¼	122	4	17	7¼	172	6	17	7¼
23	0	18	4¾	73	2	18	4¾	123	4	18	4¾	173	6	18	4¾
24	0	19	2½	74	2	19	2½	124	4	19	2½	174	6	19	2½
25	1	0	0	75	3	0	0	125	5	0	0	175	7	0	0
26	1	0	9½	76	3	0	9½	126	5	0	9½	176	7	0	9½
27	1	1	7¼	77	3	1	7¼	127	5	1	7¼	177	7	1	7¼
28	1	2	4¾	78	3	2	4¾	128	5	2	4¾	178	7	2	4¾
29	1	3	2½	79	3	3	2½	129	5	3	2½	179	7	3	2½
30	**1**	**4**	**0**	**80**	**3**	**4**	**0**	**130**	**5**	**4**	**0**	**180**	**7**	**4**	**0**
31	1	4	9½	81	3	4	9½	131	5	4	9½	181	7	4	9½
32	1	5	7¼	82	3	5	7¼	132	5	5	7¼	182	7	5	7¼
33	1	6	4¾	83	3	6	4¾	133	5	6	4¾	183	7	6	4¾
34	1	7	2½	84	3	7	2½	134	5	7	2½	184	7	7	2½
35	1	8	0	85	3	8	0	135	5	8	0	185	7	8	0
36	1	8	9½	86	3	8	9½	136	5	8	9½	186	7	8	9½
37	1	9	7¼	87	3	9	7¼	137	5	9	7¼	187	7	9	7¼
38	1	10	4¾	88	3	10	4¾	138	5	10	4¾	188	7	10	4¾
39	1	11	2½	89	3	11	2½	139	5	11	2½	189	7	11	2½
40	**1**	**12**	**0**	**90**	**3**	**12**	**0**	**140**	**5**	**12**	**0**	**190**	**7**	**12**	**0**
41	1	12	9½	91	3	12	9½	141	5	12	9½	191	7	12	9½
42	1	13	7¼	92	3	13	7¼	142	5	13	7¼	192	7	13	7¼
43	1	14	4¾	93	3	14	4¾	143	5	14	4¾	193	7	14	4¾
44	1	15	2½	94	3	15	2½	144	5	15	2½	194	7	15	2½
45	1	16	0	95	3	16	0	145	5	16	0	195	7	16	0
46	1	16	9½	96	3	16	9½	146	5	16	9½	196	7	16	9½
47	1	17	7¼	97	3	17	7¼	147	5	17	7¼	197	7	17	7¼
48	1	18	4¾	98	3	18	4¾	148	5	18	4¾	198	7	18	4¾
49	1	19	2½	99	3	19	2½	149	5	19	2½	199	7	19	2½
50	**2**	**0**	**0**	**100**	**4**	**0**	**0**	**150**	**6**	**0**	**0**	**200**	**8**	**0**	**0**

250	10	0s	0d	700	28	0s	0d	1200	48	0s	0d	2000	80	0s	0d
300	12	0	0	750	30	0	0	1400	56	0	0	2500	100	0	0
400	16	0	0	800	32	0	0	1500	60	0	0	3000	120	0	0
500	20	0	0	900	36	0	0	1600	64	0	0	4000	160	0	0
600	24	0s	0d	1000	40	0s	0d	1800	72	0s	0d	5000	200	0s	0d

96% off.

1d	0s.	0d	4/1	0s.	2	8/1	0s.	4	12/1	0s.	5¾	16/1	0s.	7¾
2d	0	0	2	0	2	2	0	4	2	0	5¾	2	0	7¾
3d	0	0	3	0	2	3	0	4	3	0	6	3	0	7¾
4d	0	0¼	4	0	2	4	0	4	4	0	6	4	0	7¾
5d	0	0¼	5	0	2	5	0	4	5	0	6	5	0	8
6d	0	0¼	4/6	0	2¼	8/6	0	4	12/6	0	6	16/6	0	8
7d	0	0¼	7	0	2¼	7	0	4	7	0	6	7	0	8
8d	0	0¼	8	0	2¼	8	0	4¼	8	0	6	8	0	8
9d	0	0¼	9	0	2¼	9	0	4¼	9	0	6	9	0	8
10d	0	0½	10	0	2¼	10	0	4¼	10	0	6¼	10	0	8
11d	0	0½	11	0	2¼	11	0	4¼	11	0	6¼	11	0	8
1/-	0s.	0½	**5/-**	0s.	2½	**9/-**	0s.	4¼	**13/-**	0s.	6¼	**17/-**	0s.	8¼
1/1	0s.	0½	5/1	0s.	2½	9/1	0s.	4¼	13/1	0s.	6¼	17/1	0s.	8¼
2	0	0½	2	0	2½	2	0	4½	2	0	6¼	2	0	8¼
3	0	0½	3	0	2½	3	0	4½	3	0	6¼	3	0	8¼
4	0	0¾	4	0	2½	4	0	4½	4	0	6½	4	0	8¼
5	0	0¾	5	0	2½	5	0	4½	5	0	6½	5	0	8¼
1/6	0	0¾	5/6	0	2¾	9/6	0	4½	13/6	0	6½	17/6	0	8½
7	0	0¾	7	0	2¾	7	0	4½	7	0	6½	7	0	8½
8	0	0¾	8	0	2¾	8	0	4¾	8	0	6½	8	0	8½
9	0	0¾	9	0	2¾	9	0	4¾	9	0	6½	9	0	8½
10	0	1	10	0	2¾	10	0	4¾	10	0	6¾	10	0	8½
11	0	1	11	0	2¾	11	0	4¾	11	0	6¾	11	0	8½
2/-	0s.	1	**6/-**	0s.	3	**10/-**	0s.	4¾	**14/-**	0s.	6¾	**18/-**	0s.	8¾
2/1	0s.	1	6/1	0s.	3	10/1	0s.	4¾	14/1	0s.	6¾	18/1	0s.	8¾
2	0	1	2	0	3	2	0	5	2	0	6¾	2	0	8¾
3	0	1	3	0	3	3	0	5	3	0	6¾	3	0	8¾
4	0	1	4	0	3	4	0	5	4	0	7	4	0	8¾
5	0	1¼	5	0	3	5	0	5	5	0	7	5	0	8¾
2/6	0	1¼	6/6	0	3	10/6	0	5	14/6	0	7	18/6	0	9
7	0	1¼	7	0	3¼	7	0	5	7	0	7	7	0	9
8	0	1¼	8	0	3¼	8	0	5	8	0	7	8	0	9
9	0	1¼	9	0	3¼	9	0	5¼	9	0	7	9	0	9
10	0	1¼	10	0	3¼	10	0	5¼	10	0	7	10	0	9
11	0	1½	11	0	3¼	11	0	5¼	11	0	7¼	11	0	9
3/-	0s.	1½	**7/-**	0s.	3¼	**11/-**	0s.	5¼	**15/-**	0s.	7¼	**19/-**	0s.	9
3/1	0s.	1½	7/1	0s.	3½	11/1	0s.	5¼	15/1	0s.	7¼	19/1	0s.	9¼
2	0	1½	2	0	3½	2	0	5¼	2	0	7¼	2	0	9¼
3	0	1½	3	0	3½	3	0	5½	3	0	7¼	3	0	9¼
4	0	1½	4	0	3½	4	0	5½	4	0	7¼	4	0	9¼
5	0	1¾	5	0	3½	5	0	5½	5	0	7½	5	0	9¼
3/6	0	1¾	7/6	0	3½	11/6	0	5½	15/6	0	7½	19/6	0	9¼
7	0	1¾	7	0	3¾	7	0	5½	7	0	7½	7	0	9½
8	0	1¾	8	0	3¾	8	0	5½	8	0	7½	8	0	9½
9	0	1¾	9	0	3¾	9	0	5¾	9	0	7½	9	0	9½
10	0	1¾	10	0	3¾	10	0	5¾	10	0	7½	10	0	9½
11	0	2	11	0	3¾	11	0	5¾	11	0	7¾	11	0	9½
4/-	0s.	2	**8/-**	0s.	3¾	**12/-**	0s.	5¾	**16/-**	0s.	7¾	**20/-**	0s.	9½

20/6	0s.	9¾	25/6	1s.	0¼	31/-	1s.	3	35/6	1s.	5	Guineas.		
21/-	0	10	26/-	1	0½	31/6	1	3	36/-	1	5¼	1.	0s.	10
22/-	0	10½	27/-	1	1	32/-	1	3¼	37/-	1	5¾	2.	1	8¼
22/6	0	10¾	27/6	1	1¼	32/6	1	3½	37/6	1	6	3.	2	6¼
23/-	0	11	28/-	1	1½	33/-	1	3¾	38/-	1	6¼	4.	3	4¼
24/-		11½	29/-	1	2	34/-	1	4¼	39/-	1	6¾	5.	4	2½
25/-	1s.	0	**30/-**	1s.	2½	**35/-**	1s.	4¾	**40/-**	1s.	7¼	6.	5s.	0½

(= $3\frac{8}{10}$%* on Gross Returns).

4⅛% £4. 2. 6 PER CENT OR PER 100. 4⅛%

£1	0s.10	£51	£2 2s. 1	£101	£4 3s. 4	£151	£6 4s. 7
2	1 7¾	52	2 2 10¾	102	4 4 1¾	152	6 5 4¾
3	2 5¾	53	2 3 8¾	103	4 4 11¾	153	6 6 2¾
4	3 3½	54	2 4 6½	104	4 5 9½	154	6 7 0½
5	4 1½	55	2 5 4½	105	4 6 7½	155	6 7 10½
6	4 11½	56	2 6 2½	106	4 7 5½	156	6 8 8½
7	5 9¼	57	2 7 0¼	107	4 8 3¼	157	6 9 6¼
8	6 7¼	58	2 7 10¼	108	4 9 1¼	158	6 10 4¼
9	7 5	59	2 8 8	109	4 9 11	159	6 11 2
10	**8s. 3**	**60**	**£2 9s. 6**	**110**	**£4 10s. 9**	**160**	**£6 12s. 0**
11	9s. 1	61	£2 10s. 4	111	£4 11s. 7	161	£6 12s.10
12	9 10¾	62	2 11 1¾	112	4 12 4¾	162	6 13 7¾
13	10 8¾	63	2 11 11¾	113	4 13 2¾	163	6 14 5¾
14	11 6½	64	2 12 9½	114	4 14 0½	164	6 15 3½
15	12 4½	65	2 13 7½	115	4 14 10½	165	6 16 1½
16	13 2½	66	2 14 5½	116	4 15 8½	166	6 16 11½
17	14 0¼	67	2 15 3¼	117	4 16 6¼	167	6 17 9¼
18	14 10¼	68	2 16 1¼	118	4 17 4¼	168	6 18 7¼
19	15 8	69	2 16 11	119	4 18 2	169	6 19 5
20	**16s. 6**	**70**	**£2 17s. 9**	**120**	**£4 19s. 0**	**170**	**£7 0s. 3**
21	17s. 4	71	£2 18s. 7	121	£4 19s.10	171	£7 1s. 1
22	18 1¾	72	2 19 4¾	122	5 0 7¾	172	7 1 10¾
23	18 11¾	73	3 0 2¾	123	5 1 5¾	173	7 2 8¾
24	19 9½	74	3 1 0½	124	5 2 3½	174	7 3 6½
25	20 7½	75	3 1 10½	125	5 3 1½	175	7 4 4½
26	21 5½	76	3 2 8½	126	5 3 11½	176	7 5 2½
27	22 3¼	77	3 3 6¼	127	5 4 9¼	177	7 6 0¼
28	23 1¼	78	3 4 4¼	128	5 5 7¼	178	7 6 10¼
29	23 11	79	3 5 2	129	5 6 5	179	7 7 8
30	**24s. 9**	**80**	**£3 6s. 0**	**130**	**£5 7s. 3**	**180**	**£7 8s. 6**
31	25s. 7	81	£3 6s.10	131	£5 8s. 1	181	£7 9s. 4
32	26 4¾	82	3 7 7¾	132	5 8 10¾	182	7 10 1¾
33	27 2¾	83	3 8 5¾	133	5 9 8¾	183	7 10 11¾
34	28 0½	84	3 9 3½	134	5 10 6½	184	7 11 9½
35	28 10½	85	3 10 1½	135	5 11 4½	185	7 12 7½
36	29 8½	86	3 10 11½	136	5 12 2½	186	7 13 5½
37	30 6¼	87	3 11 9¼	137	5 13 0¼	187	7 14 3¼
38	31 4¼	88	3 12 7¼	138	5 13 10¼	188	7 15 1¼
39	32 2	89	3 13 5	139	5 14 8	189	7 15 11
40	**33s. 0**	**90**	**£3 14s. 3**	**140**	**£5 15s. 6**	**190**	**£7 16s. 9**
41	33s.10	91	£3 15s. 1	141	£5 16s. 4	191	£7 17s. 7
42	34 7¾	92	3 15 10¾	142	5 17 1¾	192	7 18 4¾
43	35 5¾	93	3 16 8¾	143	5 17 11¾	193	7 19 2¾
44	36 3½	94	3 17 6½	144	5 18 9½	194	8 0 0½
45	37 1½	95	3 18 4½	145	5 19 7½	195	8 0 10½
46	37 11½	96	3 19 2½	146	6 0 5½	196	8 1 8½
47	38 9¼	97	4 0 0¼	147	6 1 3¼	197	8 2 6¼
48	39 7¼	98	4 0 10¼	148	6 2 1¼	198	8 3 4¼
49	40 5	99	4 1 8	149	6 2 11	199	8 4 2
50	**41s. 3**	**100**	**£4 2s. 6**	**150**	**£6 3s. 9**	**200**	**£8 5s. 0**
250	10 6s.3d	700	28 17s. 6d	1200	£49 10s. 0d	2000	£82 10s. 0
300	12 7 6	750	30 18 9	1400	57 15 0	2500	103 2 6
400	16 10 0	800	33 0 0	1500	61 17 6	3000	123 15 0
500	20 12 6	900	37 2 6	1600	66 0 0	4000	165 0 0
600	24 15s.0d	1000	£41 5s. 0d	1800	£74 5s. 0d	5000	£206 5s. 0

95⅞% off. (4%* on Gross Returns).

4⅜% £4. 7. 6 PER CENT OR PER 100. 4⅜%

No.	Amount	No.	Amount	No.	Amount	No.	Amount
£1	0s.10½	£51	£2 4s. 7½	£101	£4 8s. 4½	£151	£6 12s. 1½
2	1 9	52	2 5 6	102	4 9 3	152	6 13 0
3	2 7½	53	2 6 4½	103	4 10 1½	153	6 13 10½
4	3 6	54	2 7 3	104	4 11 0	154	6 14 9
5	4 4½	55	2 8 1½	105	4 11 10½	155	6 15 7½
6	5 3	56	2 9 0	106	4 12 9	156	6 16 6
7	6 1½	57	2 9 10½	107	4 13 7½	157	6 17 4½
8	7 0	58	2 10 9	108	4 14 6	158	6 18 3
9	7 10½	59	2 11 7½	109	4 15 4½	159	6 19 1½
10	8s. 9	60	£2 12s. 6	110	£4 16s. 3	160	£7 0s. 0
11	9s. 7½	61	£2 13s. 4½	111	£4 17s. 1½	161	£7 0s.10½
12	10 6	62	2 14 3	112	4 18 0	162	7 1 9
13	11 4½	63	2 15 1½	113	4 18 10½	163	7 2 7½
14	12 3	64	2 16 0	114	4 19 9	164	7 3 6
15	13 1½	65	2 16 10½	115	5 0 7½	165	7 4 4½
16	14 0	66	2 17 9	116	5 1 6	166	7 5 3
17	14 10½	67	2 18 7½	117	5 2 4½	167	7 6 1½
18	15 9	68	2 19 6	118	5 3 3	168	7 7 0
19	16 7½	69	3 0 4½	119	5 4 1½	169	7 7 10½
20	17s. 6	70	£3 1s. 3	120	£5 5s. 0	170	£7 8s. 9
21	18s. 4½	71	£3 2s. 1½	121	£5 5s.10½	171	£7 9s. 7½
22	19 3	72	3 3 0	122	5 6 9	172	7 10 6
23	20 1½	73	3 3 10½	123	5 7 7½	173	7 11 4½
24	21 0	74	3 4 9	124	5 8 6	174	7 12 3
25	21 10½	75	3 5 7½	125	5 9 4½	175	7 13 1½
26	22 9	76	3 6 6	126	5 10 3	176	7 14 0
27	23 7½	77	3 7 4½	127	5 11 1½	177	7 14 10½
28	24 6	78	3 8 3	128	5 12 0	178	7 15 9
29	25 4½	79	3 9 1½	129	5 12 10½	179	7 16 7½
30	26s. 3	80	£3 10s. 0	130	£5 13s. 9	180	£7 17s. 6
31	27s. 1½	81	£3 10s.10½	131	£5 14s. 7½	181	£7 18s. 4½
32	28 0	82	3 11 9	132	5 15 6	182	7 19 3
33	28 10½	83	3 12 7½	133	5 16 4½	183	8 0 1½
34	29 9	84	3 13 6	134	5 17 3	184	8 1 0
35	30 7½	85	3 14 4½	135	5 18 1½	185	8 1 10½
36	31 6	86	3 15 3	136	5 19 0	186	8 2 9
37	32 4½	87	3 16 1½	137	5 19 10½	187	8 3 7½
38	33 3	88	3 17 0	138	6 0 9	188	8 4 6
39	34 1½	89	3 17 10½	139	6 1 7½	189	8 5 4½
40	35s. 0	90	£3 18s. 9	140	£6 2s. 6	190	£8 6s. 3
41	35s.10½	91	£3 19s. 7½	141	£6 3s. 4½	191	£8 7s. 1½
42	36 9	92	4 0 6	142	6 4 3	192	8 8 0
43	37 7½	93	4 1 4½	143	6 5 1½	193	8 8 10½
44	38 6	94	4 2 3	144	6 6 0	194	8 9 9
45	39 4½	95	4 3 1½	145	6 6 10½	195	8 10 7½
46	40 3	96	4 4 0	146	6 7 9	196	8 11 6
47	41 1½	97	4 4 10½	147	6 8 7½	197	8 12 4½
48	42 0	98	4 5 9	148	6 9 6	198	8 13 3
49	42 10½	99	4 6 7½	149	6 10 4½	199	8 14 1½
50	43s. 9	100	£4 7s. 6	150	£6 11s. 3	200	£8 15s. 0

No.	Amount	No.	Amount	No.	Amount	No.	Amount
250	10 18s.9d	700	30 12s. 6d	1200	£52 10s. 0d	2000	£87 10s. 0
300	13 2 6	750	32 16 3	1400	61 5 0	2500	109 7 6
400	17 10 0	800	35 0 0	1500	65 12 6	3000	131 5 0
500	21 17 6	900	39 7 6	1600	70 0 0	4000	175 0 0
600	26 5s.0d	1000	£43 15s. 0d	1800	£78 15s. 0d	5000	£218 18s. 0

95⅝% off. (=4 2/10%* on Gross Returns).

£1	£0	0s 10d	£51	£2	2s 6d	£101	£4	4s 2d	£151	£6	5s 10
2	0	1 8	52	2	3 4	102	4	5 0	152	6	6 8
3	0	2 6	53	2	4 2	103	4	5 10	153	6	7 6
4	0	3 4	54	2	5 0	104	4	6 8	154	6	8 4
5	0	4 2	55	2	5 10	105	4	7 6	155	6	9 2
6	0	5 0	56	2	6 8	106	4	8 4	156	6	10 0
7	0	5 10	57	2	7 6	107	4	9 2	157	6	10 10
8	0	6 8	58	2	8 4	108	4	10 0	158	6	11 8
9	0	7 6	59	2	9 2	109	4	10 10	159	6	12 6
10	0	8 4	60	2	10 0	110	4	11 8	160	6	13 4
11	0	9 2	61	2	10 10	111	4	12 6	161	6	14 2
12	0	10 0	62	2	11 8	112	4	13 4	162	6	15 0
13	0	10 10	63	2	12 6	113	4	14 2	163	6	15 10
14	0	11 8	64	2	13 4	114	4	15 0	164	6	16 8
15	0	12 6	65	2	14 2	115	4	15 10	165	6	17 6
16	0	13 4	66	2	15 0	116	4	16 8	166	6	18 4
17	0	14 2	67	2	15 10	117	4	17 6	167	6	19 2
18	0	15 0	68	2	16 8	118	4	18 4	168	7	0 0
19	0	15 10	69	2	17 6	119	4	19 2	169	7	0 10
20	0	16 8	70	2	18 4	120	5	0 0	170	7	1 8
21	0	17 6	71	2	19 2	121	5	0 10	171	7	2 6
22	0	18 4	72	3	0 0	122	5	1 8	172	7	3 4
23	0	19 2	73	3	0 10	123	5	2 6	173	7	4 2
24	1	0 0	74	3	1 8	124	5	3 4	174	7	5 0
25	1	0 10	75	3	2 6	125	5	4 2	175	7	5 10
26	1	1 8	76	3	3 4	126	5	5 0	176	7	6 8
27	1	2 6	77	3	4 2	127	5	5 10	177	7	7 6
28	1	3 4	78	3	5 0	128	5	6 8	178	7	8 4
29	1	4 2	79	3	5 10	129	5	7 6	179	7	9 2
30	1	5 0	80	3	6 8	130	5	8 4	180	7	10 0
31	1	5 10	81	3	7 6	131	5	9 2	181	7	10 10
32	1	6 8	82	3	8 4	132	5	10 0	182	7	11 8
33	1	7 6	83	3	9 2	133	5	10 10	183	7	12 6
34	1	8 4	84	3	10 0	134	5	11 8	184	7	13 4
35	1	9 2	85	3	10 10	135	5	12 6	185	7	14 2
36	1	10 0	86	3	11 8	136	5	13 4	186	7	15 0
37	1	10 10	87	3	12 6	137	5	14 2	187	7	15 10
38	1	11 8	88	3	13 4	138	5	15 0	188	7	16 8
39	1	12 6	89	3	14 2	139	5	15 10	189	7	17 6
40	1	13 4	90	3	15 0	140	5	16 8	190	7	18 4
41	1	14 2	91	3	15 10	141	5	17 6	191	7	19 2
42	1	15 0	92	3	16 8	142	5	18 4	192	8	0 0
43	1	15 10	93	3	17 6	143	5	19 2	193	8	0 10
44	1	16 8	94	3	18 4	144	6	0 0	194	8	1 8
45	1	17 6	95	3	19 2	145	6	0 10	195	8	2 6
46	1	18 4	96	4	0 0	146	6	1 8	196	8	3 4
47	1	19 2	97	4	0 10	147	6	2 6	197	8	4 2
48	2	0 0	98	4	1 8	148	6	3 4	198	8	5 0
49	2	0 10	99	4	2 6	149	6	4 2	199	8	5 10
50	2	1 8	100	4	3 4	150	6	5 0	200	8	6 8

250	10	8s 4d	700	29	3s 4d	1200	50	0s 0d	2000	83	6s 8
300	12	10 0	750	31	5 0	1400	58	6 8	2500	104	3 4
400	16	13 4	800	33	6 8	1500	62	10 0	3000	125	0 0
500	20	16 8	900	37	10 0	1600	66	13 4	4000	166	13 4
600	25	0s 0d	1000	41	13s 4d	1800	75	0s 0d	5000	208	6s 8

95⅚% off.

FOUR & ONE-SIXTH % = 1/24TH.

1d	0s	0d	4/1	0s	2d	8/1	0s	4d	12/1	0s	6d	16/1	0s	8d
2d	0	0	2	0	2	2	0	4	2	0	6	2	0	8
3d	0	0⅛	3	0	2⅛	3	0	4⅛	3	0	6⅛	3	0	8⅛
4d	0	0¼	4	0	2¼	4	0	4¼	4	0	6¼	4	0	8¼
5d	0	0¼	5	0	2¼	5	0	4¼	5	0	6¼	5	0	8¼
6d	0	0¼	4/6	0	2¼	8/6	0	4¼	12/6	0	6¼	16/6	0	8¼
7d	0	0¼	7	0	2¼	7	0	4¼	7	0	6¼	7	0	8¼
8d	0	0¼	8	0	2¼	8	0	4¼	8	0	6¼	8	0	8¼
9d	0	0⅜	9	0	2⅜	9	0	4⅜	9	0	6⅜	9	0	8⅜
10d	0	0½	10	0	2½	10	0	4½	10	0	6½	10	0	8½
11d	0	0½	11	0	2½	11	0	4½	11	0	6½	11	0	8½
1/-	0	0½	**5/-**	0	2½	**9/-**	0	4½	**13/-**	0	6½	**17/-**	0	8½
1/1	0	0½	5/1	0	2½	9/1	0	4½	13/1	0	6½	17/1	0	8½
2	0	0½	2	0	2½	2	0	4½	2	0	6½	2	0	8½
3	0	0⅝	3	0	2⅝	3	0	4⅝	3	0	6⅝	3	0	8⅝
4	0	0¾	4	0	2¾	4	0	4¾	4	0	6¾	4	0	8¾
5	0	0¾	5	0	2¾	5	0	4¾	5	0	6¾	5	0	8¾
1/6	0	0¾	5/6	0	2¾	9/6	0	4¾	13/6	0	6¾	17/6	0	8¾
7	0	0¾	7	0	2¾	7	0	4¾	7	0	6¾	7	0	8¾
8	0	0¾	8	0	2¾	8	0	4¾	8	0	6¾	8	0	8¾
9	0	0⅞	9	0	2⅞	9	0	4⅞	9	0	6⅞	9	0	8⅞
10	0	1	10	0	3	10	0	5	10	0	7	10	0	9
11	0	1	11	0	3	11	0	5	11	0	7	11	0	9
2/-	0	1	**6/-**	0	3	**10/-**	0	5	**14/-**	0	7	**18/-**	0	9
2/1	0	1	6/1	0	3	10/1	0	5	14/1	0	7	18/1	0	9
2	0	1	2	0	3	2	0	5	2	0	7	2	0	9
3	0	1⅛	3	0	3⅛	3	0	5⅛	3	0	7⅛	3	0	9⅛
4	0	1¼	4	0	3¼	4	0	5¼	4	0	7¼	4	0	9¼
5	0	1¼	5	0	3¼	5	0	5¼	5	0	7¼	5	0	9¼
2/6	0	1¼	6/6	0	3¼	10/6	0	5¼	14/6	0	7¼	18/6	0	9¼
7	0	1¼	7	0	3¼	7	0	5¼	7	0	7¼	7	0	9¼
8	0	1¼	8	0	3¼	8	0	5¼	8	0	7¼	8	0	9¼
9	0	1⅜	9	0	3⅜	9	0	5⅜	9	0	7⅜	9	0	9⅜
10	0	1½	10	0	3½	10	0	5½	10	0	7½	10	0	9½
11	0	1½	11	0	3½	11	0	5½	11	0	7½	11	0	9½
3/-	0	1½	**7/-**	0	3½	**11/-**	0	5½	**15/-**	0	7½	**19/-**	0	9½
3/1	0	1½	7/1	0	3½	11/1	0	5½	15/1	0	7½	19/1	0	9½
2	0	1½	2	0	3½	2	0	5½	2	0	7½	2	0	9½
3	0	1⅝	3	0	3⅝	3	0	5⅝	3	0	7⅝	3	0	9⅝
4	0	1¾	4	0	3¾	4	0	5¾	4	0	7¾	4	0	9¾
5	0	1¾	5	0	3¾	5	0	5¾	5	0	7¾	5	0	9¾
3/6	0	1¾	7/6	0	3¾	11/6	0	5¾	15/6	0	7¾	19/6	0	9¾
7	0	1¾	7	0	3¾	7	0	5¾	7	0	7¾	7	0	9¾
8	0	1¾	8	0	3¾	8	0	5¾	8	0	7¾	8	0	9¾
9	0	1⅞	9	0	3⅞	9	0	5⅞	9	0	7⅞	9	0	9⅞
10	0	2	10	0	4	10	0	6	10	0	8	10	0	10
11	0	2	11	0	4	11	0	6	11	0	8	11	0	10
4/-	0	2	**8/-**	0	4	**12/-**	0	6	**16/-**	0	8	**20/-**	0	10

20/6	0s	10¼	25/6	1s	0¾	31/-	1s	3½	35/6	1s	5¾	42/-	1s	9
21/-	0	10½	26/-	1	1	31/6	1	3¾	36/-	1	6	45/-	1	10½
22/-	0	11	27/-	1	1½	32/-	1	4	37/-	1	6½	50/-	2	1
22/6	0	11¼	27/6	1	1¾	32/6	1	4¼	37/6	1	6¾	63/-	2	7½
23/-	0	11½	28/-	1	2	33/-	1	4½	38/-	1	7	84/-	3	6
24/-	1	0	29/-	1	2½	34/-	1	5	39/-	1	7½	105/-	4	4½
25/-	1	0½	**30/-**	1	3	**35/-**	1	5½	**40/-**	1	8	126/-	5	3

4¼% 4¼ Per Cent. 4¼%

£1	£0	0s	10¼	£51	£2	3s	4¼	£101	£4	5s	10¼	£151	£6	8s	4¼
2	0	1	8½	52	2	4	2½	102	4	6	8½	152	6	9	2½
3	0	2	6½	53	2	5	0½	103	4	7	6½	153	6	10	0½
4	0	3	4¾	54	2	5	10¾	104	4	8	4¾	154	6	10	10¾
5	0	4	3	55	2	6	9	105	4	9	3	155	6	11	9
6	0	5	1¼	56	2	7	7¼	106	4	10	1¼	156	6	12	7¼
7	0	5	11½	57	2	8	5½	107	4	10	11½	157	6	13	5½
8	0	6	9½	58	2	9	3½	108	4	11	9½	158	6	14	3½
9	0	7	7¾	59	2	10	1¾	109	4	12	7¾	159	6	15	1¾
10	0	8	6	60	2	11	0	110	4	13	6	160	6	16	0
11	0	9	4¼	61	2	11	10¼	111	4	14	4¼	161	6	16	10¼
12	0	10	2½	62	2	12	8½	112	4	15	2½	162	6	17	8½
13	0	11	0½	63	2	13	6½	113	4	16	0½	163	6	18	6½
14	0	11	10¾	64	2	14	4¾	114	4	16	10¾	164	6	19	4¾
15	0	12	9	65	2	15	3	115	4	17	9	165	7	0	3
16	0	13	7¼	66	2	16	1¼	116	4	18	7¼	166	7	1	1¼
17	0	14	5½	67	2	16	11½	117	4	19	5½	167	7	1	11½
18	0	15	3½	68	2	17	9½	118	5	0	3½	168	7	2	9½
19	0	16	1¾	69	2	18	7¾	119	5	1	1¾	169	7	3	7¾
20	0	17	0	70	2	19	6	120	5	2	0	170	7	4	6
21	0	17	10¼	71	3	0	4¼	121	5	2	10¼	171	7	5	4¼
22	0	18	8½	72	3	1	2½	122	5	3	8½	172	7	6	2½
23	0	19	6½	73	3	2	0½	123	5	4	6½	173	7	7	0½
24	1	0	4¾	74	3	2	10¾	124	5	5	4¾	174	7	7	10¾
25	1	1	3	75	3	3	9	125	5	6	3	175	7	8	9
26	1	2	1¼	76	3	4	7¼	126	5	7	1¼	176	7	9	7¼
27	1	2	11½	77	3	5	5½	127	5	7	11½	177	7	10	5½
28	1	3	9½	78	3	6	3½	128	5	8	9½	178	7	11	3½
29	1	4	7¾	79	3	7	1¾	129	5	9	7¾	179	7	12	1¾
30	1	5	6	80	3	8	0	130	5	10	6	180	7	13	0
31	1	6	4¼	81	3	8	10¼	131	5	11	4¼	181	7	13	10¼
32	1	7	2½	82	3	9	8½	132	5	12	2½	182	7	14	8½
33	1	8	0½	83	3	10	6½	133	5	13	0½	183	7	15	6½
34	1	8	10¾	84	3	11	4¾	134	5	13	10¾	184	7	16	4¾
35	1	9	9	85	3	12	3	135	5	14	9	185	7	17	3
36	1	10	7¼	86	3	13	1¼	136	5	15	7¼	186	7	18	1¼
37	1	11	5½	87	3	13	11½	137	5	16	5½	187	7	18	11½
38	1	12	3½	88	3	14	9½	138	5	17	3½	188	7	19	9½
39	1	13	1¾	89	3	15	7¾	139	5	18	1¾	189	8	0	7¾
40	1	14	0	90	3	16	6	140	5	19	0	190	8	1	6
41	1	14	10¼	91	3	17	4¼	141	5	19	10¼	191	8	2	4¼
42	1	15	8½	92	3	18	2½	142	6	0	8½	192	8	3	2½
43	1	16	6½	93	3	19	0½	143	6	1	6½	193	8	4	0½
44	1	17	4¾	94	3	19	10¾	144	6	2	4¾	194	8	4	10¾
45	1	18	3	95	4	0	9	145	6	3	3	195	8	5	9
46	1	19	1¼	96	4	1	7¼	146	6	4	1¼	196	8	6	7¼
47	1	19	11½	97	4	2	5½	147	6	4	11½	197	8	7	5½
48	2	0	9½	98	4	3	3½	148	6	5	9½	198	8	8	3½
49	2	1	7¾	99	4	4	1¾	149	6	6	7¾	199	8	9	1¾
50	2	2	6	100	4	5	0	150	6	7	6	200	8	10	0

250	10	12s	6d	700	29	15s	0d	1200	51	0s	0d	2000	85	0s	0d
300	12	15	0	750	31	17	6	1400	59	10	0	2500	106	5	0
400	17	0	0	800	34	0	0	1500	63	15	0	3000	127	10	0
500	21	5	0	900	38	5	0	1600	68	0	0	4000	170	0	0
600	25	10s	0d	1000	42	10s	0d	1800	76	10s	0d	5000	212	10s	0d

95¾% off.

4¼ Per Cent.

1d	0s.	0d	4/1	0s.	2	8/1	0s.	4	12/1	0s.	6¼	16/1	0s.	8¼
2d	0	0	2	0	2¼	2	0	4¼	2	0	6¼	2	0	8¼
3d	0	0¼	3	0	2¼	3	0	4¼	3	0	6¼	3	0	8¼
4d	0	0¼	4	0	2¼	4	0	4¼	4	0	6¼	4	0	8¼
5d	0	0¼	5	0	2¼	5	0	4¼	5	0	6¼	5	0	8¼
6d	0	0¼	4/6	0	2¼	8/6	0	4¼	12/6	0	6½	16/6	0	8½
7d	0	0¼	7	0	2¼	7	0	4½	7	0	6½	7	0	8½
8d	0	0¼	8	0	2½	8	0	4½	8	0	6½	8	0	8½
9d	0	0½	9	0	2½	9	0	4½	9	0	6½	9	0	8½
10d	0	0½	10	0	2½	10	0	4½	10	0	6½	10	0	8½
11d	0	0½	11	0	2½	11	0	4½	11	0	6½	11	0	8¾
1/-	0s.	0½	5/-	0s.	2½	9/-	0s.	4½	13/-	0s.	6¾	17/-	0s.	8¾
1/1	0s.	0½	5/1	0s.	2½	9/1	0s.	4¾	13/1	0s.	6¾	17/1	0s.	8¾
2	0	0½	2	0	2¾	2	0	4¾	2	0	6¾	2	0	8¾
3	0	0¾	3	0	2¾	3	0	4¾	3	0	6¾	3	0	8¾
4	0	0¾	4	0	2¾	4	0	4¾	4	0	6¾	4	0	8¾
5	0	0¾	5	0	2¾	5	0	4¾	5	0	6¾	5	0	9
1/6	0	0¾	5/6	0	2¾	9/6	0	4¾	13/6	0	7	17/6	0	9
7	0	0¾	7	0	2¾	7	0	5	7	0	7	7	0	9
8	0	0¾	8	0	3	8	0	5	8	0	7	8	0	9
9	0	1	9	0	3	9	0	5	9	0	7	9	0	9
10	0	1	10	0	3	10	0	5	10	0	7	10	0	9
11	0	1	11	0	3	11	0	5	11	0	7	11	0	9¼
2/-	0s.	1	6/-	0s.	3	10/-	0s.	5	14/-	0s.	7¼	18/-	0s.	9¼
2/1	0s.	1	6/1	0s.	3	10/1	0s.	5¼	14/1	0s.	7¼	18/1	0s.	9¼
2	0	1	2	0	3¼	2	0	5¼	2	0	7¼	2	0	9¼
3	0	1¼	3	0	3¼	3	0	5¼	3	0	7¼	3	0	9¼
4	0	1¼	4	0	3¼	4	0	5¼	4	0	7¼	4	0	9¼
5	0	1¼	5	0	3¼	5	0	5¼	5	0	7¼	5	0	9½
2/6	0	1¼	6/6	0	3¼	10/6	0	5¼	14/6	0	7½	18/6	0	9½
7	0	1¼	7	0	3¼	7	0	5½	7	0	7½	7	0	9½
8	0	1¼	8	0	3½	8	0	5½	8	0	7½	8	0	9½
9	0	1½	9	0	3½	9	0	5½	9	0	7½	9	0	9½
10	0	1½	10	0	3½	10	0	5½	10	0	7½	10	0	9½
11	0	1½	11	0	3½	11	0	5½	11	0	7½	11	0	9¾
3/-	0s.	1½	7/-	0s.	3½	11/-	0s.	5½	15/-	0s.	7¾	19/-	0s.	9¾
3/1	0s.	1½	7/1	0s.	3½	11/1	0s.	5¾	15/1	0s.	7¾	19/1	0s.	9¾
2	0	1½	2	0	3¾	2	0	5¾	2	0	7¾	2	0	9¾
3	0	1¾	3	0	3¾	3	0	5¾	3	0	7¾	3	0	9¾
4	0	1¾	4	0	3¾	4	0	5¾	4	0	7¾	4	0	9¾
5	0	1¾	5	0	3¾	5	0	5¾	5	0	7¾	5	0	10
3/6	0	1¾	7/6	0	3¾	11/6	0	5¾	15/6	0	8	19/6	0	10
7	0	1¾	7	0	3¾	7	0	6	7	0	8	7	0	10
8	0	1¾	8	0	4	8	0	6	8	0	8	8	0	10
9	0	2	9	0	4	9	0	6	9	0	8	9	0	10
10	0	2	10	0	4	10	0	6	10	0	8	10	0	10
11	0	2	11	0	4	11	0	6	11	0	8	11	0	10¼
4/-	0s.	2	8/-	0s.	4	12/-	0s.	6	16/-	0s.	8¼	20/-	0s.	10¼

20/6	0s.	10½	25/6	1s.	1	31/-	1s.	3¾	35/6	1s.	6	Guineas.		
21/-	0	10¾	26/-	1	1¼	31/6	1	4	36/-	1	6¼	1.	0s.	10¾
22/-	0	11¼	27/-	1	1¾	32/-	1	4¼	37/-	1	6¾	2.	1	9½
22/6	0	11½	27/6	1	2	32/6	1	4½	37/6	1	7¼	3.	2	8¼
23/-	0	11¾	28/-	1	2¼	33/-	1	4¾	38/-	1	7½	4.	3	6¾
24/-	1	0¼	29/-	1	2¾	34/-	1	5¼	39/-	1	8	5.	4	5½
25/-	1s.	0¾	30/-	1s.	3¼	35/-	1s.	5¾	40/-	1s.	8½	6.	5s.	4¼

(=4 1/10 %* on Gross Returns).

£1	£0	0s	10¾	£51	£2	5s	10¾	£101	£4	10s	10¾	£151	£6	15s	10¾
2	0	1	9½	52	2	6	9½	102	4	11	9½	152	6	16	9½
3	0	2	8½	53	2	7	8½	103	4	12	8½	153	6	17	8½
4	0	3	7¼	54	2	8	7¼	104	4	13	7¼	154	6	18	7¼
5	0	4	6	55	2	9	6	105	4	14	6	155	6	19	6
6	0	5	4¾	56	2	10	4¾	106	4	15	4¾	156	7	0	4¾
7	0	6	3½	57	2	11	3½	107	4	16	3½	157	7	1	3½
8	0	7	2½	58	2	12	2½	108	4	17	2½	158	7	2	2½
9	0	8	1¼	59	2	13	1¼	109	4	18	1¼	159	7	3	1¼
10	**0**	**9**	**0**	**60**	**2**	**14**	**0**	**110**	**4**	**19**	**0**	**160**	**7**	**4**	**0**
11	0	9	10¾	61	2	14	10¾	111	4	19	10¾	161	7	4	10¾
12	0	10	9½	62	2	15	9½	112	5	0	9½	162	7	5	9½
13	0	11	8½	63	2	16	8½	113	5	1	8½	163	7	6	8½
14	0	12	7¼	64	2	17	7¼	114	5	2	7¼	164	7	7	7¼
15	0	13	6	65	2	18	6	115	5	3	6	165	7	8	6
16	0	14	4¾	66	2	19	4¾	116	5	4	4¾	166	7	9	4¾
17	0	15	3½	67	3	0	3½	117	5	5	3½	167	7	10	3½
18	0	16	2½	68	3	1	2½	118	5	6	2½	168	7	11	2½
19	0	17	1¼	69	3	2	1¼	119	5	7	1¼	169	7	12	1¼
20	**0**	**18**	**0**	**70**	**3**	**3**	**0**	**120**	**5**	**8**	**0**	**170**	**7**	**13**	**0**
21	0	18	10¾	71	3	3	10¾	121	5	8	10¾	171	7	13	10¾
22	0	19	9½	72	3	4	9½	122	5	9	9½	172	7	14	9½
23	1	0	8½	73	3	5	8½	123	5	10	8½	173	7	15	8½
24	1	1	7¼	74	3	6	7¼	124	5	11	7¼	174	7	16	7¼
25	1	2	6	75	3	7	6	125	5	12	6	175	7	17	6
26	1	3	4¾	76	3	8	4¾	126	5	13	4¾	176	7	18	4¾
27	1	4	3½	77	3	9	3½	127	5	14	3½	177	7	19	3½
28	1	5	2½	78	3	10	2½	128	5	15	2½	178	8	0	2½
29	1	6	1¼	79	3	11	1¼	129	5	16	1¼	179	8	1	1¼
30	**1**	**7**	**0**	**80**	**3**	**12**	**0**	**130**	**5**	**17**	**0**	**180**	**8**	**2**	**0**
31	1	7	10¾	81	3	12	10¾	131	5	17	10¾	181	8	2	10¾
32	1	8	9½	82	3	13	9½	132	5	18	9½	182	8	3	9½
33	1	9	8½	83	3	14	8½	133	5	19	8½	183	8	4	8½
34	1	10	7¼	84	3	15	7¼	134	6	0	7¼	184	8	5	7¼
35	1	11	6	85	3	16	6	135	6	1	6	185	8	6	6
36	1	12	4¾	86	3	17	4¾	136	6	2	4¾	186	8	7	4¾
37	1	13	3½	87	3	18	3½	137	6	3	3½	187	8	8	3½
38	1	14	2½	88	3	19	2½	138	6	4	2½	188	8	9	2½
39	1	15	1¼	89	4	0	1¼	139	6	5	1¼	189	8	10	1¼
40	**1**	**16**	**0**	**90**	**4**	**1**	**0**	**140**	**6**	**6**	**0**	**190**	**8**	**11**	**0**
41	1	16	10¾	91	4	1	10¾	141	6	6	10¾	191	8	11	10¾
42	1	17	9½	92	4	2	9½	142	6	7	9½	192	8	12	9½
43	1	18	8½	93	4	3	8½	143	6	8	8½	193	8	13	8½
44	1	19	7¼	94	4	4	7¼	144	6	9	7¼	194	8	14	7¼
45	2	0	6	95	4	5	6	145	6	10	6	195	8	15	6
46	2	1	4¾	96	4	6	4¾	146	6	11	4¾	196	8	16	4¾
47	2	2	3½	97	4	7	3½	147	6	12	3½	197	8	17	3½
48	2	3	2½	98	4	8	2½	148	6	13	2½	198	8	18	2½
49	2	4	1¼	99	4	9	1¼	149	6	14	1¼	199	8	19	1¼
50	**2**	**5**	**0**	**100**	**4**	**10**	**0**	**150**	**6**	**15**	**0**	**200**	**9**	**0**	**0**

250	11	5s	0d	700	31	10s	0d	1200	54	0s	0d	2000	90	0s	0d
300	13	10	0	750	33	15	0	1400	63	0	0	2500	112	10	0
400	18	0	0	800	36	0	0	1500	67	10	0	3000	135	0	0
500	22	10	0	900	40	10	0	1600	72	0	0	4000	180	0	0
600	27	0s	0d	1000	45	0s	0d	1800	81	0s	0d	5000	225	0s	0d

95½% off.

1d	0s.	0d	4/1	0s.	2¼	8/1	0s.	4¼	12/1	0s.	6½	16/1	0s.	8¾
2d	0	0	2	0	2¼	2	0	4½	2	0	6½	2	0	8¾
3d	0	0¼	3	0	2¼	3	0	4½	3	0	6½	3	0	8¾
4d	0	0¼	4	0	2¼	4	0	4½	4	0	6¾	4	0	8¾
5d	0	0¼	5	0	2½	5	0	4½	5	0	6¾	5	0	8¾
6d	0	0¼	4/6	0	2½	8/6	0	4½	12/6	0	6¾	16/6	0	9
7d	0	0¼	7	0	2½	7	0	4¾	7	0	6¾	7	0	9
8d	0	0¼	8	0	2½	8	0	4¾	8	0	6¾	8	0	9
9d	0	0½	9	0	2½	9	0	4¾	9	0	7	9	0	9
10d	0	0½	10	0	2½	10	0	4¾	10	0	7	10	0	9
11d	0	0½	11	0	2¾	11	0	4¾	11	0	7	11	0	9¼
1/-	0s.	0½	**5/-**	0s.	2¾	**9/-**	0s.	4¾	**13/-**	0s.	7	**17/-**	0s.	9¼
1/1	0s.	0½	5/1	0s.	2¾	9/1	0s.	5	13/1	0s.	7	17/1	0s.	9¼
2	0	0¾	2	0	2¾	2	0	5	2	0	7	2	0	9¼
3	0	0¾	3	0	2¾	3	0	5	3	0	7¼	3	0	9¼
4	0	0¾	4	0	3	4	0	5	4	0	7¼	4	0	9¼
5	0	0¾	5	0	3	5	0	5	5	0	7¼	5	0	9½
1/6	0	0¾	5/6	0	3	9/6	0	5¼	13/6	0	7¼	17/6	0	9½
7	0	0¾	7	0	3	7	0	5¼	7	0	7¼	7	0	9½
8	0	1	8	0	3	8	0	5¼	8	0	7½	8	0	9½
9	0	1	9	0	3	9	0	5¼	9	0	7½	9	0	9½
10	0	1	10	0	3¼	10	0	5¼	10	0	7½	10	0	9¾
11	0	1	11	0	3¼	11	0	5¼	11	0	7½	11	0	9¾
2/-	0s.	1	**6/-**	0s.	3¼	**10/-**	0s.	5½	**14/-**	0s.	7½	**18/-**	0s.	9¾
2/1	0s.	1¼	6/1	0s.	3¼	10/1	0s.	5½	14/1	0s.	7½	18/1	0s.	9¾
2	0	1¼	2	0	3¼	2	0	5½	2	0	7¾	2	0	9¾
3	0	1¼	3	0	3½	3	0	5½	3	0	7¾	3	0	9¾
4	0	1¼	4	0	3½	4	0	5½	4	0	7¾	4	0	10
5	0	1¼	5	0	3½	5	0	5¾	5	0	7¾	5	0	10
2/6	0	1¼	6/6	0	3½	10/6	0	5¾	14/6	0	7¾	18/6	0	10
7	0	1½	7	0	3½	7	0	5¾	7	0	8	7	0	10
8	0	1½	8	0	3½	8	0	5¾	8	0	8	8	0	10
9	0	1½	9	0	3¾	9	0	5¾	9	0	8	9	0	10¼
10	0	1½	10	0	3¾	10	0	5¾	10	0	8	10	0	10¼
11	0	1½	11	0	3¾	11	0	6	11	0	8	11	0	10¼
3/-	0s.	1½	**7/-**	0s.	3¾	**11/-**	0s.	6	**15/-**	0s.	8	**19/-**	0s.	10¼
3/1	0s.	1¾	7/1	0s.	3¾	11/1	0s.	6	15/1	0s.	8¼	19/1	0s.	10¼
2	0	1¾	2	0	3¾	2	0	6	2	0	8¼	2	0	10¼
3	0	1¾	3	0	4	3	0	6	3	0	8¼	3	0	10½
4	0	1¾	4	0	4	4	0	6	4	0	8¼	4	0	10½
5	0	1¾	5	0	4	5	0	6¼	5	0	8¼	5	0	10½
3/6	0	2	7/6	0	4	11/6	0	6¼	15/6	0	8¼	19/6	0	10½
7	0	2	7	0	4	7	0	6¼	7	0	8½	7	0	10½
8	0	2	8	0	4¼	8	0	6¼	8	0	8½	8	0	10½
9	0	2	9	0	4¼	9	0	6¼	9	0	8½	9	0	10¾
10	0	2	10	0	4¼	10	0	6½	10	0	8½	10	0	10¾
11	0	2	11	0	4¼	11	0	6½	11	0	8½	11	0	10¾
4/-	0s.	2¼	**8/-**	0s.	4¼	**12/-**	0s.	6½	**16/-**	0s.	8¾	**20/-**	0s.	10¾

20/6	0s.	11	25/6	1s.	1¾	31/-	1s.	4¾	35/6	1s.	7¼	Guineas.		
21/-	0	11¼	26/-	1	2	31/6	1	5	36/-	1	7½	1.	0s.	11¼
22/-	1	0	27/-	1	2½	32/-	1	5¼	37/-	1	8	2.	1	10¾
22/6	1	0¼	27/6	1	2¾	32/6	1	5½	37/6	1	8¼	3.	2	10
23/-	1	0½	28/-	1	3	33/-	1	5¾	38/-	1	8½	4.	3	9¼
24/-	1	1	29/-	1	3¾	34/-	1	6¼	39/-	1	9	5.	4	8¾
25/-	1s.	1½	**30/-**	1s.	4¼	**35/-**	1s.	7	**40/-**	1s.	9½	6.	5s.	8

(=4$\frac{3}{10}$%* on Gross Returns).

4⅝% £4. 12. 6 PER CENT OR PER 100. 4⅝%

£1	0s.11	£51	£2 7s. 2	£101	£4 13s. 5	£151	£6 19s. 8
2	1 10¼	52	2 8 1¼	102	4 14 4¼	152	7 0 7¼
3	2 9¼	53	2 9 0¼	103	4 15 3¼	153	7 1 6¼
4	3 8½	54	2 9 11½	104	4 16 2½	154	7 2 5½
5	4 7½	55	2 10 10½	105	4 17 1½	155	7 3 4½
6	5 6½	56	2 11 9½	106	4 18 0½	156	7 4 3½
7	6 5¾	57	2 12 8¾	107	4 18 11¾	157	7 5 2¾
8	7 4¾	58	2 13 7¾	108	4 19 10¾	158	7 6 1¾
9	8 4	59	2 14 7	109	5 0 10	159	7 7 1
10	9s. 3	**60**	£2 15s. 6	**110**	£5 1s. 9	**160**	£7 8s. 0
11	10s. 2	61	£2 16s. 5	111	£5 2s. 8	161	£7 8s.11
12	11 1¼	62	2 17 4¼	112	5 3 7¼	162	7 9 10¼
13	12 0¼	63	2 18 3¼	113	5 4 6¼	163	7 10 9¼
14	12 11½	64	2 19 2½	114	5 5 5½	164	7 11 8½
15	13 10½	65	3 0 1½	115	5 6 4½	165	7 12 7½
16	14 9½	66	3 1 0½	116	5 7 3½	166	7 13 6½
17	15 8¾	67	3 1 11¾	117	5 8 2¾	167	7 14 5¾
18	16 7¾	68	3 2 10¾	118	5 9 1¾	168	7 15 4¾
19	17 7	69	3 3 10	119	5 10 1	169	7 16 4
20	18s. 6	**70**	£3 4s. 9	**120**	£5 11s. 0	**170**	£7 17s. 3
21	19s. 5	71	£3 5s. 8	121	£5 11s.11	171	£7 18s. 2
22	20 4¼	72	3 6 7¼	122	5 12 10¼	172	7 19 1¼
23	21 3¼	73	3 7 6¼	123	5 13 9¼	173	8 0 0¼
24	22 2½	74	3 8 5½	124	5 14 8½	174	8 0 11½
25	23 1½	75	3 9 4½	125	5 15 7½	175	8 1 10½
26	24 0½	76	3 10 3½	126	5 16 6½	176	8 2 9½
27	24 11¾	77	3 11 2¾	127	5 17 5¾	177	8 3 8¾
28	25 10¾	78	3 12 1¾	128	5 18 4¾	178	8 4 7¾
29	26 10	79	3 13 1	129	5 19 4	179	8 5 7
30	27s. 9	**80**	£3 14s. 0	**130**	£6 0s. 3	**180**	£8 6s. 6
31	28s. 8	81	£3 14s.11	131	£6 1s. 2	181	£8 7s. 5
32	29 7¼	82	3 15 10¼	132	6 2 1¼	182	8 8 4¼
33	30 6¼	83	3 16 9¼	133	6 3 0¼	183	8 9 3¼
34	31 5½	84	3 17 8½	134	6 3 11½	184	8 10 2½
35	32 4½	85	3 18 7½	135	6 4 10½	185	8 11 1½
36	33 3½	86	3 19 6½	136	6 5 9½	186	8 12 0½
37	34 2¾	87	4 0 5¾	137	6 6 8¾	187	8 12 11¾
38	35 1¾	88	4 1 4¾	138	6 7 7¾	188	8 13 10¾
39	36 1	89	4 2 4	139	6 8 7	189	8 14 10
40	37s. 0	**90**	£4 3s. 3	**140**	£6 9s. 6	**190**	£8 15s. 9
41	37s.11	91	£4 4s. 2	141	£6 10s. 5	191	£8 16s. 8
42	38 10¼	92	4 5 1¼	142	6 11 4¼	192	8 17 7¼
43	39 9¼	93	4 6 0¼	143	6 12 3¼	193	8 18 6¼
44	40 8½	94	4 6 11½	144	6 13 2½	194	8 19 5½
45	41 7½	95	4 7 10½	145	6 14 1½	195	9 0 4½
46	42 6½	96	4 8 9½	146	6 15 0½	196	9 1 3½
47	43 5¾	97	4 9 8¾	147	6 15 11¾	197	9 2 2¾
48	44 4¾	98	4 10 7¾	148	6 16 10¾	198	9 3 1¾
49	45 4	99	4 11 7	149	6 17 10	199	9 4 1
50	46s. 3	**100**	£4 12s. 6	**150**	£6 18s. 9	**200**	£9 5s. 0
250	11 11s.3d	700	32 7s. 6d	1200	£55 10s. 0d	2000	£92 10s. 0
300	13 17 6	750	34 13 9	1400	64 15 0	2500	115 12 6
400	18 10 0	800	37 0 0	1500	69 7 6	3000	138 15 0
500	23 2 6	900	41 12 6	1600	74 0 0	4000	185 0 0
600	27 15s.0d	1000	£46 5s. 0d	1800	£83 5s. 0d	5000	£231 5s. 0

95⅜% off. (=$4\frac{4}{10}$%* on Gross Returns).

1d	0s.	0d	4/1	0s.	2¼	8/1	0s.	4½	12/1	0s.	7	16/1	0s.	9¼
2d	0	0	2	0	2½	2	0	4¾	2	0	7	2	0	9¼
3d	0	0¼	3	0	2½	3	0	4¾	3	0	7	3	0	9¼
4d	0	0¼	4	0	2½	4	0	4¾	4	0	7	4	0	9¼
5d	0	0¼	5	0	2½	5	0	4¾	5	0	7	5	0	9¼
6d	0	0¼	4/6	0	2½	8/6	0	4¾	12/6	0	7¼	16/6	0	9½
7d	0	0¼	7	0	2½	7	0	5	7	0	7¼	7	0	9½
8d	0	0½	8	0	2¾	8	0	5	8	0	7¼	8	0	9½
9d	0	0½	9	0	2¾	9	0	5	9	0	7¼	9	0	9½
10d	0	0½	10	0	2¾	10	0	5	10	0	7¼	10	0	9½
11d	0	0½	11	0	2¾	11	0	5	11	0	7¼	11	0	9¾
1/-	0s.	0½	**5/-**	0s.	2¾	**9/-**	0s.	5¼	**13/-**	0s.	7½	**17/-**	0s.	9¾
1/1	0s.	0½	5/1	0s.	3	9/1	0s.	5¼	13/1	0s.	7½	17/1	0s.	9¾
2	0	0¾	2	0	3	2	0	5¼	2	0	7½	2	0	9¾
3	0	0¾	3	0	3	3	0	5¼	3	0	7½	3	0	9¾
4	0	0¾	4	0	3	4	0	5¼	4	0	7½	4	0	10
5	0	0¾	5	0	3	5	0	5¼	5	0	7¾	5	0	10
1/6	0	0¾	5/6	0	3¼	9/6	0	5½	13/6	0	7¾	17/6	0	10
7	0	1	7	0	3¼	7	0	5½	7	0	7¾	7	0	10
8	0	1	8	0	3¼	8	0	5½	8	0	7¾	8	0	10
9	0	1	9	0	3¼	9	0	5½	9	0	7¾	9	0	10
10	0	1	10	0	3¼	10	0	5½	10	0	8	10	0	10¼
11	0	1	11	0	3¼	11	0	5¾	11	0	8	11	0	10¼
2/-	0s.	1¼	**6/-**	0s.	3½	**10/-**	0s.	5¾	**14/-**	0s.	8	**18/-**	0s.	10¼
2/1	0s.	1¼	6/1	0s.	3½	10/1	0s.	5¾	14/1	0s.	8	18/1	0s.	10¼
2	0	1¼	2	0	3½	2	0	5¾	2	0	8	2	0	10¼
3	0	1¼	3	0	3½	3	0	5¾	3	0	8	3	0	10½
4	0	1¼	4	0	3½	4	0	6	4	0	8¼	4	0	10½
5	0	1½	5	0	3¾	5	0	6	5	0	8¼	5	0	10½
2/6	0	1½	6/6	0	3¾	10/6	0	6	14/6	0	8¼	18/6	0	10½
7	0	1½	7	0	3¾	7	0	6	7	0	8¼	7	0	10½
8	0	1½	8	0	3¾	8	0	6	8	0	8¼	8	0	10¾
9	0	1½	9	0	3¾	9	0	6¼	9	0	8½	9	0	10¾
10	0	1½	10	0	4	10	0	6¼	10	0	8½	10	0	10¾
11	0	1¾	11	0	4	11	0	6¼	11	0	8½	11	0	10¾
3/-	0s.	1¾	**7/-**	0s.	4	**11/-**	0s.	6¼	**15/-**	0s.	8½	**19/-**	0s.	10¾
3/1	0s.	1¾	7/1	0s.	4	11/1	0s.	6¼	15/1	0s.	8½	19/1	0s.	11
2	0	1¾	2	0	4	2	0	6¼	2	0	8¾	2	0	11
3	0	1¾	3	0	4¼	3	0	6½	3	0	8¾	3	0	11
4	0	2	4	0	4¼	4	0	6½	4	0	8¾	4	0	11
5	0	2	5	0	4¼	5	0	6½	5	0	8¾	5	0	11
3/6	0	2	7/6	0	4¼	11/6	0	6½	15/6	0	8¾	19/6	0	11
7	0	2	7	0	4¼	7	0	6½	7	0	9	7	0	11¼
8	0	2	8	0	4¼	8	0	6¾	8	0	9	8	0	11¼
9	0	2¼	9	0	4½	9	0	6¾	9	0	9	9	0	11¼
10	0	2¼	10	0	4½	10	0	6¾	10	0	9	10	0	11¼
11	0	2¼	11	0	4½	11	0	6¾	11	0	9	11	0	11¼
4/-	0s.	2¼	**8/-**	0s.	4½	**12/-**	0s.	6¾	**16/-**	0s.	9	**20/-**	0s.	11½

20/6	0s.	11¾	25/6	1s.	2½	31/-	1s.	5¾	35/6	1s.	8¼	Guineas.		
21/-	1	0	26/-	1	2¾	31/6	1	6	36/-	1	8½	1.	1s.	0
22/-	1	0½	27/-	1	3½	32/-	1	6¼	37/-	1	9	2.	2	0
22/6	1	0¾	27/6	1	3¾	32/6	1	6½	37/6	1	9½	3.	3	0
23/-	1	1	28/-	1	4	33/-	1	6¾	38/-	1	9¾	4.	4	0
24/-	1	1¾	29/-	1	4½	34/-	1	7½	39/-	1	10¼	5.	4	11¾
25/-	1s.	2¼	**30/-**	1s.	5	**35/-**	1s.	8	**40/-**	1s.	10¾	6.	5s.	11¾

(4½%* on Gross Returns).

£1	£0	1s	0d	£51	£2	11s	0d	£101	£5	1s	0d	£151	£7	11s	0d
2	0	2	0	52	2	12	0	102	5	2	0	152	7	12	0
3	0	3	0	53	2	13	0	103	5	3	0	153	7	13	0
4	0	4	0	54	2	14	0	104	5	4	0	154	7	14	0
5	0	5	0	55	2	15	0	105	5	5	0	155	7	15	0
6	0	6	0	56	2	16	0	106	5	6	0	156	7	16	0
7	0	7	0	57	2	17	0	107	5	7	0	157	7	17	0
8	0	8	0	58	2	18	0	108	5	8	0	158	7	18	0
9	0	9	0	59	2	19	0	109	5	9	0	159	7	19	0
10	0	10	0	60	3	0	0	110	5	10	0	160	8	0	0
11	0	11	0	61	3	1	0	111	5	11	0	161	8	1	0
12	0	12	0	62	3	2	0	112	5	12	0	162	8	2	0
13	0	13	0	63	3	3	0	113	5	13	0	163	8	3	0
14	0	14	0	64	3	4	0	114	5	14	0	164	8	4	0
15	0	15	0	65	3	5	0	115	5	15	0	165	8	5	0
16	0	16	0	66	3	6	0	116	5	16	0	166	8	6	0
17	0	17	0	67	3	7	0	117	5	17	0	167	8	7	0
18	0	18	0	68	3	8	0	118	5	18	0	168	8	8	0
19	0	19	0	69	3	9	0	119	5	19	0	169	8	9	0
20	1	0	0	70	3	10	0	120	6	0	0	170	8	10	0
21	1	1	0	71	3	11	0	121	6	1	0	171	8	11	0
22	1	2	0	72	3	12	0	122	6	2	0	172	8	12	0
23	1	3	0	73	3	13	0	123	6	3	0	173	8	13	0
24	1	4	0	74	3	14	0	124	6	4	0	174	8	14	0
25	1	5	0	75	3	15	0	125	6	5	0	175	8	15	0
26	1	6	0	76	3	16	0	126	6	6	0	176	8	16	0
27	1	7	0	77	3	17	0	127	6	7	0	177	8	17	0
28	1	8	0	78	3	18	0	128	6	8	0	178	8	18	0
29	1	9	0	79	3	19	0	129	6	9	0	179	8	19	0
30	1	10	0	80	4	0	0	130	6	10	0	180	9	0	0
31	1	11	0	81	4	1	0	131	6	11	0	181	9	1	0
32	1	12	0	82	4	2	0	132	6	12	0	182	9	2	0
33	1	13	0	83	4	3	0	133	6	13	0	183	9	3	0
34	1	14	0	84	4	4	0	134	6	14	0	184	9	4	0
35	1	15	0	85	4	5	0	135	6	15	0	185	9	5	0
36	1	16	0	86	4	6	0	136	6	16	0	186	9	6	0
37	1	17	0	87	4	7	0	137	6	17	0	187	9	7	0
38	1	18	0	88	4	8	0	138	6	18	0	188	9	8	0
39	1	19	0	89	4	9	0	139	6	19	0	189	9	9	0
40	2	0	0	90	4	10	0	140	7	0	0	190	9	10	0
41	2	1	0	91	4	11	0	141	7	1	0	191	9	11	0
42	2	2	0	92	4	12	0	142	7	2	0	192	9	12	0
43	2	3	0	93	4	13	0	143	7	3	0	193	9	13	0
44	2	4	0	94	4	14	0	144	7	4	0	194	9	14	0
45	2	5	0	95	4	15	0	145	7	5	0	195	9	15	0
46	2	6	0	96	4	16	0	146	7	6	0	196	9	16	0
47	2	7	0	97	4	17	0	147	7	7	0	197	9	17	0
48	2	8	0	98	4	18	0	148	7	8	0	198	9	18	0
49	2	9	0	99	4	19	0	149	7	9	0	199	9	19	0
50	2	10	0	100	5	0	0	150	7	10	0	200	10	0	0
250	12	10s	0d	700	35	0s	0d	1200	60	0s	0d	2000	100	0s	0d
300	15	0	0	750	37	10	0	1400	70	0	0	2500	125	0	0
400	20	0	0	800	40	0	0	1500	75	0	0	3000	150	0	0
500	25	0	0	900	45	0	0	1600	80	0	0	4000	200	0	0
600	30	0s	0d	1000	50	0s	0d	1800	90	0s	0d	5000	250	0s	0d

95% off.

5% FIVE PER CENT. 5%

1d	0s.	0d	4/1	0s.	2½	3/1	0s.	4¾	12/1	0s.	7¼	16/1	0s.	9¾
2d	0	0	2	0	2½	2	0	5	2	0	7¼	2	0	9¾
3d	0	0¼	3	0	2½	3	0	5	3	0	7¼	3	0	9¾
4d	0	0¼	4	0	2½	4	0	5	4	0	7½	4	0	9¾
5d	0	0¼	5	0	2¾	5	0	5	5	0	7½	5	0	9¾
6d	0	0¼	4/6	0	2¾	8/6	0	5	12/6	0	7½	16/6	0	10
7d	0	0¼	7	0	2¾	7	0	5¼	7	0	7½	7	0	10
8d	0	0½	8	0	2¾	8	0	5¼	8	0	7½	8	0	10
9d	0	0½	9	0	2¾	9	0	5¼	9	0	7¾	9	0	10
10d	0	0½	10	0	3	10	0	5¼	10	0	7¾	10	0	10
11d	0	0½	11	0	3	11	0	5¼	11	0	7¾	11	0	10¼
1/-	0s.	0½	**5/-**	0s.	3	**9/-**	0s.	5½	**13/-**	0s.	7¾	**17/-**	0s.	10¼
1/1	0s.	0¾	5/1	0s.	3	9/1	0s.	5½	13/1	0s.	7¾	17/1	0s.	10¼
2	0	0¾	2	0	3	2	0	5½	2	0	8	2	0	10¼
3	0	0¾	3	0	3¼	3	0	5½	3	0	8	3	0	10¼
4	0	0¾	4	0	3¼	4	0	5½	4	0	8	4	0	10½
5	0	0¾	5	0	3¼	5	0	5¾	5	0	8	5	0	10½
1/6	0	1	5/6	0	3¼	9/6	0	5¾	13/6	0	8	17/6	0	10½
7	0	1	7	0	3¼	7	0	5¾	7	0	8¼	7	0	10½
8	0	1	8	0	3½	8	0	5¾	8	0	8¼	8	0	10½
9	0	1	9	0	3½	9	0	5¾	9	0	8¼	9	0	10¾
10	0	1	10	0	3½	10	0	6	10	0	8¼	10	0	10¾
11	0	1¼	11	0	3½	11	0	6	11	0	8¼	11	0	10¾
2/-	0s.	1¼	**6/-**	0s.	3½	**10/-**	0s.	6	**14/-**	0s.	8½	**18/-**	0s.	10¾
2/1	0s.	1¼	6/1	0s.	3¾	10/1	0s.	6	14/1	0s.	8½	18/1	0s.	10¾
2	0	1¼	2	0	3¾	2	0	6	2	0	8½	2	0	11
3	0	1¼	3	0	3¾	3	0	6¼	3	0	8½	3	0	11
4	0	1½	4	0	3¾	4	0	6¼	4	0	8½	4	0	11
5	0	1½	5	0	3¾	5	0	6¼	5	0	8¾	5	0	11
2/6	0	1½	6/6	0	4	10/6	0	6¼	14/6	0	8¾	18/6	0	11
7	0	1½	7	0	4	7	0	6¼	7	0	8¾	7	0	11¼
8	0	1½	8	0	4	8	0	6½	8	0	8¾	8	0	11¼
9	0	1¾	9	0	4	9	0	6½	9	0	8¾	9	0	11¼
10	0	1¾	10	0	4	10	0	6½	10	0	9	10	0	11¼
11	0	1¾	11	0	4¼	11	0	6½	11	0	9	11	0	11¼
3/-	0s.	1¾	**7/-**	0s.	4¼	**11/-**	0s.	6½	**15/-**	0s.	9	**19/-**	0s.	11½
3/1	0s.	1¾	7/1	0s.	4¼	11/1	0s.	6¾	15/1	0s.	9	19/1	0s.	11½
2	0	2	2	0	4¼	2	0	6¾	2	0	9	2	0	11½
3	0	2	3	0	4¼	3	0	6¾	3	0	9¼	3	0	11½
4	0	2	4	0	4½	4	0	6¾	4	0	9¼	4	0	11½
5	0	2	5	0	4½	5	0	6¾	5	0	9¼	5	0	11¾
3/6	0	2	7/6	0	4½	11/6	0	7	15/6	0	9¼	19/6	0	11¾
7	0	2¼	7	0	4½	7	0	7	7	0	9¼	7	0	11¾
8	0	2¼	8	0	4½	8	0	7	8	0	9½	8	0	11¾
9	0	2¼	9	0	4¾	9	0	7	9	0	9½	9	0	11¾
10	0	2¼	10	0	4¾	10	0	7	10	0	9½	10	1	0
11	0	2¼	11	0	4¾	11	0	7¼	11	0	9½	11	1	0
4/-	0s.	2½	**8/-**	0s.	4¾	**12/-**	0s.	7¼	**16/-**	0s.	9½	**20/-**	1s.	0

20/6	1s.	0¼	25/6	1s.	3¼	31/-	1s.	6½	35/6	1s.	9¼	Guineas.		
21/-	1	0½	26/-	1	3½	31/6	1	7	36/-	1	9½	1.	1s.	0½
22/-	1	1¼	27/-	1	4¼	32/-	1	7¼	37/-	1	10¼	2.	2	1¼
22/6	1	1½	27/6	1	4½	32/6	1	7½	37/6	1	10½	3.	3	1¾
23/-	1	1¾	28/-	1	4¾	33/-	1	7¾	38/-	1	10¾	4.	4	2½
24/-	1	2½	29/-	1	5½	34/-	1	8½	39/-	1	11½	5.	5	3
25/-	1s.	3	**30/-**	1s.	6	**35/-**	1s.	9	**40/-**	2s.	0	6.	6s.	3½

(=4 8/10 %* on Gross Returns).

5¼ Per Cent.

5¼%

£1	£0	1s	0½	£51	£2	13s	6½	£101	£5	6s	0½	£151	£7	18s	6½
2	0	2	1¼	52	2	14	7¼	102	5	7	1¼	152	7	19	7¼
3	0	3	1¾	53	2	15	7¾	103	5	8	1¾	153	8	0	7¾
4	0	4	2½	54	2	16	8½	104	5	9	2½	154	8	1	8½
5	0	5	3	55	2	17	9	105	5	10	3	155	8	2	9
6	0	6	3½	56	2	18	9½	106	5	11	3½	156	8	3	9½
7	0	7	4¼	57	2	19	10¼	107	5	12	4¼	157	8	4	10¼
8	0	8	4¾	58	3	0	10¾	108	5	13	4¾	158	8	5	10¾
9	0	9	5½	59	3	1	11½	109	5	14	5½	159	8	6	11½
10	**0**	**10**	**6**	**60**	**3**	**3**	**0**	**110**	**5**	**15**	**6**	**160**	**8**	**8**	**0**
11	0	11	6½	61	3	4	0½	111	5	16	6½	161	8	9	0½
12	0	12	7¼	62	3	5	1¼	112	5	17	7¼	162	8	10	1¼
13	0	13	7¾	63	3	6	1¾	113	5	18	7¾	163	8	11	1¾
14	0	14	8½	64	3	7	2½	114	5	19	8½	164	8	12	2½
15	0	15	9	65	3	8	3	115	6	0	9	165	8	13	3
16	0	16	9½	66	3	9	3½	116	6	1	9½	166	8	14	3½
17	0	17	10¼	67	3	10	4¼	117	6	2	10¼	167	8	15	4¼
18	0	18	10¾	68	3	11	4¾	118	6	3	10¾	168	8	16	4¾
19	0	19	11½	69	3	12	5½	119	6	4	11½	169	8	17	5½
20	**1**	**1**	**0**	**70**	**3**	**13**	**6**	**120**	**6**	**6**	**0**	**170**	**8**	**18**	**6**
21	1	2	0½	71	3	14	6½	121	6	7	0½	171	8	19	6½
22	1	3	1¼	72	3	15	7¼	122	6	8	1¼	172	9	0	7¼
23	1	4	1¾	73	3	16	7¾	123	6	9	1¾	173	9	1	7¾
24	1	5	2½	74	3	17	8½	124	6	10	2½	174	9	2	8½
25	1	6	3	75	3	18	9	125	6	11	3	175	9	3	9
26	1	7	3½	76	3	19	9½	126	6	12	3½	176	9	4	9½
27	1	8	4¼	77	4	0	10¼	127	6	13	4¼	177	9	5	10¼
28	1	9	4¾	78	4	1	10¾	128	6	14	4¾	178	9	6	10¾
29	1	10	5½	79	4	2	11½	129	6	15	5½	179	9	7	11½
30	**1**	**11**	**6**	**80**	**4**	**4**	**0**	**130**	**6**	**16**	**6**	**180**	**9**	**9**	**0**
31	1	12	6½	81	4	5	0½	131	6	17	6½	181	9	10	0½
32	1	13	7¼	82	4	6	1¼	132	6	18	7¼	182	9	11	1¼
33	1	14	7¾	83	4	7	1¾	133	6	19	7¾	183	9	12	1¾
34	1	15	8½	84	4	8	2½	134	7	0	8½	184	9	13	2½
35	1	16	9	85	4	9	3	135	7	1	9	185	9	14	3
36	1	17	9½	86	4	10	3½	136	7	2	9½	186	9	15	3½
37	1	18	10¼	87	4	11	4¼	137	7	3	10¼	187	9	16	4¼
38	1	19	10¾	88	4	12	4¾	138	7	4	10¾	188	9	17	4¾
39	2	0	11½	89	4	13	5½	139	7	5	11½	189	9	18	5½
40	**2**	**2**	**0**	**90**	**4**	**14**	**6**	**140**	**7**	**7**	**0**	**190**	**9**	**19**	**6**
41	2	3	0½	91	4	15	6½	141	7	8	0½	191	10	0	6½
42	2	4	1¼	92	4	16	7¼	142	7	9	1¼	192	10	1	7¼
43	2	5	1¾	93	4	17	7¾	143	7	10	1¾	193	10	2	7¾
44	2	6	2½	94	4	18	8½	144	7	11	2½	194	10	3	8½
45	2	7	3	95	4	19	9	145	7	12	3	195	10	4	9
46	2	8	3½	96	5	0	9½	146	7	13	3½	196	10	5	9½
47	2	9	4¼	97	5	1	10¼	147	7	14	4¼	197	10	6	10¼
48	2	10	4¾	98	5	2	10¾	148	7	15	4¾	198	10	7	10¾
49	2	11	5½	99	5	3	11½	149	7	16	5½	199	10	8	11½
50	**2**	**12**	**6**	**100**	**5**	**5**	**0**	**150**	**7**	**17**	**6**	**200**	**10**	**10**	**0**
250	13	2s	6d	700	36	15s	0d	1200	63	0s	0d	2000	105	0s	0d
300	15	15	0	750	39	7	6	1400	73	10	0	2500	131	5	0
400	21	0	0	800	42	0	0	1500	78	15	0	3000	157	10	0
500	26	5	0	900	47	5	0	1600	84	0	0	4000	210	0	0
600	31	10s	0d	1000	52	10s	0d	1800	94	10s	0d	5000	262	10s	0

94¾% off.

1d	0s.	0d	4/1	0s.	2½	8/1	0s.	5d	12/1	0s.	7½	16/1	0s.	10¼
2d	0	0	2	0	2¾	2	0	5¼	2	0	7¾	2	0	10¼
3d	0	0¼	3	0	2¾	3	0	5¼	3	0	7¾	3	0	10¼
4d	0	0¼	4	0	2¾	4	0	5¼	4	0	7¾	4	0	10¼
5d	0	0¼	5	0	2¾	5	0	5¼	5	0	7¾	5	0	10¼
6d	0	0¼	4/6	0	2¾	8/6	0	5¼	12/6	0	8	16/6	0	10½
7d	0	0¼	7	0	3	7	0	5½	7	0	8	7	0	10½
8d	0	0½	8	0	3	8	0	5½	8	0	8	8	0	10½
9d	0	0½	9	0	3	9	0	5½	9	0	8	9	0	10½
10d	0	0½	10	0	3	10	0	5½	10	0	8	10	0	10½
11d	0	0½	11	0	3	11	0	5½	11	0	8¼	11	0	10¾
1/-	0s.	0¾	**5/-**	0s.	3¼	**9/-**	0s.	5¾	**13/-**	0s.	8¼	**17/-**	0s.	10¾
1/1	0s.	0¾	5/1	0s.	3¼	9/1	0s.	5¾	13/1	0s.	8¼	17/1	0s.	10¾
2	0	0¾	2	0	3¼	2	0	5¾	2	0	8¼	2	0	10¾
3	0	0¾	3	0	3¼	3	0	5¾	3	0	8¼	3	0	10¾
4	0	0¾	4	0	3¼	4	0	6	4	0	8½	4	0	11
5	0	1	5	0	3½	5	0	6	5	0	8½	5	0	11
1/6	0	1	5/6	0	3½	9/6	0	6	13/6	0	8½	17/6	0	11
7	0	1	7	0	3½	7	0	6	7	0	8½	7	0	11
8	0	1	8	0	3½	8	0	6	8	0	8½	8	0	11¼
9	0	1	9	0	3½	9	0	6¼	9	0	8¾	9	0	11¼
10	0	1¼	10	0	3¾	10	0	6¼	10	0	8¾	10	0	11¼
11	0	1¼	11	0	3¾	11	0	6¼	11	0	8¾	11	0	11¼
2/-	0s.	1¼	**6/-**	0s.	3¾	**10/-**	0s.	6¼	**14/-**	0s.	8¾	**18/-**	0s.	11¼
2/1	0s.	1¼	6/1	0s.	3¾	10/1	0s.	6¼	14/1	0s.	8¾	18/1	0s.	11½
2	0	1¼	2	0	4	2	0	6½	2	0	9	2	0	11½
3	0	1½	3	0	4	3	0	6½	3	0	9	3	0	11½
4	0	1½	4	0	4	4	0	6½	4	0	9	4	0	11½
5	0	1½	5	0	4	5	0	6½	5	0	9	5	0	11½
2/6	0	1½	6/6	0	4	10/6	0	6½	14/6	0	9¼	18/6	0	11¾
7	0	1¾	7	0	4¼	7	0	6¾	7	0	9¼	7	0	11¾
8	0	1¾	8	0	4¼	8	0	6¾	8	0	9¼	8	0	11¾
9	0	1¾	9	0	4¼	9	0	6¾	9	0	9¼	9	0	11¾
10	0	1¾	10	0	4¼	10	0	6¾	10	0	9¼	10	0	11¾
11	0	1¾	11	0	4¼	11	0	7	11	0	9½	11	1	0
3/-	0s.	2	**7/-**	0s.	4½	**11/-**	0s.	7	**15/-**	0s.	9½	**19/-**	1s.	0
3/1	0s.	2	7/1	0s.	4½	11/1	0s.	7	15/1	0s.	9½	19/1	1s.	0
2	0	2	2	0	4½	2	0	7	2	0	9½	2	1	0
3	0	2	3	0	4½	3	0	7	3	0	9½	3	1	0¼
4	0	2	4	0	4½	4	0	7¼	4	0	9¾	4	1	0¼
5	0	2¼	5	0	4¾	5	0	7¼	5	0	9¾	5	1	0¼
3/6	0	2¼	7/6	0	4¾	11/6	0	7¼	15/6	0	9¾	19/6	1	0¼
7	0	2¼	7	0	4¾	7	0	7¼	7	0	9¾	7	1	0¼
8	0	2¼	8	0	4¾	8	0	7¼	8	0	9¾	8	1	0½
9	0	2¼	9	0	5	9	0	7½	9	0	10	9	1	0½
10	0	2½	10	0	5	10	0	7½	10	0	10	10	1	0½
11	0	2½	11	0	5	11	0	7½	11	0	10	11	1	0½
4/-	0s.	2½	**8/-**	0s.	5	**12/-**	0s.	7½	**16/-**	0s.	10	**20/-**	1s.	0½

20/6	1s.	1	25/6	1s.	4	31/-	1s.	7½	35/6	1s.	10¼	Guineas.		
21/-	1	1¼	26/-	1	4½	31/6	1	7¾	36/-	1	10¾	1.	1s.	1¼
22/-	1	1¾	27/-	1	5	32/-	1	8¼	37/-	1	11¼	2.	2	2½
22/6	1	2¼	27/6	1	5¼	32/6	1	8½	37/6	1	11¾	3.	3	3¾
23/-	1	2½	28/-	1	5¾	33/-	1	8¾	38/-	2	0	4.	4	5
24/-	1	3	29/-	1	6¼	34/-	1	9½	39/-	2	0½	5.	5	6¼
25/-	1s.	3¾	**30/-**	1s.	7	**35/-**	1s.	10	**40/-**	2s.	1¼	6.	6s.	7½

(5%* on Gross Returns).

£1	£0	1s	1¼	£51	£2	16s	1¼	£101	£5	11s	1¼	£151	£8	6s	1¼
2	0	2	2½	52	2	17	2½	102	5	12	2½	152	8	7	2½
3	0	3	3½	53	2	18	3½	103	5	13	3½	153	8	8	3½
4	0	4	4¾	54	2	19	4¾	104	5	14	4¾	154	8	9	4¾
5	0	5	6	55	3	0	6	105	5	15	6	155	8	10	6
6	0	6	7¼	56	3	1	7¼	106	5	16	7¼	156	8	11	7¼
7	0	7	8½	57	3	2	8½	107	5	17	8½	157	8	12	8½
8	0	8	9½	58	3	3	9½	108	5	18	9½	158	8	13	9½
9	0	9	10¾	59	3	4	10¾	109	5	19	10¾	159	8	14	10¾
10	**0**	**11**	**0**	**60**	**3**	**6**	**0**	**110**	**6**	**1**	**0**	**160**	**8**	**16**	**0**
11	0	12	1¼	61	3	7	1¼	111	6	2	1¼	161	8	17	1¼
12	0	13	2½	62	3	8	2½	112	6	3	2½	162	8	18	2½
13	0	14	3½	63	3	9	3½	113	6	4	3½	163	8	19	3½
14	0	15	4¾	64	3	10	4¾	114	6	5	4¾	164	9	0	4¾
15	0	16	6	65	3	11	6	115	6	6	6	165	9	1	6
16	0	17	7¼	66	3	12	7¼	116	6	7	7¼	166	9	2	7¼
17	0	18	8½	67	3	13	8½	117	6	8	8½	167	9	3	8½
18	0	19	9½	68	3	14	9½	118	6	9	9½	168	9	4	9½
19	1	0	10¾	69	3	15	10¾	119	6	10	10¾	169	9	5	10¾
20	**1**	**2**	**0**	**70**	**3**	**17**	**0**	**120**	**6**	**12**	**0**	**170**	**9**	**7**	**0**
21	1	3	1¼	71	3	18	1¼	121	6	13	1¼	171	9	8	1¼
22	1	4	2½	72	3	19	2½	122	6	14	2½	172	9	9	2½
23	1	5	3½	73	4	0	3½	123	6	15	3½	173	9	10	3½
24	1	6	4¾	74	4	1	4¾	124	6	16	4¾	174	9	11	4¾
25	1	7	6	75	4	2	6	125	6	17	6	175	9	12	6
26	1	8	7¼	76	4	3	7¼	126	6	18	7¼	176	9	13	7¼
27	1	9	8½	77	4	4	8½	127	6	19	8½	177	9	14	8½
28	1	10	9½	78	4	5	9½	128	7	0	9½	178	9	15	9½
29	1	11	10¾	79	4	6	10¾	129	7	1	10¾	179	9	16	10¾
30	**1**	**13**	**0**	**80**	**4**	**8**	**0**	**130**	**7**	**3**	**0**	**180**	**9**	**18**	**0**
31	1	14	1¼	81	4	9	1¼	131	7	4	1¼	181	9	19	1¼
32	1	15	2½	82	4	10	2½	132	7	5	2½	182	10	0	2½
33	1	16	3½	83	4	11	3½	133	7	6	3½	183	10	1	3½
34	1	17	4¾	84	4	12	4¾	134	7	7	4¾	184	10	2	4¾
35	1	18	6	85	4	13	6	135	7	8	6	185	10	3	6
36	1	19	7¼	86	4	14	7¼	136	7	9	7¼	186	10	4	7¼
37	2	0	8½	87	4	15	8½	137	7	10	8½	187	10	5	8½
38	2	1	9½	88	4	16	9½	138	7	11	9½	188	10	6	9½
39	2	2	10¾	89	4	17	10¾	139	7	12	10¾	189	10	7	10¾
40	**2**	**4**	**0**	**90**	**4**	**19**	**0**	**140**	**7**	**14**	**0**	**190**	**10**	**9**	**0**
41	2	5	1¼	91	5	0	1¼	141	7	15	1¼	191	10	10	1¼
42	2	6	2½	92	5	1	2½	142	7	16	2½	192	10	11	2½
43	2	7	3½	93	5	2	3½	143	7	17	3½	193	10	12	3½
44	2	8	4¾	94	5	3	4¾	144	7	18	4¾	194	10	13	4¾
45	2	9	6	95	5	4	6	145	7	19	6	195	10	14	6
46	2	10	7¼	96	5	5	7¼	146	8	0	7¼	196	10	15	7¼
47	2	11	8½	97	5	6	8½	147	8	1	8½	197	10	16	8½
48	2	12	9½	98	5	7	9½	148	8	2	9½	198	10	17	9½
49	2	13	10¾	99	5	8	10¾	149	8	3	10¾	199	10	18	10¾
50	**2**	**15**	**0**	**100**	**5**	**10**	**0**	**150**	**8**	**5**	**0**	**200**	**11**	**0**	**0**

250	13	15s	0d	700	38	10s	0d	1200	66	0s	0d	2000	110	0s	0d
300	16	10	0	750	41	5	0	1400	77	0	0	2500	137	10	0
400	22	0	0	800	44	0	0	1500	82	10	0	3000	165	0	0
500	27	10	0	900	49	10	0	1600	88	0	0	4000	220	0	0
600	33	0s	0d	1000	55	0s	0d	1800	99	0s	0d	5000	275	0s	0d

94½% off.

5½ Per Cent.

1d	0s.	0d	4/1	0s.	2¾	8/1	0s.	5¼	12/1	0s.	8	16/1	0s.	10½
2d	0	0	2	0	2¾	2	0	5½	2	0	8	2	0	10¾
3d	0	0¼	3	0	2¾	3	0	5½	3	0	8	3	0	10¾
4d	0	0¼	4	0	2¾	4	0	5½	4	0	8¼	4	0	10¾
5d	0	0¼	5	0	3	5	0	5½	5	0	8¼	5	0	10¾
6d	0	0¼	4/6	0	3	8/6	0	5½	12/6	0	8¼	16/6	0	11
7d	0	0½	7	0	3	7	0	5¾	7	0	8¼	7	0	11
8d	0	0½	8	0	3	8	0	5¾	8	0	8¼	8	0	11
9d	0	0½	9	0	3¼	9	0	5¾	9	0	8½	9	0	11
10d	0	0½	10	0	3¼	10	0	5¾	10	0	8½	10	0	11
11d	0	0½	11	0	3¼	11	0	6	11	0	8½	11	0	11¼
1/-	0s.	0¾	**5/-**	0s.	3¼	**9/-**	0s.	6	**13/-**	0s.	8½	**17/-**	0s.	11¼
1/1	0s.	0¾	5/1	0s.	3¼	9/1	0s.	6	13/1	0s.	8¾	17/1	0s.	11¼
2	0	0¾	2	0	3½	2	0	6	2	0	8¾	2	0	11¼
3	0	0¾	3	0	3½	3	0	6	3	0	8¾	3	0	11½
4	0	1	4	0	3½	4	0	6¼	4	0	8¾	4	0	11½
5	0	1	5	0	3½	5	0	6¼	5	0	8¾	5	0	11½
1/6	0	1	5/6	0	3¾	9/6	0	6¼	13/6	0	9	17/6	0	11½
7	0	1	7	0	3¾	7	0	6¼	7	0	9	7	0	11½
8	0	1	8	0	3¾	8	0	6½	8	0	9	8	0	11¾
9	0	1¼	9	0	3¾	9	0	6½	9	0	9	9	0	11¾
10	0	1¼	10	0	3¾	10	0	6½	10	0	9¼	10	0	11¾
11	0	1¼	11	0	4	11	0	6½	11	0	9¼	11	0	11¾
2/-	0s.	1¼	**6/-**	0s.	4	**10/-**	0s.	6½	**14/-**	0s.	9¼	**18/-**	1s.	0
2/1	0s.	1½	6/1	0s.	4	10/1	0s.	6¾	14/1	0s.	9¼	18/1	1s.	0
2	0	1½	2	0	4	2	0	6¾	2	0	9¼	2	1	0
3	0	1½	3	0	4¼	3	0	6¾	3	0	9½	3	1	0
4	0	1½	4	0	4¼	4	0	6¾	4	0	9½	4	1	0
5	0	1½	5	0	4¼	5	0	7	5	0	9½	5	1	0¼
2/6	0	1¾	6/6	0	4¼	10/6	0	7	14/6	0	9½	18/6	1	0¼
7	0	1¾	7	0	4¼	7	0	7	7	0	9¾	7	1	0¼
8	0	1¾	8	0	4½	8	0	7	8	0	9¾	8	1	0¼
9	0	1¾	9	0	4½	9	0	7	9	0	9¾	9	1	0½
10	0	1¾	10	0	4½	10	0	7¼	10	0	9¾	10	1	0½
11	0	2	11	0	4½	11	0	7¼	11	0	9¾	11	1	0½
3/-	0s.	2	**7/-**	0s.	4½	**11/-**	0s.	7¼	**15/-**	0s.	10	**19/-**	1s.	0½
3/1	0s.	2	7/1	0s.	4¾	11/1	0s.	7¼	15/1	0s.	10	19/1	1s.	0½
2	0	2	2	0	4¾	2	0	7¼	2	0	10	2	1	0¾
3	0	2¼	3	0	4¾	3	0	7½	3	0	10	3	1	0¾
4	0	2¼	4	0	4¾	4	0	7½	4	0	10	4	1	0¾
5	0	2¼	5	0	5	5	0	7½	5	0	10¼	5	1	0¾
3/6	0	2¼	7/6	0	5	11/6	0	7½	15/6	0	10¼	19/6	1	0¾
7	0	2¼	7	0	5	7	0	7¾	7	0	10¼	7	1	1
8	0	2½	8	0	5	8	0	7¾	8	0	10¼	8	1	1
9	0	2½	9	0	5	9	0	7¾	9	0	10½	9	1	1
10	0	2½	10	0	5¼	10	0	7¾	10	0	10½	10	1	1
11	0	2½	11	0	5¼	11	0	7¾	11	0	10½	11	1	1¼
4/-	0s.	2¾	**8/-**	0s.	5¼	**12/-**	0s.	8	**16/-**	0s.	10½	**20/-**	1s.	1¼

20/6	1s.	1½	25/6	1s.	4¾	31/-	1s.	8½	35/6	1s.	11½	Guineas.		
21/-	1	1¾	26/-	1	5¼	31/6	1	8¾	36/-	1	11¾	1.	1s.	1¾
22/-	1	2½	27/-	1	5¾	32/-	1	9	37/-	2	0½	2.	2	3¾
22/6	1	2¾	27/6	1	6¼	32/6	1	9½	37/6	2	0¾	3.	3	5½
23/-	1	3¼	28/-	1	6½	33/-	1	9¾	38/-	2	1	4.	4	7½
24/-	1	3¾	29/-	1	7¼	34/-	1	10½	39/-	2	1¾	5.	5	9¼
25/-	1s.	4½	**30/-**	1s.	7¾	**35/-**	1s.	11	**40/-**	2s.	2½	6.	6s.	11¼

(= $5\frac{2}{10}$%* on Gross Returns.)

5¾%

5¾ PER CENT.

5¾%

£1	£0	1s	1¾	£51	£2	18s	7¾	£101	£5	16s	1¾	£151	£8	13s	7¾
2	0	2	3½	52	2	19	9½	102	5	17	3½	152	8	14	9½
3	0	3	5½	53	3	0	11½	103	5	18	5½	153	8	15	11½
4	0	4	7¼	54	3	2	1¼	104	5	19	7¼	154	8	17	1¼
5	0	5	9	55	3	3	3	105	6	0	9	155	8	18	3
6	0	6	10¾	56	3	4	4¾	106	6	1	10¾	156	8	19	4¾
7	0	8	0½	57	3	5	6½	107	6	3	0½	157	9	0	6½
8	0	9	2½	58	3	6	8½	108	6	4	2½	158	9	1	8½
9	0	10	4¼	59	3	7	10¼	109	6	5	4¼	159	9	2	10¼
10	**0**	**11**	**6**	**60**	**3**	**9**	**0**	**110**	**6**	**6**	**6**	**160**	**9**	**4**	**0**
11	0	12	7¾	61	3	10	1¾	111	6	7	7¾	161	9	5	1¾
12	0	13	9½	62	3	11	3½	112	6	8	9½	162	9	6	3½
13	0	14	11½	63	3	12	5½	113	6	9	11½	163	9	7	5½
14	0	16	1¼	64	3	13	7¼	114	6	11	1¼	164	9	8	7¼
15	0	17	3	65	3	14	9	115	6	12	3	165	9	9	9
16	0	18	4¾	66	3	15	10¾	116	6	13	4¾	166	9	10	10¾
17	0	19	6½	67	3	17	0½	117	6	14	6½	167	9	12	0½
18	1	0	8½	68	3	18	2½	118	6	15	8½	168	9	13	2½
19	1	1	10¼	69	3	19	4¼	119	6	16	10¼	169	9	14	4¼
20	**1**	**3**	**0**	**70**	**4**	**0**	**6**	**120**	**6**	**18**	**0**	**170**	**9**	**15**	**6**
21	1	4	1¾	71	4	1	7¾	121	6	19	1¾	171	9	16	7¾
22	1	5	3½	72	4	2	9½	122	7	0	3½	172	9	17	9½
23	1	6	5½	73	4	3	11½	123	7	1	5½	173	9	18	11½
24	1	7	7¼	74	4	5	1¼	124	7	2	7¼	174	10	0	1¼
25	1	8	9	75	4	6	3	125	7	3	9	175	10	1	3
26	1	9	10¾	76	4	7	4¾	126	7	4	10¾	176	10	2	4¾
27	1	11	0½	77	4	8	6½	127	7	6	0½	177	10	3	6½
28	1	12	2½	78	4	9	8½	128	7	7	2½	178	10	4	8½
29	1	13	4¼	79	4	10	10¼	129	7	8	4¼	179	10	5	10¼
30	**1**	**14**	**6**	**80**	**4**	**12**	**0**	**130**	**7**	**9**	**6**	**180**	**10**	**7**	**0**
31	1	15	7¾	81	4	13	1¾	131	7	10	7¾	181	10	8	1¾
32	1	16	9½	82	4	14	3½	132	7	11	9½	182	10	9	3½
33	1	17	11½	83	4	15	5½	133	7	12	11½	183	10	10	5½
34	1	19	1¼	84	4	16	7¼	134	7	14	1¼	184	10	11	7¼
35	2	0	3	85	4	17	9	135	7	15	3	185	10	12	9
36	2	1	4¾	86	4	18	10¾	136	7	16	4¾	186	10	13	10¾
37	2	2	6½	87	5	0	0½	137	7	17	6½	187	10	15	0½
38	2	3	8½	88	5	1	2½	138	7	18	8½	188	10	16	2½
39	2	4	10¼	89	5	2	4¼	139	7	19	10¼	189	10	17	4¼
40	**2**	**6**	**0**	**90**	**5**	**3**	**6**	**140**	**8**	**1**	**0**	**190**	**10**	**18**	**6**
41	2	7	1¾	91	5	4	7¾	141	8	2	1¾	191	10	19	7¾
42	2	8	3½	92	5	5	9½	142	8	3	3½	192	11	0	9½
43	2	9	5½	93	5	6	11½	143	8	4	5½	193	11	1	11½
44	2	10	7¼	94	5	8	1¼	144	8	5	7¼	194	11	3	1¼
45	2	11	9	95	5	9	3	145	8	6	9	195	11	4	3
46	2	12	10¾	96	5	10	4¾	146	8	7	10¾	196	11	5	4¾
47	2	14	0½	97	5	11	6½	147	8	9	0½	197	11	6	6½
48	2	15	2½	98	5	12	8½	148	8	10	2½	198	11	7	8½
49	2	16	4¼	99	5	13	10¼	149	8	11	4¼	199	11	8	10¼
50	**2**	**17**	**6**	**100**	**5**	**15**	**0**	**150**	**8**	**12**	**6**	**200**	**11**	**10**	**0**

250	14	7s	6d	700	40	5s	0d	1200	69	0s	0d	2000	115	0s	0d
300	17	5	0	750	43	2	6	1400	80	10	0	2500	143	15	0
400	23	0	0	800	46	0	0	1500	86	5	0	3000	172	10	0
500	28	15	0	900	51	15	0	1600	92	0	0	4000	230	0	0
600	34	10s	0d	1000	57	10s	0d	1800	103	10s	0d	5000	287	10s	0d

94¼% off.

1d	0s.	0d	4/1	0s.	2¾	8/1	0s.	5½	12/1	0s.	8¼	16/1	0s.	11
2d	0	0	2	0	3	2	0	5¾	2	0	8½	2	0	11¼
3d	0	0¼	3	0	3	3	0	5¾	3	0	8½	3	0	11¼
4d	0	0¼	4	0	3	4	0	5¾	4	0	8½	4	0	11¼
5d	0	0¼	5	0	3	5	0	5¾	5	0	8½	5	0	11¼
6d	0	0¼	4/6	0	3	8/6	0	5¾	12/6	0	8¾	16/6	0	11½
7d	0	0½	7	0	3¼	7	0	6	7	0	8¾	7	0	11½
8d	0	0½	8	0	3¼	8	0	6	8	0	8¾	8	0	11½
9d	0	0½	9	0	3¼	9	0	6	9	0	8¾	9	0	11½
10d	0	0½	10	0	3¼	10	0	6	10	0	8¾	10	0	11½
11d	0	0¾	11	0	3½	11	0	6¼	11	0	9	11	0	11¾
1/-	0s.	0¾	**5/-**	0s.	3½	**9/-**	0s.	6¼	**13/-**	0s.	9	**17/-**	0s.	11¾
1/1	0s.	0¾	5/1	0s.	3½	9/1	0s.	6¼	13/1	0s.	9	17/1	0s.	11¾
2	0	0¾	2	0	3½	2	0	6¼	2	0	9	2	0	11¾
3	0	0¾	3	0	3½	3	0	6½	3	0	9¼	3	1	0
4	0	1	4	0	3¾	4	0	6½	4	0	9¼	4	1	0
5	0	1	5	0	3¾	5	0	6½	5	0	9¼	5	1	0
1/6	0	1	5/6	0	3¾	9/6	0	6½	13/6	0	9¼	17/6	1	0
7	0	1	7	0	3¾	7	0	6½	7	0	9¼	7	1	0¼
8	0	1¼	8	0	4	8	0	6¾	8	0	9½	8	1	0¼
9	0	1¼	9	0	4	9	0	6¾	9	0	9½	9	1	0¼
10	0	1¼	10	0	4	10	0	6¾	10	0	9½	10	1	0¼
11	0	1¼	11	0	4	11	0	6¾	11	0	9½	11	1	0¼
2/-	0s.	1½	**6/-**	0s.	4¼	**10/-**	0s.	7	**14/-**	0s.	9¾	**18/-**	1s.	0½
2/1	0s.	1½	6/1	0s.	4¼	10/1	0s.	7	14/1	0s.	9¾	18/1	1s.	0½
2	0	1½	2	0	4¼	2	0	7	2	0	9¾	2	1	0½
3	0	1½	3	0	4¼	3	0	7	3	0	9¾	3	1	0½
4	0	1½	4	0	4¼	4	0	7¼	4	0	10	4	1	0¾
5	0	1¾	5	0	4½	5	0	7¼	5	0	10	5	1	0¾
2/6	0	1¾	6/6	0	4½	10/6	0	7¼	14/6	0	10	18/6	1	0¾
7	0	1¾	7	0	4½	7	0	7¼	7	0	10	7	1	0¾
8	0	1¾	8	0	4½	8	0	7¼	8	0	10	8	1	1
9	0	2	9	0	4¾	9	0	7½	9	0	10¼	9	1	1
10	0	2	10	0	4¾	10	0	7½	10	0	10¼	10	1	1
11	0	2	11	0	4¾	11	0	7½	11	0	10¼	11	1	1
3/-	0s.	2	**7/-**	0s.	4¾	**11/-**	0s.	7½	**15/-**	0s.	10¼	**19/-**	1s.	1
3/1	0s.	2¼	7/1	0s.	5	11/1	0s.	7¾	15/1	0s.	10½	19/1	1s.	1¼
2	0	2¼	2	0	5	2	0	7¾	2	0	10½	2	1	1¼
3	0	2¼	3	0	5	3	0	7¾	3	0	10½	3	1	1¼
4	0	2¼	4	0	5	4	0	7¾	4	0	10½	4	1	1¼
5	0	2¼	5	0	5	5	0	8	5	0	10¾	5	1	1½
3/6	0	2½	7/6	0	5¼	11/6	0	8	15/6	0	10¾	19/6	1	1½
7	0	2½	7	0	5¼	7	0	8	7	0	10¾	7	1	1½
8	0	2½	8	0	5¼	8	0	8	8	0	10¾	8	1	1½
9	0	2½	9	0	5¼	9	0	8	9	0	10¾	9	1	1¾
10	0	2¾	10	0	5½	10	0	8¼	10	0	11	10	1	1¾
11	0	2¾	11	0	5½	11	0	8¼	11	0	11	11	1	1¾
4/-	0s.	2¾	**8/-**	0s.	5½	**12/-**	0s.	8¼	**16/-**	0s.	11	**20/-**	1s.	1¾

20/6	1s.	2¼	25/6	1s.	5½	31/-	1s.	9½	35/6	2s.	0½	Guineas.		
21/-	1	2½	26/-	1	6	31/6	1	9¾	36/-	2	0¾	1.	1s.	2½
22/-	1	3¼	27/-	1	6¾	32/-	1	10	37/-	2	1½	2.	2	5
22/6	1	3½	27/6	1	7	32/6	1	10½	37/6	2	2	3.	3	7½
23/-	1	3¾	28/-	1	7¼	33/-	1	10¾	38/-	2	2¼	4.	4	10
24/-	1	4½	29/-	1	8	34/-	1	11½	39/-	2	3	5.	6	0½
25/-	1s.	5¼	**30/-**	1s.	8¾	**35/-**	2s.	0¼	**40/-**	2s.	3½	6.	7s.	3

(=5 4/10 %* on Gross Returns)

6% 6 PER CENT. 6%

£	£	s	d	£	£	s	d	£	£	s	d	£	£	s	d
1	0	1	2½	51	3	1	2½	101	6	1	2½	151	9	1	2½
2	0	2	4¾	52	3	2	4¾	102	6	2	4¾	152	9	2	4¾
3	0	3	7¼	53	3	3	7¼	103	6	3	7¼	153	9	3	7¼
4	0	4	9½	54	3	4	9½	104	6	4	9½	154	9	4	9½
5	0	6	0	55	3	6	0	105	6	6	0	155	9	6	0
6	0	7	2½	56	3	7	2½	106	6	7	2½	156	9	7	2½
7	0	8	4¾	57	3	8	4¾	107	6	8	4¾	157	9	8	4¾
8	0	9	7¼	58	3	9	7¼	108	6	9	7¼	158	9	9	7¼
9	0	10	9½	59	3	10	9½	109	6	10	9½	159	9	10	9½
10	0	12	0	60	3	12	0	110	6	12	0	160	9	12	0
11	0	13	2½	61	3	13	2½	111	6	13	2½	161	9	13	2½
12	0	14	4¾	62	3	14	4¾	112	6	14	4¾	162	9	14	4¾
13	0	15	7¼	63	3	15	7¼	113	6	15	7¼	163	9	15	7¼
14	0	16	9½	64	3	16	9½	114	6	16	9½	164	9	16	9½
15	0	18	0	65	3	18	0	115	6	18	0	165	9	18	0
16	0	19	2½	66	3	19	2½	116	6	19	2½	166	9	19	2½
17	1	0	4¾	67	4	0	4¾	117	7	0	4¾	167	10	0	4¾
18	1	1	7¼	68	4	1	7¼	118	7	1	7¼	168	10	1	7¼
19	1	2	9½	69	4	2	9½	119	7	2	9½	169	10	2	9½
20	1	4	0	70	4	4	0	120	7	4	0	170	10	4	0
21	1	5	2½	71	4	5	2½	121	7	5	2½	171	10	5	2½
22	1	6	4¾	72	4	6	4¾	122	7	6	4¾	172	10	6	4¾
23	1	7	7¼	73	4	7	7¼	123	7	7	7¼	173	10	7	7¼
24	1	8	9½	74	4	8	9½	124	7	8	9½	174	10	8	9½
25	1	10	0	75	4	10	0	125	7	10	0	175	10	10	0
26	1	11	2½	76	4	11	2½	126	7	11	2½	176	10	11	2½
27	1	12	4¾	77	4	12	4¾	127	7	12	4¾	177	10	12	4¾
28	1	13	7¼	78	4	13	7¼	128	7	13	7¼	178	10	13	7¼
29	1	14	9½	79	4	14	9½	129	7	14	9½	179	10	14	9½
30	1	16	0	80	4	16	0	130	7	16	0	180	10	16	0
31	1	17	2½	81	4	17	2½	131	7	17	2½	181	10	17	2½
32	1	18	4¾	82	4	18	4¾	132	7	18	4¾	182	10	18	4¾
33	1	19	7¼	83	4	19	7¼	133	7	19	7¼	183	10	19	7¼
34	2	0	9½	84	5	0	9½	134	8	0	9½	184	11	0	9½
35	2	2	0	85	5	2	0	135	8	2	0	185	11	2	0
36	2	3	2½	86	5	3	2½	136	8	3	2½	186	11	3	2½
37	2	4	4¾	87	5	4	4¾	137	8	4	4¾	187	11	4	4¾
38	2	5	7¼	88	5	5	7¼	138	8	5	7¼	188	11	5	7¼
39	2	6	9½	89	5	6	9½	139	8	6	9½	189	11	6	9½
40	2	8	0	90	5	8	0	140	8	8	0	190	11	8	0
41	2	9	2½	91	5	9	2½	141	8	9	2½	191	11	9	2½
42	2	10	4¾	92	5	10	4¾	142	8	10	4¾	192	11	10	4¾
43	2	11	7¼	93	5	11	7¼	143	8	11	7¼	193	11	11	7¼
44	2	12	9½	94	5	12	9½	144	8	12	9½	194	11	12	9½
45	2	14	0	95	5	14	0	145	8	14	0	195	11	14	0
46	2	15	2½	96	5	15	2½	146	8	15	2½	196	11	15	2½
47	2	16	4¾	97	5	16	4¾	147	8	16	4¾	197	11	16	4¾
48	2	17	7¼	98	5	17	7¼	148	8	17	7¼	198	11	17	7¼
49	2	18	9½	99	5	18	9½	149	8	18	9½	199	11	18	9½
50	3	0	0	100	6	0	0	150	9	0	0	200	12	0	0

£	£	s	d	£	£	s	d	£	£	s	d	£	£	s	d
250	15	0s	0d	700	42	0s	0d	1200	72	0s	0d	2000	120	0s	0d
300	18	0	0	750	45	0	0	1400	84	0	0	2500	150	0	0
400	24	0	0	800	48	0	0	1500	90	0	0	3000	180	0	0
500	30	0	0	900	54	0	0	1600	96	0	0	4000	240	0	0
600	36	0s	0d	1000	60	0s	0d	1800	108	0s	0d	5000	300	0s	0d

94% off.

1d	0s.	0d	4/1	0s.	3d	8/1	0s.	5¾	12/1	0s.	8¾	16/1	0s.	11½
2d	0	0	2	0	3	2	0	6	2	0	8¾	2	0	11¾
3d	0	0¼	3	0	3	3	0	6	3	0	8¾	3	0	11¾
4d	0	0¼	4	0	3	4	0	6	4	0	9	4	0	11¾
5d	0	0¼	5	0	3¼	5	0	6	5	0	9	5	0	11¾
6d	0	0¼	4/6	0	3¼	8/6	0	6	12/6	0	9	16/6	1	0
7d	0	0½	7	0	3¼	7	0	6¼	7	0	9	7	1	0
8d	0	0½	8	0	3¼	8	0	6¼	8	0	9	8	1	0
9d	0	0½	9	0	3½	9	0	6¼	9	0	9¼	9	1	0
10d	0	0½	10	0	3½	10	0	6¼	10	0	9¼	10	1	0
11d	0	0¾	11	0	3½	11	0	6½	11	0	9¼	11	1	0¼
1/-	0s.	0¾	**5/-**	0s.	3½	**9/-**	0s.	6½	**13/-**	0s.	9¼	**17/-**	1s.	0¼
1/1	0s.	0¾	5/1	0s.	3¾	9/1	0s.	6½	13/1	0s.	9½	17/1	1s.	0¼
2	0	0¾	2	0	3¾	2	0	6½	2	0	9½	2	1	0¼
3	0	1	3	0	3¾	3	0	6¾	3	0	9½	3	1	0½
4	0	1	4	0	3¾	4	0	6¾	4	0	9½	4	1	0½
5	0	1	5	0	4	5	0	6¾	5	0	9¾	5	1	0½
1/6	0	1	5/6	0	4	9/6	0	6¾	13/6	0	9¾	17/6	1	0½
7	0	1¼	7	0	4	7	0	7	7	0	9¾	7	1	0¾
8	0	1¼	8	0	4	8	0	7	8	0	9¾	8	1	0¾
9	0	1¼	9	0	4¼	9	0	7	9	0	10	9	1	0¾
10	0	1¼	10	0	4¼	10	0	7	10	0	10	10	1	0¾
11	0	1½	11	0	4¼	11	0	7¼	11	0	10	11	1	1
2/-	0s.	1½	**6/-**	0s.	4¼	**10/-**	0s.	7¼	**14/-**	0s.	10	**18/-**	1s.	1
2/1	0s.	1½	6/1	0s.	4½	10/1	0s.	7¼	14/1	0s.	10¼	18/1	1s.	1
2	0	1½	2	0	4½	2	0	7¼	2	0	10¼	2	1	1
3	0	1½	3	0	4½	3	0	7½	3	0	10¼	3	1	1¼
4	0	1¾	4	0	4½	4	0	7½	4	0	10¼	4	1	1¼
5	0	1¾	5	0	4½	5	0	7½	5	0	10½	5	1	1¼
2/6	0	1¾	6/6	0	4¾	10/6	0	7½	14/6	0	10½	18/6	1	1¼
7	0	1¾	7	0	4¾	7	0	7½	7	0	10½	7	1	1½
8	0	2	8	0	4¾	8	0	7¾	8	0	10½	8	1	1½
9	0	2	9	0	4¾	9	0	7¾	9	0	10½	9	1	1½
10	0	2	10	0	5	10	0	7¾	10	0	10¾	10	1	1½
11	0	2	11	0	5	11	0	7¾	11	0	10¾	11	1	1½
3/-	0s.	2¼	**7/-**	0s.	5	**11/-**	0s.	8	**15/-**	0s.	10¾	**19/-**	1s.	1¾
3/1	0s.	2¼	7/1	0s.	5	11/1	0s.	8	15/1	0s.	10¾	19/1	1s.	1¾
2	0	2¼	2	0	5¼	2	0	8	2	0	11	2	1	1¾
3	0	2¼	3	0	5¼	3	0	8	3	0	11	3	1	1¾
4	0	2½	4	0	5¼	4	0	8¼	4	0	11	4	1	2
5	0	2½	5	0	5¼	5	0	8¼	5	0	11	5	1	2
3/6	0	2½	7/6	0	5½	11/6	0	8¼	15/6	0	11¼	19/6	1	2
7	0	2½	7	0	5½	7	0	8¼	7	0	11¼	7	1	2
8	0	2¾	8	0	5½	8	0	8½	8	0	11¼	8	1	2¼
9	0	2¾	9	0	5½	9	0	8½	9	0	11¼	9	1	2¼
10	0	2¾	10	0	5¾	10	0	8½	10	0	11½	10	1	2¼
11	0	2¾	11	0	5¾	11	0	8½	11	0	11½	11	1	2¼
4/-	0s.	3	**8/-**	0s.	5¾	**12/-**	0s.	8¾	**16/-**	0s.	11½	**20/-**	1s.	2½

20/6	1s.	2¾	25/6	1s.	6¼	31/-	1s.	10¼	35/6	2s.	1½	Guineas.		
21/-	1	3	26/-	1	6¾	31/6	1	10¾	36/-	2	2	1.	1s.	3
22/-	1	3¾	27/-	1	7½	32/-	1	11	37/-	2	2¾	2.	2	6¼
22/6	1	4¼	27/6	1	7¾	32/6	1	11½	37/6	2	3	3.	3	9¼
23/-	1	4½	28/-	1	8¼	33/-	1	11¾	38/-	2	3¼	4.	5	0½
24/-	1	5¼	29/-	1	9	34/-	2	0½	39/-	2	4	5.	6	3½
25/-	1s.	6	**30/-**	1s.	9½	**35/-**	2s.	1¼	**40/-**	2s.	4¾	6.	7s.	6¾

(= $5\frac{7}{10}$%* on Gross Retnrns).

£	£ s d	£	£ s d	£	£ s d	£	£ s d
£1	£0 1s 3	£51	£3 3s 9	£101	£6 6s 3	£151	£9 8s 9
2	0 2 6	52	3 5 0	102	6 7 6	152	9 10 0
3	0 3 9	53	3 6 3	103	6 8 9	153	9 11 3
4	0 5 0	54	3 7 6	104	6 10 0	154	9 12 6
5	0 6 3	55	3 8 9	105	6 11 3	155	9 13 9
6	0 7 6	56	3 10 0	106	6 12 6	156	9 15 0
7	0 8 9	57	3 11 3	107	6 13 9	157	9 16 3
8	0 10 0	58	3 12 6	108	6 15 0	158	9 17 6
9	0 11 3	59	3 13 9	109	6 16 3	159	9 18 9
10	0 12 6	60	3 15 0	110	6 17 6	160	10 0 0
11	0 13 9	61	3 16 3	111	6 18 9	161	10 1 3
12	0 15 0	62	3 17 6	112	7 0 0	162	10 2 6
13	0 16 3	63	3 18 9	113	7 1 3	163	10 3 9
14	0 17 6	64	4 0 0	114	7 2 6	164	10 5 0
15	0 18 9	65	4 1 3	115	7 3 9	165	10 6 3
16	1 0 0	66	4 2 6	116	7 5 0	166	10 7 6
17	1 1 3	67	4 3 9	117	7 6 3	167	10 8 9
18	1 2 6	68	4 5 0	118	7 7 6	168	10 10 0
19	1 3 9	69	4 6 3	119	7 8 9	169	10 11 3
20	1 5 0	70	4 7 6	120	7 10 0	170	10 12 6
21	1 6 3	71	4 8 9	121	7 11 3	171	10 13 9
22	1 7 6	72	4 10 0	122	7 12 6	172	10 15 0
23	1 8 9	73	4 11 3	123	7 13 9	173	10 16 3
24	1 10 0	74	4 12 6	124	7 15 0	174	10 17 6
25	1 11 3	75	4 13 9	125	7 16 3	175	10 18 9
26	1 12 6	76	4 15 0	126	7 17 6	176	11 0 0
27	1 13 9	77	4 16 3	127	7 18 9	177	11 1 3
28	1 15 0	78	4 17 6	128	8 0 0	178	11 2 6
29	1 16 3	79	4 18 9	129	8 1 3	179	11 3 9
30	1 17 6	80	5 0 0	130	8 2 6	180	11 5 0
31	1 18 9	81	5 1 3	131	8 3 9	181	11 6 3
32	2 0 0	82	5 2 6	132	8 5 0	182	11 7 6
33	2 1 3	83	5 3 9	133	8 6 3	183	11 8 9
34	2 2 6	84	5 5 0	134	8 7 6	184	11 10 0
35	2 3 9	85	5 6 3	135	8 8 9	185	11 11 3
36	2 5 0	86	5 7 6	136	8 10 0	186	11 12 6
37	2 6 3	87	5 8 9	137	8 11 3	187	11 13 9
38	2 7 6	88	5 10 0	138	8 12 6	188	11 15 0
39	2 8 9	89	5 11 3	139	8 13 9	189	11 16 3
40	2 10 0	90	5 12 6	140	8 15 0	190	11 17 6
41	2 11 3	91	5 13 9	141	8 16 3	191	11 18 9
42	2 12 6	92	5 15 0	142	8 17 6	192	12 0 0
43	2 13 9	93	5 16 3	143	8 18 9	193	12 1 3
44	2 15 0	94	5 17 6	144	9 0 0	194	12 2 6
45	2 16 3	95	5 18 9	145	9 1 3	195	12 3 9
46	2 17 6	96	6 0 0	146	9 2 6	196	12 5 0
47	2 18 9	97	6 1 3	147	9 3 9	197	12 6 3
48	3 0 0	98	6 2 6	148	9 5 0	198	12 7 6
49	3 1 3	99	6 3 9	149	9 6 3	199	12 8 9
50	3 2 6	100	6 5 0	150	9 7 6	200	12 10 0
250	15 12s 6d	700	43 15s 0d	1200	75 0s 0d	2000	125 0s 0d
300	18 15 0	750	46 17 6	1400	87 10 0	2500	156 5 0
400	25 0 0	800	50 0 0	1500	93 15 0	3000	187 10 0
500	31 5 0	900	56 5 0	1600	100 0 0	4000	250 0 0
600	37 10s 0d	1000	62 10s 0d	1800	112 10s 0d	5000	312 10s 0d

93¾% off.   (6¼%=1-16th)

1d	0s.	0	4/1	0s.	3	8/1	0s.	6	12/1	0s.	9	16/1	1s.	0
2d	0	0¼	2	0	3¼	2	0	6¼	2	0	9¼	2	1	0¼
3d	0	0¼	3	0	3¼	3	0	6¼	3	0	9¼	3	1	0¼
4d	0	0¼	4	0	3¼	4	0	6¼	4	0	9¼	4	1	0¼
5d	0	0¼	5	0	3¼	5	0	6¼	5	0	9¼	5	1	0¼
6d	0	0½	4/6	0	3½	8/6	0	6½	12/6	0	9½	16/6	1	0½
7d	0	0½	7	0	3½	7	0	6½	7	0	9½	7	1	0½
8d	0	0½	8	0	3½	8	0	6½	8	0	9½	8	1	0½
9d	0	0½	9	0	3½	9	0	6½	9	0	9½	9	1	0½
10d	0	0¾	10	0	3¾	10	0	6¾	10	0	9¾	10	1	0¾
11d	0	0¾	11	0	3¾	11	0	6¾	11	0	9¾	11	1	0¾
1/-	0s.	0¾	**5/-**	0s.	3¾	**9/-**	0s.	6¾	**13/-**	0s.	9¾	**17/-**	1s.	0¾
1/1	0s.	0¾	5/1	0s.	3¾	9/1	0s.	6¾	13/1	0s.	9¾	17/1	1s.	0¾
2	0	1	2	0	4	2	0	7	2	0	10	2	1	1
3	0	1	3	0	4	3	0	7	3	0	10	3	1	1
4	0	1	4	0	4	4	0	7	4	0	10	4	1	1
5	0	1	5	0	4	5	0	7	5	0	10	5	1	1
1/6	0	1¼	5/6	0	4¼	9/6	0	7¼	13/6	0	10¼	17/6	1	1¼
7	0	1¼	7	0	4¼	7	0	7¼	7	0	10¼	7	1	1¼
8	0	1¼	8	0	4¼	8	0	7¼	8	0	10¼	8	1	1¼
9	0	1¼	9	0	4¼	9	0	7¼	9	0	10¼	9	1	1¼
10	0	1½	10	0	4½	10	0	7½	10	0	10½	10	1	1½
11	0	1½	11	0	4½	11	0	7½	11	0	10½	11	1	1½
2/-	0s.	1½	**6/-**	0s.	4½	**10/-**	0s.	7½	**14/-**	0s.	10½	**18/-**	1s.	1½
2/1	0s.	1½	6/1	0s.	4½	10/1	0s.	7½	14/1	0s.	10½	18/1	1s.	1½
2	0	1¾	2	0	4¾	2	0	7¾	2	0	10¾	2	1	1¾
3	0	1¾	3	0	4¾	3	0	7¾	3	0	10¾	3	1	1¾
4	0	1¾	4	0	4¾	4	0	7¾	4	0	10¾	4	1	1¾
5	0	1¾	5	0	4¾	5	0	7¾	5	0	10¾	5	1	1¾
2/6	0	2	6/6	0	5	10/6	0	8	14/6	0	11	18/6	1	2
7	0	2	7	0	5	7	0	8	7	0	11	7	1	2
8	0	2	8	0	5	8	0	8	8	0	11	8	1	2
9	0	2	9	0	5	9	0	8	9	0	11	9	1	2
10	0	2¼	10	0	5¼	10	0	8¼	10	0	11¼	10	1	2¼
11	0	2¼	11	0	5¼	11	0	8¼	11	0	11¼	11	1	2¼
3/-	0s.	2¼	**7/-**	0s.	5¼	**11/-**	0s.	8¼	**15/-**	0s.	11¼	**19/-**	1s.	2¼
3/1	0s.	2¼	7/1	0s.	5¼	11/1	0s.	8¼	15/1	0s.	11¼	19/1	1s.	2¼
2	0	2½	2	0	5½	2	0	8½	2	0	11½	2	1	2½
3	0	2½	3	0	5½	3	0	8½	3	0	11½	3	1	2½
4	0	2½	4	0	5½	4	0	8½	4	0	11½	4	1	2½
5	0	2½	5	0	5½	5	0	8½	5	0	11½	5	1	2½
3/6	0	2¾	7/6	0	5¾	11/6	0	8¾	15/6	0	11¾	19/6	1	2¾
7	0	2¾	7	0	5¾	7	0	8¾	7	0	11¾	7	1	2¾
8	0	2¾	8	0	5¾	8	0	8¾	8	0	11¾	8	1	2¾
9	0	2¾	9	0	5¾	9	0	8¾	9	0	11¾	9	1	2¾
10	0	3	10	0	6	10	0	9	10	1	0	10	1	3
11	0	3	11	0	6	11	0	9	11	1	0	11	1	3
4/-	0s.	3	**8/-**	0s.	6	**12/-**	0s.	9	**16/-**	1s.	0	**20/-**	1s.	3

20/6	1s.	3½	25/6	1s.	7¼	31/-	1s.	11¼	35/6	2s.	2¾	Guineas.		
21/-	1	3¾	26/-	1	7½	31/6	1	11¾	36/-	2	3	1.	1s.	3¾
22/-	1	4½	27/-	1	8¼	32/-	2	0	37/-	2	3¾	2.	2	7½
22/6	1	5	27/6	1	8¾	32/6	2	0½	37/6	2	4¼	3.	3	11¼
23/-	1	5¼	28/-	1	9	33/-	2	0¾	38/-	2	4½	4.	5	3
24/-	1	6	29/-	1	9¾	34/-	2	1½	39/-	2	5¼	5.	6	6¾
25/-	1s.	6¾	**30/-**	1s.	10½	**35/-**	2s.	2¼	**40/-**	2s.	6	6.	7s.	10½

(=5$\frac{9}{10}$%* on Gross Returns).

6½% SIX PDS. TEN SHGS. PER CENT. £6.10%

£1	0	1s.	3½	£51	3	6s.	3½	£101	6	11s.	3½	£151	9	16s.	3½
2	0	2	7¼	52	3	7	7¼	102	6	12	7¼	152	9	17	7¼
3	0	3	10¾	53	3	8	10¾	103	6	13	10¾	153	9	18	10¾
4	0	5	2½	54	3	10	2½	104	6	15	2½	154	10	0	2½
5	0	6	6	55	3	11	6	105	6	16	6	155	10	1	6
6	0	7	9½	56	3	12	9½	106	6	17	9½	156	10	2	9½
7	0	9	1¼	57	3	14	1¼	107	6	19	1¼	157	10	4	1¼
8	0	10	4¾	58	3	15	4¾	108	7	0	4¾	158	10	5	4¾
9	0	11	8½	59	3	16	8½	109	7	1	8½	159	10	6	8½
10	0	13s.	0d	**60**	3	18s.	0d	**110**	7	3s.	0d	**160**	10	8s.	0d
11	0	14s.	3½	61	3	19s.	3½	111	7	4s.	3½	161	10	9s.	3½
12	0	15	7¼	62	4	0	7¼	112	7	5	7¼	162	10	10	7¼
13	0	16	10¾	63	4	1	10¾	113	7	6	10¾	163	10	11	10¾
14	0	18	2½	64	4	3	2½	114	7	8	2½	164	10	13	2½
15	0	19	6	65	4	4	6	115	7	9	6	165	10	14	6
16	1	0	9½	66	4	5	9½	116	7	10	9½	166	10	15	9½
17	1	2	1¼	67	4	7	1¼	117	7	12	1¼	167	10	17	1¼
18	1	3	4¾	68	4	8	4¾	118	7	13	4¾	168	10	18	4¾
19	1	4	8½	69	4	9	8½	119	7	14	8½	169	10	19	8½
20	1	6s.	0d	**70**	4	11s.	0d	**120**	7	16s.	0d	**170**	11	1s.	0d
21	1	7s.	3½	71	4	12s.	3½	121	7	17s.	3½	171	11	2s.	3½
22	1	8	7¼	72	4	13	7¼	122	7	18	7¼	172	11	3	7¼
23	1	9	10¾	73	4	14	10¾	123	7	19	10¾	173	11	4	10¾
24	1	11	2½	74	4	16	2½	124	8	1	2½	174	11	6	2½
25	1	12	6	75	4	17	6	125	8	2	6	175	11	7	6
26	1	13	9½	76	4	18	9½	126	8	3	9½	176	11	8	9½
27	1	15	1¼	77	5	0	1¼	127	8	5	1¼	177	11	10	1¼
28	1	16	4¾	78	5	1	4¾	128	8	6	4¾	178	11	11	4¾
29	1	17	8½	79	5	2	8½	129	8	7	8½	179	11	12	8½
30	1	19s.	0d	**80**	5	4s.	0d	**130**	8	9s.	0d	**180**	11	14s.	0d
31	2	0s.	3½	81	5	5s.	3½	131	8	10s.	3½	181	11	15s.	3½
32	2	1	7¼	82	5	6	7¼	132	8	11	7¼	182	11	16	7¼
33	2	2	10¾	83	5	7	10¾	133	8	12	10¾	183	11	17	10¾
34	2	4	2½	84	5	9	2½	134	8	14	2½	184	11	19	2½
35	2	5	6	85	5	10	6	135	8	15	6	185	12	0	6
36	2	6	9½	86	5	11	9½	136	8	16	9½	186	12	1	9½
37	2	8	1¼	87	5	13	1¼	137	8	18	1¼	187	12	3	1¼
38	2	9	4¾	88	5	14	4¾	138	8	19	4¾	188	12	4	4¾
39	2	10	8½	89	5	15	8½	139	9	0	8½	189	12	5	8½
40	2	12s.	0d	**90**	5	17s.	0d	**140**	9	2s.	0d	**190**	12	7s.	0d
41	2	13s.	3½	91	5	18s.	3½	141	9	3s.	3½	191	12	8s.	3½
42	2	14	7¼	92	5	19	7¼	142	9	4	7¼	192	12	9	7¼
43	2	15	10¾	93	6	0	10¾	143	9	5	10¾	193	12	10	10¾
44	2	17	2½	94	6	2	2½	144	9	7	2½	194	12	12	2½
45	2	18	6	95	6	3	6	145	9	8	6	195	12	13	6
46	2	19	9½	96	6	4	9½	146	9	9	9½	196	12	14	9½
47	3	1	1¼	97	6	6	1¼	147	9	11	1¼	197	12	16	1¼
48	3	2	4¾	98	6	7	4¾	148	9	12	4¾	198	12	17	4¾
49	3	3	8½	99	6	8	8½	149	9	13	8½	199	12	18	8½
50	3	5s.	0d	**100**	6	10s.	0d	**150**	9	15s.	0d	**200**	13	0s.	0d
250	16	5s.	0d	700	45	10s.	0d	1200	78	0s.	0d	2000	130	0s.	0d
300	19	10	0	750	48	15	0	1400	91	0	0	2500	162	10	0
400	26	0	0	800	52	0	0	1500	97	10	0	3000	195	0	0
500	32	10	0	900	58	10	0	1600	104	0	0	4000	260	0	0
600	39	0s.	0d	1000	65	0s.	0d	1800	117	0s.	0d	5000	325	0s.	0d

1d	0s.	0	**4/1**	0s.	3¼	**8/1**	0s.	6¼	**12/1**	0s.	9½	**16/1**	1s.	0½
2d	0	0¼	**2**	0	3¼	**2**	0	6¼	**2**	0	9½	**2**	1	0½
3d	0	0¼	**3**	0	3¼	**3**	0	6½	**3**	0	9½	**3**	1	0¾
4d	0	0¼	**4**	0	3½	**4**	0	6½	**4**	0	9½	**4**	1	0¾
5d	0	0¼	**5**	0	3½	**5**	0	6½	**5**	0	9¾	**5**	1	0¾
6d	0	0½	**4/6**	0	3½	**8/6**	0	6¾	**12/6**	0	9¾	**16/6**	1	0¾
7d	0	0½	**7**	0	3½	**7**	0	6¾	**7**	0	9¾	**7**	1	1
8d	0	0½	**8**	0	3¾	**8**	0	6¾	**8**	0	10	**8**	1	1
9d	0	0½	**9**	0	3¾	**9**	0	6¾	**9**	0	10	**9**	1	1
10d	0	0¾	**10**	0	3¾	**10**	0	7	**10**	0	10	**10**	1	1¼
11d	0	0¾	**11**	0	3¾	**11**	0	7	**11**	0	10	**11**	1	1¼
1/-	0s.	0¾	**5/-**	0s.	4	**9/-**	0s.	7	**13/-**	0s.	10¼	**17/-**	1s.	1¼
1/1	0s.	0¾	**5/1**	0s.	4	**9/1**	0s.	7	**13/1**	0s.	10¼	**17/1**	1s.	1¼
2	0	1	**2**	0	4	**2**	0	7¼	**2**	0	10¼	**2**	1	1½
3	0	1	**3**	0	4	**3**	0	7¼	**3**	0	10¼	**3**	1	1½
4	0	1	**4**	0	4¼	**4**	0	7¼	**4**	0	10½	**4**	1	1½
5	0	1	**5**	0	4¼	**5**	0	7¼	**5**	0	10½	**5**	1	1½
1/6	0	1¼	**5/6**	0	4¼	**9/6**	0	7½	**13/6**	0	10½	**17/6**	1	1¾
7	0	1¼	**7**	0	4¼	**7**	0	7½	**7**	0	10½	**7**	1	1¾
8	0	1¼	**8**	0	4½	**8**	0	7½	**8**	0	10¾	**8**	1	1¾
9	0	1¼	**9**	0	4½	**9**	0	7½	**9**	0	10¾	**9**	1	1¾
10	0	1½	**10**	0	4½	**10**	0	7¾	**10**	0	10¾	**10**	1	2
11	0	1½	**11**	0	4½	**11**	0	7¾	**11**	0	10¾	**11**	1	2
2/-	0s.	1½	**6/-**	0s.	4¾	**10/-**	0s.	7¾	**14/-**	0s.	11	**18/-**	1s.	2
2/1	0s.	1¾	**6/1**	0s.	4¾	**10/1**	0s.	7¾	**14/1**	0s.	11	**18/1**	1s.	2
2	0	1¾	**2**	0	4¾	**2**	0	8	**2**	0	11	**2**	1	2¼
3	0	1¾	**3**	0	5	**3**	0	8	**3**	0	11	**3**	1	2¼
4	0	1¾	**4**	0	5	**4**	0	8	**4**	0	11¼	**4**	1	2¼
5	0	2	**5**	0	5	**5**	0	8¼	**5**	0	11¼	**5**	1	2¼
2/6	0	2	**6/6**	0	5	**10/6**	0	8¼	**14/6**	0	11¼	**18/6**	1	2½
7	0	2	**7**	0	5¼	**7**	0	8¼	**7**	0	11½	**7**	1	2½
8	0	2	**8**	0	5¼	**8**	0	8¼	**8**	0	11½	**8**	1	2½
9	0	2¼	**9**	0	5¼	**9**	0	8½	**9**	0	11½	**9**	1	2¾
10	0	2¼	**10**	0	5¼	**10**	0	8½	**10**	0	11½	**10**	1	2¾
11	0	2¼	**11**	0	5½	**11**	0	8½	**11**	0	11¾	**11**	1	2¾
3/-	0s.	2¼	**7/-**	0s.	5½	**11/-**	0s.	8½	**15/-**	0s.	11¾	**19/-**	1s.	2¾
3/1	0s.	2½	**7/1**	0s.	5½	**11/1**	0s.	8¾	**15/1**	0s.	11¾	**19/1**	1s.	3
2	0	2½	**2**	0	5½	**2**	0	8¾	**2**	0	11¾	**2**	1	3
3	0	2½	**3**	0	5¾	**3**	0	8¾	**3**	1	0	**3**	1	3
4	0	2½	**4**	0	5¾	**4**	0	8¾	**4**	1	0	**4**	1	3
5	0	2¾	**5**	0	5¾	**5**	0	9	**5**	1	0	**5**	1	3¼
3/6	0	2¾	**7/6**	0	5¾	**11/6**	0	9	**15/6**	1	0	**19/6**	1	3¼
7	0	2¾	**7**	0	6	**7**	0	9	**7**	1	0¼	**7**	1	3¼
8	0	2¾	**8**	0	6	**8**	0	9	**8**	1	0¼	**8**	1	3¼
9	0	3	**9**	0	6	**9**	0	9¼	**9**	1	0¼	**9**	1	3½
10	0	3	**10**	0	6	**10**	0	9¼	**10**	1	0¼	**10**	1	3½
11	0	3	**11**	0	6¼	**11**	0	9¼	**11**	1	0½	**11**	1	3½
4/-	0s.	3	**8/-**	0s.	6¼	**12/-**	0s.	9¼	**16/-**	1s.	0½	**20/-**	1s.	3½

20/6	1s.	4	**25/6**	1s.	8	**31/-**	2s.	0¼	**35/6**	2s.	3¾	Guineas.		
21/-	1	4½	**26/-**	1	8¼	**31/6**	2	0½	**36/-**	2	4	**1.**	1s.	4½
22/-	1	5¼	**27/-**	1	9	**32/-**	2	1	**37/-**	2	4¾	**2.**	2	8¾
22/6	1	5½	**27/6**	1	9½	**32/6**	2	1¼	**37/6**	2	5¼	**3.**	4	1¼
23/-	1	6	**28/-**	1	9¾	**33/-**	2	1¾	**38/-**	2	5¾	**4.**	5	5½
24/-	1	6¾	**29/-**	1	10½	**34/-**	2	2½	**39/-**	2	6½	**5.**	6	10
25/-	1s.	7½	**30/-**	1s.	11½	**35/-**	2s.	3¼	**40/-**	2s.	7¼	**6.**	8s.	2¼

(=6 1/16%* on Gross Returns).

£	£	s	d	£	£	s	d	£	£	s	d	£	£	s	d
£1	0	1	4¼	£51	3	8	10¼	£101	6	16	4¼	£151	10	3	10¼
2	0	2	8½	52	3	10	2½	102	6	17	8½	152	10	5	2½
3	0	4	0½	53	3	11	6½	103	6	19	0½	153	10	6	6½
4	0	5	4¾	54	3	12	10¾	104	7	0	4¾	154	10	7	10¾
5	0	6	9	55	3	14	3	105	7	1	9	155	10	9	3
6	0	8	1¼	56	3	15	7¼	106	7	3	1¼	156	10	10	7¼
7	0	9	5½	57	3	16	11½	107	7	4	5½	157	10	11	11½
8	0	10	9½	58	3	18	3½	108	7	5	9½	158	10	13	3½
9	0	12	1¾	59	3	19	7¾	109	7	7	1¾	159	10	14	7¾
10	0	13	6	**60**	4	1	0	**110**	7	8	6	**160**	10	16	0
11	0	14	10¼	61	4	2	4¼	111	7	9	10¼	161	10	17	4¼
12	0	16	2½	62	4	3	8½	112	7	11	2½	162	10	18	8½
13	0	17	6½	63	4	5	0½	113	7	12	6½	163	11	0	0½
14	0	18	10¾	64	4	6	4¾	114	7	13	10¾	164	11	1	4¾
15	1	0	3	65	4	7	9	115	7	15	3	165	11	2	9
16	1	1	7¼	66	4	9	1¼	116	7	16	7¼	166	11	4	1¼
17	1	2	11½	67	4	10	5½	117	7	17	11½	167	11	5	5½
18	1	4	3½	68	4	11	9½	118	7	19	3½	168	11	6	9½
19	1	5	7¾	69	4	13	1¾	119	8	0	7¾	169	11	8	1¾
20	1	7	0	**70**	4	14	6	**120**	8	2	0	**170**	11	9	6
21	1	8	4¼	71	4	15	10¼	121	8	3	4¼	171	11	10	10¼
22	1	9	8½	72	4	17	2½	122	8	4	8½	172	11	12	2½
23	1	11	0½	73	4	18	6½	123	8	6	0½	173	11	13	6½
24	1	12	4¾	74	4	19	10¾	124	8	7	4¾	174	11	14	10¾
25	1	13	9	75	5	1	3	125	8	8	9	175	11	16	3
26	1	15	1¼	76	5	2	7¼	126	8	10	1¼	176	11	17	7¼
27	1	16	5½	77	5	3	11½	127	8	11	5½	177	11	18	11½
28	1	17	9½	78	5	5	3½	128	8	12	9½	178	12	0	3½
29	1	19	1¾	79	5	6	7¾	129	8	14	1¾	179	12	1	7¾
30	2	0	6	**80**	5	8	0	**130**	8	15	6	**180**	12	3	0
31	2	1	10¼	81	5	9	4¼	131	8	16	10¼	181	12	4	4¼
32	2	3	2½	82	5	10	8½	132	8	18	2½	182	12	5	8½
33	2	4	6½	83	5	12	0½	133	8	19	6½	183	12	7	0½
34	2	5	10¾	84	5	13	4¾	134	9	0	10¾	184	12	8	4¾
35	2	7	3	85	5	14	9	135	9	2	3	185	12	9	9
36	2	8	7¼	86	5	16	1¼	136	9	3	7¼	186	12	11	1¼
37	2	9	11½	87	5	17	5½	137	9	4	11½	187	12	12	5½
38	2	11	3½	88	5	18	9½	138	9	6	3½	188	12	13	9½
39	2	12	7¾	89	6	0	1¾	139	9	7	7¾	189	12	15	1¾
40	2	14	0	**90**	6	1	6	**140**	9	9	0	**190**	12	16	6
41	2	15	4¼	91	6	2	10¼	141	9	10	4¼	191	12	17	10¼
42	2	16	8½	92	6	4	2½	142	9	11	8½	192	12	19	2½
43	2	18	0½	93	6	5	6½	143	9	13	0½	193	13	0	6½
44	2	19	4¾	94	6	6	10¾	144	9	14	4¾	194	13	1	10¾
45	3	0	9	95	6	8	3	145	9	15	9	195	13	3	3
46	3	2	1¼	96	6	9	7¼	146	9	17	1¼	196	13	4	7¼
47	3	3	5½	97	6	10	11½	147	9	18	5½	197	13	5	11½
48	3	4	9½	98	6	12	3½	148	9	19	9½	198	13	7	3½
49	3	6	1¾	99	6	13	7¾	149	10	1	1¾	199	13	8	7¾
50	3	7	6	**100**	6	15	0	**150**	10	2	6	**200**	13	10	0

250	16	17s	6d	700	47	5s	0d	1200	81	0s	0d	2000	135	0s	0
300	20	5	0	750	50	12	6	1400	94	10	0	2500	168	15	0
400	27	0	0	800	54	0	0	1500	101	5	0	3000	202	10	0
500	33	15	0	900	60	15	0	1600	108	0	0	4000	270	0	0
600	40	10s	0d	1000	67	10s	0d	1800	121	10s	0d	5000	337	10s	0

93¼% off

6¾% 6¾ PER CENT. 6¾%

1d	0s	0	4/1	0s	3¼	8/1	0s	6½	12/1	0s	9¾	16/1	1s	1
2d	0	0¼	2	0	3½	2	0	6½	2	0	9¾	2	1	1
3d	0	0¼	3	0	3½	3	0	6¾	3	0	10	3	1	1¼
4d	0	0¼	4	0	3½	4	0	6¾	4	0	10	4	1	1¼
5d	0	0¼	5	0	3½	5	0	6¾	5	0	10	5	1	1¼
6d	0	0½	4/6	0	3¾	8/6	0	7	12/6	0	10¼	16/6	1	1¼
7d	0	0½	7	0	3¾	7	0	7	7	0	10¼	7	1	1½
8d	0	0½	8	0	3¾	8	0	7	8	0	10¼	8	1	1½
9d	0	0½	9	0	3¾	9	0	7	9	0	10¼	9	1	1½
10d	0	0¾	10	0	4	10	0	7¼	10	0	10½	10	1	1¾
11d	0	0¾	11	0	4	11	0	7¼	11	0	10½	11	1	1¾
1/-	0	0¾	5/-	0	4	9/-	0	7¼	13/-	0	10½	17/-	1	1¾
1/1	0	1	5/1	0	4	1	0	7¼	1	0	10½	1	1	1¾
2	0	1	2	0	4¼	2	0	7½	2	0	10¾	2	1	2
3	0	1	3	0	4¼	3	0	7½	3	0	10¾	3	1	2
4	0	1	4	0	4¼	4	0	7½	4	0	10¾	4	1	2
5	0	1¼	5	0	4½	5	0	7¾	5	0	10¾	5	1	2
1/6	0	1¼	5/6	0	4½	9/6	0	7¾	13/6	0	11	17/6	1	2¼
7	0	1¼	7	0	4½	7	0	7¾	7	0	11	7	1	2¼
8	0	1¼	8	0	4½	8	0	7¾	8	0	11	8	1	2¼
9	0	1½	9	0	4¾	9	0	8	9	0	11¼	9	1	2½
10	0	1½	10	0	4¾	10	0	8	10	0	11¼	10	1	2½
11	0	1½	11	0	4¾	11	0	8	11	0	11¼	11	1	2½
2/-	0	1½	6/-	0	4¾	10/-	0	8	14/-	0	11¼	18/-	1	2½
2/1	0	1¾	1	0	5	10/1	0	8¼	1	0	11½	1	1	2¾
2	0	1¾	2	0	5	2	0	8¼	2	0	11½	2	1	2¾
3	0	1¾	3	0	5	3	0	8¼	3	0	11½	3	1	2¾
4	0	2	4	0	5¼	4	0	8¼	4	0	11½	4	1	2¾
5	0	2	5	0	5¼	5	0	8½	5	0	11¾	5	1	3
2/6	0	2	6/6	0	5¼	10/6	0	8½	14/6	0	11¾	18/6	1	3
7	0	2	7	0	5¼	7	0	8½	7	0	11¾	7	1	3
8	0	2¼	8	0	5½	8	0	8¾	8	1	0	8	1	3
9	0	2¼	9	0	5½	9	0	8¾	9	1	0	9	1	3¼
10	0	2¼	10	0	5½	10	0	8¾	10	1	0	10	1	3¼
11	0	2¼	11	0	5½	11	0	8¾	11	1	0	11	1	3¼
3/-	0	2½	7/-	0	5¾	11/-	0	9	15/-	1	0¼	19/-	1	3½
3/1	0	2½	1	0	5¾	1	0	9	15/1	1	0¼	1	1	3½
2	0	2½	2	0	5¾	2	0	9	2	1	0¼	2	1	3½
3	0	2¾	3	0	5¾	3	0	9	3	1	0¼	3	1	3½
4	0	2¾	4	0	6	4	0	9¼	4	1	0½	4	1	3¾
5	0	2¾	5	0	6	5	0	9¼	5	1	0½	5	1	3¾
3/6	0	2¾	7/6	0	6	11/6	0	9¼	15/6	1	0½	19/6	1	3¾
7	0	3	7	0	6¼	7	0	9½	7	1	0½	7	1	3¾
8	0	3	8	0	6¼	8	0	9½	8	1	0¾	8	1	4
9	0	3	9	0	6¼	9	0	9½	9	1	0¾	9	1	4
10	0	3	10	0	6¼	10	0	9½	10	1	0¾	10	1	4
11	0	3¼	11	0	6½	11	0	9¾	11	1	1	11	1	4¼
4/-	0	3¼	8/-	0	6½	12/-	0	9¾	16/-	1	1	20/-	1	4¼

20/6	1s	4½	25/6	1s	8¾	31/-	2s	1	35/6	2s	4¾	Guineas.		
21/-	1	5	26/-	1	9	31/6	2	1½	36/-	2	5¼	1.	1s	5
22/-	1	5¾	27/-	1	9¾	32/-	2	2	37/-	2	6	2.	2	10
22/6	1	6¼	27/6	1	10¼	32/6	2	2¼	37/6	2	6½	3.	4	3
23/-	1	6¾	28/-	1	10¾	33/-	2	2¾	38/-	2	6¾	4.	5	8
24/-	1	7½	29/-	1	11½	34/-	2	3½	39/-	2	7½	5.	7	1
25/-	1s	8¼	30/-	2s	0¼	35/-	2s	4¼	40/-	2s	8½	6.	8	6

(=6 3/10% on Gross Returns).

7 Per Cent

£1	£0	1s	4¾	£51	£3	11s	4¾	£101	£7	1s	4¾	£151	10	11s	4¾
2	0	2	9½	52	3	12	9½	102	7	2	9½	152	10	12	9½
3	0	4	2½	53	3	14	2½	103	7	4	2½	153	10	14	2½
4	0	5	7¼	54	3	15	7¼	104	7	5	7¼	154	10	15	7¼
5	0	7	0	55	3	17	0	105	7	7	0	155	10	17	0
6	0	8	4¾	56	3	18	4¾	106	7	8	4¾	156	10	18	4¾
7	0	9	9½	57	3	19	9½	107	7	9	9½	157	10	19	9½
8	0	11	2½	o8	4	1	2½	108	7	11	2½	158	11	1	2½
9	0	12	7¼	59	4	2	7¼	109	7	12	7¼	159	11	2	7¼
10	**0**	**14**	**0**	**60**	**4**	**4**	**0**	**110**	**7**	**14**	**0**	**160**	**11**	**4**	**0**
11	0	15	4¾	61	4	5	4¾	111	7	15	4¾	161	11	5	4¾
12	0	16	9½	62	4	6	9½	112	7	16	9½	162	11	6	9½
13	0	18	2½	63	4	8	2½	113	7	18	2½	163	11	8	2½
14	0	19	7¼	64	4	9	7¼	114	7	19	7¼	164	11	9	7¼
15	1	1	0	65	4	11	0	115	8	1	0	165	11	11	0
16	1	2	4¾	66	4	12	4¾	116	8	2	4¾	166	11	12	4¾
17	1	3	9½	67	4	13	9½	117	8	3	9½	167	11	13	9½
18	1	5	2½	68	4	15	2½	118	8	5	2½	168	11	15	2½
19	1	6	7¼	69	4	16	7¼	119	8	6	7¼	169	11	16	7¼
20	**1**	**8**	**0**	**70**	**4**	**18**	**0**	**120**	**8**	**8**	**0**	**170**	**11**	**18**	**0**
21	1	9	4¾	71	4	19	4¾	121	8	9	4¾	171	11	19	4¾
22	1	10	9½	72	5	0	9½	122	8	10	9½	172	12	0	9½
23	1	12	2½	73	5	2	2½	123	8	12	2½	173	12	2	2½
24	1	13	7¼	74	5	3	7¼	124	8	13	7¼	174	12	3	7¼
25	1	15	0	75	5	5	0	125	8	15	0	175	12	5	0
26	1	16	4¾	76	5	6	4¾	126	8	16	4¾	176	12	6	4¾
27	1	17	9½	77	5	7	9½	127	8	17	9½	177	12	7	9½
28	1	19	2½	78	5	9	2½	128	8	19	2½	178	12	9	2½
29	2	0	7¼	79	5	10	7¼	129	9	0	7¼	179	12	10	7¼
30	**2**	**2**	**0**	**80**	**5**	**12**	**0**	**130**	**9**	**2**	**0**	**180**	**12**	**12**	**0**
31	2	3	4¾	81	5	13	4¾	131	9	3	4¾	181	12	13	4¾
32	2	4	9½	82	5	14	9½	132	9	4	9½	182	12	14	9½
33	2	6	2½	83	5	16	2½	133	9	6	2½	183	12	16	2½
34	2	7	7¼	84	5	17	7¼	134	9	7	7¼	184	12	17	7¼
35	2	9	0	85	5	19	0	135	9	9	0	185	12	19	0
36	2	10	4¾	86	6	0	4¾	136	9	10	4¾	186	13	0	4¾
37	2	11	9½	87	6	1	9½	137	9	11	9½	187	13	1	9½
38	2	13	2½	88	6	3	2½	138	9	13	2½	188	13	3	2½
39	2	14	7¼	89	6	4	7¼	139	9	14	7¼	189	13	4	7¼
40	**2**	**16**	**0**	**90**	**6**	**6**	**0**	**140**	**9**	**16**	**0**	**190**	**13**	**6**	**0**
41	2	17	4¾	91	6	7	4¾	141	9	17	4¾	191	13	7	4¾
42	2	18	9½	92	6	8	9½	142	9	18	9½	192	13	8	9½
43	3	0	2½	93	6	10	2½	143	10	0	2½	193	13	10	2½
44	3	1	7¼	94	6	11	7¼	144	10	1	7¼	194	13	11	7¼
45	3	3	0	95	6	13	0	145	10	3	0	195	13	13	0
46	3	4	4¾	96	6	14	4¾	146	10	4	4¾	196	13	14	4¾
47	3	5	9½	97	6	15	9½	147	10	5	9½	197	13	15	9½
48	3	7	2½	98	6	17	2½	148	10	7	2½	198	13	17	2½
49	3	8	7¼	99	6	18	7¼	149	10	8	7¼	199	13	18	7¼
50	**3**	**10**	**0**	**100**	**7**	**0**	**0**	**150**	**10**	**10**	**0**	**200**	**14**	**0**	**0**

250	17	10s	0d	700	49	0s	0d	1200	84	0s	0d	2000	140	0s	0d
300	21	0	0	750	52	10	0	1400	98	0	0	2500	175	0	0
400	28	0	0	800	56	0	0	1500	105	0	0	3000	210	0	0
500	35	0	0	900	63	0	0	1600	112	0	0	4000	280	0	0
600	42	0s	0d	1000	70	0s	0d	1800	126	0s	0d	5000	350	0s	0d

93% off.

7% Seven Per Cent. 7%

1d	0s.	0	4/1	0s.	3½	8/1	0s.	6¾	12/1	0s.	10¼	16/1	1s.	1½
2d	0	0¼	2	0	3½	2	0	6¾	2	0	10¼	2	1	1½
3d	0	0¼	3	0	3½	3	0	7	3	0	10¼	3	1	1¾
4d	0	0¼	4	0	3¾	4	0	7	4	0	10¼	4	1	1¾
5d	0	0¼	5	0	3¾	5	0	7	5	0	10½	5	1	1¾
6d	0	0½	4/6	0	3¾	8/6	0	7¼	12/6	0	10½	16/6	1	1¾
7d	0	0½	7	0	3¾	7	0	7¼	7	0	10½	7	1	2
8d	0	0½	8	0	4	8	0	7¼	8	0	10¾	8	1	2
9d	0	0¾	9	0	4	9	0	7¼	9	0	10¾	9	1	2
10d	0	0¾	10	0	4	10	0	7½	10	0	10¾	10	1	2¼
11d	0	0¾	11	0	4¼	11	0	7½	11	0	10¾	11	1	2¼
1/-	0s.	0¾	**5/-**	0s.	4¼	**9/-**	0s.	7½	**13/-**	0s.	11	**17/-**	1s.	2¼
1/1	0s.	1	5/1	0s.	4¼	9/1	0s.	7¾	13/1	0s.	11	17/1	1s.	2¼
2	0	1	2	0	4¼	2	0	7¾	2	0	11	2	1	2½
3	0	1	3	0	4½	3	0	7¾	3	0	11¼	3	1	2½
4	0	1	4	0	4½	4	0	7¾	4	0	11¼	4	1	2½
5	0	1¼	5	0	4½	5	0	8	5	0	11¼	5	1	2¾
1/6	0	1¼	5/6	0	4½	9/6	0	8	13/6	0	11¼	17/6	1	2¾
7	0	1¼	7	0	4¾	7	0	8	7	0	11½	7	1	2¾
8	0	1½	8	0	4¾	8	0	8	8	0	11½	8	1	2¾
9	0	1½	9	0	4¾	9	0	8¼	9	0	11½	9	1	3
10	0	1½	10	0	5	10	0	8¼	10	0	11½	10	1	3
11	0	1½	11	0	5	11	0	8¼	11	0	11¾	11	1	3
2/-	0s.	1¾	**6/-**	0s.	5	**10/-**	0s.	8½	**14/-**	0s.	11¾	**18/-**	1s.	3
2/1	0s.	1¾	6/1	0s.	5	10/1	0s.	8½	14/1	0s.	11¾	18/1	1s.	3¼
2	0	1¾	2	0	5¼	2	0	8½	2	1	0	2	1	3¼
3	0	2	3	0	5¼	3	0	8½	3	1	0	3	1	3¼
4	0	2	4	0	5¼	4	0	8¾	4	1	0	4	1	3½
5	0	2	5	0	5½	5	0	8¾	5	1	0	5	1	3½
2/6	0	2	6/6	0	5½	10/6	0	8¾	14/6	1	0¼	18/6	1	3½
7	0	2¼	7	0	5½	7	0	9	7	1	0¼	7	1	3½
8	0	2¼	8	0	5½	8	0	9	8	1	0¼	8	1	3¾
9	0	2¼	9	0	5¾	9	0	9	9	1	0½	9	1	3¾
10	0	2½	10	0	5¾	10	0	9	10	1	0½	10	1	3¾
11	0	2½	11	0	5¾	11	0	9¼	11	1	0½	11	1	4
3/-	0s.	2½	**7/-**	0s.	6	**11/-**	0s.	9¼	**15/-**	1s.	0½	**19/-**	1s.	4
3/1	0s.	2½	7/1	0s.	6	11/1	0s.	9¼	15/1	1s.	0¾	19/1	1s.	4
2	0	2¾	2	0	6	2	0	9½	2	1	0¾	2	1	4
3	0	2¾	3	0	6	3	0	9½	3	1	0¾	3	1	4¼
4	0	2¾	4	0	6¼	4	0	9½	4	1	1	4	1	4¼
5	0	2¾	5	0	6¼	5	0	9½	5	1	1	5	1	4¼
3/6	0	3	7/6	0	6¼	11/6	0	9¾	15/6	1	1	19/6	1	4½
7	0	3	7	0	6¼	7	0	9¾	7	1	1	7	1	4½
8	0	3	8	0	6½	8	0	9¾	8	1	1¼	8	1	4½
9	0	3¼	9	0	6½	9	0	9¾	9	1	1¼	9	1	4½
10	0	3¼	10	0	6½	10	0	10	10	1	1¼	10	1	4¾
11	0	3¼	11	0	6¾	11	0	10	11	1	1¼	11	1	4¾
4/-	0s.	3¼	**8/-**	0s.	6¾	**12/-**	0s.	10	**16/-**	1s.	1½	**20/-**	1s.	4¾

20/6	1s.	5¼	25/6	1s.	9½	31/-	2s.	2	35/6	2s.	5¾	Guineas.		
21/-	1	5¾	26/-	1	9¾	31/6	2	2½	36/-	2	6¼	1.	1s.	5¾
22/-	1	6½	27/-	1	10¾	32/-	2	3	37/-	2	7	2.	2	11¼
22/6	1	7	27/6	1	11	32/6	2	3¼	37/6	2	7½	3.	4	5
23/-	1	7¼	28/-	1	11½	33/-	2	3¾	38/-	2	8	4.	5	10½
24/-	1	8¼	29/-	2	0¼	34/-	2	4½	39/-	2	8¾	5.	7	4¼
25/-	1s.	9	**30/-**	2s.	1¼	**35/-**	2s.	5½	**40/-**	2s.	9½	6.	8s.	9¾

(6½%* on Gross Returns).

£1	£0	1s	5½	£51	£3	13s	11½	£101	£7	6s	5½	£151	10	18s	11½
2	0	2	10¾	52	3	15	4¾	102	7	7	10¾	152	11	0	4¾
3	0	4	4¼	53	3	16	10¼	103	7	9	4¼	153	11	1	10¼
4	0	5	9½	54	3	18	3½	104	7	10	9½	154	11	3	3½
5	0	7	3	55	3	19	9	105	7	12	3	155	11	4	9
6	0	8	8½	56	4	1	2½	106	7	13	8½	156	11	6	2½
7	0	10	1¾	57	4	2	7¾	107	7	15	1¾	157	11	7	7¾
8	0	11	7¼	58	4	4	1¼	108	7	16	7¼	158	11	9	1¼
9	0	13	0½	59	4	5	6½	109	7	18	0½	159	11	10	6½
10	**0**	**14**	**6**	**60**	**4**	**7**	**0**	**110**	**7**	**19**	**6**	**160**	**11**	**12**	**0**
11	0	15	11½	61	4	8	5½	111	8	0	11½	161	11	13	5½
12	0	17	4¾	62	4	9	10¾	112	8	2	4¾	162	11	14	10¾
13	0	18	10¼	63	4	11	4¼	113	8	3	10¼	163	11	16	4¼
14	1	0	3½	64	4	12	9½	114	8	5	3½	164	11	17	9½
15	1	1	9	65	4	14	3	115	8	6	9	165	11	19	3
16	1	3	2½	66	4	15	8½	116	8	8	2½	166	12	0	8½
17	1	4	7¾	67	4	17	1¾	117	8	9	7¾	167	12	2	1¾
18	1	6	1¼	68	4	18	7¼	118	8	11	1¼	168	12	3	7¼
19	1	7	6½	69	5	0	0½	119	8	12	6½	169	12	5	0½
20	**1**	**9**	**0**	**70**	**5**	**1**	**6**	**120**	**8**	**14**	**0**	**170**	**12**	**6**	**6**
21	1	10	5½	71	5	2	11½	121	8	15	5½	171	12	7	11½
22	1	11	10¾	72	5	4	4¾	122	8	16	10¾	172	12	9	4¾
23	1	13	4¼	73	5	5	10¼	123	8	18	4¼	173	12	10	10¼
24	1	14	9½	74	5	7	3½	124	8	19	9½	174	12	12	3½
25	1	16	3	75	5	8	9	125	9	1	3	175	12	13	9
26	1	17	8½	76	5	10	2½	126	9	2	8½	176	12	15	2½
27	1	19	1¾	77	5	11	7¾	127	9	4	1¾	177	12	16	7¾
28	2	0	7¼	78	5	13	1¼	128	9	5	7¼	178	12	18	1¼
29	2	2	0½	79	5	14	6½	129	9	7	0½	179	12	19	6½
30	**2**	**3**	**6**	**80**	**5**	**16**	**0**	**130**	**9**	**8**	**6**	**180**	**13**	**1**	**0**
31	2	4	11½	81	5	17	5½	131	9	9	11½	181	13	2	5½
32	2	6	4¾	82	5	18	10¾	132	9	11	4¾	182	13	3	10¾
33	2	7	10¼	83	6	0	4¼	133	9	12	10¼	183	13	5	4¼
34	2	9	3½	84	6	1	9½	134	9	14	3½	184	13	6	9½
35	2	10	9	85	6	3	3	135	9	15	9	185	13	8	3
36	2	12	2½	86	6	4	8½	136	9	17	2½	186	13	9	8½
37	2	13	7¾	87	6	6	1¾	137	9	18	7¾	187	13	11	1¾
38	2	15	1¼	88	6	7	7¼	138	10	0	1¼	188	13	12	7¼
39	2	16	6½	89	6	9	0½	139	10	1	6½	189	13	14	0½
40	**2**	**18**	**0**	**90**	**6**	**10**	**6**	**140**	**10**	**3**	**0**	**190**	**13**	**15**	**6**
41	2	19	5½	91	6	11	11½	141	10	4	5½	191	13	16	11½
42	3	0	10¾	92	6	13	4¾	142	10	5	10¾	192	13	18	4¾
43	3	2	4¼	93	6	14	10¼	143	10	7	4¼	193	13	19	10¼
44	3	3	9½	94	6	16	3½	144	10	8	9½	194	14	1	3½
45	3	5	3	95	6	17	9	145	10	10	3	195	14	2	9
46	3	6	8½	96	6	19	2½	146	10	11	8½	196	14	4	2½
47	3	8	1¾	97	7	0	7¾	147	10	13	1¾	197	14	5	7¾
48	3	9	7¼	98	7	2	1¼	148	10	14	7¼	198	14	7	1¼
49	3	11	0½	99	7	3	6½	149	10	16	0½	199	14	8	6½
50	**3**	**12**	**6**	**100**	**7**	**5**	**0**	**150**	**10**	**17**	**6**	**200**	**14**	**10**	**0**

250	18	2s	6d	700	50	15s	0d	1200	87	0s	0d	2000	145	0s	0
300	21	15	0	750	54	7	6	1400	101	10	0	2500	181	5	0
400	29	0	0	800	58	0	0	1500	108	15	0	3000	217	10	0
500	36	5	0	900	65	5	0	1600	116	0	0	4000	290	0	0
600	43	10s	0d	1000	72	10s	0d	1800	130	10s	0d	5000	362	10s	0

92¾% off

7¼ Per Cent.

1d	0s	0d	4/1	0s	3½	8/1	0s	7	12/1	0s	10½	16/1	1s	2
2d	0	0¼	2	0	3¾	2	0	7	2	0	10½	2	1	2
3d	0	0¼	3	0	3¾	3	0	7¼	3	0	10¾	3	1	2¼
4d	0	0¼	4	0	3¾	4	0	7¼	4	0	10¾	4	1	2¼
5d	0	0¼	5	0	3¾	5	0	7¼	5	0	10¾	5	1	2¼
6d	0	0½	4/6	0	4	8/6	0	7½	12/6	0	11	16/6	1	2¼
7d	0	0½	7	0	4	7	0	7½	7	0	11	7	1	2½
8d	0	0½	8	0	4	8	0	7½	8	0	11	8	1	2½
9d	0	0¾	9	0	4¼	9	0	7½	9	0	11	9	1	2½
10d	0	0¾	10	0	4¼	10	0	7¾	10	0	11¼	10	1	2¾
11d	0	0¾	11	0	4¼	11	0	7¾	11	0	11¼	11	1	2¾
1/-	**0**	**0¾**	**5/-**	**0**	**4¼**	**9/-**	**0**	**7¾**	**13/-**	**0**	**11¼**	**17/-**	**1**	**2¾**
1/1	0	1	5/1	0	4½	1	0	8	1	0	11½	1	1	2¾
2	0	1	2	0	4½	2	0	8	2	0	11½	2	1	3
3	0	1	3	0	4½	3	0	8	3	0	11½	3	1	3
4	0	1¼	4	0	4¾	4	0	8	4	0	11½	4	1	3
5	0	1¼	5	0	4¾	5	0	8¼	5	0	11¾	5	1	3¼
1/6	0	1¼	5/6	0	4¾	9/6	0	8¼	13/6	0	11¾	17/6	1	3¼
7	0	1½	7	0	4¾	7	0	8¼	7	0	11¾	7	1	3¼
8	0	1½	8	0	5	8	0	8½	8	1	0	8	1	3¼
9	0	1½	9	0	5	9	0	8½	9	1	0	9	1	3½
10	0	1½	10	0	5	10	0	8½	10	1	0	10	1	3½
11	0	1¾	11	0	5¼	11	0	8¾	11	1	0	11	1	3½
2/-	**0**	**1¾**	**6/-**	**0**	**5¼**	**10/-**	**0**	**8¾**	**14/-**	**1**	**0¼**	**18/-**	**1**	**3¾**
2/1	0	1¾	1	0	5¼	10/1	0	8¾	1	1	0¼	1	1	3¾
2	0	2	2	0	5¼	2	0	8¾	2	1	0¼	2	1	3¾
3	0	2	3	0	5½	3	0	9	3	1	0½	3	1	4
4	0	2	4	0	5½	4	0	9	4	1	0½	4	1	4
5	0	2	5	0	5½	5	0	9	5	1	0½	5	1	4
2/6	0	2¼	6/6	0	5¾	10/6	0	9¼	14/6	1	0½	18/6	1	4
7	0	2¼	7	0	5¾	7	0	9¼	7	1	0¾	7	1	4¼
8	0	2¼	8	0	5¾	8	0	9¼	8	1	0¾	8	1	4¼
9	0	2½	9	0	5¾	9	0	9¼	9	1	0¾	9	1	4¼
10	0	2½	10	0	6	10	0	9½	10	1	1	10	1	4½
11	0	2½	11	0	6	11	0	9½	11	1	1	11	1	4½
3/-	**0**	**2½**	**7/-**	**0**	**6**	**11/-**	**0**	**9½**	**15/-**	**1**	**1**	**19/-**	**1**	**4½**
3/1	0	2¾	1	0	6¼	1	0	9¾	15/1	1	1	1	1	4½
2	0	2¾	2	0	6¼	2	0	9¾	2	1	1¼	2	1	4¾
3	0	2¾	3	0	6¼	3	0	9¾	3	1	1¼	3	1	4¾
4	0	3	4	0	6½	4	0	9¾	4	1	1¼	4	1	4¾
5	0	3	5	0	6½	5	0	10	5	1	1½	5	1	5
3/6	0	3	7/6	0	6½	11/6	0	10	15/6	1	1½	19/6	1	5
7	0	3	7	0	6½	7	0	10	7	1	1½	7	1	5
8	0	3¼	8	0	6¾	8	0	10¼	8	1	1¾	8	1	5
9	0	3¼	9	0	6¾	9	0	10¼	9	1	1¾	9	1	5¼
10	0	3¼	10	0	6¾	10	0	10¼	10	1	1¾	10	1	5¼
11	0	3½	11	0	7	11	0	10¼	11	1	1¾	11	1	5¼
4/-	**0**	**3½**	**8/-**	**0**	**7**	**12/-**	**0**	**10½**	**16/-**	**1**	**2**	**20/-**	**1**	**5½**

20/6	1s	5¾	25/6	1s	10¼	31/-	2s	3	35/6	2s	7	Guineas.		
21/-	1	6¼	26/-	1	10½	31/6	2	3½	36/-	2	7¼	1.	1s	6¼
22/-	1	7¼	27/-	1	11½	32/-	2	3¾	37/-	2	8¼	2.	3	0½
22/6	1	7½	27/6	2	0	32/6	2	4¼	37/6	2	8¾	3.	4	6¾
23/-	1	8	28/-	2	0¼	33/-	2	4¾	38/-	2	9	4.	6	1
24/-	1	9	29/-	2	1¼	34/-	2	5½	39/-	2	10	5.	7	7¼
25/-	1s	9¾	**30/-**	2s	2	**35/-**	2s	6½	**40/-**	2s	10¾	6.	9	1½

(=$6\frac{8}{10}$% on Gross Returns).

£1	£0	1s 6	£51	£3	16s 6	£101	£7	11s 6	£151	11	6s 6
2	0	3 0	52	3	18 0	102	7	13 0	152	11	8 0
3	0	4 6	53	3	19 6	103	7	14 6	153	11	9 6
4	0	6 0	54	4	1 0	104	7	16 0	154	11	11 0
5	0	7 6	55	4	2 6	105	7	17 6	155	11	12 6
6	0	9 0	56	4	4 0	106	7	19 0	156	11	14 0
7	0	10 6	57	4	5 6	107	8	0 6	157	11	15 6
8	0	12 0	58	4	7 0	108	8	2 0	158	11	17 0
9	0	13 6	59	4	8 6	109	8	3 6	159	11	18 6
10	0	15 0	60	4	10 0	110	8	5 0	160	12	0 0
11	0	16 6	61	4	11 6	111	8	6 6	161	12	1 6
12	0	18 0	62	4	13 0	112	8	8 0	162	12	3 0
13	0	19 6	63	4	14 6	113	8	9 6	163	12	4 6
14	1	1 0	64	4	16 0	114	8	11 0	164	12	6 0
15	1	2 6	65	4	17 6	115	8	12 6	165	12	7 6
16	1	4 0	66	4	19 0	116	8	14 0	166	12	9 0
17	1	5 6	67	5	0 6	117	8	15 6	167	12	10 6
18	1	7 0	68	5	2 0	118	8	17 0	168	12	12 0
19	1	8 6	69	5	3 6	119	8	18 6	169	12	13 6
20	1	10 0	70	5	5 0	120	9	0 0	170	12	15 0
21	1	11 6	71	5	6 6	121	9	1 6	171	12	16 6
22	1	13 0	72	5	8 0	122	9	3 0	172	12	18 0
23	1	14 6	73	5	9 6	123	9	4 6	173	12	19 6
24	1	16 0	74	5	11 0	124	9	6 0	174	13	1 0
25	1	17 6	75	5	12 6	125	9	7 6	175	13	2 6
26	1	19 0	76	5	14 0	126	9	9 0	176	13	4 0
27	2	0 6	77	5	15 6	127	9	10 6	177	13	5 6
28	2	2 0	78	5	17 0	128	9	12 0	178	13	7 0
29	2	3 6	79	5	18 6	129	9	13 6	179	13	8 6
30	2	5 0	80	6	0 0	130	9	15 0	180	13	10 0
31	2	6 6	81	6	1 6	131	9	16 6	181	13	11 6
32	2	8 0	82	6	3 0	132	9	18 0	182	13	13 0
33	2	9 6	83	6	4 6	133	9	19 6	183	13	14 6
34	2	11 0	84	6	6 0	134	10	1 0	184	13	16 0
35	2	12 6	85	6	7 6	135	10	2 6	185	13	17 6
36	2	14 0	86	6	9 0	136	10	4 0	186	13	19 0
37	2	15 6	87	6	10 6	137	10	5 6	187	14	0 6
38	2	17 0	88	6	12 0	138	10	7 0	188	14	2 0
39	2	18 6	89	6	13 6	139	10	8 6	189	14	3 6
40	3	0 0	90	6	15 0	140	10	10 0	190	14	5 0
41	3	1 6	91	6	16 6	141	10	11 6	191	14	6 6
42	3	3 0	92	6	18 0	142	10	13 0	192	14	8 0
43	3	4 6	93	6	19 6	143	10	14 6	193	14	9 6
44	3	6 0	94	7	1 0	144	10	16 0	194	14	11 0
45	3	7 6	95	7	2 6	145	10	17 6	195	14	12 6
46	3	9 0	96	7	4 0	146	10	19 0	196	14	14 0
47	3	10 6	97	7	5 6	147	11	0 6	197	14	15 6
48	3	12 0	98	7	7 0	148	11	2 0	198	14	17 0
49	3	13 6	99	7	8 6	149	11	3 6	199	14	18 6
50	3	15 0	100	7	10 0	150	11	5 0	200	15	0 0

250	18 15s 0d	700	52 10s 0d	1200	90 0s 0d	2000	150 0s 0d
300	22 10 0	750	56 5 0	1400	105 0 0	2500	187 10 0
400	30 0 0	800	60 0 0	1500	112 10 0	3000	225 0 0
500	37 10 0	900	67 10 0	1600	120 0 0	4000	300 0 0
600	45 0s 0d	1000	75 0s 0d	1800	135 0s 0d	5000	375 0s 0d

92½% off

7½% 7½ Per Cent. 7½%

1d	0s.	0	4/1	0s.	3¾	8/1	0s.	7¼	12/1	0s.	11	16/1	1s.	2½
2d	0	0¼	2	0	3¾	2	0	7¼	2	0	11	2	1	2½
3d	0	0¼	3	0	3¾	3	0	7½	3	0	11	3	1	2¾
4d	0	0¼	4	0	4	4	0	7½	4	0	11	4	1	2¾
5d	0	0½	5	0	4	5	0	7½	5	0	11¼	5	1	2¾
6d	0	0½	4/6	0	4	8/6	0	7¾	12/6	0	11¼	16/6	1	2¾
7d	0	0½	7	0	4¼	7	0	7¾	7	0	11¼	7	1	3
8d	0	0½	8	0	4¼	8	0	7¾	8	0	11½	8	1	3
9d	0	0¾	9	0	4¼	9	0	8	9	0	11½	9	1	3
10d	0	0¾	10	0	4¼	10	0	8	10	0	11½	10	1	3¼
11d	0	0¾	11	0	4½	11	0	8	11	0	11¾	11	1	3¼
1/-	0s.	1	**5/-**	0s.	4½	**9/-**	0s.	8	**13/-**	0s.	11¾	**17/-**	1s.	3¼
1/1	0s.	1	5/1	0s.	4½	9/1	0s.	8¼	13/1	0s.	11¾	17/1	1s.	3½
2	0	1	2	0	4¾	2	0	8¼	2	0	11¾	2	1	3½
3	0	1¼	3	0	4¾	3	0	8¼	3	1	0	3	1	3½
4	0	1¼	4	0	4¾	4	0	8½	4	1	0	4	1	3½
5	0	1¼	5	0	5	5	0	8½	5	1	0	5	1	3¾
1/6	0	1¼	5/6	0	5	9/6	0	8½	13/6	1	0¼	17/6	1	3¾
7	0	1½	7	0	5	7	0	8¾	7	1	0¼	7	1	3¾
8	0	1½	8	0	5	8	0	8¾	8	1	0¼	8	1	4
9	0	1½	9	0	5¼	9	0	8¾	9	1	0½	9	1	4
10	0	1¾	10	0	5¼	10	0	8¾	10	1	0½	10	1	4
11	0	1¾	11	0	5¼	11	0	9	11	1	0½	11	1	4¼
2/-	0s.	1¾	**6/-**	0s.	5½	**10/-**	0s.	9	**14/-**	1s.	0½	**18/-**	1s.	4¼
2/1	0s.	2	6/1	0s.	5½	10/1	0s.	9	14/1	1s.	0¾	18/1	1s.	4¼
2	0	2	2	0	5½	2	0	9¼	2	1	0¾	2	1	4¼
3	0	2	3	0	5¾	3	0	9¼	3	1	0¾	3	1	4½
4	0	2	4	0	5¾	4	0	9¼	4	1	1	4	1	4½
5	0	2¼	5	0	5¾	5	0	9½	5	1	1	5	1	4½
2/6	0	2¼	6/6	0	5¾	10/6	0	9½	14/6	1	1	18/6	1	4¾
7	0	2¼	7	0	6	7	0	9½	7	1	1¼	7	1	4¾
8	0	2½	8	0	6	8	0	9½	8	1	1¼	8	1	4¾
9	0	2½	9	0	6	9	0	9¾	9	1	1¼	9	1	5
10	0	2½	10	0	6¼	10	0	9¾	10	1	1¼	10	1	5
11	0	2¾	11	0	6¼	11	0	9¾	11	1	1½	11	1	5
3/-	0s.	2¾	**7/-**	0s.	6¼	**11/-**	0s.	10	**15/-**	1s.	1½	**19/-**	1s.	5
3/1	0s.	2¾	7/1	0s.	6½	11/1	0s.	10	15/1	1s.	1½	19/1	1s.	5¼
2	0	2¾	2	0	6½	2	0	10	2	1	1¾	2	1	5¼
3	0	3	3	0	6½	3	0	10¼	3	1	1¾	3	1	5¼
4	0	3	4	0	6½	4	0	10¼	4	1	1¾	4	1	5½
5	0	3	5	0	6¾	5	0	10¼	5	1	2	5	1	5½
3/6	0	3¼	7/6	0	6¾	11/6	0	10¼	15/6	1	2	19/6	1	5½
7	0	3¼	7	0	6¾	7	0	10½	7	1	2	7	1	5¾
8	0	3¼	8	0	7	8	0	10½	8	1	2	8	1	5¾
9	0	3½	9	0	7	9	0	10½	9	1	2¼	9	1	5¾
10	0	3½	10	0	7	10	0	10¾	10	1	2¼	10	1	5¾
11	0	3½	11	0	7¼	11	0	10¾	11	1	2¼	11	1	6
4/-	0s.	3½	**8/-**	0s.	7¼	**12/-**	0s.	10¾	**16/-**	1s.	2½	**20/-**	1s.	6

20/6	1s.	6½	25/6	1s.	11	31/-	2s.	4	35/6	2s.	8	Guineas.		
21/-	1	7	26/-	1	11½	31/6	2	4¼	36/-	2	8½	1.	1s.	7
22/-	1	7¾	27/-	2	0¼	32/-	2	4¾	37/-	2	9¼	2.	3	1¾
22/6	1	8¼	27/6	2	0¾	32/6	2	5¼	37/6	2	9¾	3.	4	8¾
23/-	1	8¾	28/-	2	1¼	33/-	2	5¾	38/-	2	10¼	4.	6	3½
24/-	1	9½	29/-	2	2	34/-	2	6½	39/-	2	11	5.	7	10½
25/-	1s.	10½	**30/-**	2s.	3	**35/-**	2s.	7½	**40/-**	3s.	0	6.	9s.	5½

(7%* on Gross Returns).

£1	£0	1s	6½	£51	£3	19s	0½	£101	£7	16s	6½	£151	11	14s	0½
2	0	3	1¼	52	4	0	7¼	102	7	18	1¼	152	11	15	7¼
3	0	4	7¾	53	4	2	1¾	103	7	19	7¾	153	11	17	1¾
4	0	6	2½	54	4	3	8½	104	8	1	2½	154	11	18	8½
5	0	7	9	55	4	5	3	105	8	2	9	155	12	0	3
6	0	9	3½	56	4	6	9½	106	8	4	3½	156	12	1	9½
7	0	10	10¼	57	4	8	4¼	107	8	5	10¼	157	12	3	4¼
8	0	12	4¾	58	4	9	10¾	108	8	7	4¾	158	12	4	10¾
9	0	13	11½	59	4	11	5½	109	8	8	11½	159	12	6	5½
10	0	15	6	60	4	13	0	110	8	10	6	160	12	8	0
11	0	17	0½	61	4	14	6½	111	8	12	0½	161	12	9	6½
12	0	18	7¼	62	4	16	1¼	112	8	13	7¼	162	12	11	1¼
13	1	0	1¾	63	4	17	7¾	113	8	15	1¾	163	12	12	7¾
14	1	1	8½	64	4	19	2½	114	8	16	8½	164	12	14	2½
15	1	3	3	65	5	0	9	115	8	18	3	165	12	15	9
16	1	4	9½	66	5	2	3½	116	8	19	9½	166	12	17	3½
17	1	6	4¼	67	5	3	10¼	117	9	1	4¼	167	12	18	10¼
18	1	7	10¾	68	5	5	4¾	118	9	2	10¾	168	13	0	4¾
19	1	9	5½	69	5	6	11½	119	9	4	5½	169	13	1	11½
20	1	11	0	70	5	8	6	120	9	6	0	170	13	3	6
21	1	12	6½	71	5	10	0½	121	9	7	6½	171	13	5	0½
22	1	14	1¼	72	5	11	7¼	122	9	9	1¼	172	13	6	7¼
23	1	15	7¾	73	5	13	1¾	123	9	10	7¾	173	13	8	1¾
24	1	17	2½	74	5	14	8½	124	9	12	2½	174	13	9	8½
25	1	18	9	75	5	16	3	125	9	13	9	175	13	11	3
26	2	0	3½	76	5	17	9½	126	9	15	3½	176	13	12	9½
27	2	1	10¼	77	5	19	4¼	127	9	16	10¼	177	13	14	4¼
28	2	3	4¾	78	6	0	10¾	128	9	18	4¾	178	13	15	10¾
29	2	4	11½	79	6	2	5½	129	9	19	11½	179	13	17	5½
30	2	6	6	80	6	4	0	130	10	1	6	180	13	19	0
31	2	8	0½	81	6	5	6½	131	10	3	0½	181	14	0	6½
32	2	9	7¼	82	6	7	1¼	132	10	4	7¼	182	14	2	1¼
33	2	11	1¾	83	6	8	7¾	133	10	6	1¾	183	14	3	7¾
34	2	12	8½	84	6	10	2½	134	10	7	8½	184	14	5	2½
35	2	14	3	85	6	11	9	135	10	9	3	185	14	6	9
36	2	15	9½	86	6	13	3½	136	10	10	9½	186	14	8	3½
37	2	17	4¼	87	6	14	10¼	137	10	12	4¼	187	14	9	10¼
38	2	18	10¾	88	6	16	4¾	138	10	13	10¾	188	14	11	4¾
39	3	0	5½	89	6	17	11½	139	10	15	5½	189	14	12	11½
40	3	2	0	90	6	19	6	140	10	17	0	190	14	14	6
41	3	3	6½	91	7	1	0½	141	10	18	6½	191	14	16	0½
42	3	5	1¼	92	7	2	7¼	142	11	0	1¼	192	14	17	7¼
43	3	6	7¾	93	7	4	1¾	143	11	1	7¾	193	14	19	1¾
44	3	8	2½	94	7	5	8½	144	11	3	2½	194	15	0	8½
45	3	9	9	95	7	7	3	145	11	4	9	195	15	2	3
46	3	11	3½	96	7	8	9½	146	11	6	3½	196	15	3	9½
47	3	12	10¼	97	7	10	4¼	147	11	7	10¼	197	15	5	4¼
48	3	14	4¾	98	7	11	10¾	148	11	9	4¾	198	15	6	10¾
49	3	15	11½	99	7	13	5½	149	11	10	11½	199	15	8	5½
50	3	17	6	100	7	15	0	150	11	12	6	200	15	10	0

250	19	7s	6d	700	54	5s	0d	1200	93	0s	0d	2000	155	0s	0
300	23	5	0	750	58	2	6	1400	108	10	0	2500	193	15	0
400	31	0	0	800	62	0	0	1500	116	5	0	3000	232	10	0
500	38	15	0	900	69	15	0	1600	124	0	0	4000	310	0	0
600	46	10s	0d	1000	77	10s	0d	1800	139	10s	0d	5000	387	10s	0

92¼% off

7¾ Per Cent.

7¾%

1d	0s	0	4/1	0s	3¾	8/1	0s	7½	12/1	0s	11¼	16/1	1s	3
2d	0	0¼	2	0	4	2	0	7½	2	0	11¼	2	1	3
3d	0	0¼	3	0	4	3	0	7¾	3	0	11½	3	1	3
4d	0	0¼	4	0	4	4	0	7¾	4	0	11½	4	1	3¼
5d	0	0½	5	0	4	5	0	7¾	5	0	11½	5	1	3¼
6d	0	0½	4/6	0	4¼	8/6	0	8	12/6	0	11¾	16/6	1	3¼
7d	0	0½	7	0	4¼	7	0	8	7	0	11¾	7	1	3½
8d	0	0½	8	0	4¼	8	0	8	8	0	11¾	8	1	3½
9d	0	0¾	9	0	4½	9	0	8¼	9	0	11¾	9	1	3½
10d	0	0¾	10	0	4½	10	0	8¼	10	1	0	10	1	3¾
11d	0	0¾	11	0	4½	11	0	8¼	11	1	0	11	1	3¾
1/-	**0**	**1**	**5/-**	**0**	**4¾**	**9/-**	**0**	**8¼**	**13/-**	**1**	**0**	**17/-**	**1**	**3¾**
1/1	0	1	5/1	0	4¾	9/1	0	8½	13/1	1	0¼	17/1	1	4
2	0	1	2	0	4¾	2	0	8½	2	1	0¼	2	1	4
3	0	1¼	3	0	5	3	0	8½	3	1	0¼	3	1	4
4	0	1¼	4	0	5	4	0	8¾	4	1	0½	4	1	4
5	0	1¼	5	0	5	5	0	8¾	5	1	0½	5	1	4¼
1/6	0	1½	5/6	0	5	9/6	0	8¾	13/6	1	0½	17/6	1	4¼
7	0	1½	7	0	5¼	7	0	9	7	1	0¾	7	1	4¼
8	0	1½	8	0	5¼	8	0	9	8	1	0¾	8	1	4½
9	0	1¾	9	0	5¼	9	0	9	9	1	0¾	9	1	4½
10	0	1¾	10	0	5½	10	0	9¼	10	1	0¾	10	1	4½
11	0	1¾	11	0	5½	11	0	9¼	11	1	1	11	1	4¾
2/-	**0**	**1¾**	**6/-**	**0**	**5½**	**10/-**	**0**	**9¼**	**14/-**	**1**	**1**	**18/-**	**1**	**4¾**
2/1	0	2	6/1	0	5¾	10/1	0	9½	14/1	1	1	18/1	1	4¾
2	0	2	2	0	5¾	2	0	9½	2	1	1¼	2	1	5
3	0	2	3	0	5¾	3	0	9½	3	1	1¼	3	1	5
4	0	2¼	4	0	6	4	0	9½	4	1	1¼	4	1	5
5	0	2¼	5	0	6	5	0	9¾	5	1	1½	5	1	5¼
2/6	0	2¼	6/6	0	6	10/6	0	9¾	14/6	1	1½	18/6	1	5¼
7	0	2½	7	0	6	7	0	9¾	7	1	1½	7	1	5¼
8	0	2½	8	0	6¼	8	0	10	8	1	1¾	8	1	5¼
9	0	2½	9	0	6¼	9	0	10	9	1	1¾	9	1	5½
10	0	2¾	10	0	6¼	10	0	10	10	1	1¾	10	1	5½
11	0	2¾	11	0	6½	11	0	10¼	11	1	1¾	11	1	5½
3/-	**0**	**2¾**	**7/-**	**0**	**6½**	**11/-**	**0**	**10¼**	**15/-**	**1**	**2**	**19/-**	**1**	**5¾**
3/1	0	2¾	7/1	0	6½	11/1	0	10¼	15/1	1	2	19/1	1	5¾
2	0	3	2	0	6¾	2	0	10½	2	1	2	2	1	5¾
3	0	3	3	0	6¾	3	0	10½	3	1	2¼	3	1	6
4	0	3	4	0	6¾	4	0	10½	4	1	2¼	4	1	6
5	0	3¼	5	0	7	5	0	10½	5	1	2¼	5	1	6
3/6	0	3¼	7/6	0	7	11/6	0	10¾	15/6	1	2½	19/6	1	6¼
7	0	3¼	7	0	7	7	0	10¾	7	1	2½	7	1	6¼
8	0	3½	8	0	7¼	8	0	10¾	8	1	2½	8	1	6¼
9	0	3½	9	0	7¼	9	0	11	9	1	2¾	9	1	6¼
10	0	3½	10	0	7¼	10	0	11	10	1	2¾	10	1	6½
11	0	3¾	11	0	7¼	11	0	11	11	1	2¾	11	1	6½
4/-	**0**	**3¾**	**8/-**	**0**	**7½**	**12/-**	**0**	**11¼**	**16/-**	**1**	**3**	**20/-**	**1**	**6½**

												Guineas			
20/6	1s	7	25/6	1s	11¾	31/-	2s	4¾	35/6	2s	9				
21/-	1	7½	26/-	2	0¼	31/6	2	5¼	36/-	2	9½	**1.**	£0	1	7½
22/-	1	8½	27/-	2	1	32/-	2	5¾	37/-	2	10½	**2.**	0	3	3
22/6	1	9	27/6	2	1½	32/6	2	6¼	37/6	2	11	**3.**	0	4	10½
23/-	1	9½	28/-	2	2	33/-	2	6¾	38/-	2	11¼	**4.**	0	6	6
24/-	1	10¼	29/-	2	3	34/-	2	7½	39/-	3	0¼	**5.**	0	8	1¾
25/-	1s	11¼	**30/-**	2s	4	**35/-**	2s	8½	**40/-**	3s	1¼	**6.**	£0	9	9¼

(=7 2/10% on Gross Returns).

£	£	s	d	£	£	s	d	£	£	s	d	£	£	s	d
1	£0	1s	7¼	51	£4	1s	7¼	101	£8	1s	7¼	151	12	1s	7¼
2	0	3	2½	52	4	3	2½	102	8	3	2½	152	12	3	2½
3	0	4	9½	53	4	4	9½	103	8	4	9½	153	12	4	9½
4	0	6	4¾	54	4	6	4¾	104	8	6	4¾	154	12	6	4¾
5	0	8	0	55	4	8	0	105	8	8	0	155	12	8	0
6	0	9	7¼	56	4	9	7¼	106	8	9	7¼	156	12	9	7¼
7	0	11	2½	57	4	11	2½	107	8	11	2½	157	12	11	2½
8	0	12	9½	58	4	12	9½	108	8	12	9½	158	12	12	9½
9	0	14	4¾	59	4	14	4¾	109	8	14	4¾	159	12	14	4¾
10	0	16	0	60	4	16	0	110	8	16	0	160	12	16	0
11	0	17	7¼	61	4	17	7¼	111	8	17	7¼	161	12	17	7¼
12	0	19	2½	62	4	19	2½	112	8	19	2½	162	12	19	2½
13	1	0	9½	63	5	0	9½	113	9	0	9½	163	13	0	9½
14	1	2	4¾	64	5	2	4¾	114	9	2	4¾	164	13	2	4¾
15	1	4	0	65	5	4	0	115	9	4	0	165	13	4	0
16	1	5	7¼	66	5	5	7¼	116	9	5	7¼	166	13	5	7¼
17	1	7	2½	67	5	7	2½	117	9	7	2½	167	13	7	2½
18	1	8	9½	68	5	8	9½	118	9	8	9½	168	13	8	9½
19	1	10	4¾	69	5	10	4¾	119	9	10	4¾	169	13	10	4¾
20	1	12	0	70	5	12	0	120	9	12	0	170	13	12	0
21	1	13	7¼	71	5	13	7¼	121	9	13	7¼	171	13	13	7¼
22	1	15	2½	72	5	15	2½	122	9	15	2½	172	13	15	2½
23	1	16	9½	73	5	16	9½	123	9	16	9½	173	13	16	9½
24	1	18	4¾	74	5	18	4¾	124	9	18	4¾	174	13	18	4¾
25	2	0	0	75	6	0	0	125	10	0	0	175	14	0	0
26	2	1	7¼	76	6	1	7¼	126	10	1	7¼	176	14	1	7¼
27	2	3	2½	77	6	3	2½	127	10	3	2½	177	14	3	2½
28	2	4	9½	78	6	4	9½	128	10	4	9½	178	14	4	9½
29	2	6	4¾	79	6	6	4¾	129	10	6	4¾	179	14	6	4¾
30	2	8	0	80	6	8	0	130	10	8	0	180	14	8	0
31	2	9	7¼	81	6	9	7¼	131	10	9	7¼	181	14	9	7¼
32	2	11	2½	82	6	11	2½	132	10	11	2½	182	14	11	2½
33	2	12	9½	83	6	12	9½	133	10	12	9½	183	14	12	9½
34	2	14	4¾	84	6	14	4¾	134	10	14	4¾	184	14	14	4¾
35	2	16	0	85	6	16	0	135	10	16	0	185	14	16	0
36	2	17	7¼	86	6	17	7¼	136	10	17	7¼	186	14	17	7¼
37	2	19	2½	87	6	19	2½	137	10	19	2½	187	14	19	2½
38	3	0	9½	88	7	0	9½	138	11	0	9½	188	15	0	9½
39	3	2	4¾	89	7	2	4¾	139	11	2	4¾	189	15	2	4¾
40	3	4	0	90	7	4	0	140	11	4	0	190	15	4	0
41	3	5	7¼	91	7	5	7¼	141	11	5	7¼	191	15	5	7¼
42	3	7	2½	92	7	7	2½	142	11	7	2½	192	15	7	2½
43	3	8	9½	93	7	8	9½	143	11	8	9½	193	15	8	9½
44	3	10	4¾	94	7	10	4¾	144	11	10	4¾	194	15	10	4¾
45	3	12	0	95	7	12	0	145	11	12	0	195	15	12	0
46	3	13	7¼	96	7	13	7¼	146	11	13	7¼	196	15	13	7¼
47	3	15	2½	97	7	15	2½	147	11	15	2½	197	15	15	2½
48	3	16	9½	98	7	16	9½	148	11	16	9½	198	15	16	9½
49	3	18	4¾	99	7	18	4¾	149	11	18	4¾	199	15	18	4¾
50	4	0	0	100	8	0	0	150	12	0	0	200	16	0	0

£	£	s	d	£	£	s	d	£	£	s	d	£	£	s	d
250	20	0s	0d	700	56	0s	0d	1200	96	0s	0d	2000	160	0s	0d
300	24	0	0	750	60	0	0	1400	112	0	0	2500	200	0	0
400	32	0	0	800	64	0	0	1500	120	0	0	3000	240	0	0
500	40	0	0	900	72	0	0	1600	128	0	0	4000	320	0	0
600	48	0s	0d	1000	80	0s	0d	1800	144	0s	0d	5000	400	0s	0d

92% off.

8% EIGHT PER CENT. 8%

1d	0s.	0	4/1	0s.	4	8/1	0s.	7¾	12/1	0s.	11½	16/1	1s.	3½
2d	0	0¼	2	0	4	2	0	7¾	2	0	11¾	2	1	3½
3d	0	0¼	3	0	4	3	0	8	3	0	11¾	3	1	3½
4d	0	0¼	4	0	4¼	4	0	8	4	0	11¾	4	1	3¾
5d	0	0½	5	0	4¼	5	0	8	5	1	0	5	1	3¾
6d	0	0½	4/6	0	4¼	8/6	0	8¼	12/6	1	0	16/6	1	3¾
7d	0	0½	7	0	4½	7	0	8¼	7	1	0	7	1	4
8d	0	0¾	8	0	4½	8	0	8¼	8	1	0¼	8	1	4
9d	0	0¾	9	0	4½	9	0	8½	9	1	0¼	9	1	4
10d	0	0¾	10	0	4¾	10	0	8½	10	1	0¼	10	1	4¼
11d	0	1	11	0	4¾	11	0	8½	11	1	0½	11	1	4¼
1/-	0s.	1	**5/-**	0s.	4¾	**9/-**	0s.	8¾	**13/-**	1s.	0½	**17/-**	1s.	4¼
1/1	0s.	1	5/1	0s.	5	9/1	0s.	8¾	13/1	1s.	0½	17/1	1s.	4½
2	0	1	2	0	5	2	0	8¾	2	1	0¾	2	1	4½
3	0	1¼	3	0	5	3	0	9	3	1	0¾	3	1	4½
4	0	1¼	4	0	5	4	0	9	4	1	0¾	4	1	4¾
5	0	1¼	5	0	5¼	5	0	9	5	1	1	5	1	4¾
1/6	0	1½	5/6	0	5¼	9/6	0	9	13/6	1	1	17/6	1	4¾
7	0	1½	7	0	5¼	7	0	9¼	7	1	1	7	1	5
8	0	1½	8	0	5½	8	0	9¼	8	1	1	8	1	5
9	0	1¾	9	0	5½	9	0	9¼	9	1	1¼	9	1	5
10	0	1¾	10	0	5½	10	0	9½	10	1	1¼	10	1	5
11	0	1¾	11	0	5¾	11	0	9½	11	1	1¼	11	1	5¼
2/-	0s.	2	**6/-**	0s.	5¾	**10/-**	0s.	9½	**14/-**	1s.	1½	**18/-**	1s.	5¼
2/1	0s.	2	6/1	0s.	5¾	10/1	0s.	9¾	14/1	1s.	1½	18/1	1s.	5¼
2	0	2	2	0	6	2	0	9¾	2	1	1½	2	1	5½
3	0	2¼	3	0	6	3	0	9¾	3	1	1¾	3	1	5½
4	0	2¼	4	0	6	4	0	10	4	1	1¾	4	1	5½
5	0	2¼	5	0	6¼	5	0	10	5	1	1¾	5	1	5¾
2/6	0	2½	6/6	0	6¼	10/6	0	10	14/6	1	2	18/6	1	5¾
7	0	2½	7	0	6¼	7	0	10¼	7	1	2	7	1	5¾
8	0	2½	8	0	6½	8	0	10¼	8	1	2	8	1	6
9	0	2¾	9	0	6½	9	0	10¼	9	1	2¼	9	1	6
10	0	2¾	10	0	6½	10	0	10½	10	1	2¼	10	1	6
11	0	2¾	11	0	6¾	11	0	10½	11	1	2¼	11	1	6¼
3/-	0s.	3	**7/-**	0s.	6¾	**11/-**	0s.	10½	**15/-**	1s.	2½	**19/-**	1s.	6¼
3/1	0s.	3	7/1	0s.	6¾	11/1	0s.	10¾	15/1	1s.	2½	19/1	1s.	6¼
2	0	3	2	0	7	2	0	10¾	2	1	2½	2	1	6½
3	0	3	3	0	7	3	0	10¾	3	1	2¾	3	1	6½
4	0	3¼	4	0	7	4	0	11	4	1	2¾	4	1	6½
5	0	3¼	5	0	7	5	0	11	5	1	2¾	5	1	6¾
3/6	0	3¼	7/6	0	7¼	11/6	0	11	15/6	1	3	19/6	1	6¾
7	0	3½	7	0	7¼	7	0	11	7	1	3	7	1	6¾
8	0	3½	8	0	7¼	8	0	11¼	8	1	3	8	1	7
9	0	3½	9	0	7½	9	0	11¼	9	1	3	9	1	7
10	0	3¾	10	0	7½	10	0	11¼	10	1	3¼	10	1	7
11	0	3¾	11	0	7½	11	0	11½	11	1	3¼	11	1	7
4/-	0s.	3¾	**8/-**	0s.	7¾	**12/-**	0s.	11½	**16/-**	1s.	3¼	**20/-**	1s.	7¼

20/6	1s.	7¾	25/6	2s.	0½	31/-	2s.	5¾	35/6	2s.	10	Guineas.		
21/-	1	8¼	26/-	2	1	31/6	2	6¼	36/-	2	10½	1.	1s.	8¼
22/-	1	9	27/-	2	2	32/-	2	6¾	37/-	2	11½	2.	3	4¼
22/6	1	9½	27/6	2	2½	32/6	2	7¼	37/6	3	0	3.	5	0½
23/-	1	10	28/-	2	3	33/-	2	7¾	38/-	3	0½	4.	6	8¾
24/-	1	11	29/-	2	3¾	34/-	2	8¾	39/-	3	1½	5.	8	4¾
25/-	2s.	0	**30/-**	2s.	4¾	**35/-**	2s.	9½	**40/-**	3s.	2½	6.	10s.	1

(=7 4/10 %* on Gross Returns).

£	£ s d	£	£ s d	£	£ s d	£	£ s d
£1	£0 1s 8	£51	£4 5s 0	£101	£8 8s 4	£151	12 11s 8
2	0 3 4	52	4 6 8	102	8 10 0	152	12 13 4
3	0 5 0	53	4 8 4	103	8 11 8	153	12 15 0
4	0 6 8	54	4 10 0	104	8 13 4	154	12 16 8
5	0 8 4	55	4 11 8	105	8 15 0	155	12 18 4
6	0 10 0	56	4 13 4	106	8 16 8	156	13 0 0
7	0 11 8	57	4 15 0	107	8 18 4	157	13 1 8
8	0 13 4	58	4 16 8	108	9 0 0	158	13 3 4
9	0 15 0	59	4 18 4	109	9 1 8	159	13 5 0
10	0 16 8	60	5 0 0	110	9 3 4	160	13 6 8
11	0 18 4	61	5 1 8	111	9 5 0	161	13 8 4
12	1 0 0	62	5 3 4	112	9 6 8	162	13 10 0
13	1 1 8	63	5 5 0	113	9 8 4	163	13 11 8
14	1 3 4	64	5 6 8	114	9 10 0	164	13 13 4
15	1 5 0	65	5 8 4	115	9 11 8	165	13 15 0
16	1 6 8	66	5 10 0	116	9 13 4	166	13 16 8
17	1 8 4	67	5 11 8	117	9 15 0	167	13 18 4
18	1 10 0	68	5 13 4	118	9 16 8	168	14 0 0
19	1 11 8	69	5 15 0	119	9 18 4	169	14 1 8
20	1 13 4	70	5 16 8	120	10 0 0	170	14 3 4
21	1 15 0	71	5 18 4	121	10 1 8	171	14 5 0
22	1 16 8	72	6 0 0	122	10 3 4	172	14 6 8
23	1 18 4	73	6 1 8	123	10 5 0	173	14 8 4
24	2 0 0	74	6 3 4	124	10 6 8	174	14 10 0
25	2 1 8	75	6 5 0	125	10 8 4	175	14 11 8
26	2 3 4	76	6 6 8	126	10 10 0	176	14 13 4
27	2 5 0	77	6 8 4	127	10 11 8	177	14 15 0
28	2 6 8	78	6 10 0	128	10 13 4	178	14 16 8
29	2 8 4	79	6 11 8	129	10 15 0	179	14 18 4
30	2 10 0	80	6 13 4	130	10 16 8	180	15 0 0
31	2 11 8	81	6 15 0	131	10 18 4	181	15 1 8
32	2 13 4	82	6 16 8	132	11 0 0	182	15 3 4
33	2 15 0	83	6 18 4	133	11 1 8	183	15 5 0
34	2 16 8	84	7 0 0	134	11 3 4	184	15 6 8
35	2 18 4	85	7 1 8	135	11 5 0	185	15 8 4
36	3 0 0	86	7 3 4	136	11 6 8	186	15 10 0
37	3 1 8	87	7 5 0	137	11 8 4	187	15 11 8
38	3 3 4	88	7 6 8	138	11 10 0	188	15 13 4
39	3 5 0	89	7 8 4	139	11 11 8	189	15 15 0
40	3 6 8	90	7 10 0	140	11 13 4	190	15 16 8
41	3 8 4	91	7 11 8	141	11 15 0	191	15 18 4
42	3 10 0	92	7 13 4	142	11 16 8	192	16 0 0
43	3 11 8	93	7 15 0	143	11 18 4	193	16 1 8
44	3 13 4	94	7 16 8	144	12 0 0	194	16 3 4
45	3 15 0	95	7 18 4	145	12 1 8	195	16 5 0
46	3 16 8	96	8 0 0	146	12 3 4	196	16 6 8
47	3 18 4	97	8 1 8	147	12 5 0	197	16 8 4
48	4 0 0	98	8 3 4	148	12 6 8	198	16 10 0
49	4 1 8	99	8 5 0	149	12 8 4	199	16 11 8
50	4 3 4	100	8 6 8	150	12 10 0	200	16 13 4

£	£ s d	£	£ s d	£	£ s d	£	£ s d
250	20 16s 8d	700	58 6s 8d	1200	100 0s 0d	2000	166 13s 4
300	25 0 0	750	62 10 0	1400	116 13 4	2500	208 6 8
400	33 6 8	800	66 13 4	1500	125 0 0	3000	250 0 0
500	41 13 4	900	75 0 0	1600	133 6 8	4000	333 6 8
600	50 0s 0d	1000	83 6s 8d	1800	150 0s 0d	5000	416 13s 4

91⅔% off.   (8⅓% = 1·12tn).

1d	0s	0d	4/1	0s	4d	8/1	0s	8d	12/1	1s	0d	16/1	1s	4d
2d	0	0¼	2	0	4¼	2	0	8¼	2	1	0¼	2	1	4¼
3d	0	0¼	3	0	4¼	3	0	8¼	3	1	0¼	3	1	4¼
4d	0	0¼	4	0	4¼	4	0	8¼	4	1	0¼	4	1	4¼
5d	0	0½	5	0	4½	5	0	8½	5	1	0½	5	1	4½
6d	0	0½	4/6	0	4½	8/6	0	8½	12/6	1	0½	16/6	1	4½
7d	0	0½	7	0	4½	7	0	8½	7	1	0½	7	1	4½
8d	0	0¾	8	0	4¾	8	0	8¾	8	1	0¾	8	1	4¾
9d	0	0¾	9	0	4¾	9	0	8¾	9	1	0¾	9	1	4¾
10d	0	0¾	10	0	4¾	10	0	8¾	10	1	0¾	10	1	4¾
11d	0	1	11	0	5	11	0	9	11	1	1	11	1	5
1/-	**0**	**1**	**5/-**	**0**	**5**	**9/-**	**0**	**9**	**13/-**	**1**	**1**	**17/-**	**1**	**5**
1/1	0	1	5/1	0	5	9/1	0	9	13/1	1	1	17/1	1	5
2	0	1¼	2	0	5¼	2	0	9¼	2	1	1¼	2	1	5¼
3	0	1¼	3	0	5¼	3	0	9¼	3	1	1¼	3	1	5¼
4	0	1¼	4	0	5¼	4	0	9¼	4	1	1¼	4	1	5¼
5	0	1½	5	0	5½	5	0	9½	5	1	1½	5	1	5½
1/6	0	1½	5/6	0	5½	9/6	0	9½	13/6	1	1½	17/6	1	5½
7	0	1½	7	0	5½	7	0	9½	7	1	1½	7	1	5½
8	0	1¾	8	0	5¾	8	0	9¾	8	1	1¾	8	1	5¾
9	0	1¾	9	0	5¾	9	0	9¾	9	1	1¾	9	1	5¾
10	0	1¾	10	0	5¾	10	0	9¾	10	1	1¾	10	1	5¾
11	0	2	11	0	6	11	0	10	11	1	2	11	1	6
2/-	**0**	**2**	**6/-**	**0**	**6**	**10/-**	**0**	**10**	**14/-**	**1**	**2**	**18/-**	**1**	**6**
2/1	0	2	6/1	0	6	10/1	0	10	14/1	1	2	18/1	1	6
2	0	2¼	2	0	6¼	2	0	10¼	2	1	2¼	2	1	6¼
3	0	2¼	3	0	6¼	3	0	10¼	3	1	2¼	3	1	6¼
4	0	2¼	4	0	6¼	4	0	10¼	4	1	2¼	4	1	6¼
5	0	2½	5	0	6½	5	0	10½	5	1	2½	5	1	6½
2/6	0	2½	6/6	0	6½	10/6	0	10½	14/6	1	2½	18/6	1	6½
7	0	2½	7	0	6½	7	0	10½	7	1	2½	7	1	6½
8	0	2¾	8	0	6¾	8	0	10¾	8	1	2¾	8	1	6¾
9	0	2¾	9	0	6¾	9	0	10¾	9	1	2¾	9	1	6¾
10	0	2¾	10	0	6¾	10	0	10¾	10	1	2¾	10	1	6¾
11	0	3	11	0	7	11	0	11	11	1	3	11	1	7
3/-	**0**	**3**	**7/-**	**0**	**7**	**11/-**	**0**	**11**	**15/-**	**1**	**3**	**19/-**	**1**	**7**
3/1	0	3	7/1	0	7	11/1	0	11	15/1	1	3	19/1	1	7
2	0	3¼	2	0	7¼	2	0	11¼	2	1	3¼	2	1	7¼
3	0	3¼	3	0	7¼	3	0	11¼	3	1	3¼	3	1	7¼
4	0	3¼	4	0	7¼	4	0	11¼	4	1	3¼	4	1	7¼
5	0	3½	5	0	7½	5	0	11½	5	1	3½	5	1	7½
3/6	0	3½	7/6	0	7½	11/6	0	11½	15/6	1	3½	19/6	1	7½
7	0	3½	7	0	7½	7	0	11½	7	1	3½	7	1	7½
8	0	3¾	8	0	7¾	8	0	11¾	8	1	3¾	8	1	7¾
9	0	3¾	9	0	7¾	9	0	11¾	9	1	3¾	9	1	7¾
10	0	3¾	10	0	7¾	10	0	11¾	10	1	3¾	10	1	7¾
11	0	4	11	0	8	11	1	0	11	1	4	11	1	8
4/-	**0**	**4**	**8/-**	**0**	**8**	**12/-**	**1**	**0**	**16/-**	**1**	**4**	**20/-**	**1**	**8**

20/6	1s	8½	25/6	2s	1½	31/-	2s	7	35/6	2s	11½	Guineas.			
21/-	1	9	26/-	2	2	31/6	2	7½	36/-	3	0	1.	£0	1s	9
22/-	1	10	27/-	2	3	32/-	2	8	37/-	3	1	2.	0	3	6
22/6	1	10½	27/6	2	3½	32/6	2	8½	37/6	3	1½	3.	0	5	3
23/-	1	11	28/-	2	4	33/-	2	9	38/-	3	2	4.	0	7	0
24/-	2	0	29/-	2	5	34/-	2	10	39/-	3	3	5.	0	8	9
25/-	2	1	**30/-**	2	6	**35/-**	2	11	**40/-**	3	4	6.	£0	10	6

($7\frac{11}{13}$%* on Gross Returns).

8½ Per Cent.

£1	£0	1s	8½	£51	£4	6s	8½	£101	£8	11s	8½	£151	12	16s	8½
2	0	3	4¾	52	4	8	4¾	102	8	13	4¾	152	12	18	4¾
3	0	5	1¼	53	4	10	1¼	103	8	15	1¼	153	13	0	1¼
4	0	6	9½	54	4	11	9½	104	8	16	9½	154	13	1	9½
5	0	8	6	55	4	13	6	105	8	18	6	155	13	3	6
6	0	10	2½	56	4	15	2½	106	9	0	2½	156	13	5	2½
7	0	11	10¾	57	4	16	10¾	107	9	1	10¾	157	13	6	10¾
8	0	13	7¼	58	4	18	7¼	108	9	3	7¼	158	13	8	7¼
9	0	15	3½	59	5	0	3½	109	9	5	3½	159	13	10	3½
10	**0**	**17**	**0**	**60**	**5**	**2**	**0**	**110**	**9**	**7**	**0**	**160**	**13**	**12**	**0**
11	0	18	8½	61	5	3	8½	111	9	8	8½	161	13	13	8½
12	1	0	4¾	62	5	5	4¾	112	9	10	4¾	162	13	15	4¾
13	1	2	1¼	63	5	7	1¼	113	9	12	1¼	163	13	17	1¼
14	1	3	9½	64	5	8	9½	114	9	13	9½	164	13	18	9½
15	1	5	6	65	5	10	6	115	9	15	6	165	14	0	6
16	1	7	2½	66	5	12	2½	116	9	17	2½	166	14	2	2½
17	1	8	10¾	67	5	13	10¾	117	9	18	10¾	167	14	3	10¾
18	1	10	7¼	68	5	15	7¼	118	10	0	7¼	168	14	5	7¼
19	1	12	3½	69	5	17	3½	119	10	2	3½	169	14	7	3½
20	**1**	**14**	**0**	**70**	**5**	**19**	**0**	**120**	**10**	**4**	**0**	**170**	**14**	**9**	**0**
21	1	15	8½	71	6	0	8½	121	10	5	8½	171	14	10	8½
22	1	17	4¾	72	6	2	4¾	122	10	7	4¾	172	14	12	4¾
23	1	19	1¼	73	6	4	1¼	123	10	9	1¼	173	14	14	1¼
24	2	0	9½	74	6	5	9½	124	10	10	9½	174	14	15	9½
25	2	2	6	75	6	7	6	125	10	12	6	175	14	17	6
26	2	4	2½	76	6	9	2½	126	10	14	2½	176	14	19	2½
27	2	5	10¾	77	6	10	10¾	127	10	15	10¾	177	15	0	10¾
28	2	7	7¼	78	6	12	7¼	128	10	17	7¼	178	15	2	7¼
29	2	9	3½	79	6	14	3½	129	10	19	3½	179	15	4	3½
30	**2**	**11**	**0**	**80**	**6**	**16**	**0**	**130**	**11**	**1**	**0**	**180**	**15**	**6**	**0**
31	2	12	8½	81	6	17	8½	131	11	2	8½	181	15	7	8½
32	2	14	4¾	82	6	19	4¾	132	11	4	4¾	182	15	9	4¾
33	2	16	1¼	83	7	1	1¼	133	11	6	1¼	183	15	11	1¼
34	2	17	9½	84	7	2	9½	134	11	7	9½	184	15	12	9½
35	2	19	6	85	7	4	6	135	11	9	6	185	15	14	6
36	3	1	2½	86	7	6	2½	136	11	11	2½	186	15	16	2½
37	3	2	10¾	87	7	7	10¾	137	11	12	10¾	187	15	17	10¾
38	3	4	7¼	88	7	9	7¼	138	11	14	7¼	188	15	19	7¼
39	3	6	3½	89	7	11	3½	139	11	16	3½	189	16	1	3½
40	**3**	**8**	**0**	**90**	**7**	**13**	**0**	**140**	**11**	**18**	**0**	**190**	**16**	**3**	**0**
41	3	9	8½	91	7	14	8½	141	11	19	8½	191	16	4	8½
42	3	11	4¾	92	7	16	4¾	142	12	1	4¾	192	16	6	4¾
43	3	13	1¼	93	7	18	1¼	143	12	3	1¼	193	16	8	1¼
44	3	14	9½	94	7	19	9½	144	12	4	9½	194	16	9	9½
45	3	16	6	95	8	1	6	145	12	6	6	195	16	11	6
46	3	18	2½	96	8	3	2½	146	12	8	2½	196	16	13	2½
47	3	19	10¾	97	8	4	10¾	147	12	9	10¾	197	16	14	10¾
48	4	1	7¼	98	8	6	7¼	148	12	11	7¼	198	16	16	7¼
49	4	3	3½	99	8	8	3½	149	12	13	3½	199	16	18	3½
50	**4**	**5**	**0**	**100**	**8**	**10**	**0**	**150**	**12**	**15**	**0**	**200**	**17**	**0**	**0**

250	21	5s	0d	700	59	10s	0d	1200	102	0s	0d	2000	170	0s	0
300	25	10	0	750	63	15	0	1400	119	0	0	2500	212	10	0
400	34	0	0	800	68	0	0	1500	127	10	0	3000	255	0	0
500	42	10	0	900	76	10	0	1600	136	0	0	4000	340	0	0
600	51	0s	0d	1000	85	0s	0d	1800	153	0s	0d	5000	425	0s	0

91½% off

8½ Per Cent.

8½%

1d	0s	0d	4/1	0s	4¼	8/1	0s	8¼	12/1	1s	0¼	16/1	1s	4½
2d	0	0¼	2	0	4¼	2	0	8¼	2	1	0½	2	1	4½
3d	0	0¼	3	0	4¼	3	0	8½	3	1	0½	3	1	4½
4d	0	0¼	4	0	4½	4	0	8½	4	1	0½	4	1	4¾
5d	0	0½	5	0	4½	5	0	8½	5	1	0¾	5	1	4¾
6d	0	0½	4/6	0	4½	8/6	0	8¾	12/6	1	0¾	16/6	1	4¾
7d	0	0½	7	0	4¾	7	0	8¾	7	1	0¾	7	1	5
8d	0	0¾	8	0	4¾	8	0	8¾	8	1	1	8	1	5
9d	0	0¾	9	0	4¾	9	0	9	9	1	1	9	1	5
10d	0	0¾	10	0	5	10	0	9	10	1	1	10	1	5¼
11d	0	1	11	0	5	11	0	9	11	1	1¼	11	1	5¼
1/-	**0**	**1**	**5/-**	**0**	**5**	**9/-**	**0**	**9¼**	**13/-**	**1**	**1¼**	**17/-**	**1**	**5¼**
1/1	0	1	5/1	0	5¼	1	0	9¼	1	1	1¼	1	1	5½
2	0	1¼	2	0	5¼	2	0	9¼	2	1	1½	2	1	5½
3	0	1¼	3	0	5¼	3	0	9½	3	1	1½	3	1	5½
4	0	1¼	4	0	5½	4	0	9½	4	1	1½	4	1	5¾
5	0	1½	5	0	5½	5	0	9½	5	1	1¾	5	1	5¾
1/6	0	1½	5/6	0	5½	9/6	0	9¾	13/6	1	1¾	17/6	1	5¾
7	0	1½	7	0	5¾	7	0	9¾	7	1	1¾	7	1	6
8	0	1¾	8	0	5¾	8	0	9¾	8	1	2	8	1	6
9	0	1¾	9	0	5¾	9	0	10	9	1	2	9	1	6
10	0	1¾	10	0	6	10	0	10	10	1	2	10	1	6¼
11	0	2	11	0	6	11	0	10	11	1	2¼	11	1	6¼
2/-	**0**	**2**	**6/-**	**0**	**6**	**10/-**	**0**	**10¼**	**14/-**	**1**	**2¼**	**18/-**	**1**	**6¼**
2/1	0	2¼	1	0	6¼	10/1	0	10¼	1	1	2¼	1	1	6½
2	0	2¼	2	0	6¼	2	0	10¼	2	1	2½	2	1	6½
3	0	2¼	3	0	6½	3	0	10½	3	1	2½	3	1	6½
4	0	2½	4	0	6½	4	0	10½	4	1	2½	4	1	6¾
5	0	2½	5	0	6½	5	0	10¾	5	1	2¾	5	1	6¾
2/6	0	2½	6/6	0	6¾	10/6	0	10¾	14/6	1	2¾	18/6	1	6¾
7	0	2¾	7	0	6¾	7	0	10¾	7	1	3	7	1	7
8	0	2¾	8	0	6¾	8	0	11	8	1	3	8	1	7
9	0	2¾	9	0	7	9	0	11	9	1	3	9	1	7¼
10	0	3	10	0	7	10	0	11	10	1	3¼	10	1	7¼
11	0	3	11	0	7	11	0	11¼	11	1	3¼	11	1	7¼
3/-	**0**	**3**	**7/-**	**0**	**7¼**	**11/-**	**0**	**11¼**	**15/-**	**1**	**3¼**	**19/-**	**1**	**7½**
3/1	0	3¼	1	0	7¼	1	0	11¼	15/1	1	3½	1	1	7½
2	0	3¼	2	0	7¼	2	0	11½	2	1	3½	2	1	7½
3	0	3¼	3	0	7½	3	0	11½	3	1	3½	3	1	7¾
4	0	3½	4	0	7½	4	0	11½	4	1	3¾	4	1	7¾
5	0	3½	5	0	7½	5	0	11¾	5	1	3¾	5	1	7¾
3/6	0	3½	7/6	0	7¾	11/6	0	11¾	15/6	1	3¾	19/6	1	8
7	0	3¾	7	0	7¾	7	0	11¾	7	1	4	7	1	8
8	0	3¾	8	0	7¾	8	1	0	8	1	4	8	1	8
9	0	3¾	9	0	8	9	1	0	9	1	4	9	1	8¼
10	0	4	10	0	8	10	1	0	10	1	4¼	10	1	8¼
11	0	4	11	0	8	11	1	0¼	11	1	4¼	11	1	8¼
4/-	**0**	**4**	**8/-**	**0**	**8¼**	**12/-**	**1**	**0¼**	**16/-**	**1**	**4¼**	**20/-**	**1**	**8½**

20/6	1s	9	25/6	2s	2	31/-	2s	7½	35/6	3s	0¼	Guineas.		
21/-	1	9½	26/-	2	2½	31/6	2	8¼	36/-	3	0¾	1.	1s	9½
22/-	1	10½	27/-	2	3½	32/-	2	8¾	37/-	3	1¾	2.	3	6¾
22/6	1	11	27/6	2	4	32/6	2	9¼	37/6	3	2¼	3.	5	4¼
23/-	1	11½	28/-	2	4½	33/-	2	9¾	38/-	3	2¾	4.	7	1¾
24/-	2	0½	29/-	2	5½	34/-	2	10¾	39/-	3	3¾	5.	8	11
25/-	2s	1½	**30/-**	2s	6½	**35/-**	2s	11¾	**40/-**	3s	4¾	6.	10	8½

(=7 8/10% on Gross Returns).

£			£			£			£		
£1	0	1s. 9	£51	4	9s. 3	£101	£8	16s. 9	£151	13	4s. 3
2	0	3 6	52	4	11 0	102	8	18 6	152	13	6 0
3	0	5 3	53	4	12 9	103	9	0 3	153	13	7 9
4	0	7 0	54	4	14 6	104	9	2 0	154	13	9 6
5	0	8 9	55	4	16 3	105	9	3 9	155	13	11 3
6	0	10 6	56	4	18 0	106	9	5 6	156	13	13 0
7	0	12 3	57	4	19 9	107	9	7 3	157	13	14 9
8	0	14 0	58	5	1 6	108	9	9 0	158	13	16 6
9	0	15 9	59	5	3 3	109	9	10 9	159	13	18 3
10	0	17s. 6	60	5	5s. 0	110	9	12s. 6	160	14	0s. 0
11	0	19 3	61	5	6 9	111	9	14 3	161	14	1 9
12	1	1 0	62	5	8 6	112	9	16 0	162	14	3 6
13	1	2 9	63	5	10 3	113	9	17 9	163	14	5 3
14	1	4 6	64	5	12 0	114	9	19 6	164	14	7 0
15	1	6 3	65	5	13 9	115	10	1 3	165	14	8 9
16	1	8 0	66	5	15 6	116	10	3 0	166	14	10 6
17	1	9 9	67	5	17 3	117	10	4 9	167	14	12 3
18	1	11 6	68	5	19 0	118	10	6 6	168	14	14 0
19	1	13 3	69	6	0 9	119	10	8 3	169	14	15 9
20	1	15s. 0	70	6	2s. 6	120	10	10s. 0	170	14	17s. 6
21	1	16 9	71	6	4 3	121	10	11 9	171	14	19 3
22	1	18 6	72	6	6 0	122	10	13 6	172	15	1 0
23	2	0 3	73	6	7 9	123	10	15 3	173	15	2 9
24	2	2 0	74	6	9 6	124	10	17 0	174	15	4 6
25	2	3 9	75	6	11 3	125	10	18 9	175	15	6 3
26	2	5 6	76	6	13 0	126	11	0 6	176	15	8 0
27	2	7 3	77	6	14 9	127	11	2 3	177	15	9 9
28	2	9 0	78	6	16 6	128	11	4 0	178	15	11 6
29	2	10 9	79	6	18 3	129	11	5 9	179	15	13 3
30	2	12s. 6	80	7	0s. 0	130	11	7s. 6	180	15	15s. 0
31	2	14 3	81	7	1 9	131	11	9 3	181	15	16 9
32	2	16 0	82	7	3 6	132	11	11 0	182	15	18 6
33	2	17 9	83	7	5 3	133	11	12 9	183	16	0 3
34	2	19 6	84	7	7 0	134	11	14 6	184	16	2 0
35	3	1 3	85	7	8 9	135	11	16 3	185	16	3 9
36	3	3 0	86	7	10 6	136	11	18 0	186	16	5 6
37	3	4 9	87	7	12 3	137	11	19 9	187	16	7 3
38	3	6 6	88	7	14 0	138	12	1 6	188	16	9 0
39	3	8 3	89	7	15 9	139	12	3 3	189	16	10 9
40	3	10s. 0	90	7	17s. 6	140	12	5s. 0	190	16	12s. 6
41	3	11 9	91	7	19 3	141	12	6 9	191	16	14 3
42	3	13 6	92	8	1 0	142	12	8 6	192	16	16 0
43	3	15 3	93	8	2 9	143	12	10 3	193	16	17 9
44	3	17 0	94	8	4 6	144	12	12 0	194	16	19 6
45	3	18 9	95	8	6 3	145	12	13 9	195	17	1 3
46	4	0 6	96	8	8 0	146	12	15 6	196	17	3 0
47	4	2 3	97	8	9 9	147	12	17 3	197	17	4 9
48	4	4 0	98	8	11 6	148	12	19 0	198	17	6 6
49	4	5 9	99	8	13 3	149	13	0 9	199	17	8 3
50	4	7s. 6	100	8	15s. 0	150	13	2s. 6	200	17	10s. 0

£			£			£			£		
250	£21	17 6	700	£61	5 0	1200	105	0 0	2000	175	0 0
300	26	5 0	750	65	12 6	1400	122	10 0	2500	218	15 0
400	35	0 0	800	70	0 0	1500	131	5 0	3000	262	10 0
500	43	15 0	900	78	15 0	1600	140	0 0	4000	350	0 0
600	52	10 0	1000	87	10 0	1800	157	10 0	5000	437	10 0

91¼% off.

8¾ Per Cent.

1d	0s.	0	4/1	0s.	4¼	8/1	0s.	8½	12/1	1s.	0¾	16/1	1s.	5
2d	0	0¼	2	0	4½	2	0	8½	2	1	0¾	2	1	5
3d	0	0¼	3	0	4½	3	0	8¾	3	1	0¾	3	1	5
4d	0	0¼	4	0	4½	4	0	8¾	4	1	1	4	1	5¼
5d	0	0½	5	0	4¾	5	0	8¾	5	1	1	5	1	5¼
6d	0	0½	4/6	0	4¾	8/6	0	9	12/6	1	1¼	16/6	1	5¼
7d	0	0½	7	0	4¾	7	0	9	7	1	1¼	7	1	5½
8d	0	0¾	8	0	5	8	0	9	8	1	1¼	8	1	5½
9d	0	0¾	9	0	5	9	0	9¼	9	1	1½	9	1	5½
10d	0	1	10	0	5	10	0	9¼	10	1	1½	10	1	5¾
11d	0	1	11	0	5¼	11	0	9¼	11	1	1½	11	1	5¾
1/-	0s.	1	**5/-**	0s.	5¼	**9/-**	0s.	9½	**13/-**	1s.	1¾	**17/-**	1s.	5¾
1/1	0	1¼	5/1	0	5¼	9/1	0	9½	13/1	1	1¾	17/1	1	6
2	0	1¼	2	0	5½	2	0	9¾	2	1	1¾	2	1	6
3	0	1¼	3	0	5½	3	0	9¾	3	1	2	3	1	6
4	0	1½	4	0	5½	4	0	9¾	4	1	2	4	1	6¼
5	0	1½	5	0	5¾	5	0	10	5	1	2	5	1	6¼
1/6	0	1½	5/6	0	5¾	9/6	0	10	13/6	1	2¼	17/6	1	6½
7	0	1¾	7	0	5¾	7	0	10	7	1	2¼	7	1	6½
8	0	1¾	8	0	6	8	0	10¼	8	1	2¼	8	1	6½
9	0	1¾	9	0	6	9	0	10¼	9	1	2½	9	1	6¾
10	0	2	10	0	6¼	10	0	10¼	10	1	2½	10	1	6¾
11	0	2	11	0	6¼	11	0	10½	11	1	2½	11	1	6¾
2/-	0s.	2	**6/-**	0s.	6¼	**10/-**	0s.	10½	**14/-**	1s.	2¾	**18/-**	1s.	7
2/1	0	2¼	6/1	0	6½	10/1	0	10½	14/1	1	2¾	18/1	1	7
2	0	2¼	2	0	6½	2	0	10¾	2	1	3	2	1	7
3	0	2¼	3	0	6½	3	0	10¾	3	1	3	3	1	7¼
4	0	2½	4	0	6¾	4	0	10¾	4	1	3	4	1	7¼
5	0	2½	5	0	6¾	5	0	11	5	1	3¼	5	1	7¼
2/6	0	2¾	6/6	0	6¾	10/6	0	11	14/6	1	3¼	18/6	1	7½
7	0	2¾	7	0	7	7	0	11	7	1	3¼	7	1	7½
8	0	2¾	8	0	7	8	0	11¼	8	1	3½	8	1	7½
9	0	3	9	0	7	9	0	11¼	9	1	3½	9	1	7¾
10	0	3	10	0	7¼	10	0	11½	10	1	3½	10	1	7¾
11	0	3	11	0	7¼	11	0	11½	11	1	3¾	11	1	7¾
3/-	0s.	3¼	**7/-**	0s.	7¼	**11/-**	0s.	11½	**15/-**	1s	3¾	**19/-**	1s.	8
3/1	0	3¼	7/1	0	7½	11/1	0	11¾	15/1	1	3¾	19/1	1	8
2	0	3¼	2	0	7½	2	0	11¾	2	1	4	2	1	8¼
3	0	3½	3	0	7½	3	0	11¾	3	1	4	3	1	8¼
4	0	3½	4	0	7¾	4	1	0	4	1	4	4	1	8¼
5	0	3½	5	0	7¾	5	1	0	5	1	4¼	5	1	8½
3/6	0	3¾	7/6	0	8	11/6	1	0	15/6	1	4¼	19/6	1	8½
7	0	3¾	7	0	8	7	1	0¼	7	1	4¼	7	1	8½
8	0	3¾	8	0	8	8	1	0¼	8	1	4½	8	1	8¾
9	0	4	9	0	8¼	9	1	0¼	9	1	4½	9	1	8¾
10	0	4	10	0	8¼	10	1	0½	10	1	4¾	10	1	8¾
11	0	4	11	0	8¼	11	1	0½	11	1	4¾	11	1	9
4/-	0s.	4¼	**8/-**	0s.	8½	**12/-**	1s.	0½	**16/-**	1s.	4¾	**20/-**	1s.	9

20/6	1s.	9½	25/6	2s.	2¾	31/-	2s.	8½	35/6	3s.	1¼	Guineas.		
21/-	1	10	26/-	2	3¼	31/6	2	9	36/-	3	1¾	1.	1s.	10
22/-	1	11	27/-	2	4¼	32/-	2	9½	37/-	3	2¾	2.	3	8
22/6	1	11¾	27/6	2	5	32/6	2	10¼	37/6	3	3½	3.	5	6¼
23/-	2	0¼	28/-	2	5½	33/-	2	10¾	38/-	3	4	4.	7	4¼
24/-	2	1¼	29/-	2	6½	34/-	2	11¾	39/-	3	5	5.	9	2¼
25/-	2s.	2¼	**30/-**	2s.	7½	**35/-**	3s.	0¾	**40/-**	3s.	6	6.	11s.	0¼

(=8$\frac{1}{10}$%* on Gross Returns).

£1	£0	1s	9½	£51	£4	11s	9½	£101	£9	1s	9½	£151	13	11s	9½
2	0	3	7¼	52	4	13	7¼	102	9	3	7¼	152	13	13	7¼
3	0	5	4¾	53	4	15	4¾	103	9	5	4¾	153	13	15	4¾
4	0	7	2½	54	4	17	2½	104	9	7	2½	154	13	17	2½
5	0	9	0	55	4	19	0	105	9	9	0	155	13	19	0
6	0	10	9½	56	5	0	9½	106	9	10	9½	156	14	0	9½
7	0	12	7¼	57	5	2	7¼	107	9	12	7¼	157	14	2	7¼
8	0	14	4¾	58	5	4	4¾	108	9	14	4¾	158	14	4	4¾
9	0	16	2½	59	5	6	2½	109	9	16	2½	159	14	6	2½
10	**0**	**18**	**0**	**60**	**5**	**8**	**0**	**110**	**9**	**18**	**0**	**160**	**14**	**8**	**0**
11	0	19	9½	61	5	9	9½	111	9	19	9½	161	14	9	9½
12	1	1	7¼	62	5	11	7¼	112	10	1	7¼	162	14	11	7¼
13	1	3	4¾	63	5	13	4¾	113	10	3	4¾	163	14	13	4¾
14	1	5	2½	64	5	15	2½	114	10	5	2½	164	14	15	2½
15	1	7	0	65	5	17	0	115	10	7	0	165	14	17	0
16	1	8	9½	66	5	18	9½	116	10	8	9½	166	14	18	9½
17	1	10	7¼	67	6	0	7¼	117	10	10	7¼	167	15	0	7¼
18	1	12	4¾	68	6	2	4¾	118	10	12	4¾	168	15	2	4¾
19	1	14	2½	69	6	4	2½	119	10	14	2½	169	15	4	2½
20	**1**	**16**	**0**	**70**	**6**	**6**	**0**	**120**	**10**	**16**	**0**	**170**	**15**	**6**	**0**
21	1	17	9½	71	6	7	9½	121	10	17	9½	171	15	7	9½
22	1	19	7¼	72	6	9	7¼	122	10	19	7¼	172	15	9	7¼
23	2	1	4¾	73	6	11	4¾	123	11	1	4¾	173	15	11	4¾
24	2	3	2½	74	6	13	2½	124	11	3	2½	174	15	13	2½
25	2	5	0	75	6	15	0	125	11	5	0	175	15	15	0
26	2	6	9½	76	6	16	9½	126	11	6	9½	176	15	16	9½
27	2	8	7¼	77	6	18	7¼	127	11	8	7¼	177	15	18	7¼
28	2	10	4¾	78	7	0	4¾	128	11	10	4¾	178	16	0	4¾
29	2	12	2½	79	7	2	2½	129	11	12	2½	179	16	2	2½
30	**2**	**14**	**0**	**80**	**7**	**4**	**0**	**130**	**11**	**14**	**0**	**180**	**16**	**4**	**0**
31	2	15	9½	81	7	5	9½	131	11	15	9½	181	16	5	9½
32	2	17	7¼	82	7	7	7¼	132	11	17	7¼	182	16	7	7¼
33	2	19	4¾	83	7	9	4¾	133	11	19	4¾	183	16	9	4¾
34	3	1	2½	84	7	11	2½	134	12	1	2½	184	16	11	2½
35	3	3	0	85	7	13	0	135	12	3	0	185	16	13	0
36	3	4	9½	86	7	14	9½	136	12	4	9½	186	16	14	9½
37	3	6	7¼	87	7	16	7¼	137	12	6	7¼	187	16	16	7¼
38	3	8	4¾	88	7	18	4¾	138	12	8	4¾	188	16	18	4¾
39	3	10	2½	89	8	0	2½	139	12	10	2½	189	17	0	2½
40	**3**	**12**	**0**	**90**	**8**	**2**	**0**	**140**	**12**	**12**	**0**	**190**	**17**	**2**	**0**
41	3	13	9½	91	8	3	9½	141	12	13	9½	191	17	3	9½
42	3	15	7¼	92	8	5	7¼	142	12	15	7¼	192	17	5	7¼
43	3	17	4¾	93	8	7	4¾	143	12	17	4¾	193	17	7	4¾
44	3	19	2½	94	8	9	2½	144	12	19	2½	194	17	9	2½
45	4	1	0	95	8	11	0	145	13	1	0	195	17	11	0
46	4	2	9½	96	8	12	9½	146	13	2	9½	196	17	12	9½
47	4	4	7¼	97	8	14	7¼	147	13	4	7¼	197	17	14	7¼
48	4	6	4¾	98	8	16	4¾	148	13	6	4¾	198	17	16	4¾
49	4	8	2½	99	8	18	2½	149	13	8	2½	199	17	18	2½
50	**4**	**10**	**0**	**100**	**9**	**0**	**0**	**150**	**13**	**10**	**0**	**200**	**18**	**0**	**0**

250	22	10s	0d	700	63	0s	0d	1200	108	0s	0d	2000	180	0s	0d
300	27	0	0	750	67	10	0	1400	126	0	0	2500	225	0	0
400	36	0	0	800	72	0	0	1500	135	0	0	3000	270	0	0
500	45	0	0	900	81	0	0	1600	144	0	0	4000	360	0	0
600	54	0s	0d	1000	90	0s	0d	1800	162	0s	0d	5000	450	0s	0d

91% off.

9% Nine Per Cent. 9%

1d	0s.	0	4/1	0s.	4½	8/1	0s.	8¾	12/1	1s.	1	16/1	1s.	5½
2d	0	0¼	2	0	4½	2	0	8¾	2	1	1¼	2	1	5½
3d	0	0¼	3	0	4½	3	0	9	3	1	1¼	3	1	5½
4d	0	0¼	4	0	4¾	4	0	9	4	1	1¼	4	1	5¾
5d	0	0½	5	0	4¾	5	0	9	5	1	1½	5	1	5¾
6d	0	0½	4/6	0	4¾	8/6	0	9¼	12/6	1	1½	16/6	1	5¾
7d	0	0¾	7	0	5	7	0	9¼	7	1	1½	7	1	6
8d	0	0¾	8	0	5	8	0	9¼	8	1	1¾	8	1	6
9d	0	0¾	9	0	5¼	9	0	9½	9	1	1¾	9	1	6
10d	0	1	10	0	5¼	10	0	9½	10	1	1¾	10	1	6¼
11d	0	1	11	0	5¼	11	0	9¾	11	1	2	11	1	6¼
1/-	0s.	1	**5/-**	0s.	5½	**9/-**	0s.	9¾	**13/-**	1s.	2	**17/-**	1s.	6¼
1/1	0s.	1¼	5/1	0s.	5½	9/1	0s.	9¾	13/1	1s.	2¼	17/1	1s.	6½
2	0	1¼	2	0	5½	2	0	10	2	1	2¼	2	1	6½
3	0	1¼	3	0	5¾	3	0	10	3	1	2¼	3	1	6¾
4	0	1½	4	0	5¾	4	0	10	4	1	2½	4	1	6¾
5	0	1½	5	0	5¾	5	0	10¼	5	1	2½	5	1	6¾
1/6	0	1½	5/6	0	6	9/6	0	10¼	13/6	1	2½	17/6	1	7
7	0	1¾	7	0	6	7	0	10¼	7	1	2¾	7	1	7
8	0	1¾	8	0	6	8	0	10½	8	1	2¾	8	1	7
9	0	2	9	0	6¼	9	0	10½	9	1	2¾	9	1	7¼
10	0	2	10	0	6¼	10	0	10½	10	1	3	10	1	7¼
11	0	2	11	0	6½	11	0	10¾	11	1	3	11	1	7¼
2/-	0s.	2¼	**6/-**	0s.	6½	**10/-**	0s.	10¾	**14/-**	1s.	3	**18/-**	1s.	7½
2/1	0s.	2¼	6/1	0s.	6½	10/1	0s.	11	14/1	1s.	3¼	18/1	1s.	7½
2	0	2¼	2	0	6¾	2	0	11	2	1	3¼	2	1	7½
3	0	2½	3	0	6¾	3	0	11	3	1	3½	3	1	7¾
4	0	2½	4	0	6¾	4	0	11¼	4	1	3½	4	1	7¾
5	0	2½	5	0	7	5	0	11¼	5	1	3½	5	1	8
2/6	0	2¾	6/6	0	7	10/6	0	11¼	14/6	1	3¾	18/6	1	8
7	0	2¾	7	0	7	7	0	11½	7	1	3¾	7	1	8
8	0	3	8	0	7¼	8	0	11½	8	1	3¾	8	1	8¼
9	0	3	9	0	7¼	9	0	11½	9	1	4	9	1	8¼
10	0	3	10	0	7½	10	0	11¾	10	1	4	10	1	8¼
11	0	3¼	11	0	7½	11	0	11¾	11	1	4	11	1	8½
3/-	0s.	3¼	**7/-**	0s.	7½	**11/-**	1s.	0	**15/-**	1s.	4¼	**19/-**	1s.	8½
3/1	0s.	3¼	7/1	0s.	7¾	11/1	1s.	0	15/1	1s.	4¼	19/1	1s.	8½
2	0	3½	2	0	7¾	2	1	0	2	1	4½	2	1	8¾
3	0	3½	3	0	7¾	3	1	0¼	3	1	4½	3	1	8¾
4	0	3½	4	0	8	4	1	0¼	4	1	4½	4	1	9
5	0	3¾	5	0	8	5	1	0¼	5	1	4¾	5	1	9
3/6	0	3¾	7/6	0	8	11/6	1	0½	15/6	1	4¾	19/6	1	9
7	0	3¾	7	0	8¼	7	1	0½	7	1	4¾	7	1	9¼
8	0	4	8	0	8¼	8	1	0½	8	1	5	8	1	9¼
9	0	4	9	0	8¼	9	1	0¾	9	1	5	9	1	9¼
10	0	4¼	10	0	8½	10	1	0¾	10	1	5	10	1	9½
11	0	4¼	11	0	8½	11	1	0¾	11	1	5¼	11	1	9½
4/-	0s.	4¼	**8/-**	0s.	8¾	**12/-**	1s.	1	**16/-**	1s.	5¼	**20/-**	1s.	9½

												Guineas.	
20/6	1s.	10¼	25/6	2s.	3½	31/-	2s.	9½	35/6	3s.	2¼		
21/-	1	10¾	26/-	2	4	31/6	2	10	36/-	3	3	1.	1s. 10¾
22/-	1	11¾	27/-	2	5¼	32/-	2	10½	37/-	3	4	2.	3 9¼
22/6	2	0¼	27/6	2	5¾	32/6	2	11	37/6	3	4½	3.	5 8
23/-	2	0¾	28/-	2	6¼	33/-	2	11¾	38/-	3	5	4.	7 6¾
24/-	2	2	29/-	2	7¼	34/-	3	0¾	39/-	3	6	5.	9 5½
25/-	2s.	3	**30/-**	2s.	8½	**35/-**	3s.	1¾	**40/-**	3s.	7¼	6.	11s. 4

(=8 3/10%* on Gross Returns).

£	£ s d	£	£ s d	£	£ s d	£	£ s d
£1	£0 1s10¾	£51	£4 16s10¾	£101	£9 11s10¾	£151	14 6s10¾
2	0 3 9½	52	4 18 9½	102	9 13 9½	152	14 8 9½
3	0 5 8½	53	5 0 8½	103	9 15 8½	153	14 10 8½
4	0 7 7¼	54	5 2 7¼	104	9 17 7¼	154	14 12 7¼
5	0 9 6	55	5 4 6	105	9 19 6	155	14 14 6
6	0 11 4¾	56	5 6 4¾	106	10 1 4¾	156	14 16 4¾
7	0 13 3½	57	5 8 3½	107	10 3 3½	157	14 18 3½
8	0 15 2½	58	5 10 2½	108	10 5 2½	158	15 0 2½
9	0 17 1¼	59	5 12 1¼	109	10 7 1¼	159	15 2 1¼
10	0 19 0	60	5 14 0	110	10 9 0	160	15 4 0
11	1 0 10¾	61	5 15 10¾	111	10 10 10¾	161	15 5 10¾
12	1 2 9½	62	5 17 9½	112	10 12 9½	162	15 7 9½
13	1 4 8½	63	5 19 8½	113	10 14 8½	163	15 9 8½
14	1 6 7¼	64	6 1 7¼	114	10 16 7¼	164	15 11 7¼
15	1 8 6	65	6 3 6	115	10 18 6	165	15 13 6
16	1 10 4¾	66	6 5 4¾	116	11 0 4¾	166	15 15 4¾
17	1 12 3½	67	6 7 3½	117	11 2 3½	167	15 17 3½
18	1 14 2½	68	6 9 2½	118	11 4 2½	168	15 19 2½
19	1 16 1¼	69	6 11 1¼	119	11 6 1¼	169	16 1 1¼
20	1 18 0	70	6 13 0	120	11 8 0	170	16 3 0
21	1 19 10¾	71	6 14 10¾	121	11 9 10¾	171	16 4 10¾
22	2 1 9½	72	6 16 9½	122	11 11 9½	172	16 6 9½
23	2 3 8½	73	6 18 8½	123	11 13 8½	173	16 8 8½
24	2 5 7¼	74	7 0 7¼	124	11 15 7¼	174	16 10 7¼
25	2 7 6	75	7 2 6	125	11 17 6	175	16 12 6
26	2 9 4¾	76	7 4 4¾	126	11 19 4¾	176	16 14 4¾
27	2 11 3½	77	7 6 3½	127	12 1 3½	177	16 16 3½
28	2 13 2½	78	7 8 2½	128	12 3 2½	178	16 18 2½
29	2 15 1¼	79	7 10 1¼	129	12 5 1¼	179	17 0 1¼
30	2 17 0	80	7 12 0	130	12 7 0	180	17 2 0
31	2 18 10¾	81	7 13 10¾	131	12 8 10¾	181	17 3 10¾
32	3 0 9½	82	7 15 9½	132	12 10 9½	182	17 5 9½
33	3 2 8½	83	7 17 8½	133	12 12 8½	183	17 7 8½
34	3 4 7¼	84	7 19 7¼	134	12 14 7¼	184	17 9 7¼
35	3 6 6	85	8 1 6	135	12 16 6	185	17 11 6
36	3 8 4¾	86	8 3 4¾	136	12 18 4¾	186	17 13 4¾
37	3 10 3½	87	8 5 3½	137	13 0 3½	187	17 15 3½
38	3 12 2½	88	8 7 2½	138	13 2 2½	188	17 17 2½
39	3 14 1¼	89	8 9 1¼	139	13 4 1¼	189	17 19 1¼
40	3 16 0	90	8 11 0	140	13 6 0	190	18 1 0
41	3 17 10¾	91	8 12 10¾	141	13 7 10¾	191	18 2 10¾
42	3 19 9½	92	8 14 9½	142	13 9 9½	192	18 4 9½
43	4 1 8½	93	8 16 8½	143	13 11 8½	193	18 6 8½
44	4 3 7¼	94	8 18 7¼	144	13 13 7¼	194	18 8 7¼
45	4 5 6	95	9 0 6	145	13 15 6	195	18 10 6
46	4 7 4¾	96	9 2 4¾	146	13 17 4¾	196	18 12 4¾
47	4 9 3½	97	9 4 3½	147	13 19 3½	197	18 14 3½
48	4 11 2½	98	9 6 2½	148	14 1 2½	198	18 16 2½
49	4 13 1¼	99	9 8 1¼	149	14 3 1¼	199	18 18 1¼
50	4 15 0	100	9 10 0	150	14 5 0	200	19 0 0

£	£ s d	£	£ s d	£	£ s d	£	£ s d
250	23 15s 0d	700	66 10s 0d	1200	114 0s 0d	2000	190 0s 0
300	28 10 0	750	71 5 0	1400	133 0 0	2500	237 10 0
400	38 0 0	800	76 0 0	1500	142 10 0	3000	285 0 0
500	47 10 0	900	85 10 0	1600	152 0 0	4000	380 0 0
600	57 0s 0d	1000	95 0s 0d	1800	171 0s 0d	5000	475 0s 0

90½% off

9½ Per Cent.

9½%

1d	0s	0d	4/1	0s	4¾	8/1	0s	9¼	12/1	1s	1¾	16/1	1s	6¼
2d	0	0¼	2	0	4¾	2	0	9¼	2	1	1¾	2	1	6½
3d	0	0¼	3	0	4¾	3	0	9½	3	1	2	3	1	6½
4d	0	0½	4	0	5	4	0	9½	4	1	2	4	1	6½
5d	0	0½	5	0	5	5	0	9½	5	1	2¼	5	1	6¾
6d	0	0½	4/6	0	5¼	8/6	0	9¾	12/6	1	2¼	16/6	1	6¾
7d	0	0¾	7	0	5¼	7	0	9¾	7	1	2¼	7	1	7
8d	0	0¾	8	0	5¼	8	0	10	8	1	2½	8	1	7
9d	0	0¾	9	0	5½	9	0	10	9	1	2½	9	1	7
10d	0	1	10	0	5½	10	0	10	10	1	2¾	10	1	7¼
11d	0	1	11	0	5½	11	0	10¼	11	1	2¾	11	1	7¼
1/-	**0**	**1¼**	**5/-**	**0**	**5¾**	**9/-**	**0**	**10¼**	**13/-**	**1**	**2¾**	**17/-**	**1**	**7½**
1/1	0	1¼	5/1	0	5¾	1	0	10¼	1	1	3	1	1	7½
2	0	1¼	2	0	6	2	0	10½	2	1	3	2	1	7½
3	0	1½	3	0	6	3	0	10½	3	1	3	3	1	7¾
4	0	1½	4	0	6	4	0	10¾	4	1	3¼	4	1	7¾
5	0	1½	5	0	6¼	5	0	10¾	5	1	3¼	5	1	7¾
1/6	0	1¾	5/6	0	6¼	9/6	0	10¾	13/6	1	3½	17/6	1	8
7	0	1¾	7	0	6¼	7	0	11	7	1	3½	7	1	8
8	0	2	8	0	6½	8	0	11	8	1	3½	8	1	8¼
9	0	2	9	0	6½	9	0	11	9	1	3¾	9	1	8¼
10	0	2	10	0	6¾	10	0	11¼	10	1	3¾	10	1	8¼
11	0	2¼	11	0	6¾	11	0	11¼	11	1	3¾	11	1	8½
2/-	**0**	**2¼**	**6/-**	**0**	**6¾**	**10/-**	**0**	**11½**	**14/-**	**1**	**4**	**18/-**	**1**	**8½**
2/1	0	2½	1	0	7	10/1	0	11½	1	1	4	1	1	8½
2	0	2½	2	0	7	2	0	11½	2	1	4¼	2	1	8¾
3	0	2½	3	0	7¼	3	0	11¾	3	1	4¼	3	1	8¾
4	0	2¾	4	0	7¼	4	0	11¾	4	1	4¼	4	1	9
5	0	2¾	5	0	7¼	5	1	0	5	1	4½	5	1	9
2/6	0	2¾	6/6	0	7½	10/6	1	0	14/6	1	4½	18/6	1	9
7	0	3	7	0	7½	7	1	0	7	1	4¾	7	1	9¼
8	0	3	8	0	7½	8	1	0¼	8	1	4¾	8	1	9¼
9	0	3¼	9	0	7¾	9	1	0¼	9	1	4¾	9	1	9½
10	0	3¼	10	0	7¾	10	1	0¼	10	1	5	10	1	9½
11	0	3¼	11	0	8	11	1	0½	11	1	5	11	1	9½
3/-	**0**	**3½**	**7/-**	**0**	**8**	**11/-**	**1**	**0½**	**15/-**	**1**	**5**	**19/-**	**1**	**9¾**
3/1	0	3½	1	0	8	1	1	0¾	15/1	1	5¼	1	1	9¾
2	0	3½	2	0	8¼	2	1	0¾	2	1	5¼	2	1	9¾
3	0	3¾	3	0	8¼	3	1	0¾	3	1	5½	3	1	10
4	0	3¾	4	0	8¼	4	1	1	4	1	5½	4	1	10
5	0	4	5	0	8½	5	1	1	5	1	5½	5	1	10¼
3/6	0	4	7/6	0	8½	11/6	1	1	15/6	1	5¾	19/6	1	10¼
7	0	4	7	0	8¾	7	1	1¼	7	1	5¾	7	1	10¼
8	0	4¼	8	0	8¾	8	1	1¼	8	1	5¾	8	1	10½
9	0	4¼	9	0	8¾	9	1	1½	9	1	6	9	1	10½
10	0	4¼	10	0	9	10	1	1½	10	1	6	10	1	10½
11	0	4½	11	0	9	11	1	1½	11	1	6¼	11	1	10¾
4/-	**0**	**4½**	**8/-**	**0**	**9**	**12/-**	**1**	**1¾**	**16/-**	**1**	**6¼**	**20/-**	**1**	**10¾**

20/6	1s	11¼	25/6	2s	5	31/-	2s	11¼	35/6	3s	4½	Guineas.		
21/-	2	0	26/-	2	5¾	31/6	3	0	36/-	3	5	1.	2s	0
22/-	2	1	27/-	2	6¾	32/-	3	0½	37/-	3	6¼	2.	4	0
22/6	2	1¾	27/6	2	7¼	32/6	3	1	37/6	3	6¾	3.	5	11¾
23/-	2	2¼	28/-	2	8	33/-	3	1½	38/-	3	7¼	4.	7	11¾
24/-	2	3¼	29/-	2	9	34/-	3	2¾	39/-	3	8½	5.	9	11¾
25/-	2s	4½	**30/-**	2s	10¼	**35/-**	3s	4	**40/-**	3s	9½	6.	11	11¾

(=8 7/10% on Gross Returns).

£				£				£				£			
£1	£0	2s.	0	£51	£5	2s.	0	£101	10	2s.	0	£151	£15	2s.	0
2	0	4	0	52	5	4	0	102	10	4	0	152	15	4	0
3	0	6	0	53	5	6	0	103	10	6	0	153	15	6	0
4	0	8	0	54	5	8	0	104	10	8	0	154	15	8	0
5	0	10	0	55	5	10	0	105	10	10	0	155	15	10	0
6	0	12	0	56	5	12	0	106	10	12	0	156	15	12	0
7	0	14	0	57	5	14	0	107	10	14	0	157	15	14	0
8	0	16	0	58	5	16	0	108	10	16	0	158	15	16	0
9	0	18	0	59	5	18	0	109	10	18	0	159	15	18	0
10	£1	0s.	0	60	£6	0s.	0	110	11	0s.	0	160	£16	0s.	0
11	£1	2s.	0	61	£6	2s.	0	111	11	2s.	0	161	£16	2s.	0
12	1	4	0	62	6	4	0	112	11	4	0	162	16	4	0
13	1	6	0	63	6	6	0	113	11	6	0	163	16	6	0
14	1	8	0	64	6	8	0	114	11	8	0	164	16	8	0
15	1	10	0	65	6	10	0	115	11	10	0	165	16	10	0
16	1	12	0	66	6	12	0	116	11	12	0	166	16	12	0
17	1	14	0	67	6	14	0	117	11	14	0	167	16	14	0
18	1	16	0	68	6	16	0	118	11	16	0	168	16	16	0
19	1	18	0	69	6	18	0	119	11	18	0	169	16	18	0
20	£2	0s.	0	70	£7	0s.	0	120	12	0s.	0	170	£17	0s.	0
21	£2	2s.	0	71	£7	2s.	0	121	12	2s.	0	171	£17	2s.	0
22	2	4	0	72	7	4	0	122	12	4	0	172	17	4	0
23	2	6	0	73	7	6	0	123	12	6	0	173	17	6	0
24	2	8	0	74	7	8	0	124	12	8	0	174	17	8	0
25	2	10	0	75	7	10	0	125	12	10	0	175	17	10	0
26	2	12	0	76	7	12	0	126	12	12	0	176	17	12	0
27	2	14	0	77	7	14	0	127	12	14	0	177	17	14	0
28	2	16	0	78	7	16	0	128	12	16	0	178	17	16	0
29	2	18	0	79	7	18	0	129	12	18	0	179	17	18	0
30	£3	0s.	0	80	£8	0s.	0	130	13	0s.	0	180	£18	0s.	0
31	£3	2s.	0	81	£8	2s.	0	131	13	2s.	0	181	£18	2s	0
32	3	4	0	82	8	4	0	132	13	4	0	182	18	4	0
33	3	6	0	83	8	6	0	133	13	6	0	183	18	6	0
34	3	8	0	84	8	8	0	134	13	8	0	184	18	8	0
35	3	10	0	85	8	10	0	135	13	10	0	185	18	10	0
36	3	12	0	86	8	12	0	136	13	12	0	186	18	12	0
37	3	14	0	87	8	14	0	137	13	14	0	187	18	14	0
38	3	16	0	88	8	16	0	138	13	16	0	188	18	16	0
39	3	18	0	89	8	18	0	139	13	18	0	189	18	18	0
40	£4	0s.	0	90	£9	0s.	0	140	14	0s.	0	190	£19	0s	0
41	£4	2s.	0	91	£9	2s.	0	141	14	2s.	0	191	£19	2s.	0
42	4	4	0	92	9	4	0	142	14	4	0	192	19	4	0
43	4	6	0	93	9	6	0	143	14	6	0	193	19	6	0
44	4	8	0	94	9	8	0	144	14	8	0	194	19	8	0
45	4	10	0	95	9	10	0	145	14	10	0	195	19	10	0
46	4	12	0	96	9	12	0	146	14	12	0	196	19	12	0
47	4	14	0	97	9	14	0	147	14	14	0	197	19	14	0
48	4	16	0	98	9	16	0	148	14	16	0	198	19	16	0
49	4	18	0	99	9	18	0	149	14	18	0	199	19	18	0
50	£5	0s.	0	100	10	0s.	0	150	15	0s.	0	200	£20	0s.	0
250	£25	0s.	0d	700	£70	0s.	0d	1200	120	0s.	0d	2000	£200	0s.	0
300	30	0	0	750	75	0	0	1400	140	0	0	2500	250	0	0
400	40	0	0	800	80	0	0	1500	150	0	0	3000	300	0	0
500	50	0	0	900	90	0	0	1600	160	0	0	4000	400	0	0
600	£60	0s.	0d	1000	100	0s.	0d	1800	180	0s.	0d	5000	£500	0s.	0

90% off.

10% TEN PER CENT. 10%

1d	0s.	0	4/1	0s.	5	8/1	0s.	9¾	12/1	1s.	2½	16/1	1s.	7¼
2d	0	0¼	2	0	5	2	0	9¾	2	1	2½	2	1	7½
3d	0	0¼	3	0	5	3	0	10	3	1	2¾	3	1	7½
4d	0	0½	4	0	5¼	4	0	10	4	1	2¾	4	1	7½
5d	0	0½	5	0	5¼	5	0	10	5	1	3	5	1	7¾
6d	0	0½	4/6	0	5½	8/6	0	10¼	12/6	1	3	16/6	1	7¾
7d	0	0¾	7	0	5½	7	0	10¼	7	1	3	7	1	8
8d	0	0¾	8	0	5½	8	0	10½	8	1	3¼	8	1	8
9d	0	1	9	0	5¾	9	0	10½	9	1	3¼	9	1	8
10d	0	1	10	0	5¾	10	0	10½	10	1	3½	10	1	8¼
11d	0	1	11	0	6	11	0	10¾	11	1	3½	11	1	8¼
1/-	0s.	1¼	**5/-**	0s.	6	**9/-**	0s.	10¾	**13/-**	1s.	3½	**17/-**	1s.	8½
1/1	0s.	1¼	5/1	0s.	6	9/1	0s.	11	13/1	1s.	3¾	17/1	1s.	8½
2	0	1½	2	0	6¼	2	0	11	2	1	3¾	2	1	8½
3	0	1½	3	0	6¼	3	0	11	3	1	4	3	1	8¾
4	0	1½	4	0	6½	4	0	11¼	4	1	4	4	1	8¾
5	0	1¾	5	0	6½	5	0	11¼	5	1	4	5	1	9
1/6	0	1¾	5/6	0	6½	9/6	0	11½	13/6	1	4¼	17/6	1	9
7	0	2	7	0	6¾	7	0	11½	7	1	4¼	7	1	9
8	0	2	8	0	6¾	8	0	11½	8	1	4½	8	1	9¼
9	0	2	9	0	7	9	0	11¾	9	1	4½	9	1	9¼
10	0	2¼	10	0	7	10	0	11¾	10	1	4½	10	1	9½
11	0	2¼	11	0	7	11	1	0	11	1	4¾	11	1	9½
2/-	0s.	2½	**6/-**	0s.	7¼	**10/-**	1s.	0	**14/-**	1s.	4¾	**18/-**	1s.	9½
2/1	0s.	2½	6/1	0s.	7¼	10/1	1s.	0	14/1	1s.	5	18/1	1s.	9¾
2	0	2½	2	0	7½	2	1	0¼	2	1	5	2	1	9¾
3	0	2¾	3	0	7½	3	1	0¼	3	1	5	3	1	10
4	0	2¾	4	0	7½	4	1	0½	4	1	5¼	4	1	10
5	0	3	5	0	7¾	5	1	0½	5	1	5¼	5	1	10
2/6	0	3	6/6	0	7¾	10/6	1	0½	14/6	1	5½	18/6	1	10¼
7	0	3	7	0	8	7	1	0¾	7	1	5½	7	1	10¼
8	0	3¼	8	0	8	8	1	0¾	8	1	5½	8	1	10½
9	0	3¼	9	0	8	9	1	1	9	1	5¾	9	1	10½
10	0	3½	10	0	8¼	10	1	1	10	1	5¾	10	1	10½
11	0	3½	11	0	8¼	11	1	1	11	1	6	11	1	10¾
3/-	0s.	3½	**7/-**	0s.	8½	**11/-**	1s.	1¼	**15/-**	1s.	6	**19/-**	1s.	10¾
3/1	0s.	3¾	7/1	0s.	8½	11/1	1s.	1¼	15/1	1s.	6	19/1	1s.	11
2	0	3¾	2	0	8½	2	1	1½	2	1	6¼	2	1	11
3	0	4	3	0	8¾	3	1	1½	3	1	6¼	3	1	11
4	0	4	4	0	8¾	4	1	1½	4	1	6½	4	1	11¼
5	0	4	5	0	9	5	1	1¾	5	1	6½	5	1	11¼
3/6	0	4¼	7/6	0	9	11/6	1	1¾	15/6	1	6½	19/6	1	11½
7	0	4¼	7	0	9	7	1	2	7	1	6¾	7	1	11½
8	0	4½	8	0	9¼	8	1	2	8	1	6¾	8	1	11½
9	0	4½	9	0	9¼	9	1	2	9	1	7	9	1	11¾
10	0	4½	10	0	9½	10	1	2¼	10	1	7	10	1	11¾
11	0	4¾	11	0	9½	11	1	2¼	11	1	7	11	2	0
4/-	0s.	4¾	**8/-**	0s.	9½	**12/-**	1s.	2½	**16/-**	1s.	7¼	**20/-**	2s.	0

20/6	2s.	0½	25/6	2s.	6½	31/-	3s.	1¼	35/6	3s.	6½	Guineas.		
21/-	2	1¼	26/-	2	7¼	31/6	3	1¾	36/-	3	7¼	1.	2s.	1¼
22/-	2	2½	27/-	2	8½	32/-	3	2½	37/-	3	8½	2.	4	2½
22/6	2	3	27/6	2	9	32/6	3	3	37/6	3	9	3.	6	3½
23/-	2	3½	28/-	2	9½	33/-	3	3½	38/-	3	9½	4.	8	4¾
24/-	2	4¾	29/-	2	10¾	34/-	3	4¾	39/-	3	10¾	5.	10	6
25/-	2s.	6	**30/-**	3s.	0	**35/-**	3s.	6	**40/-**	4s.	0	6.	12s.	7¼

(=9$\frac{1}{11}$%* on Gross Returns).

10½ Per Cent.

£1	£0	2s	1¼	£51	£5	7s	1¼	£101	10	12s	1¼	£151	15	17s	1¼
2	0	4	2½	52	5	9	2½	102	10	14	2½	152	15	19	2½
3	0	6	3½	53	5	11	3½	103	10	16	3½	153	16	1	3½
4	0	8	4¾	54	5	13	4¾	104	10	18	4¾	154	16	3	4¾
5	0	10	6	55	5	15	6	105	11	0	6	155	16	5	6
6	0	12	7¼	56	5	17	7¼	106	11	2	7¼	156	16	7	7¼
7	0	14	8½	57	5	19	8½	107	11	4	8½	157	16	9	8½
8	0	16	9½	58	6	1	9½	108	11	6	9½	158	16	11	9½
9	0	18	10¾	59	6	3	10¾	109	11	8	10¾	159	16	13	10¾
10	**1**	**1**	**0**	**60**	**6**	**6**	**0**	**110**	**11**	**11**	**0**	**160**	**16**	**16**	**0**
11	1	3	1¼	61	6	8	1¼	111	11	13	1¼	161	16	18	1¼
12	1	5	2½	62	6	10	2½	112	11	15	2½	162	17	0	2½
13	1	7	3½	63	6	12	3½	113	11	17	3½	163	17	2	3½
14	1	9	4¾	64	6	14	4¾	114	11	19	4¾	164	17	4	4¾
15	1	11	6	65	6	16	6	115	12	1	6	165	17	6	6
16	1	13	7¼	66	6	18	7¼	116	12	3	7¼	166	17	8	7¼
17	1	15	8½	67	7	0	8½	117	12	5	8½	167	17	10	8½
18	1	17	9½	68	7	2	9½	118	12	7	9½	168	17	12	9½
19	1	19	10¾	69	7	4	10¾	119	12	9	10¾	169	17	14	10¾
20	**2**	**2**	**0**	**70**	**7**	**7**	**0**	**120**	**12**	**12**	**0**	**170**	**17**	**17**	**0**
21	2	4	1¼	71	7	9	1¼	121	12	14	1¼	171	17	19	1¼
22	2	6	2½	72	7	11	2½	122	12	16	2½	172	18	1	2½
23	2	8	3½	73	7	13	3½	123	12	18	3½	173	18	3	3½
24	2	10	4¾	74	7	15	4¾	124	13	0	4¾	174	18	5	4¾
25	2	12	6	75	7	17	6	125	13	2	6	175	18	7	6
26	2	14	7¼	76	7	19	7¼	126	13	4	7¼	176	18	9	7¼
27	2	16	8½	77	8	1	8½	127	13	6	8½	177	18	11	8½
28	2	18	9½	78	8	3	9½	128	13	8	9½	178	18	13	9½
29	3	0	10¾	79	8	5	10¾	129	13	10	10¾	179	18	15	10¾
30	**3**	**3**	**0**	**80**	**8**	**8**	**0**	**130**	**13**	**13**	**0**	**180**	**18**	**18**	**0**
31	3	5	1¼	81	8	10	1¼	131	13	15	1¼	181	19	0	1¼
32	3	7	2½	82	8	12	2½	132	13	17	2½	182	19	2	2½
33	3	9	3½	83	8	14	3½	133	13	19	3½	183	19	4	3½
34	3	11	4¾	84	8	16	4¾	134	14	1	4¾	184	19	6	4¾
35	3	13	6	85	8	18	6	135	14	3	6	185	19	8	6
36	3	15	7¼	86	9	0	7¼	136	14	5	7¼	186	19	10	7¼
37	3	17	8½	87	9	2	8½	137	14	7	8½	187	19	12	8½
38	3	19	9½	88	9	4	9½	138	14	9	9½	188	19	14	9½
39	4	1	10¾	89	9	6	10¾	139	14	11	10¾	189	19	16	10¾
40	**4**	**4**	**0**	**90**	**9**	**9**	**0**	**140**	**14**	**14**	**0**	**190**	**19**	**19**	**0**
41	4	6	1¼	91	9	11	1¼	141	14	16	1¼	191	20	1	1¼
42	4	8	2½	92	9	13	2½	142	14	18	2½	192	20	3	2½
43	4	10	3½	93	9	15	3½	143	15	0	3½	193	20	5	3½
44	4	12	4¾	94	9	17	4¾	144	15	2	4¾	194	20	7	4¾
45	4	14	6	95	9	19	6	145	15	4	6	195	20	9	6
46	4	16	7¼	96	10	1	7¼	146	15	6	7¼	196	20	11	7¼
47	4	18	8½	97	10	3	8½	147	15	8	8½	197	20	13	8½
48	5	0	9½	98	10	5	9½	148	15	10	9½	198	20	15	9½
49	5	2	10¾	99	10	7	10¾	149	15	12	10¾	199	20	17	10¾
50	**5**	**5**	**0**	**100**	**10**	**10**	**0**	**150**	**15**	**15**	**0**	**200**	**21**	**0**	**0**

250	26	5s	0d	700	73	10s	0d	1200	126	0s	0d	2000	210	0s	0
300	31	10	0	750	78	15	0	1400	147	0	0	2500	262	10	0
400	42	0	0	800	84	0	0	1500	157	10	0	3000	315	0	0
500	52	10	0	900	94	10	0	1600	168	0	0	4000	420	0	0
600	63	0s	0d	1000	105	0s	0d	1800	189	0s	0d	5000	525	0s	0

89½% off

1d	0s	0d	4/1	0s	5¼	8/1	0s	10¼	12/1	1s	3¼	16/1	1s	8¼
2d	0	0¼	2	0	5¼	2	0	10¼	2	1	3¼	2	1	8¼
3d	0	0¼	3	0	5¼	3	0	10½	3	1	3½	3	1	8½
4d	0	0½	4	0	5½	4	0	10½	4	1	3½	4	1	8½
5d	0	0½	5	0	5½	5	0	10½	5	1	3¾	5	1	8¾
6d	0	0¾	4/6	0	5¾	8/6	0	10¾	12/6	1	3¾	16/6	1	8¾
7d	0	0¾	7	0	5¾	7	0	10¾	7	1	3¾	7	1	9
8d	0	0¾	8	0	6	8	0	11	8	1	4	8	1	9
9d	0	1	9	0	6	9	0	11	9	1	4	9	1	9
10d	0	1	10	0	6	10	0	11¼	10	1	4¼	10	1	9¼
11d	0	1¼	11	0	6¼	11	0	11¼	11	1	4¼	11	1	9¼
1/-	**0**	**1¼**	**5/-**	**0**	**6¼**	**9/-**	**0**	**11¼**	**13/-**	**1**	**4½**	**17/-**	**1**	**9½**
1/1	0	1¼	5/1	0	6½	1	0	11½	1	1	4½	1	1	9½
2	0	1½	2	0	6½	2	0	11½	2	1	4½	2	1	9¾
3	0	1½	3	0	6½	3	0	11¾	3	1	4¾	3	1	9¾
4	0	1¾	4	0	6¾	4	0	11¾	4	1	4¾	4	1	9¾
5	0	1¾	5	0	6¾	5	0	11¾	5	1	5	5	1	10
1/6	0	2	5/6	0	7	9/6	1	0	13/6	1	5	17/6	1	10
7	0	2	7	0	7	7	1	0	7	1	5	7	1	10¼
8	0	2	8	0	7¼	8	1	0¼	8	1	5¼	8	1	10¼
9	0	2¼	9	0	7¼	9	1	0¼	9	1	5¼	9	1	10¼
10	0	2¼	10	0	7¼	10	1	0½	10	1	5½	10	1	10½
11	0	2½	11	0	7½	11	1	0½	11	1	5½	11	1	10½
2/-	**0**	**2½**	**6/-**	**0**	**7½**	**10/-**	**1**	**0½**	**14/-**	**1**	**5¾**	**18/-**	**1**	**10¾**
2/1	0	2¾	1	0	7¾	10/1	1	0¾	1	1	5¾	1	1	10¾
2	0	2¾	2	0	7¾	2	1	0¾	2	1	5¾	2	1	11
3	0	2¾	3	0	8	3	1	1	3	1	6	3	1	11
4	0	3	4	0	8	4	1	1	4	1	6	4	1	11
5	0	3	5	0	8	5	1	1¼	5	1	6¼	5	1	11¼
2/6	0	3¼	6/6	0	8¼	10/6	1	1¼	14/6	1	6¼	18/6	1	11¼
7	0	3¼	7	0	8¼	7	1	1¼	7	1	6½	7	1	11½
8	0	3¼	8	0	8½	8	1	1½	8	1	6½	8	1	11½
9	0	3½	9	0	8½	9	1	1½	9	1	6½	9	1	11¾
10	0	3½	10	0	8½	10	1	1¾	10	1	6¾	10	1	11¾
11	0	3¾	11	0	8¾	11	1	1¾	11	1	6¾	11	1	11¾
3/-	**0**	**3¾**	**7/-**	**0**	**8¾**	**11/-**	**1**	**1¾**	**15/-**	**1**	**7**	**19/-**	**2**	**0**
3/1	0	4	1	0	9	1	1	2	15/1	1	7	1	2	0
2	0	4	2	0	9	2	1	2	2	1	7	2	2	0¼
3	0	4	3	0	9¼	3	1	2¼	3	1	7¼	3	2	0¼
4	0	4¼	4	0	9¼	4	1	2¼	4	1	7¼	4	2	0¼
5	0	4¼	5	0	9¼	5	1	2½	5	1	7½	5	2	0½
3/6	0	4½	7/6	0	9½	11/6	1	2½	15/6	1	7½	19/6	2	0½
7	0	4½	7	0	9½	7	1	2½	7	1	7¾	7	2	0¾
8	0	4½	8	0	9¾	8	1	2¾	8	1	7¾	8	2	0¾
9	0	4¾	9	0	9¾	9	1	2¾	9	1	7¾	9	2	1
10	0	4¾	10	0	9¾	10	1	3	10	1	8	10	2	1
11	0	5	11	0	10	11	1	3	11	1	8	11	2	1
4/-	**0**	**5**	**8/-**	**0**	**10**	**12/-**	**1**	**3**	**16/-**	**1**	**8¼**	**20/-**	**2**	**1¼**

20/6	2s	1¾	25/6	2s	8¼	31/-	3s	3	35/6	3s	8¾	Guineas.		
21/-	2	2½	26/-	2	8¾	31/6	3	3¾	36/-	3	9¼	1.	2s	2½
22/-	2	3¾	27/-	2	10	32/-	3	4¼	37/-	3	10½	2.	4	5
22/6	2	4¼	27/6	2	10¾	32/6	3	5	37/6	3	11¼	3.	6	7½
23/-	2	5	28/-	2	11¼	33/-	3	5½	38/-	4	0	4.	8	9¾
24/-	2	6¼	29/-	3	0½	34/-	3	6¾	39/-	4	1¼	5.	11	0¼
25/-	2s	7½	**30/-**	3s	1¾	**35/-**	3s	8	**40/-**	4s	2½	6.	13	2¾

(=9½% on Gross Returns).

£	Amount			£	Amount			£	Amount			£	Amount		
1	0	2s.	2½	51	5	12s.	2½	101	11	2s.	2½	151	16	12s.	2½
2	0	4	4¾	52	5	14	4¾	102	11	4	4¾	152	16	14	4¾
3	0	6	7¼	53	5	16	7¼	103	11	6	7¼	153	16	16	7¼
4	0	8	9½	54	5	18	9½	104	11	8	9½	154	16	18	9½
5	0	11	0	55	6	1	0	105	11	11	0	155	17	1	0
6	0	13	2½	56	6	3	2½	106	11	13	2½	156	17	3	2½
7	0	15	4¾	57	6	5	4¾	107	11	15	4¾	157	17	5	4¾
8	0	17	7¼	58	6	7	7¼	108	11	17	7¼	158	17	7	7¼
9	0	19	9½	59	6	9	9½	109	11	19	9½	159	17	9	9½
10	1	2s.	0	60	6	12s.	0	110	12	2s.	0	160	17	12s.	0
11	1	4	2½	61	6	14	2½	111	12	4	2½	161	17	14	2½
12	1	6	4¾	62	6	16	4¾	112	12	6	4¾	162	17	16	4¾
13	1	8	7¼	63	6	18	7¼	113	12	8	7¼	163	17	18	7¼
14	1	10	9½	64	7	0	9½	114	12	10	9½	164	18	0	9½
15	1	13	0	65	7	3	0	115	12	13	0	165	18	3	0
16	1	15	2½	66	7	5	2½	116	12	15	2½	166	18	5	2½
17	1	17	4¾	67	7	7	4¾	117	12	17	4¾	167	18	7	4¾
18	1	19	7¼	68	7	9	7¼	118	12	19	7¼	168	18	9	7¼
19	2	1	9½	69	7	11	9½	119	13	1	9½	169	18	11	9½
20	2	4s.	0	70	7	14s.	0	120	13	4s.	0	170	18	14s.	0
21	2	6	2½	71	7	16	2½	121	13	6	2½	171	18	16	2½
22	2	8	4¾	72	7	18	4¾	122	13	8	4¾	172	18	18	4¾
23	2	10	7¼	73	8	0	7¼	123	13	10	7¼	173	19	0	7¼
24	2	12	9½	74	8	2	9½	124	13	12	9½	174	19	2	9½
25	2	15	0	75	8	5	0	125	13	15	0	175	19	5	0
26	2	17	2½	76	8	7	2½	126	13	17	2½	176	19	7	2½
27	2	19	4¾	77	8	9	4¾	127	13	19	4¾	177	19	9	4¾
28	3	1	7¼	78	8	11	7¼	128	14	1	7¼	178	19	11	7¼
29	3	3	9½	79	8	13	9½	129	14	3	9½	179	19	13	9½
30	3	6s.	0	80	8	16s.	0	130	14	6s.	0	180	19	16s.	0
31	3	8	2½	81	8	18	2½	131	14	8	2½	181	19	18	2½
32	3	10	4¾	82	9	0	4¾	132	14	10	4¾	182	20	0	4¾
33	3	12	7¼	83	9	2	7¼	133	14	12	7¼	183	20	2	7¼
34	3	14	9½	84	9	4	9½	134	14	14	9½	184	20	4	9½
35	3	17	0	85	9	7	0	135	14	17	0	185	20	7	0
36	3	19	2½	86	9	9	2½	136	14	19	2½	186	20	9	2½
37	4	1	4¾	87	9	11	4¾	137	15	1	4¾	187	20	11	4¾
38	4	3	7¼	88	9	13	7¼	138	15	3	7¼	188	20	13	7¼
39	4	5	9½	89	9	15	9½	139	15	5	9½	189	20	15	9½
40	4	8s.	0	90	9	18s.	0	140	15	8s.	0	190	20	18s.	0
41	4	10	2½	91	10	0	2½	141	15	10	2½	191	21	0	2½
42	4	12	4¾	92	10	2	4¾	142	15	12	4¾	192	21	2	4¾
43	4	14	7¼	93	10	4	7¼	143	15	14	7¼	193	21	4	7¼
44	4	16	9½	94	10	6	9½	144	15	16	9½	194	21	6	9½
45	4	19	0	95	10	9	0	145	15	19	0	195	21	9	0
46	5	1	2½	96	10	11	2½	146	16	1	2½	196	21	11	2½
47	5	3	4¾	97	10	13	4¾	147	16	3	4¾	197	21	13	4¾
48	5	5	7¼	98	10	15	7¼	148	16	5	7¼	198	21	15	7¼
49	5	7	9½	99	10	17	9½	149	16	7	9½	199	21	17	9½
50	5	10s.	0	100	11	0s.	0	150	16	10s.	0	200	22	0s.	0

£	Amount			£	Amount			£	Amount			£	Amount		
250	£27	10	0	700	£77	0	0	1200	132	0	0	2000	220	0	0
300	33	0	0	750	82	10	0	1400	154	0	0	2500	275	0	0
400	44	0	0	800	88	0	0	1500	165	0	0	3000	330	0	0
500	55	0	0	900	99	0	0	1600	176	0	0	4000	440	0	0
600	66	0	0	1000	110	0	0	1800	198	0	0	5000	550	0	0

89% off.

11% **11 Per Cent.** 11%

1d	0s. 0	4/1	0s. 5½	8/1	0s.10¾	12/1	1s. 4	16/1	1s. 9¼
2d	0 0¼	2	0 5½	2	0 10¾	2	1 4	2	1 9¼
3d	0 0¼	3	0 5½	3	0 11	3	1 4¼	3	1 9½
4d	0 0½	4	0 5¾	4	0 11	4	1 4¼	4	1 9½
5d	0 0½	5	0 5¾	5	0 11	5	1 4½	5	1 9¾
6d	0 0¾	4/6	0 6	8/6	0 11¼	12/6	1 4½	16/6	1 9¾
7d	0 0¾	7	0 6	7	0 11¼	7	1 4½	7	1 10
8d	0 1	8	0 6¼	8	0 11½	8	1 4¾	8	1 10
9d	0 1	9	0 6¼	9	0 11½	9	1 4¾	9	1 10
10d	0 1	10	0 6½	10	0 11¾	10	1 5	10	1 10¼
11d	0 1¼	11	0 6½	11	0 11¾	11	1 5	11	1 10¼
1/-	0s. 1¼	**5/-**	0s. 6½	**9/-**	1s. 0	**13/-**	1s. 5¼	**17/-**	1s.10½
1/1	0 1½	5/1	0 6¾	9/1	1 0	13/1	1 5¼	17/1	1 10½
2	0 1½	2	0 6¾	2	1 0	2	1 5½	2	1 10¾
3	0 1¾	3	0 7	3	1 0¼	3	1 5½	3	1 10¾
4	0 1¾	4	0 7	4	1 0¼	4	1 5½	4	1 11
5	0 1¾	5	0 7¼	5	1 0½	5	1 5¾	5	1 11
1/6	0 2	5/6	0 7¼	9/6	1 0½	13/6	1 5¾	17/6	1 11
7	0 2	7	0 7¼	7	1 0¾	7	1 6	7	1 11¼
8	0 2¼	8	0 7½	8	1 0¾	8	1 6	8	1 11¼
9	0 2¼	9	0 7½	9	1 0¾	9	1 6¼	9	1 11½
10	0 2½	10	0 7¾	10	1 1	10	1 6¼	10	1 11½
11	0 2½	11	0 7¾	11	1 1	11	1 6¼	11	1 11¾
2/-	0s. 2¾	**6/-**	0s. 8	**10/-**	1s. 1¼	**14/-**	1s. 6½	**18/-**	1s.11¾
2/1	0 2¾	6/1	0 8	10/1	1 1¼	14/1	1 6½	18/1	1 11¾
2	0 2¾	2	0 8¼	2	1 1½	2	1 6¾	2	2 0
3	0 3	3	0 8¼	3	1 1½	3	1 6¾	3	2 0
4	0 3	4	0 8¼	4	1 1¾	4	1 7	4	2 0¼
5	0 3¼	5	0 8½	5	1 1¾	5	1 7	5	2 0¼
2/6	0 3¼	6/6	0 8½	10/6	1 1¾	14/6	1 7¼	18/6	2 0½
7	0 3½	7	0 8¾	7	1 2	7	1 7¼	7	2 0½
8	0 3½	8	0 8¾	8	1 2	8	1 7¼	8	2 0¾
9	0 3¾	9	0 9	9	1 2¼	9	1 7½	9	2 0¾
10	0 3¾	10	0 9	10	1 2¼	10	1 7½	10	2 0¾
11	0 3¾	11	0 9¼	11	1 2½	11	1 7¾	11	2 1
3/-	0s. 4	**7/-**	0s. 9¼	**11/-**	1s. 2½	**15/-**	1s 7¾	**19/-**	2s. 1
3/1	0 4	7/1	0 9¼	11/1	1 2¾	15/1	1 8	19/1	2 1¼
2	0 4¼	2	0 9½	2	1 2¾	2	1 8	2	2 1¼
3	0 4¼	3	0 9½	3	1 2¾	3	1 8¼	3	2 1½
4	0 4½	4	0 9¾	4	1 3	4	1 8¼	4	2 1½
5	0 4½	5	0 9¾	5	1 3	5	1 8¼	5	2 1¾
3/6	0 4½	7/6	0 10	11/6	1 3¼	15/6	1 8½	19/6	2 1¾
7	0 4¾	7	0 10	7	1 3¼	7	1 8½	7	2 1¾
8	0 4¾	8	0 10	8	1 3½	8	1 8¾	8	2 2
9	0 5	9	0 10¼	9	1 3½	9	1 8¾	9	2 2
10	0 5	10	0 10¼	10	1 3½	10	1 9	10	2 2¼
11	0 5¼	11	0 10½	11	1 3¾	11	1 9	11	2 2¼
4/-	0s. 5¼	**8/-**	0s.10½	**12/-**	1s. 3¾	**16/-**	1s. 9	**20/-**	2s. 2½

20/6	2s. 3	25/6	2s. 9¾	31/-	3s. 5	35/6	3s. 10¾	Guineas.	
21/-	2 3¾	26/-	2 10¼	31/6	3 5½	36/-	3 11½	1.	2s. 3¾
22/-	2 5	27/-	2 11¾	32/-	3 6¼	37/-	4 0¾	2.	4 7½
22/6	2 5¾	27/6	3 0¼	32/6	3 7	37/6	4 1½	3.	6 11¼
23/-	2 6¼	28/-	3 1	33/-	3 7½	38/-	4 2¼	4.	9 3
24/-	2 7¾	29/-	3 2¼	34/-	3 9	39/-	4 3½	5.	11 6½
25/-	2s. 9	**30/-**	3s. 3½	**35/-**	3s. 10¼	**40/-**	4s. 4¾	6.	13s. 10¼

(=$9\frac{9}{10}$%* on Gross Returns.)

£				£				£				£			
1	0	2s.	3	51	5	14s.	9	101	11	7s.	3	151	16	19s.	9
2	0	4	6	52	5	17	0	102	11	9	6	152	17	2	0
3	0	6	9	53	5	19	3	103	11	11	9	153	17	4	3
4	0	9	0	54	6	1	6	104	11	14	0	154	17	6	6
5	0	11	3	55	6	3	9	105	11	16	3	155	17	8	9
6	0	13	6	56	6	6	0	106	11	18	6	156	17	11	0
7	0	15	9	57	6	8	3	107	12	0	9	157	17	13	3
8	0	18	0	58	6	10	6	108	12	3	0	158	17	15	6
9	1	0	3	59	6	12	9	109	12	5	3	159	17	17	9
10	1	2s.	6	60	6	15s.	0	110	12	7s.	6	160	18	0s.	0
11	1	4	9	61	6	17	3	111	12	9	9	161	18	2	3
12	1	7	0	62	6	19	6	112	12	12	0	162	18	4	6
13	1	9	3	63	7	1	9	113	12	14	3	163	18	6	9
14	1	11	6	64	7	4	0	114	12	16	6	164	18	9	0
15	1	13	9	65	7	6	3	115	12	18	9	165	18	11	3
16	1	16	0	66	7	8	6	116	13	1	0	166	18	13	6
17	1	18	3	67	7	10	9	117	13	3	3	167	18	15	9
18	2	0	6	68	7	13	0	118	13	5	6	168	18	18	0
19	2	2	9	69	7	15	3	119	13	7	9	169	19	0	3
20	2	5s.	0	70	7	17s.	6	120	13	10s.	0	170	19	2s.	6
21	2	7	3	71	7	19	9	121	13	12	3	171	19	4	9
22	2	9	6	72	8	2	0	122	13	14	6	172	19	7	0
23	2	11	9	73	8	4	3	123	13	16	9	173	19	9	3
24	2	14	0	74	8	6	6	124	13	19	0	174	19	11	6
25	2	16	3	75	8	8	9	125	14	1	3	175	19	13	9
26	2	18	6	76	8	11	0	126	14	3	6	176	19	16	0
27	3	0	9	77	8	13	3	127	14	5	9	177	19	18	3
28	3	3	0	78	8	15	6	128	14	8	0	178	20	0	6
29	3	5	3	79	8	17	9	129	14	10	3	179	20	2	9
30	3	7s.	6	80	9	0s.	0	130	14	12s.	6	180	20	5s.	0
31	3	9	9	81	9	2	3	131	14	14	9	181	20	7	3
32	3	12	0	82	9	4	6	132	14	17	0	182	20	9	6
33	3	14	3	83	9	6	9	133	14	19	3	183	20	11	9
34	3	16	6	84	9	9	0	134	15	1	6	184	20	14	0
35	3	18	9	85	9	11	3	135	15	3	9	185	20	16	3
36	4	1	0	86	9	13	6	136	15	6	0	186	20	18	6
37	4	3	3	87	9	15	9	137	15	8	3	187	21	0	9
38	4	5	6	88	9	18	0	138	15	10	6	188	21	3	0
39	4	7	9	89	10	0	3	139	15	12	9	189	21	5	3
40	4	10s.	0	90	10	2s.	6	140	15	15s.	0	190	21	7s.	6
41	4	12	3	91	10	4	9	141	15	17	3	191	21	9	9
42	4	14	6	92	10	7	0	142	15	19	6	192	21	12	0
43	4	16	9	93	10	9	3	143	16	1	9	193	21	14	3
44	4	19	0	94	10	11	6	144	16	4	0	194	21	16	6
45	5	1	3	95	10	13	9	145	16	6	3	195	21	18	9
46	5	3	6	96	10	16	0	146	16	8	6	196	22	1	0
47	5	5	9	97	10	18	3	147	16	10	9	197	22	3	3
48	5	8	0	98	11	0	6	148	16	13	0	198	22	5	6
49	5	10	3	99	11	2	9	149	16	15	3	199	22	7	9
50	5	12s.	6	100	11	5s.	0	150	16	17s.	6	200	22	10s.	0

250	£28	2	6	700	£78	15	0	1200	135	0	0	2000	225	0	0
300	33	15	0	750	84	7	6	1400	157	10	0	2500	281	5	0
400	45	0	0	800	90	0	0	1500	168	15	0	3000	337	10	0
500	56	5	0	900	101	5	0	1600	180	0	0	4000	450	0	0
600	67	10	0	1000	112	10	0	1800	202	10	0	5000	562	10	0

88¾% off.

11¼ Per Cent.

11¼%

1d	0s.	0	4/1	0s.	5½	8/1	0s.	11	12/1	1s.	4¼	16/1	1s.	9¾
2d	0	0¼	2	0	5¾	2	0	11	2	1	4½	2	1	9¾
3d	0	0¼	3	0	5¾	3	0	11¼	3	1	4½	3	1	10
4d	0	0½	4	0	5¾	4	0	11¼	4	1	4¾	4	1	10
5d	0	0½	5	0	6	5	0	11¼	5	1	4¾	5	1	10¼
6d	0	0¾	4/6	0	6	8/6	0	11½	12/6	1	5	16/6	1	10¼
7d	0	0¾	7	0	6¼	7	0	11½	7	1	5	7	1	10½
8d	0	1	8	0	6¼	8	0	11¾	8	1	5	8	1	10½
9d	0	1	9	0	6½	9	0	11¾	9	1	5¼	9	1	10½
10d	0	1¼	10	0	6½	10	1	0	10	1	5¼	10	1	10¾
11d	0	1¼	11	0	6¾	11	1	0	11	1	5½	11	1	10¾
1/-	0s.	1¼	**5/-**	0s.	6¾	**9/-**	1s.	0¼	**13/-**	1s.	5½	**17/-**	1s.	11
1/1	0	1½	5/1	0	6¾	9/1	1	0¼	13/1	1	5¾	17/1	1	11
2	0	1½	2	0	7	2	1	0½	2	1	5¾	2	1	11¼
3	0	1¾	3	0	7	3	1	0½	3	1	6	3	1	11¼
4	0	1¾	4	0	7¼	4	1	0½	4	1	6	4	1	11½
5	0	2	5	0	7¼	5	1	0¾	5	1	6	5	1	11½
1/6	0	2	5/6	0	7½	9/6	1	0¾	13/6	1	6¼	17/6	1	11¾
7	0	2¼	7	0	7½	7	1	1	7	1	6¼	7	1	11¾
8	0	2¼	8	0	7¾	8	1	1	8	1	6½	8	1	11¾
9	0	2¼	9	0	7¾	9	1	1¼	9	1	6½	9	2	0
10	0	2½	10	0	8	10	1	1¼	10	1	6¾	10	2	0
11	0	2½	11	0	8	11	1	1½	11	1	6¾	11	2	0¼
2/-	0s.	2¾	**6/-**	0s.	8	**10/-**	1s.	1½	**14/-**	1s.	7	**18/-**	2s.	0¼
2/1	0	2¾	6/1	0	8¼	10/1	1	1½	14/1	1	7	18/1	2	0½
2	0	3	2	0	8¼	2	1	1¾	2	1	7¼	2	2	0½
3	0	3	3	0	8½	3	1	1¾	3	1	7¼	3	2	0¾
4	0	3¼	4	0	8½	4	1	2	4	1	7¼	4	2	0¾
5	0	3¼	5	0	8¾	5	1	2	5	1	7½	5	2	0¾
2/6	0	3½	6/6	0	8¾	10/6	1	2¼	14/6	1	7½	18/6	2	1
7	0	3½	7	0	9	7	1	2¼	7	1	7¾	7	2	1
8	0	3½	8	0	9	8	1	2½	8	1	7¾	8	2	1¼
9	0	3¾	9	0	9	9	1	2½	9	1	8	9	2	1¼
10	0	3¾	10	0	9¼	10	1	2¾	10	1	8	10	2	1½
11	0	4	11	0	9¼	11	1	2¾	11	1	8¼	11	2	1½
3/-	0s.	4	**7/-**	0s.	9½	**11/-**	1s.	2¾	**15/-**	1s	8¼	**19/-**	2s.	1¾
3/1	0	4¼	7/1	0	9½	11/1	1	3	15/1	1	8¼	19/1	2	1¾
2	0	4¼	2	0	9¾	2	1	3	2	1	8½	2	2	2
3	0	4½	3	0	9¾	3	1	3¼	3	1	8½	3	2	2
4	0	4½	4	0	10	4	1	3¼	4	1	8¾	4	2	2
5	0	4½	5	0	10	5	1	3½	5	1	8¾	5	2	2¼
3/6	0	4¾	7/6	0	10¼	11/6	1	3½	15/6	1	9	19/6	2	2¼
7	0	4¾	7	0	10¼	7	1	3¾	7	1	9	7	2	2½
8	0	5	8	0	10¼	8	1	3¾	8	1	9¼	8	2	2½
9	0	5	9	0	10½	9	1	3¾	9	1	9¼	9	2	2¾
10	0	5¼	10	0	10½	10	1	4	10	1	9½	10	2	2¾
11	0	5¼	11	0	10¾	11	1	4	11	1	9½	11	2	3
4/-	0s.	5½	**8/-**	0s.	10¾	**12/-**	1s.	4¼	**16/-**	1s.	9½	**20/-**	2s.	3

20/6	2s.	3¾	25/6	2s.	10½	31/-	3s.	5¾	35/6	4s.	0	Guineas.		
21/-	2	4½	26/-	2	11	31/6	3	6½	36/-	4	0½	1.	2s.	4½
22/-	2	5¾	27/-	3	0½	32/-	3	7¼	37/-	4	2	2.	4	8¾
22/6	2	6½	27/6	3	1¼	32/6	3	8	37/6	4	2¾	3.	7	1
23/-	2	7	28/-	3	1¾	33/-	3	8½	38/-	4	3¼	4.	9	5½
24/-	2	8½	29/-	3	3¼	34/-	3	10	39/-	4	4¾	5.	11	9¾
25/-	2s.	9¾	**30/-**	3s.	4½	**35/-**	3s.	11¼	**40/-**	4s.	6	6.	14s.	2

(=10 1/10 %* on Gross Returns.)

£1	£0	2s	3½	£51	£5	17s	3½	£101	11	12s	3½	£151	17	7s	3½
2	0	4	7¼	52	5	19	7¼	102	11	14	7¼	152	17	9	7¼
3	0	6	10¾	53	6	1	10¾	103	11	16	10¾	153	17	11	10¾
4	0	9	2½	54	6	4	2½	104	11	19	2½	154	17	14	2½
5	0	11	6	55	6	6	6	105	12	1	6	155	17	16	6
6	0	13	9½	56	6	8	9½	106	12	3	9½	156	17	18	9½
7	0	16	1¼	57	6	11	1¼	107	12	6	1¼	157	18	1	1¼
8	0	18	4¾	58	6	13	4¾	108	12	8	4¾	158	18	3	4¾
9	1	0	8½	59	6	15	8½	109	12	10	8½	159	18	5	8½
10	**1**	**3**	**0**	**60**	**6**	**18**	**0**	**110**	**12**	**13**	**0**	**160**	**18**	**8**	**0**
11	1	5	3½	61	7	0	3½	111	12	15	3½	161	18	10	3½
12	1	7	7¼	62	7	2	7¼	112	12	17	7¼	162	18	12	7¼
13	1	9	10¾	63	7	4	10¾	113	12	19	10¾	163	18	14	10¾
14	1	12	2½	64	7	7	2½	114	13	2	2½	164	18	17	2½
15	1	14	6	65	7	9	6	115	13	4	6	165	18	19	6
16	1	16	9½	66	7	11	9½	116	13	6	9½	166	19	1	9½
17	1	19	1¼	67	7	14	1¼	117	13	9	1¼	167	19	4	1¼
18	2	1	4¾	68	7	16	4¾	118	13	11	4¾	168	19	6	4¾
19	2	3	8½	69	7	18	8½	119	13	13	8½	169	19	8	8½
20	**2**	**6**	**0**	**70**	**8**	**1**	**0**	**120**	**13**	**16**	**0**	**170**	**19**	**11**	**0**
21	2	8	3½	71	8	3	3½	121	13	18	3½	171	19	13	3½
22	2	10	7¼	72	8	5	7¼	122	14	0	7¼	172	19	15	7¼
23	2	12	10¾	73	8	7	10¾	123	14	2	10¾	173	19	17	10¾
24	2	15	2½	74	8	10	2½	124	14	5	2½	174	20	0	2½
25	2	17	6	75	8	12	6	125	14	7	6	175	20	2	6
26	2	19	9½	76	8	14	9½	126	14	9	9½	176	20	4	9½
27	3	2	1¼	77	8	17	1¼	127	14	12	1¼	177	20	7	1¼
28	3	4	4¾	78	8	19	4¾	128	14	14	4¾	178	20	9	4¾
29	3	6	8½	79	9	1	8½	129	14	16	8½	179	20	11	8½
30	**3**	**9**	**0**	**80**	**9**	**4**	**0**	**130**	**14**	**19**	**0**	**180**	**20**	**14**	**0**
31	3	11	3½	81	9	6	3½	131	15	1	3½	181	20	16	3½
32	3	13	7¼	82	9	8	7¼	132	15	3	7¼	182	20	18	7¼
33	3	15	10¾	83	9	10	10¾	133	15	5	10¾	183	21	0	10¾
34	3	18	2½	84	9	13	2½	134	15	8	2½	184	21	3	2½
35	4	0	6	85	9	15	6	135	15	10	6	185	21	5	6
36	4	2	9½	86	9	17	9½	136	15	12	9½	186	21	7	9½
37	4	5	1¼	87	10	0	1¼	137	15	15	1¼	187	21	10	1¼
38	4	7	4¾	88	10	2	4¾	138	15	17	4¾	188	21	12	4¾
39	4	9	8½	89	10	4	8½	139	15	19	8½	189	21	14	8½
40	**4**	**12**	**0**	**90**	**10**	**7**	**0**	**140**	**16**	**2**	**0**	**190**	**21**	**17**	**0**
41	4	14	3½	91	10	9	3½	141	16	4	3½	191	21	19	3½
42	4	16	7¼	92	10	11	7¼	142	16	6	7¼	192	22	1	7¼
43	4	18	10¾	93	10	13	10¾	143	16	8	10¾	193	22	3	10¾
44	5	1	2½	94	10	16	2½	144	16	11	2½	194	22	6	2½
45	5	3	6	95	10	18	6	145	16	13	6	195	22	8	6
46	5	5	9½	96	11	0	9½	146	16	15	9½	196	22	10	9½
47	5	8	1¼	97	11	3	1¼	147	16	18	1¼	197	22	13	1¼
48	5	10	4¾	98	11	5	4¾	148	17	0	4¾	198	22	15	4¾
49	5	12	8½	99	11	7	8½	149	17	2	8½	199	22	17	8½
50	**5**	**15**	**0**	**100**	**11**	**10**	**0**	**150**	**17**	**5**	**0**	**200**	**23**	**0**	**0**

250	28	15s	0d	700	80	10s	0d	1200	138	0s	0d	2000	230	0s	0
300	34	10	0	750	86	5	0	1400	161	0	0	2500	287	10	0
400	46	0	0	800	92	0	0	1500	172	10	0	3000	345	0	0
500	57	10	0	900	103	10	0	1600	184	0	0	4000	460	0	0
600	69	0s	0d	1000	115	0s	0d	1800	207	0s	0d	5000	575	0s	0

88½% off

11½ PER CENT.

11½%

	s	d		s	d		s	d		s	d		s	d
1d	0s	0d	4/1	0s	5¾	8/1	0s	11¼	12/1	1s	4¾	16/1	1s	10¼
2d	0	0¼	2	0	5¾	2	0	11¼	2	1	4¾	2	1	10¼
3d	0	0¼	3	0	5¾	3	0	11½	3	1	5	3	1	10½
4d	0	0½	4	0	6	4	0	11½	4	1	5	4	1	10½
5d	0	0½	5	0	6	5	0	11½	5	1	5¼	5	1	10¾
6d	0	0¾	4/6	0	6¼	8/6	0	11¾	12/6	1	5¼	16/6	1	10¾
7d	0	0¾	7	0	6¼	7	0	11¾	7	1	5¼	7	1	11
8d	0	1	8	0	6½	8	1	0	8	1	5½	8	1	11
9d	0	1	9	0	6½	9	1	0	9	1	5½	9	1	11
10d	0	1¼	10	0	6¾	10	1	0¼	10	1	5¾	10	1	11¼
11d	0	1¼	11	0	6¾	11	1	0¼	11	1	5¾	11	1	11¼
1/-	**0**	**1½**	**5/-**	**0**	**7**	**9/-**	**1**	**0½**	**13/-**	**1**	**6**	**17/-**	**1**	**11½**
1/1	0	1½	5/1	0	7	1	1	0½	1	1	6	1	1	11½
2	0	1½	2	0	7¼	2	1	0¾	2	1	6¼	2	1	11¾
3	0	1¾	3	0	7¼	3	1	0¾	3	1	6¼	3	1	11¾
4	0	1¾	4	0	7¼	4	1	1	4	1	6½	4	2	0
5	0	2	5	0	7½	5	1	1	5	1	6½	5	2	0
1/6	0	2	5/6	0	7½	9/6	1	1	13/6	1	6¾	17/6	2	0¼
7	0	2¼	7	0	7¾	7	1	1¼	7	1	6¾	7	2	0¼
8	0	2¼	8	0	7¾	8	1	1¼	8	1	7	8	2	0½
9	0	2½	9	0	8	9	1	1½	9	1	7	9	2	0½
10	0	2½	10	0	8	10	1	1½	10	1	7	10	2	0½
11	0	2¾	11	0	8¼	11	1	1¾	11	1	7¼	11	2	0¾
2/-	**0**	**2¾**	**6/-**	**0**	**8¼**	**10/-**	**1**	**1¾**	**14/-**	**1**	**7¼**	**18/-**	**2**	**0¾**
2/1	0	3	1	0	8½	10/1	1	2	1	1	7½	1	2	1
2	0	3	2	0	8½	2	1	2	2	1	7½	2	2	1
3	0	3	3	0	8¾	3	1	2¼	3	1	7¾	3	2	1¼
4	0	3¼	4	0	8¾	4	1	2¼	4	1	7¾	4	2	1¼
5	0	3¼	5	0	8¾	5	1	2½	5	1	8	5	2	1½
2/6	0	3½	6/6	0	9	10/6	1	2½	14/6	1	8	18/6	2	1½
7	0	3½	7	0	9	7	1	2½	7	1	8¼	7	2	1¾
8	0	3¾	8	0	9¼	8	1	2¾	8	1	8¼	8	2	1¾
9	0	3¾	9	0	9¼	9	1	2¾	9	1	8¼	9	2	2
10	0	4	10	0	9½	10	1	3	10	1	8½	10	2	2
11	0	4	11	0	9½	11	1	3	11	1	8½	11	2	2
3/-	**0**	**4¼**	**7/-**	**0**	**9¾**	**11/-**	**1**	**3¼**	**15/-**	**1**	**8¾**	**19/-**	**2**	**2¼**
3/1	0	4¼	1	0	9¾	1	1	3¼	15/1	1	8¾	1	2	2¼
2	0	4¼	2	0	10	2	1	3½	2	1	9	2	2	2½
3	0	4½	3	0	10	3	1	3½	3	1	9	3	2	2½
4	0	4½	4	0	10	4	1	3¾	4	1	9¼	4	2	2¾
5	0	4¾	5	0	10¼	5	1	3¾	5	1	9¼	5	2	2¾
3/6	0	4¾	7/6	0	10¼	11/6	1	3¾	15/6	1	9½	19/6	2	3
7	0	5	7	0	10½	7	1	4	7	1	9½	7	2	3
8	0	5	8	0	10½	8	1	4	8	1	9½	8	2	3¼
9	0	5¼	9	0	10¾	9	1	4¼	9	1	9¾	9	2	3¼
10	0	5¼	10	0	10¾	10	1	4¼	10	1	9¾	10	2	3¼
11	0	5½	11	0	11	11	1	4½	11	1	10	11	2	3½
4/-	**0**	**5½**	**8/-**	**0**	**11**	**12/-**	**1**	**4½**	**16/-**	**1**	**10**	**20/-**	**2**	**3½**

												Guineas.		
20/6	2s	4¼	25/6	2s	11¼	31/-	3s	6¾	35/6	4s	1	1.	2s	5
21/-	2	5	26/-	3	0	31/6	3	7½	36/-	4	1¾	2.	4	10
22/-	2	6¼	27/-	3	1¼	32/-	3	8¼	37/-	4	3	3.	7	3
22/6	2	7	27/6	3	2	32/6	3	8¾	37/6	4	3¾	4.	9	8
23/-	2	7¾	28/-	3	2¾	33/-	3	9½	38/-	4	4½	5.	12	1
24/-	2	9	29/-	3	4	34/-	3	11	39/-	4	5¾	6.	14	6
25/-	2s	10½	**30/-**	3s	5½	**35/-**	4s	0¼	**40/-**	4s	7¼			

(=$10\frac{3}{10}$% on Gross Returns).

£1	0	2s.	4¾	£51	6	2s.	4¾	£101	12	2s.	4¾	£151	18	2s.	4¾
2	0	4	9½	52	6	4	9½	102	12	4	9½	152	18	4	9½
3	0	7	2½	53	6	7	2½	103	12	7	2½	153	18	7	2½
4	0	9	7¼	54	6	9	7¼	104	12	9	7¼	154	18	9	7¼
5	0	12	0	55	6	12	0	105	12	12	0	155	18	12	0
6	0	14	4¾	56	6	14	4¾	106	12	14	4¾	156	18	14	4¾
7	0	16	9½	57	6	16	9½	107	12	16	9½	157	18	16	9½
8	0	19	2½	58	6	19	2½	108	12	19	2½	158	18	19	2½
9	1	1	7¼	59	7	1	7¼	109	13	1	7¼	159	19	1	7¼
10	1	4s.	0	**60**	7	4s.	0	**110**	13	4s.	0	**160**	19	4s.	0
11	1	6	4¾	61	7	6	4¾	111	13	6	4¾	161	19	6	4¾
12	1	8	9½	62	7	8	9½	112	13	8	9½	162	19	8	9½
13	1	11	2½	63	7	11	2½	113	13	11	2½	163	19	11	2½
14	1	13	7¼	64	7	13	7¼	114	13	13	7¼	164	19	13	7¼
15	1	16	0	65	7	16	0	115	13	16	0	165	19	16	0
16	1	18	4¾	66	7	18	4¾	116	13	18	4¾	166	19	18	4¾
17	2	0	9½	67	8	0	9½	117	14	0	9½	167	20	0	9½
18	2	3	2½	68	8	3	2½	118	14	3	2½	168	20	3	2½
19	2	5	7¼	69	8	5	7¼	119	14	5	7¼	169	20	5	7¼
20	2	8s.	0	**70**	8	8s.	0	**120**	14	8s.	0	**170**	20	8s.	0
21	2	10	4¾	71	8	10	4¾	121	14	10	4¾	171	20	10	4¾
22	2	12	9½	72	8	12	9½	122	14	12	9½	172	20	12	9½
23	2	15	2½	73	8	15	2½	123	14	15	2½	173	20	15	2½
24	2	17	7¼	74	8	17	7¼	124	14	17	7¼	174	20	17	7¼
25	3	0	0	75	9	0	0	125	15	0	0	175	21	0	0
26	3	2	4¾	76	9	2	4¾	126	15	2	4¾	176	21	2	4¾
27	3	4	9½	77	9	4	9½	127	15	4	9½	177	21	4	9½
28	3	7	2½	78	9	7	2½	128	15	7	2½	178	21	7	2½
29	3	9	7¼	79	9	9	7¼	129	15	9	7¼	179	21	9	7¼
30	3	12s.	0	**80**	9	12s.	0	**130**	15	12s.	0	**180**	21	12s.	0
31	3	14	4¾	81	9	14	4¾	131	15	14	4¾	181	21	14	4¾
32	3	16	9½	82	9	16	9½	132	15	16	9½	182	21	16	9½
33	3	19	2½	83	9	19	2½	133	15	19	2½	183	21	19	2½
34	4	1	7¼	84	10	1	7¼	134	16	1	7¼	184	22	1	7¼
35	4	4	0	85	10	4	0	135	16	4	0	185	22	4	0
36	4	6	4¾	86	10	6	4¾	136	16	6	4¾	186	22	6	4¾
37	4	8	9½	87	10	8	9½	137	16	8	9½	187	22	8	9½
38	4	11	2½	88	10	11	2½	138	16	11	2½	188	22	11	2½
39	4	13	7¼	89	10	13	7¼	139	16	13	7¼	189	22	13	7¼
40	4	16s.	0	**90**	10	16s.	0	**140**	16	16s.	0	**190**	22	16s.	0
41	4	18	4¾	91	10	18	4¾	141	16	18	4¾	191	22	18	4¾
42	5	0	9½	92	11	0	9½	142	17	0	9½	192	23	0	9½
43	5	3	2½	93	11	3	2½	143	17	3	2½	193	23	3	2½
44	5	5	7¼	94	11	5	7¼	144	17	5	7¼	194	23	5	7¼
45	5	8	0	95	11	8	0	145	17	8	0	195	23	8	0
46	5	10	4¾	96	11	10	4¾	146	17	10	4¾	196	23	10	4¾
47	5	12	9½	97	11	12	9½	147	17	12	9½	197	23	12	9½
48	5	15	2½	98	11	15	2½	148	17	15	2½	198	23	15	2½
49	5	17	7¼	99	11	17	7¼	149	17	17	7¼	199	23	17	7¼
50	6	0s.	0	**100**	12	0s.	0	**150**	18	0s.	0	**200**	24	0s.	0
250	£30	0	0	700	£84	0	0	1200	144	0	0	2000	240	0	0
300	36	0	0	750	90	0	0	1400	168	0	0	2500	300	0	0
400	48	0	0	800	96	0	0	1500	180	0	0	3000	360	0	0
500	60	0	0	900	108	0	0	1600	192	0	0	4000	480	0	0
600	72	0	0	1000	120	0	0	1800	216	0	0	5000	600	0	0

88% off.

12% 12 Per Cent. 12%

1d	0s.	0	4/1	0s.	6	8/1	0s.	11¾	12/1	1s.	5½	16/1	1s.	11¼
2d	0	0¼	2	0	6	2	0	11¾	2	1	5½	2	1	11¼
3d	0	0¼	3	0	6	3	1	0	3	1	5¾	3	1	11½
4d	0	0½	4	0	6¼	4	1	0	4	1	5¾	4	1	11½
5d	0	0½	5	0	6¼	5	1	0	5	1	6	5	1	11¾
6d	0	0¾	4/6	0	6½	8/6	1	0¼	12/6	1	6	16/6	1	11¾
7d	0	0¾	7	0	6½	7	1	0¼	7	1	6	7	2	0
8d	0	1	8	0	6¾	8	1	0½	8	1	6¼	8	2	0
9d	0	1	9	0	6¾	9	1	0½	9	1	6¼	9	2	0
10d	0	1¼	10	0	7	10	1	0¾	10	1	6½	10	2	0¼
11d	0	1¼	11	0	7	11	1	0¾	11	1	6½	11	2	0¼
1/-	0s.	1½	**5/-**	0s.	7¼	**9/-**	1s.	1	**13/-**	1s.	6¾	**17/-**	2s.	0½
1/1	0	1½	5/1	0	7¼	9/1	1	1	13/1	1	6¾	17/1	2	0½
2	0	1¾	2	0	7½	2	1	1¼	2	1	7	2	2	0¾
3	0	1¾	3	0	7½	3	1	1¼	3	1	7	3	2	0¾
4	0	2	4	0	7¾	4	1	1½	4	1	7¼	4	2	1
5	0	2	5	0	7¾	5	1	1½	5	1	7¼	5	2	1
1/6	0	2¼	5/6	0	8	9/6	1	1¾	13/6	1	7½	17/6	2	1¼
7	0	2¼	7	0	8	7	1	1¾	7	1	7½	7	2	1¼
8	0	2½	8	0	8¼	8	1	2	8	1	7¾	8	2	1½
9	0	2½	9	0	8¼	9	1	2	9	1	7¾	9	2	1½
10	0	2¾	10	0	8½	10	1	2¼	10	1	8	10	2	1¾
11	0	2¾	11	0	8½	11	1	2¼	11	1	8	11	2	1¾
2/-	0s.	3	**6/-**	0s.	8¾	**10/-**	1s.	2½	**14/-**	1s.	8¼	**18/-**	2s.	2
2/1	0	3	6/1	0	8¾	10/1	1	2½	14/1	1	8¼	18/1	2	2
2	0	3	2	0	9	2	1	2¾	2	1	8½	2	2	2¼
3	0	3¼	3	0	9	3	1	2¾	3	1	8½	3	2	2¼
4	0	3¼	4	0	9	4	1	3	4	1	8¾	4	2	2½
5	0	3½	5	0	9¼	5	1	3	5	1	8¾	5	2	2½
2/6	0	3½	6/6	0	9¼	10/6	1	3	14/6	1	9	18/6	2	2¾
7	0	3¾	7	0	9½	7	1	3¼	7	1	9	7	2	2¾
8	0	3¾	8	0	9½	8	1	3¼	8	1	9	8	2	3
9	0	4	9	0	9¾	9	1	3½	9	1	9¼	9	2	3
10	0	4	10	0	9¾	10	1	3½	10	1	9¼	10	2	3
11	0	4¼	11	0	10	11	1	3¾	11	1	9½	11	2	3¼
3/-	0s.	4¼	**7/-**	0s.	10	**11/-**	1s.	3¾	**15/-**	1s	9½	**19/-**	2s.	3¼
3/1	0	4½	7/1	0	10¼	11/1	1	4	15/1	1	9¾	19/1	2	3½
2	0	4½	2	0	10¼	2	1	4	2	1	9¾	2	2	3½
3	0	4¾	3	0	10½	3	1	4¼	3	1	10	3	2	3¾
4	0	4¾	4	0	10½	4	1	4¼	4	1	10	4	2	3¾
5	0	5	5	0	10¾	5	1	4½	5	1	10¼	5	2	4
3/6	0	5	7/6	0	10¾	11/6	1	4½	15/6	1	10¼	19/6	2	4
7	0	5¼	7	0	11	7	1	4¾	7	1	10½	7	2	4¼
8	0	5¼	8	0	11	8	1	4¾	8	1	10½	8	2	4¼
9	0	5½	9	0	11¼	9	1	5	9	1	10¾	9	2	4½
10	0	5½	10	0	11¼	10	1	5	10	1	10¾	10	2	4½
11	0	5¾	11	0	11½	11	1	5¼	11	1	11	11	2	4¾
4/-	0s.	5¾	**8/-**	0s.	11½	**12/-**	1s.	5¼	**16/-**	1s.	11	**20/-**	2s	4¾

20/6	2s.	5½	25/6	3s.	0¾	31/-	3s.	8¾	35/6	4s.	3	Guineas		
21/-	2	6¼	26/-	3	1½	31/6	3	9¼	36/-	4	3¾	1.	2s.	6¼
22/-	2	7¾	27/-	3	3	32/-	3	10	37/-	4	5¼	2.	5	0½
22/6	2	8½	27/6	3	3½	32/6	3	10¾	37/6	4	6	3.	7	6¾
23/-	2	9	28/-	3	4¼	33/-	3	11½	38/-	4	6¾	4.	10	1
24/-	2	10½	29/-	3	5¾	34/-	4	1	39/-	4	8¼	5.	12	7¼
25/-	3s.	0	**30/-**	3s.	7¼	**35/-**	4s.	2½	**40/-**	4s.	9½	6.	15s.	1½

(= $10\frac{7}{10}$%* on Gross Returns.)

£	£ s. d.	£	£ s. d.	£	£ s. d.	£	£ s. d.
£1	£0 2s. 6	£51	£6 7s. 6	£101	12 12s. 6	£151	£18 17s. 6
2	0 5 0	52	6 10 0	102	12 15 0	152	19 0 0
3	0 7 6	53	6 12 6	103	12 17 6	153	19 2 6
4	0 10 0	54	6 15 0	104	13 0 0	154	19 5 0
5	0 12 6	55	6 17 6	105	13 2 6	155	19 7 6
6	0 15 0	56	7 0 0	106	13 5 0	156	19 10 0
7	0 17 6	57	7 2 6	107	13 7 6	157	19 12 6
8	1 0 0	58	7 5 0	108	13 10 0	158	19 15 0
9	1 2 6	59	7 7 6	109	13 12 6	159	19 17 6
10	£1 5s. 0	60	£7 10s. 0	110	13 15s. 0	160	£20 0s. 0
11	£1 7s. 6	61	£7 12s. 6	111	13 17s. 6	161	£20 2s. 6
12	1 10 0	62	7 15 0	112	14 0 0	162	20 5 0
13	1 12 6	63	7 17 6	113	14 2 6	163	20 7 6
14	1 15 0	64	8 0 0	114	14 5 0	164	20 10 0
15	1 17 6	65	8 2 6	115	14 7 6	165	20 12 6
16	2 0 0	66	8 5 0	116	14 10 0	166	20 15 0
17	2 2 6	67	8 7 6	117	14 12 6	167	20 17 6
18	2 5 0	68	8 10 0	118	14 15 0	168	21 0 0
19	2 7 6	69	8 12 6	119	14 17 6	169	21 2 6
20	£2 10s. 0	70	£8 15s. 0	120	15 0s. 0	170	£21 5s. 0
21	£2 12s. 6	71	£8 17s. 6	121	15 2s. 6	171	£21 7s. 6
22	2 15 0	72	9 0 0	122	15 5 0	172	21 10 0
23	2 17 6	73	9 2 6	123	15 7 6	173	21 12 6
24	3 0 0	74	9 5 0	124	15 10 0	174	21 15 0
25	3 2 6	75	9 7 6	125	15 12 6	175	21 17 6
26	3 5 0	76	9 10 0	126	15 15 0	176	22 0 0
27	3 7 6	77	9 12 6	127	15 17 6	177	22 2 6
28	3 10 0	78	9 15 0	128	16 0 0	178	22 5 0
29	3 12 6	79	9 17 6	129	16 2 6	179	22 7 6
30	£3 15s. 0	80	10 0s. 0	130	16 5s. 0	180	£22 10s. 0
31	£3 17s. 6	81	10 2s. 6	131	16 7s. 6	181	£22 12s 6
32	4 0 0	82	10 5 0	132	16 10 0	182	22 15 0
33	4 2 6	83	10 7 6	133	16 12 6	183	22 17 6
34	4 5 0	84	10 10 0	134	16 15 0	184	23 0 0
35	4 7 6	85	10 12 6	135	16 17 6	185	23 2 6
36	4 10 0	86	10 15 0	136	17 0 0	186	23 5 0
37	4 12 6	87	10 17 6	137	17 2 6	187	23 7 6
38	4 15 0	88	11 0 0	138	17 5 0	188	23 10 0
39	4 17 6	89	11 2 6	139	17 7 6	189	23 12 6
40	£5 0s. 0	90	11 5s. 0	140	17 10s. 0	190	£23 15s. 0
41	£5 2s. 6	91	11 7s. 6	141	17 12s. 6	191	£23 17s. 6
42	5 5 0	92	11 10 0	142	17 15 0	192	24 0 0
43	5 7 6	93	11 12 6	143	17 17 6	193	24 2 6
44	5 10 0	94	11 15 0	144	18 0 0	194	24 5 0
45	5 12 6	95	11 17 6	145	18 2 6	195	24 7 6
46	5 15 0	96	12 0 0	146	18 5 0	196	24 10 0
47	5 17 6	97	12 2 6	147	18 7 6	197	24 12 6
48	6 0 0	98	12 5 0	148	18 10 0	198	24 15 0
49	6 2 6	99	12 7 6	149	18 12 6	199	24 17 6
50	£6 5s. 0	100	12 10s. 0	150	18 15s. 0	200	£25 0s 0

£	£ s. d.	£	£ s. d.	£	£ s. d.	£	£ s. d.
250	£31 5s. 0d	700	£87 10s.0d	1200	150 0s.0d	2000	£250 0s. 0d
300	37 10 0	750	93 15 0	1400	175 0 0	2500	312 10 0
400	50 0 0	800	100 0 0	1500	187 10 0	3000	375 0 0
500	62 10 0	900	112 10 0	1600	200 0 0	4000	500 0 0
600	£75 0s. 0d	1000	125 0s. 0d	1800	225 0s.0d	5000	£625 0s. 0

87½% off.   (12½%=1-8th)

12½% 12½ Per Cent. 12½%

1d	0s.	0¼	4/1	0s.	6¼	8/1	1s.	0¼	12/1	1s.	6¼	16/1	2s.	0¼
2d	0	0¼	2	0	6¼	2	1	0¼	2	1	6¼	2	2	0¼
3d	0	0½	3	0	6½	3	1	0½	3	1	6½	3	2	0½
4d	0	0½	4	0	6½	4	1	0½	4	1	6½	4	2	0½
5d	0	0¾	5	0	6¾	5	1	0¾	5	1	6¾	5	2	0¾
6d	0	0¾	4/6	0	6¾	8/6	1	0¾	12/6	1	6¾	16/6	2	0¾
7d	0	1	7	0	7	7	1	1	7	1	7	7	2	1
8d	0	1	8	0	7	8	1	1	8	1	7	8	2	1
9d	0	1¼	9	0	7¼	9	1	1¼	9	1	7¼	9	2	1¼
10d	0	1¼	10	0	7¼	10	1	1¼	10	1	7¼	10	2	1¼
11d	0	1½	11	0	7½	11	1	1½	11	1	7½	11	2	1½
1/-	0s.	1½	**5/-**	0s.	7½	**9/-**	1s.	1½	**13/-**	1s.	7½	**17/-**	2s.	1½
1/1	0s.	1¾	5/1	0s.	7¾	9/1	1s.	1¾	13/1	1s.	7¾	17/1	2s.	1¾
2	0	1¾	2	0	7¾	2	1	1¾	2	1	7¾	2	2	1¾
3	0	2	3	0	8	3	1	2	3	1	8	3	2	2
4	0	2	4	0	8	4	1	2	4	1	8	4	2	2
5	0	2¼	5	0	8¼	5	1	2¼	5	1	8¼	5	2	2¼
1/6	0	2¼	5/6	0	8¼	9/6	1	2¼	13/6	1	8¼	17/6	2	2¼
7	0	2½	7	0	8½	7	1	2½	7	1	8½	7	2	2½
8	0	2½	8	0	8½	8	1	2½	8	1	8½	8	2	2½
9	0	2¾	9	0	8¾	9	1	2¾	9	1	8¾	9	2	2¾
10	0	2¾	10	0	8¾	10	1	2¾	10	1	8¾	10	2	2¾
11	0	3	11	0	9	11	1	3	11	1	9	11	2	3
2/-	0s.	3	**6/-**	0s.	9	**10/-**	1s.	3	**14/-**	1s.	9	**18/-**	2s.	3
2/1	0s.	3¼	6/1	0s.	9¼	10/1	1s.	3¼	14/1	1s.	9¼	18/1	2s.	3¼
2	0	3¼	2	0	9¼	2	1	3¼	2	1	9¼	2	2	3¼
3	0	3½	3	0	9½	3	1	3½	3	1	9½	3	2	3½
4	0	3½	4	0	9½	4	1	3½	4	1	9½	4	2	3½
5	0	3¾	5	0	9¾	5	1	3¾	5	1	9¾	5	2	3¾
2/6	0	3¾	6/6	0	9¾	10/6	1	3¾	14/6	1	9¾	18/6	2	3¾
7	0	4	7	0	10	7	1	4	7	1	10	7	2	4
8	0	4	8	0	10	8	1	4	8	1	10	8	2	4
9	0	4¼	9	0	10¼	9	1	4¼	9	1	10¼	9	2	4¼
10	0	4¼	10	0	10¼	10	1	4¼	10	1	10¼	10	2	4¼
11	0	4½	11	0	10½	11	1	4½	11	1	10½	11	2	4½
3/-	0s.	4½	**7/-**	0s.	10½	**11/-**	1s.	4½	**15/-**	1s.	10½	**19/-**	2s.	4½
3/1	0s.	4¾	7/1	0s.	10¾	11/1	1s.	4¾	15/1	1s.	10¾	19/1	2s.	4¾
2	0	4¾	2	0	10¾	2	1	4¾	2	1	10¾	2	2	4¾
3	0	5	3	0	11	3	1	5	3	1	11	3	2	5
4	0	5	4	0	11	4	1	5	4	1	11	4	2	5
5	0	5¼	5	0	11¼	5	1	5¼	5	1	11¼	5	2	5¼
3/6	0	5¼	7/6	0	11¼	11/6	1	5¼	15/6	1	11¼	19/6	2	5¼
7	0	5½	7	0	11½	7	1	5½	7	1	11½	7	2	5½
8	0	5½	8	0	11½	8	1	5½	8	1	11½	8	2	5½
9	0	5¾	9	0	11¾	9	1	5¾	9	1	11¾	9	2	5¾
10	0	5¾	10	0	11¾	10	1	5¾	10	1	11¾	10	2	5¾
11	0	6	11	1	0	11	1	6	11	2	0	11	2	6
4/-	0s.	6	**8/-**	1s.	0	**12/-**	1s.	6	**16/-**	2s.	0	**20/-**	2s.	6

20/6	2s.	6¾	25/6	3s.	2¼	31/-	3s.	10½	35/6	4s.	5¼	Guineas.		
21/-	2	7½	26/-	3	3	31/6	3	11¼	36/-	4	6	1.	2s.	7½
22/-	2	9	27/-	3	4½	32/-	4	0	37/-	4	7½	2.	5	3
22/6	2	9¾	27/6	3	5¼	32/6	4	0¾	37/6	4	8¼	3.	7	10½
23/-	2	10½	28/-	3	6	33/-	4	1½	38/-	4	9	4.	10	6
24/-	3	0	29/-	3	7½	34/-	4	3	39/-	4	10½	5.	13	1½
25/-	3s.	1½	**30/-**	3s.	9	**35/-**	4s.	4½	**40/-**	5s.	0	6.	15s.	9

(=$11\frac{1}{10}$%* on Gross Returns).

Amt	£	s.	d.	Amt	£	s.	d.	Amt	£	s.	d.	Amt	£	s.	d.
£1	0	2s.	7¼	£51	6	12s.	7¼	£101	13	2s.	7¼	£151	19	12s.	7¼
2	0	5	2½	52	6	15	2½	102	13	5	2½	152	19	15	2½
3	0	7	9½	53	6	17	9½	103	13	7	9½	153	19	17	9½
4	0	10	4¾	54	7	0	4¾	104	13	10	4¾	154	20	0	4¾
5	0	13	0	55	7	3	0	105	13	13	0	155	20	3	0
6	0	15	7¼	56	7	5	7¼	106	13	15	7¼	156	20	5	7¼
7	0	18	2½	57	7	8	2½	107	13	18	2½	157	20	8	2½
8	1	0	9½	58	7	10	9½	108	14	0	9½	158	20	10	9½
9	1	3	4¾	59	7	13	4¾	109	14	3	4¾	159	20	13	4¾
10	1	6s.	0	60	7	16s.	0	110	14	6s.	0	160	20	16s.	0
11	1	8	7¼	61	7	18	7¼	111	14	8	7¼	161	20	18	7¼
12	1	11	2½	62	8	1	2½	112	14	11	2½	162	21	1	2½
13	1	13	9½	63	8	3	9½	113	14	13	9½	163	21	3	9½
14	1	16	4¾	64	8	6	4¾	114	14	16	4¾	164	21	6	4¾
15	1	19	0	65	8	9	0	115	14	19	0	165	21	9	0
16	2	1	7¼	66	8	11	7¼	116	15	1	7¼	166	21	11	7¼
17	2	4	2½	67	8	14	2½	117	15	4	2½	167	21	14	2½
18	2	6	9½	68	8	16	9½	118	15	6	9½	168	21	16	9½
19	2	9	4¾	69	8	19	4¾	119	15	9	4¾	169	21	19	4¾
20	2	12s.	0	70	9	2s.	0	120	15	12s.	0	170	22	2s.	0
21	2	14	7¼	71	9	4	7¼	121	15	14	7¼	171	22	4	7¼
22	2	17	2½	72	9	7	2½	122	15	17	2½	172	22	7	2½
23	2	19	9½	73	9	9	9½	123	15	19	9½	173	22	9	9½
24	3	2	4¾	74	9	12	4¾	124	16	2	4¾	174	22	12	4¾
25	3	5	0	75	9	15	0	125	16	5	0	175	22	15	0
26	3	7	7¼	76	9	17	7¼	126	16	7	7¼	176	22	17	7¼
27	3	10	2½	77	10	0	2½	127	16	10	2½	177	23	0	2½
28	3	12	9½	78	10	2	9½	128	16	12	9½	178	23	2	9½
29	3	15	4¾	79	10	5	4¾	129	16	15	4¾	179	23	5	4¾
30	3	18s.	0	80	10	8s.	0	130	16	18s.	0	180	23	8s.	0
31	4	0	7¼	81	10	10	7¼	131	17	0	7¼	181	23	10	7¼
32	4	3	2½	82	10	13	2½	132	17	3	2½	182	23	13	2½
33	4	5	9½	83	10	15	9½	133	17	5	9½	183	23	15	9½
34	4	8	4¾	84	10	18	4¾	134	17	8	4¾	184	23	18	4¾
35	4	11	0	85	11	1	0	135	17	11	0	185	24	1	0
36	4	13	7¼	86	11	3	7¼	136	17	13	7¼	186	24	3	7¼
37	4	16	2½	87	11	6	2½	137	17	16	2½	187	24	6	2½
38	4	18	9½	88	11	8	9½	138	17	18	9½	188	24	8	9½
39	5	1	4¾	89	11	11	4¾	139	18	1	4¾	189	24	11	4¾
40	5	4s.	0	90	11	14s.	0	140	18	4s.	0	190	24	14s.	0
41	5	6	7¼	91	11	16	7¼	141	18	6	7¼	191	24	16	7¼
42	5	9	2½	92	11	19	2½	142	18	9	2½	192	24	19	2½
43	5	11	9½	93	12	1	9½	143	18	11	9½	193	25	1	9½
44	5	14	4¾	94	12	4	4¾	144	18	14	4¾	194	25	4	4¾
45	5	17	0	95	12	7	0	145	18	17	0	195	25	7	0
46	5	19	7¼	96	12	9	7¼	146	18	19	7¼	196	25	9	7¼
47	6	2	2½	97	12	12	2½	147	19	2	2½	197	25	12	2½
48	6	4	9½	98	12	14	9½	148	19	4	9½	198	25	14	9½
49	6	7	4¾	99	12	17	4¾	149	19	7	4¾	199	25	17	4¾
50	6	10s.	0	100	13	0s.	0	150	19	10s.	0	200	26	0s.	0

Amt	£	s.	d.	Amt	£	s.	d.	Amt	£	s.	d.	Amt	£	s.	d.
250	£32	10	0	700	£91	0	0	1200	156	0	0	2000	260	0	0
300	39	0	0	750	97	10	0	1400	182	0	0	2500	325	0	0
400	52	0	0	800	104	0	0	1500	195	0	0	3000	390	0	0
500	65	0	0	900	117	0	0	1600	208	0	0	4000	520	0	0
600	78	0	0	1000	130	0	0	1800	234	0	0	5000	650	0	0

87% off.

13% 13 Per Cent. 13%

1d	0s.	0¼	4/1	0s.	6¼	8/1	1s.	0½	12/1	1s.	6¾	16/1	2s.	1
2d	0	0¼	2	0	6½	2	1	0¾	2	1	7	2	2	1¼
3d	0	0½	3	0	6¾	3	1	0¾	3	1	7	3	2	1¼
4d	0	0½	4	0	6¾	4	1	1	4	1	7¼	4	2	1½
5d	0	0¾	5	0	7	5	1	1¼	5	1	7¼	5	2	1½
6d	0	0¾	4/6	0	7	8/6	1	1¼	12/6	1	7½	16/6	2	1¾
7d	0	1	7	0	7¼	7	1	1½	7	1	7¾	7	2	1¾
8d	0	1	8	0	7¼	8	1	1½	8	1	7¾	8	2	2
9d	0	1¼	9	0	7½	9	1	1¾	9	1	8	9	2	2¼
10d	0	1¼	10	0	7½	10	1	1¾	10	1	8	10	2	2¼
11d	0	1½	11	0	7¾	11	1	2	11	1	8¼	11	2	2½
1/-	0s.	1½	**5/-**	0s.	7¾	**9/-**	1s.	2	**13/-**	1s.	8¼	**17/-**	2s.	2½
1/1	0	1¾	5/1	0	8	9/1	1	2¼	13/1	1	8½	17/1	2	2¾
2	0	1¾	2	0	8	2	1	2¼	2	1	8½	2	2	2¾
3	0	2	3	0	8¼	3	1	2½	3	1	8¾	3	2	3
4	0	2	4	0	8¼	4	1	2½	4	1	8¾	4	2	3
5	0	2¼	5	0	8½	5	1	2¾	5	1	9	5	2	3¼
1/6	0	2¼	5/6	0	8½	9/6	1	2¾	13/6	1	9	17/6	2	3¼
7	0	2½	7	0	8¾	7	1	3	7	1	9¼	7	2	3½
8	0	2½	8	0	8¾	8	1	3	8	1	9¼	8	2	3½
9	0	2¾	9	0	9	9	1	3¼	9	1	9½	9	2	3¾
10	0	2¾	10	0	9	10	1	3¼	10	1	9½	10	2	3¾
11	0	3	11	0	9¼	11	1	3½	11	1	9¾	11	2	4
2/-	0s.	3	**6/-**	0s.	9¼	**10/-**	1s.	3½	**14/-**	1s.	9¾	**18/-**	2s.	4
2/1	0	3¼	6/1	0	9½	10/1	1	3¾	14/1	1	10	18/1	2	4¼
2	0	3½	2	0	9½	2	1	3¾	2	1	10	2	2	4¼
3	0	3½	3	0	9¾	3	1	4	3	1	10¼	3	2	4½
4	0	3¾	4	0	10	4	1	4	4	1	10¼	4	2	4½
5	0	3¾	5	0	10	5	1	4¼	5	1	10½	5	2	4¾
2/6	0	4	6/6	0	10¼	10/6	1	4½	14/6	1	10½	18/6	2	4¾
7	0	4	7	0	10¼	7	1	4½	7	1	10¾	7	2	5
8	0	4¼	8	0	10½	8	1	4¾	8	1	11	8	2	5
9	0	4¼	9	0	10½	9	1	4¾	9	1	11	9	2	5¼
10	0	4½	10	0	10¾	10	1	5	10	1	11¼	10	2	5¼
11	0	4½	11	0	10¾	11	1	5	11	1	11¼	11	2	5½
3/-	0s.	4¾	**7/-**	0s.	11	**11/-**	1s.	5¼	**15/-**	1s.	11½	**19/-**	2s.	5¾
3/1	0	4¾	7/1	0	11	11/1	1	5¼	15/1	1	11½	19/1	2	5¾
2	0	5	2	0	11¼	2	1	5½	2	1	11¾	2	2	6
3	0	5	3	0	11¼	3	1	5½	3	1	11¾	3	2	6
4	0	5¼	4	0	11½	4	1	5¾	4	2	0	4	2	6¼
5	0	5¼	5	0	11½	5	1	5¾	5	2	0	5	2	6¼
3/6	0	5½	7/6	0	11¾	11/6	1	6	15/6	2	0¼	19/6	2	6½
7	0	5½	7	0	11¾	7	1	6	7	2	0¼	7	2	6½
8	0	5¾	8	1	0	8	1	6¼	8	2	0½	8	2	6¾
9	0	5¾	9	1	0	9	1	6¼	9	2	0½	9	2	6¾
10	0	6	10	1	0¼	10	1	6½	10	2	0¾	10	2	7
11	0	6	11	1	0¼	11	1	6½	11	2	0¾	11	2	7
4/-	0s.	6¼	**8/-**	1s.	0½	**12/-**	1s.	6¾	**16/-**	2s.	1	**20/-**	2s.	7¼

20/6	2s.	8	25/6	3s.	3¾	31/-	4s.	0¼	35/6	4s.	7½	Guineas.		
21/-	2	8¾	26/-	3	4½	31/6	4	1¼	36/-	4	8¼	1.	2s.	8¾
22/-	2	10¼	27/-	3	6	32/-	4	2	37/-	4	9¾	2.	5	5½
22/6	2	11	27/6	3	7	32/6	4	2¾	37/6	4	10½	3.	8	2¼
23/-	3	0	28/-	3	7¾	33/-	4	3½	38/-	4	11¼	4.	10	11
24/-	3	1½	29/-	3	9¼	34/-	4	5	39/-	5	0¾	5.	13	7¾
25/-	3s.	3	**30/-**	3s.	10¾	**35/-**	4s.	6½	**40/-**	5s.	2½	6.	16s.	4½

(=11½%* on Gross Returns.)

13½ Per Cent.

£1	£0	2s	8½	£51	£6	17s	8½	£101	13	12s	8½	£151	20	7s	8½
2	0	5	4¾	52	7	0	4¾	102	13	15	4¾	152	20	10	4¾
3	0	8	1¼	53	7	3	1¼	103	13	18	1¼	153	20	13	1¼
4	0	10	9½	54	7	5	9½	104	14	0	9½	154	20	15	9½
5	0	13	6	55	7	8	6	105	14	3	6	155	20	18	6
6	0	16	2½	56	7	11	2½	106	14	6	2½	156	21	1	2½
7	0	18	10¾	57	7	13	10¾	107	14	8	10¾	157	21	3	10¾
8	1	1	7¼	58	7	16	7¼	108	14	11	7¼	158	21	6	7¼
9	1	4	3½	59	7	19	3½	109	14	14	3½	159	21	9	3½
10	**1**	**7**	**0**	**60**	**8**	**2**	**0**	**110**	**14**	**17**	**0**	**160**	**21**	**12**	**0**
11	1	9	8½	61	8	4	8½	111	14	19	8½	161	21	14	8½
12	1	12	4¾	62	8	7	4¾	112	15	2	4¾	162	21	17	4¾
13	1	15	1¼	63	8	10	1¼	113	15	5	1¼	163	22	0	1¼
14	1	17	9½	64	8	12	9½	114	15	7	9½	164	22	2	9½
15	2	0	6	65	8	15	6	115	15	10	6	165	22	5	6
16	2	3	2½	66	8	18	2½	116	15	13	2½	166	22	8	2½
17	2	5	10¾	67	9	0	10¾	117	15	15	10¾	167	22	10	10¾
18	2	8	7¼	68	9	3	7¼	118	15	18	7¼	168	22	13	7¼
19	2	11	3½	69	9	6	3½	119	16	1	3½	169	22	16	3½
20	**2**	**14**	**0**	**70**	**9**	**9**	**0**	**120**	**16**	**4**	**0**	**170**	**22**	**19**	**0**
21	2	16	8½	71	9	11	8½	121	16	6	8½	171	23	1	8½
22	2	19	4¾	72	9	14	4¾	122	16	9	4¾	172	23	4	4¾
23	3	2	1¼	73	9	17	1¼	123	16	12	1¼	173	23	7	1¼
24	3	4	9½	74	9	19	9½	124	16	14	9½	174	23	9	9½
25	3	7	6	75	10	2	6	125	16	17	6	175	23	12	6
26	3	10	2½	76	10	5	2½	126	17	0	2½	176	23	15	2½
27	3	12	10¾	77	10	7	10¾	127	17	2	10¾	177	23	17	10¾
28	3	15	7¼	78	10	10	7¼	128	17	5	7¼	178	24	0	7¼
29	3	18	3½	79	10	13	3½	129	17	8	3½	179	24	3	3½
30	**4**	**1**	**0**	**80**	**10**	**16**	**0**	**130**	**17**	**11**	**0**	**180**	**24**	**6**	**0**
31	4	3	8½	81	10	18	8½	131	17	13	8½	181	24	8	8½
32	4	6	4¾	82	11	1	4¾	132	17	16	4¾	182	24	11	4¾
33	4	9	1¼	83	11	4	1¼	133	17	19	1¼	183	24	14	1¼
34	4	11	9½	84	11	6	9½	134	18	1	9½	184	24	16	9½
35	4	14	6	85	11	9	6	135	18	4	6	185	24	19	6
36	4	17	2½	86	11	12	2½	136	18	7	2½	186	25	2	2½
37	4	19	10¾	87	11	14	10¾	137	18	9	10¾	187	25	4	10¾
38	5	2	7¼	88	11	17	7¼	138	18	12	7¼	188	25	7	7¼
39	5	5	3½	89	12	0	3½	139	18	15	3½	189	25	10	3½
40	**5**	**8**	**0**	**90**	**12**	**3**	**0**	**140**	**18**	**18**	**0**	**190**	**25**	**13**	**0**
41	5	10	8½	91	12	5	8½	141	19	0	8½	191	25	15	8½
42	5	13	4¾	92	12	8	4¾	142	19	3	4¾	192	25	18	4¾
43	5	16	1¼	93	12	11	1¼	143	19	6	1¼	193	26	1	1¼
44	5	18	9½	94	12	13	9½	144	19	8	9½	194	26	3	9½
45	6	1	6	95	12	16	6	145	19	11	6	195	26	6	6
46	6	4	2½	96	12	19	2½	146	19	14	2½	196	26	9	2½
47	6	6	10¾	97	13	1	10¾	147	19	16	10¾	197	26	11	10¾
48	6	9	7¼	98	13	4	7¼	148	19	19	7¼	198	26	14	7¼
49	6	12	3½	99	13	7	3½	149	20	2	3½	199	26	17	3½
50	**6**	**15**	**0**	**100**	**13**	**10**	**0**	**150**	**20**	**5**	**0**	**200**	**27**	**0**	**0**

250	33	15s	0d	700	94	10s	0d	1200	162	0s	0d	2000	270	0s	0
300	40	10	0	750	101	5	0	1400	189	0	0	2500	337	10	0
400	54	0	0	800	108	0	0	1500	202	10	0	3000	405	0	0
500	67	10	0	900	121	10	0	1600	216	0	0	4000	540	0	0
600	81	0s	0d	1000	135	0s	0d	1800	243	0s	0d	5000	675	0s	0

86½% off

13½% **13½ Per Cent.** 13½%

1d	0s	0¼	4/1	0s	6½	8/1	1s	1	12/1	1s	7½	16/1	2s	2
2d	0	0¼	2	0	6¾	2	1	1¼	2	1	7¾	2	2	2¼
3d	0	0½	3	0	7	3	1	1¼	3	1	7¾	3	2	2¼
4d	0	0½	4	0	7	4	1	1½	4	1	8	4	2	2½
5d	0	0¾	5	0	7¼	5	1	1¾	5	1	8	5	2	2½
6d	0	0¾	4/6	0	7¼	8/6	1	1¾	12/6	1	8¼	16/6	2	2¾
7d	0	1	7	0	7½	7	1	2	7	1	8½	7	2	2¾
8d	0	1	8	0	7½	8	1	2	8	1	8½	8	2	3
9d	0	1¼	9	0	7¾	9	1	2¼	9	1	8¾	9	2	3¼
10d	0	1¼	10	0	7¾	10	1	2¼	10	1	8¾	10	2	3¼
11d	0	1½	11	0	8	11	1	2½	11	1	9	11	2	3½
1/-	**0**	**1½**	**5/-**	**0**	**8**	**9/-**	**1**	**2½**	**13/-**	**1**	**9**	**17/-**	**2**	**3½**
1/1	0	1¾	5/1	0	8¼	1	1	2¾	1	1	9¼	1	2	3¾
2	0	2	2	0	8¼	2	1	2¾	2	1	9¼	2	2	3¾
3	0	2	3	0	8½	3	1	3	3	1	9½	3	2	4
4	0	2¼	4	0	8¾	4	1	3	4	1	9½	4	2	4
5	0	2¼	5	0	8¾	5	1	3¼	5	1	9¾	5	2	4¼
1/6	0	2½	5/6	0	9	9/6	1	3½	13/6	1	9¾	17/6	2	4¼
7	0	2½	7	0	9	7	1	3½	7	1	10	7	2	4½
8	0	2¾	8	0	9¼	8	1	3¾	8	1	10¼	8	2	4½
9	0	2¾	9	0	9¼	9	1	3¾	9	1	10¼	9	2	4¾
10	0	3	10	0	9½	10	1	4	10	1	10½	10	2	5
11	0	3	11	0	9½	11	1	4	11	1	10½	11	2	5
2/-	**0**	**3¼**	**6/-**	**0**	**9¾**	**10/-**	**1**	**4¼**	**14/-**	**1**	**10¾**	**18/-**	**2**	**5¼**
2/1	0	3½	1	0	9¾	10/1	1	4¼	1	1	10¾	1	2	5¼
2	0	3½	2	0	10	2	1	4½	2	1	11	2	2	5½
3	0	3¾	3	0	10¼	3	1	4½	3	1	11	3	2	5½
4	0	3¾	4	0	10¼	4	1	4¾	4	1	11¼	4	2	5¾
5	0	4	5	0	10½	5	1	5	5	1	11¼	5	2	5¾
2/6	0	4	6/6	0	10½	10/6	1	5	14/6	1	11½	18/6	2	6
7	0	4¼	7	0	10¾	7	1	5¼	7	1	11¾	7	2	6
8	0	4¼	8	0	10¾	8	1	5¼	8	1	11¾	8	2	6¼
9	0	4½	9	0	11	9	1	5½	9	2	0	9	2	6½
10	0	4½	10	0	11	10	1	5½	10	2	0	10	2	6½
11	0	4¾	11	0	11¼	11	1	5¾	11	2	0¼	11	2	6¾
3/-	**0**	**4¾**	**7/-**	**0**	**11¼**	**11/-**	**1**	**5¾**	**15/-**	**2**	**0¼**	**19/-**	**2**	**6¾**
3/1	0	5	1	0	11½	1	1	6	15/1	2	0½	1	2	7
2	0	5¼	2	0	11½	2	1	6	2	2	0½	2	2	7
3	0	5¼	3	0	11¾	3	1	6¼	3	2	0¾	3	2	7¼
4	0	5½	4	1	0	4	1	6¼	4	2	0¾	4	2	7¼
5	0	5½	5	1	0	5	1	6½	5	2	1	5	2	7½
3/6	0	5¾	7/6	1	0¼	11/6	1	6¾	15/6	2	1	19/6	2	7½
7	0	5¾	7	1	0¼	7	1	6¾	7	2	1¼	7	2	7¾
8	0	6	8	1	0½	8	1	7	8	2	1½	8	2	7¾
9	0	6	9	1	0½	9	1	7	9	2	1½	9	2	8
10	0	6¼	10	1	0¾	10	1	7¼	10	2	1¾	10	2	8¼
11	0	6¼	11	1	0¾	11	1	7¼	11	2	1¾	11	2	8¼
4/-	**0**	**6½**	**8/-**	**1**	**1**	**12/-**	**1**	**7½**	**16/-**	**2**	**2**	**20/-**	**2**	**8½**

20/6	2s	9¼	25/6	3s	5¼	31/-	4s	2¼	35/6	4s	9½	Guineas.		
21/-	2	10	26/-	3	6	31/6	4	3	36/-	4	10¼	1.	2s	10
22/-	2	11¾	27/-	3	7¾	32/-	4	3¾	37/-	5	0	2.	5	8
22/6	3	0½	27/6	3	8½	32/6	4	4¾	37/6	5	0¾	3.	8	6
23/-	3	1¼	28/-	3	9¼	33/-	4	5½	38/-	5	1½	4.	11	4
24/-	3	3	29/-	3	11	34/-	4	7	39/-	5	3¼	5.	14	2
25/-	3s	4½	**30/-**	4s	0½	**35/-**	4s	8¾	**40/-**	5s	4¾	6.	17	0

(=11 9/10% on Gross Returns).

13¾% 13¾ PER CENT. 13¾%

£	£ s. d.	£	£ s. d.	£	£ s. d.	£	£ s. d.
1	0 2s. 9	51	7 0s. 3	101	13 17s. 9	151	20 15s. 3
2	0 5 6	52	7 3 0	102	14 0 6	152	20 18 0
3	0 8 3	53	7 5 9	103	14 3 3	153	21 0 9
4	0 11 0	54	7 8 6	104	14 6 0	154	21 3 6
5	0 13 9	55	7 11 3	105	14 8 9	155	21 6 3
6	0 16 6	56	7 14 0	106	14 11 6	156	21 9 0
7	0 19 3	57	7 16 9	107	14 14 3	157	21 11 9
8	1 2 0	58	7 19 6	108	14 17 0	158	21 14 6
9	1 4 9	59	8 2 3	109	14 19 9	159	21 17 3
10	1 7s. 6	60	8 5s. 0	110	15 2s. 6	160	22 0s. 0
11	1 10 3	61	8 7 9	111	15 5 3	161	22 2 9
12	1 13 0	62	8 10 6	112	15 8 0	162	22 5 6
13	1 15 9	63	8 13 3	113	15 10 9	163	22 8 3
14	1 18 6	64	8 16 0	114	15 13 6	164	22 11 0
15	2 1 3	65	8 18 9	115	15 16 3	165	22 13 9
16	2 4 0	66	9 1 6	116	15 19 0	166	22 16 6
17	2 6 9	67	9 4 3	117	16 1 9	167	22 19 3
18	2 9 6	68	9 7 0	118	16 4 6	168	23 2 0
19	2 12 3	69	9 9 9	119	16 7 3	169	23 4 9
20	2 15s. 0	70	9 12s. 6	120	16 10s. 0	170	23 7s. 6
21	2 17 9	71	9 15 3	121	16 12 9	171	23 10 3
22	3 0 6	72	9 18 0	122	16 15 6	172	23 13 0
23	3 3 3	73	10 0 9	123	16 18 3	173	23 15 9
24	3 6 0	74	10 3 6	124	17 1 0	174	23 18 6
25	3 8 9	75	10 6 3	125	17 3 9	175	24 1 3
26	3 11 6	76	10 9 0	126	17 6 6	176	24 4 0
27	3 14 3	77	10 11 9	127	17 9 3	177	24 6 9
28	3 17 0	78	10 14 6	128	17 12 0	178	24 9 6
29	3 19 9	79	10 17 3	129	17 14 9	179	24 12 3
30	4 2s. 6	80	11 0s. 0	130	17 17s. 6	180	24 15s. 0
31	4 5 3	81	11 2 9	131	18 0 3	181	24 17 9
32	4 8 0	82	11 5 6	132	18 3 0	182	25 0 6
33	4 10 9	83	11 8 3	133	18 5 9	183	25 3 3
34	4 13 6	84	11 11 0	134	18 8 6	184	25 6 0
35	4 16 3	85	11 13 9	135	18 11 3	185	25 8 9
36	4 19 0	86	11 16 6	136	18 14 0	186	25 11 6
37	5 1 9	87	11 19 3	137	18 16 9	187	25 14 3
38	5 4 6	88	12 2 0	138	18 19 6	188	25 17 0
39	5 7 3	89	12 4 9	139	19 2 3	189	25 19 9
40	5 10s. 0	90	12 7s. 6	140	19 5s. 0	190	26 2s. 6
41	5 12 9	91	12 10 3	141	19 7 9	191	26 5 3
42	5 15 6	92	12 13 0	142	19 10 6	192	26 8 0
43	5 18 3	93	12 15 9	143	19 13 3	193	26 10 9
44	6 1 0	94	12 18 6	144	19 16 0	194	26 13 6
45	6 3 9	95	13 1 3	145	19 18 9	195	26 16 3
46	6 6 6	96	13 4 0	146	20 1 6	196	26 19 0
47	6 9 3	97	13 6 9	147	20 4 3	197	27 1 9
48	6 12 0	98	13 9 6	148	20 7 0	198	27 4 6
49	6 14 9	99	13 12 3	149	20 9 9	199	27 7 3
50	6 17s. 6	100	13 15s. 0	150	20 12s. 6	200	27 10s. 0

£	£ s. d.	£	£ s. d.	£	£ s. d.	£	£ s. d.
250	£34 7 6	700	£96 5 0	1200	165 0 0	2000	275 0 0
300	41 5 0	750	103 2 6	1400	192 10 0	2500	343 15 0
400	55 0 0	800	110 0 0	1500	206 5 0	3000	412 10 0
500	68 15 0	900	123 15 0	1600	220 0 0	4000	550 0 0
600	82 10 0	1000	137 10 0	1800	247 10 0	5000	687 10 0

86⅓% off.

13¾% 13¾ Per Cent. 13¾%

1d	0s.	0¼	4/1	0s.	6¾	8/1	1s.	1¼	12/1	1s.	8	16/1	2s.	2½
2d	0	0¼	2	0	7	2	1	1½	2	1	8	2	2	2¾
3d	0	0½	3	0	7	3	1	1½	3	1	8¼	3	2	2¾
4d	0	0½	4	0	7¼	4	1	1¾	4	1	8¼	4	2	3
5d	0	0¾	5	0	7¼	5	1	2	5	1	8½	5	2	3
6d	0	0¾	4/6	0	7½	8/6	1	2	12/6	1	8¾	16/6	2	3¼
7d	0	1	7	0	7½	7	1	2¼	7	1	8¾	7	2	3¼
8d	0	1	8	0	7¾	8	1	2¼	8	1	9	8	2	3½
9d	0	1¼	9	0	7¾	9	1	2½	9	1	9	9	2	3¾
10d	0	1½	10	0	8	10	1	2½	10	1	9¼	10	2	3¾
11d	0	1½	11	0	8	11	1	2¾	11	1	9¼	11	2	4
1/-	0s.	1¾	**5/-**	0s.	8¼	**9/-**	1s.	2¾	**13/-**	1s.	9½	**17/-**	2s.	4
1/1	0	1¾	5/1	0	8½	9/1	1	3	13/1	1	9½	17/1	2	4¼
2	0	2	2	0	8½	2	1	3¼	2	1	9¾	2	2	4¼
3	0	2	3	0	8¾	3	1	3¼	3	1	9¾	3	2	4½
4	0	2¼	4	0	8¾	4	1	3½	4	1	10	4	2	4½
5	0	2¼	5	0	9	5	1	3½	5	1	10¼	5	2	4¾
1/6	0	2½	5/6	0	9	9/6	1	3¾	13/6	1	10¼	17/6	2	5
7	0	2½	7	0	9¼	7	1	3¾	7	1	10½	7	2	5
8	0	2¾	8	0	9¼	8	1	4	8	1	10½	8	2	5¼
9	0	3	9	0	9½	9	1	4	9	1	10¾	9	2	5¼
10	0	3	10	0	9¾	10	1	4¼	10	1	10¾	10	2	5½
11	0	3¼	11	0	9¾	11	1	4¼	11	1	11	11	2	5½
2/-	0s.	3¼	**6/-**	0s.	10	**10/-**	1s.	4½	**14/-**	1s.	11	**18/-**	2s.	5¾
2/1	0	3½	6/1	0	10	10/1	1	4¾	14/1	1	11¼	18/1	2	5¾
2	0	3½	2	0	10¼	2	1	4¾	2	1	11½	2	2	6
3	0	3¾	3	0	10¼	3	1	5	3	1	11½	3	2	6
4	0	3¾	4	0	10½	4	1	5	4	1	11¾	4	2	6¼
5	0	4	5	0	10½	5	1	5¼	5	1	11¾	5	2	6½
2/6	0	4¼	6/6	0	10¾	10/6	1	5¼	14/6	2	0	18/6	2	6½
7	0	4¼	7	0	10¾	7	1	5½	7	2	0	7	2	6¾
8	0	4½	8	0	11	8	1	5½	8	2	0¼	8	2	6¾
9	0	4½	9	0	11¼	9	1	5¾	9	2	0¼	9	2	7
10	0	4¾	10	0	11¼	10	1	6	10	2	0½	10	2	7
11	0	4¾	11	0	11½	11	1	6	11	2	0½	11	2	7¼
3/-	0s.	5	**7/-**	0s.	11½	**11/-**	1s.	6¼	**15/-**	2s.	0¾	**19/-**	2s.	7¼
3/1	0	5	7/1	0	11¾	11/1	1	6¼	15/1	2	1	19/1	2	7½
2	0	5¼	2	0	11¾	2	1	6½	2	2	1	2	2	7¾
3	0	5¼	3	1	0	3	1	6½	3	2	1¼	3	2	7¾
4	0	5½	4	1	0	4	1	6¾	4	2	1¼	4	2	8
5	0	5¾	5	1	0¼	5	1	6¾	5	2	1½	5	2	8
3/6	0	5¾	7/6	1	0½	11/6	1	7	15/6	2	1½	19/6	2	8¼
7	0	6	7	1	0½	7	1	7	7	2	1¾	7	2	8¼
8	0	6	8	1	0¾	8	1	7¼	8	2	1¾	8	2	8½
9	0	6¼	9	1	0¾	9	1	7½	9	2	2	9	2	8½
10	0	6¼	10	1	1	10	1	7½	10	2	2¼	10	2	8¾
11	0	6½	11	1	1	11	1	7¾	11	2	2¼	11	2	8¾
4/-	0s.	6½	**8/-**	1s.	1¼	**12/-**	1s.	7¾	**16/-**	2s.	2½	**20/-**	2s.	9

20/6	2s.	9¾	25/6	3s.	6	31/-	4s.	3¼	35/6	4s.	10½	Guineas.		
21/-	2	10¾	26/-	3	7	31/6	4	4	36/-	4	11½	1.	2s.	10¾
22/-	3	0¼	27/-	3	8½	32/-	4	4¾	37/-	5	1	2.	5	9¼
22/6	3	1¼	27/6	3	9½	32/6	4	5¾	37/6	5	2	3.	8	8
23/-	3	2	28/-	3	10¼	33/-	4	6½	38/-	5	2¾	4.	11	6½
24/-	3	3½	29/-	3	11¾	34/-	4	8	39/-	5	4¼	5.	14	5¼
25/-	3s.	5¼	**30/-**	4s.	1½	**35/-**	4s.	9¾	**40/-**	5s.	6	6.	17s.	4

(=12 1/10%* on Gross Returns.)

£	s. d.	£	s. d.	£	s. d.	£	s. d.
1	0 2s. 9½	51	7 2s. 9½	101	14 2s. 9½	151	21 2s. 9½
2	0 5 7¼	52	7 5 7¼	102	14 5 7¼	152	21 5 7¼
3	0 8 4¾	53	7 8 4¾	103	14 8 4¾	153	21 8 4¾
4	0 11 2½	54	7 11 2½	104	14 11 2½	154	21 11 2½
5	0 14 0	55	7 14 0	105	14 14 0	155	21 14 0
6	0 16 9½	56	7 16 9½	106	14 16 9½	156	21 16 9½
7	0 19 7¼	57	7 19 7¼	107	14 19 7¼	157	21 19 7¼
8	1 2 4¾	58	8 2 4¾	108	15 2 4¾	158	22 2 4¾
9	1 5 2½	59	8 5 2½	109	15 5 2½	159	22 5 2½
10	1 8s. 0	60	8 8s. 0	110	15 8s. 0	160	22 8s. 0
11	1 10 9½	61	8 10 9½	111	15 10 9½	161	22 10 9½
12	1 13 7¼	62	8 13 7¼	112	15 13 7¼	162	22 13 7¼
13	1 16 4¾	63	8 16 4¾	113	15 16 4¾	163	22 16 4¾
14	1 19 2½	64	8 19 2½	114	15 19 2½	164	22 19 2½
15	2 2 0	65	9 2 0	115	16 2 0	165	23 2 0
16	2 4 9½	66	9 4 9½	116	16 4 9½	166	23 4 9½
17	2 7 7¼	67	9 7 7¼	117	16 7 7¼	167	23 7 7¼
18	2 10 4¾	68	9 10 4¾	118	16 10 4¾	168	23 10 4¾
19	2 13 2½	69	9 13 2½	119	16 13 2½	169	23 13 2½
20	2 16s. 0	70	9 16s. 0	120	16 16s. 0	170	23 16s. 0
21	2 18 9½	71	9 18 9½	121	16 18 9½	171	23 18 9½
22	3 1 7¼	72	10 1 7¼	122	17 1 7¼	172	24 1 7¼
23	3 4 4¾	73	10 4 4¾	123	17 4 4¾	173	24 4 4¾
24	3 7 2½	74	10 7 2½	124	17 7 2½	174	24 7 2½
25	3 10 0	75	10 10 0	125	17 10 0	175	24 10 0
26	3 12 9½	76	10 12 9½	126	17 12 9½	176	24 12 9½
27	3 15 7¼	77	10 15 7¼	127	17 15 7¼	177	24 15 7¼
28	3 18 4¾	78	10 18 4¾	128	17 18 4¾	178	24 18 4¾
29	4 1 2½	79	11 1 2½	129	18 1 2½	179	25 1 2½
30	4 4s. 0	80	11 4s. 0	130	18 4s. 0	180	25 4s. 0
31	4 6 9½	81	11 6 9½	131	18 6 9½	181	25 6 9½
32	4 9 7¼	82	11 9 7¼	132	18 9 7¼	182	25 9 7¼
33	4 12 4¾	83	11 12 4¾	133	18 12 4¾	183	25 12 4¾
34	4 15 2½	84	11 15 2½	134	18 15 2½	184	25 15 2½
35	4 18 0	85	11 18 0	135	18 18 0	185	25 18 0
36	5 0 9½	86	12 0 9½	136	19 0 9½	186	26 0 9½
37	5 3 7¼	87	12 3 7¼	137	19 3 7¼	187	26 3 7¼
38	5 6 4¾	88	12 6 4¾	138	19 6 4¾	188	26 6 4¾
39	5 9 2½	89	12 9 2½	139	19 9 2½	189	26 9 2½
40	5 12s. 0	90	12 12s. 0	140	19 12s. 0	190	26 12s. 0
41	5 14 9½	91	12 14 9½	141	19 14 9½	191	26 14 9½
42	5 17 7¼	92	12 17 7¼	142	19 17 7¼	192	26 17 7¼
43	6 0 4¾	93	13 0 4¾	143	20 0 4¾	193	27 0 4¾
44	6 3 2½	94	13 3 2½	144	20 3 2½	194	27 3 2½
45	6 6 0	95	13 6 0	145	20 6 0	195	27 6 0
46	6 8 9½	96	13 8 9½	146	20 8 9½	196	27 8 9½
47	6 11 7¼	97	13 11 7¼	147	20 11 7¼	197	27 11 7¼
48	6 14 4¾	98	13 14 4¾	148	20 14 4¾	198	27 14 4¾
49	6 17 2½	99	13 17 2½	149	20 17 2½	199	27 17 2½
50	7 0s. 0	100	14 0s. 0	150	21 0s. 0	200	28 0s. 0

£	£ s. d.	£	£ s. d.	£	£ s. d.	£	£ s. d.
250	£35 0 0	700	£98 0 0	1200	168 0 0	2000	280 0 0
300	42 0 0	750	105 0 0	1400	196 0 0	2500	350 0 0
400	56 0 0	800	112 0 0	1500	210 0 0	3000	420 0 0
500	70 0 0	900	126 0 0	1600	224 0 0	4000	560 0 0
600	84 0 0	1000	140 0 0	1800	252 0 0	5000	700 0 0

86% off.

1d	0s.	0¼	4/1	0s.	6¾	8/1	1s.	1½	12/1	1s.	8¼	16/1	2s.	3
2d	0	0¼	2	0	7	2	1	1¾	2	1	8½	2	2	3¼
3d	0	0½	3	0	7¼	3	1	1¾	3	1	8½	3	2	3¼
4d	0	0½	4	0	7¼	4	1	2	4	1	8¾	4	2	3½
5d	0	0¾	5	0	7½	5	1	2¼	5	1	8¾	5	2	3½
6d	0	0¾	4/6	0	7½	8/6	1	2¼	12/6	1	9	16/6	2	3¾
7d	0	1	7	0	7¾	7	1	2½	7	1	9¼	7	2	3¾
8d	0	1	8	0	7¾	8	1	2½	8	1	9¼	8	2	4
9d	0	1¼	9	0	8	9	1	2¾	9	1	9½	9	2	4¼
10d	0	1½	10	0	8	10	1	2¾	10	1	9½	10	2	4¼
11d	0	1½	11	0	8¼	11	1	3	11	1	9¾	11	2	4½
1/-	0s.	1¾	**5/-**	0s.	8½	**9/-**	1s.	3	**13/-**	1s.	9¾	**17/-**	2s.	4½
1/1	0	1¾	5/1	0	8½	9/1	1	3¼	13/1	1	10	17/1	2	4¾
2	0	2	2	0	8¾	2	1	3½	2	1	10	2	2	4¾
3	0	2	3	0	8¾	3	1	3½	3	1	10¼	3	2	5
4	0	2¼	4	0	9	4	1	3¾	4	1	10½	4	2	5
5	0	2½	5	0	9	5	1	3¾	5	1	10½	5	2	5¼
1/6	0	2½	5/6	0	9¼	9/6	1	4	13/6	1	10¾	17/6	2	5½
7	0	2¾	7	0	9½	7	1	4	7	1	10¾	7	2	5½
8	0	2¾	8	0	9½	8	1	4¼	8	1	11	8	2	5¾
9	0	3	9	0	9¾	9	1	4½	9	1	11	9	2	5¾
10	0	3	10	0	9¾	10	1	4½	10	1	11¼	10	2	6
11	0	3¼	11	0	10	11	1	4¾	11	1	11½	11	2	6
2/-	0s.	3¼	**6/-**	0s.	10	**10/-**	1s.	4¾	**14/-**	1s.	11½	**18/-**	2s.	6¼
2/1	0	3½	6/1	0	10¼	10/1	1	5	14/1	1	11¾	18/1	2	6½
2	0	3¾	2	0	10¼	2	1	5	2	1	11¾	2	2	6½
3	0	3¾	3	0	10½	3	1	5¼	3	2	0	3	2	6¾
4	0	4	4	0	10¾	4	1	5¼	4	2	0	4	2	6¾
5	0	4	5	0	10¾	5	1	5½	5	2	0¼	5	2	7
2/6	0	4¼	6/6	0	11	10/6	1	5¾	14/6	2	0¼	18/6	2	7
7	0	4¼	7	0	11	7	1	5¾	7	2	0½	7	2	7¼
8	0	4½	8	0	11¼	8	1	6	8	2	0¾	8	2	7¼
9	0	4½	9	0	11¼	9	1	6	9	2	0¾	9	2	7½
10	0	4¾	10	0	11½	10	1	6¼	10	2	1	10	2	7¾
11	0	5	11	0	11½	11	1	6¼	11	2	1	11	2	7¾
3/-	0s.	5	**7/-**	0s.	11¾	**11/-**	1s.	6½	**15/-**	2s.	1¼	**19/-**	2s.	8
3/1	0	5¼	7/1	1	0	11/1	1	6½	15/1	2	1¼	19/1	2	8
2	0	5¼	2	1	0	2	1	6¾	2	2	1½	2	2	8¼
3	0	5½	3	1	0¼	3	1	7	3	2	1½	3	2	8¼
4	0	5½	4	1	0¼	4	1	7	4	2	1¾	4	2	8½
5	0	5¾	5	1	0½	5	1	7¼	5	2	2	5	2	8½
3/6	0	6	7/6	1	0½	11/6	1	7¼	15/6	2	2	19/6	2	8¾
7	0	6	7	1	0¾	7	1	7½	7	2	2¼	7	2	9
8	0	6¼	8	1	1	8	1	7½	8	2	2¼	8	2	9
9	0	6¼	9	1	1	9	1	7¾	9	2	2½	9	2	9¼
10	0	6½	10	1	1¼	10	1	8	10	2	2½	10	2	9¼
11	0	6½	11	1	1¼	11	1	8	11	2	2¾	11	2	9½
4/-	0s.	6¾	**8/-**	1s.	1½	**12/-**	1s.	8¼	**16/-**	2s.	3	**20/-**	2s.	9½

20/6	2s.	10½	25/6	3s.	6¾	31/-	4s.	4	35/6	4s.	11¾	Guineas.		
21/-	2	11¼	26/-	3	7¾	31/6	4	5	36/-	5	0½	1.	2s.	11¼
22/-	3	1	27/-	3	9¼	32/-	4	5¾	37/-	5	2¼	2.	5	10½
22/6	3	1¾	27/6	3	10¼	32/6	4	6½	37/6	5	3	3.	8	9¾
23/-	3	2¾	28/-	3	11	33/-	4	7½	38/-	5	3¾	4.	11	9
24/-	3	4¼	29/-	4	0¾	34/-	4	9	39/-	5	5½	5.	14	8½
25/-	3s.	6	**30/-**	4s.	2½	**35/-**	4s.	10¾	**40/-**	5s.	7¼	6.	17s.	7¾

(= 12$\frac{3}{10}$%* on Gross Returns.)

£1	£0	2s	10¼	£51	£7	5s	8½	£101	14	8s	6¾	£151	21	11s	5¼
2	0	5	8½	52	7	8	6¾	102	14	11	5¼	152	21	14	3½
3	0	8	6¾	53	7	11	5¼	103	14	14	3½	153	21	17	1¾
4	0	11	5¼	54	7	14	3½	104	14	17	1¾	154	22	0	0
5	0	14	3½	55	7	17	1¾	105	15	0	0	155	22	2	10¼
6	0	17	1¾	56	8	0	0	106	15	2	10¼	156	22	5	8½
7	1	0	0	57	8	2	10¼	107	15	5	8½	157	22	8	6¾
8	1	2	10¼	58	8	5	8½	108	15	8	6¾	158	22	11	5¼
9	1	5	8½	59	8	8	6¾	109	15	11	5¼	159	22	14	3½
10	**1**	**8**	**6¾**	**60**	**8**	**11**	**5¼**	**110**	**15**	**14**	**3½**	**160**	**22**	**17**	**1¾**
11	1	11	5¼	61	8	14	3½	111	15	17	1¾	161	23	0	0
12	1	14	3½	62	8	17	1¾	112	16	0	0	162	23	2	10¼
13	1	17	1¾	63	9	0	0	113	16	2	10¼	163	23	5	8½
14	2	0	0	64	9	2	10¼	114	16	5	8½	164	23	8	6¾
15	2	2	10¼	65	9	5	8½	115	16	8	6¾	165	23	11	5¼
16	2	5	8½	66	9	8	6¾	116	16	11	5¼	166	23	14	3½
17	2	8	6¾	67	9	11	5¼	117	16	14	3½	167	23	17	1¾
18	2	11	5¼	68	9	14	3½	118	16	17	1¾	168	24	0	0
19	2	14	3½	69	9	17	1¾	119	17	0	0	169	24	2	10¼
20	**2**	**17**	**1¾**	**70**	**10**	**0**	**0**	**120**	**17**	**2**	**10¼**	**170**	**24**	**5**	**8½**
21	3	0	0	71	10	2	10¼	121	17	5	8½	171	24	8	6¾
22	3	2	10¼	72	10	5	8½	122	17	8	6¾	172	24	11	5¼
23	3	5	8½	73	10	8	6¾	123	17	11	5¼	173	24	14	3½
24	3	8	6¾	74	10	11	5¼	124	17	14	3½	174	24	17	1¾
25	3	11	5¼	75	10	14	3½	125	17	17	1¾	175	25	0	0
26	3	14	3½	76	10	17	1¾	126	18	0	0	176	25	2	10¼
27	3	17	1¾	77	11	0	0	127	18	2	10¼	177	25	5	8½
28	4	0	0	78	11	2	10¼	128	18	5	8½	178	25	8	6¾
29	4	2	10¼	79	11	5	8½	129	18	8	6¾	179	25	11	5¼
30	**4**	**5**	**8½**	**80**	**11**	**8**	**6¾**	**130**	**18**	**11**	**5¼**	**180**	**25**	**14**	**3½**
31	4	8	6¾	81	11	11	5¼	131	18	14	3½	181	25	17	1¾
32	4	11	5¼	82	11	14	3½	132	18	17	1¾	182	26	0	0
33	4	14	3½	83	11	17	1¾	133	19	0	0	183	26	2	10¼
34	4	17	1¾	84	12	0	0	134	19	2	10¼	184	26	5	8½
35	5	0	0	85	12	2	10¼	135	19	5	8½	185	26	8	6¾
36	5	2	10¼	86	12	5	8½	136	19	8	6¾	186	26	11	5¼
37	5	5	8½	87	12	8	6¾	137	19	11	5¼	187	26	14	3½
38	5	8	6¾	88	12	11	5¼	138	19	14	3½	188	26	17	1¾
39	5	11	5¼	89	12	14	3½	139	19	17	1¾	189	27	0	0
40	**5**	**14**	**3½**	**90**	**12**	**17**	**1¾**	**140**	**20**	**0**	**0**	**190**	**27**	**2**	**10¼**
41	5	17	1¾	91	13	0	0	141	20	2	10¼	191	27	5	8½
42	6	0	0	92	13	2	10¼	142	20	5	8½	192	27	8	6¾
43	6	2	10¼	93	13	5	8½	143	20	8	6¾	193	27	11	5¼
44	6	5	8½	94	13	8	6¾	144	20	11	5¼	194	27	14	3½
45	6	8	6¾	95	13	11	5¼	145	20	14	3½	195	27	17	1¾
46	6	11	5¼	96	13	14	3½	146	20	17	1¾	196	28	0	0
47	6	14	3½	97	13	17	1¾	147	21	0	0	197	28	2	10¼
48	6	17	1¾	98	14	0	0	148	21	2	10¼	198	28	5	8½
49	7	0	0	99	14	2	10¼	149	21	5	8½	199	28	8	6¾
50	**7**	**2**	**10¼**	**100**	**14**	**5**	**8½**	**150**	**21**	**8**	**6¾**	**200**	**28**	**11**	**5¼**
250	35	14s	3½	700	100	0	0	1200	171	8	6¾	2000	285	14	3½
300	42	17	1¾	750	107	2	10¼	1400	200	0	0	2500	357	2	10¼
400	57	2	10¼	800	114	5	8½	1500	214	5	8½	3000	428	11	5¼
500	71	8	6¾	900	128	11	5¼	1600	228	11	5¼	4000	571	8	6¾
600	85	14s	3½	1000	142	17	1¾	1800	257	2	10¼	5000	714	5	8½

$85\frac{5}{7}\%$ off.

1d	0s	0¼	4/1	0s	7	8/1	1s	1¾	12/1	1s	8¾	16/1	2s	3½
2d	0	0¼	2	0	7¼	2	1	2	2	1	8¾	2	2	3¾
3d	0	0½	3	0	7¼	3	1	2¼	3	1	9	3	2	3¾
4d	0	0½	4	0	7½	4	1	2¼	4	1	9¼	4	2	4
5d	0	0¾	5	0	7½	5	1	2½	5	1	9¼	5	2	4¼
6d	0	0¾	4/6	0	7¾	8/6	1	2½	12/6	1	9½	16/6	2	4¼
7d	0	1	7	0	7¾	7	1	2¾	7	1	9½	7	2	4½
8d	0	1¼	8	0	8	8	1	2¾	8	1	9¾	8	2	4½
9d	0	1¼	9	0	8¼	9	1	3	9	1	9¾	9	2	4¾
10d	0	1½	10	0	8¼	10	1	3¼	10	1	10	10	2	4¾
11d	0	1½	11	0	8½	11	1	3¼	11	1	10¼	11	2	5
1/-	0	1¾	**5/-**	0	8½	**9/-**	1	3½	**13/-**	1	10¼	**17/-**	2	5¼
1/1	0	1¾	5/1	0	8¾	9/1	1	3½	13/1	1	10½	17/1	2	5¼
2	0	2	2	0	8¾	2	1	3¾	2	1	10½	2	2	5½
3	0	2¼	3	0	9	3	1	3¾	3	1	10¾	3	2	5½
4	0	2¼	4	0	9¼	4	1	4	4	1	10¾	4	2	5¾
5	0	2½	5	0	9¼	5	1	4¼	5	1	11	5	2	5¾
1/6	0	2½	5/6	0	9½	9/6	1	4¼	13/6	1	11¼	17/6	2	6
7	0	2¾	7	0	9½	7	1	4½	7	1	11¼	7	2	6¼
8	0	2¾	8	0	9¾	8	1	4½	8	1	11½	8	2	6¼
9	0	3	9	0	9¾	9	1	4¾	9	1	11½	9	2	6½
10	0	3¼	10	0	10	10	1	4¾	10	1	11¾	10	2	6½
11	0	3¼	11	0	10¼	11	1	5	11	1	11¾	11	2	6¾
2/-	0	3½	**6/-**	0	10¼	**10/-**	1	5¼	**14/-**	2	0	**18/-**	2	6¾
2/1	0	3½	6/1	0	10½	10/1	1	5¼	14/1	2	0¼	18/1	2	7
2	0	3¾	2	0	10½	2	1	5½	2	2	0¼	2	2	7¼
3	0	3¾	3	0	10¾	3	1	5½	3	2	0½	3	2	7¼
4	0	4	4	0	10¾	4	1	5¾	4	2	0½	4	2	7½
5	0	4¼	5	0	11	5	1	5¾	5	2	0¾	5	2	7½
2/6	0	4¼	6/6	0	11¼	10/6	1	6	14/6	2	0¾	18/6	2	7¾
7	0	4½	7	0	11¼	7	1	6¼	7	2	1	7	2	7¾
8	0	4½	8	0	11½	8	1	6¼	8	2	1¼	8	2	8
9	0	4¾	9	0	11½	9	1	6½	9	2	1¼	9	2	8¼
10	0	4¾	10	0	11¾	10	1	6½	10	2	1½	10	2	8¼
11	0	5	11	0	11¾	11	1	6¾	11	2	1½	11	2	8½
3/-	0	5¼	**7/-**	1	0	**11/-**	1	6¾	**15/-**	2	1¾	**19/-**	2	8½
3/1	0	5¼	7/1	1	0¼	11/1	1	7	15/1	2	1¾	19/1	2	8¾
2	0	5½	2	1	0¼	2	1	7¼	2	2	2	2	2	8¾
3	0	5½	3	1	0½	3	1	7¼	3	2	2¼	3	2	9
4	0	5¾	4	1	0½	4	1	7½	4	2	2¼	4	2	9¼
5	0	5¾	5	1	0¾	5	1	7½	5	2	2½	5	2	9¼
3/6	0	6	7/6	1	0¾	11/6	1	7¾	15/6	2	2½	19/6	2	9½
7	0	6¼	7	1	1	7	1	7¾	7	2	2¾	7	2	9½
8	0	6¼	8	1	1¼	8	1	8	8	2	2¾	8	2	9¾
9	0	6½	9	1	1¼	9	1	8¼	9	2	3	9	2	9¾
10	0	6½	10	1	1½	10	1	8¼	10	2	3¼	10	2	10
11	0	6¾	11	1	1½	11	1	8½	11	2	3¼	11	2	10¼
4/-	0	6¾	**8/-**	1	1¾	**12/-**	1	8½	**16/-**	2	3½	**20/-**	2	10¼

20/6	2s	11¼	25/6	3s	7¾	31/-	4s	5¼	35/6	5s	0¾	42/-	6s	0
21/-	3	0	26/-	3	8½	31/6	4	6	36/-	5	1¾	45/-	6	5
22/-	3	1¾	27/-	3	10¼	32/-	4	6¾	37/-	5	3½	50/-	7	1¾
22/6	3	2½	27/6	3	11¼	32/6	4	7¾	37/6	5	4¼	63/-	9	0
23/-	3	3½	28/-	4	0	33/-	4	8½	38/-	5	5¼	84/-	12	0
24/-	3	5¼	29/-	4	1¾	34/-	4	10¼	39/-	5	6¾	105/-	15	0
25/-	3	6¾	**30/-**	4	3½	**35/-**	5	0	**40/-**	5	8½	126/-	18	0

£1	£0	2s	10¾	£51	£7	7s	10¾	£101	14	12s	10¾	£151	21	17s	10¾
2	0	5	9½	52	7	10	9½	102	14	15	9½	152	22	0	9½
3	0	8	8½	53	7	13	8½	103	14	18	8½	153	22	3	8½
4	0	11	7¼	54	7	16	7¼	104	15	1	7¼	154	22	6	7¼
5	0	14	6	55	7	19	6	105	15	4	6	155	22	9	6
6	0	17	4¾	56	8	2	4¾	106	15	7	4¾	156	22	12	4¾
7	1	0	3½	57	8	5	3½	107	15	10	3½	157	22	15	3½
8	1	3	2½	58	8	8	2½	108	15	13	2½	158	22	18	2½
9	1	6	1¼	59	8	11	1¼	109	15	16	1¼	159	23	1	1¼
10	**1**	**9**	**0**	**60**	**8**	**14**	**0**	**110**	**15**	**19**	**0**	**160**	**23**	**4**	**0**
11	1	11	10¾	61	8	16	10¾	111	16	1	10¾	161	23	6	10¾
12	1	14	9½	62	8	19	9½	112	16	4	9½	162	23	9	9½
13	1	17	8½	63	9	2	8½	113	16	7	8½	163	23	12	8½
14	2	0	7¼	64	9	5	7¼	114	16	10	7¼	164	23	15	7¼
15	2	3	6	65	9	8	6	115	16	13	6	165	23	18	6
16	2	6	4¾	66	9	11	4¾	116	16	16	4¾	166	24	1	4¾
17	2	9	3½	67	9	14	3½	117	16	19	3½	167	24	4	3½
18	2	12	2½	68	9	17	2½	118	17	2	2½	168	24	7	2½
19	2	15	1¼	69	10	0	1¼	119	17	5	1¼	169	24	10	1¼
20	**2**	**18**	**0**	**70**	**10**	**3**	**0**	**120**	**17**	**8**	**0**	**170**	**24**	**13**	**0**
21	3	0	10¾	71	10	5	10¾	121	17	10	10¾	171	24	15	10¾
22	3	3	9½	72	10	8	9½	122	17	13	9½	172	24	18	9½
23	3	6	8½	73	10	11	8½	123	17	16	8½	173	25	1	8½
24	3	9	7¼	74	10	14	7¼	124	17	19	7¼	174	25	4	7¼
25	3	12	6	75	10	17	6	125	18	2	6	175	25	7	6
26	3	15	4¾	76	11	0	4¾	126	18	5	4¾	176	25	10	4¾
27	3	18	3½	77	11	3	3½	127	18	8	3½	177	25	13	3½
28	4	1	2½	78	11	6	2½	128	18	11	2½	178	25	16	2½
29	4	4	1¼	79	11	9	1¼	129	18	14	1¼	179	25	19	1¼
30	**4**	**7**	**0**	**80**	**11**	**12**	**0**	**130**	**18**	**17**	**0**	**180**	**26**	**2**	**0**
31	4	9	10¾	81	11	14	10¾	131	18	19	10¾	181	26	4	10¾
32	4	12	9½	82	11	17	9½	132	19	2	9½	182	26	7	9½
33	4	15	8½	83	12	0	8½	133	19	5	8½	183	26	10	8½
34	4	18	7¼	84	12	3	7¼	134	19	8	7¼	184	26	13	7¼
35	5	1	6	85	12	6	6	135	19	11	6	185	26	16	6
36	5	4	4¾	86	12	9	4¾	136	19	14	4¾	186	26	19	4¾
37	5	7	3½	87	12	12	3½	137	19	17	3½	187	27	2	3½
38	5	10	2½	88	12	15	2½	138	20	0	2½	188	27	5	2½
39	5	13	1¼	89	12	18	1¼	139	20	3	1¼	189	27	8	1¼
40	**5**	**16**	**0**	**90**	**13**	**1**	**0**	**140**	**20**	**6**	**0**	**190**	**27**	**11**	**0**
41	5	18	10¾	91	13	3	10¾	141	20	8	10¾	191	27	13	10¾
42	6	1	9½	92	13	6	9½	142	20	11	9½	192	27	16	9½
43	6	4	8½	93	13	9	8½	143	20	14	8½	193	27	19	8½
44	6	7	7¼	94	13	12	7¼	144	20	17	7¼	194	28	2	7¼
45	6	10	6	95	13	15	6	145	21	0	6	195	28	5	6
46	6	13	4¾	96	13	18	4¾	146	21	3	4¾	196	28	8	4¾
47	6	16	3½	97	14	1	3½	147	21	6	3½	197	28	11	3½
48	6	19	2½	98	14	4	2½	148	21	9	2½	198	28	14	2½
49	7	2	1¼	99	14	7	1¼	149	21	12	1¼	199	28	17	1¼
50	**7**	**5**	**0**	**100**	**14**	**10**	**0**	**150**	**21**	**15**	**0**	**200**	**29**	**0**	**0**

250	36	5s	0d	700	101	10s	0d	1200	174	0s	0d	2000	290	0s	0
300	43	10	0	750	108	15	0	1400	203	0	0	2500	362	10	0
400	58	0	0	800	116	0	0	1500	217	10	0	3000	435	0	0
500	72	10	0	900	130	10	0	1600	232	0	0	4000	580	0	0
600	87	0s	0d	1000	145	0s	0d	1800	261	0s	0d	5000	725	0s	0

85½% off

14½% 14½ Per Cent. 14½%

1d	0s	0¼	4/1	0s	7	8/1	1s	2	12/1	1s	9	16/1	2s	4
2d	0	0¼	2	0	7¼	2	1	2¼	2	1	9¼	2	2	4¼
3d	0	0½	3	0	7½	3	1	2¼	3	1	9¼	3	2	4¼
4d	0	0½	4	0	7½	4	1	2½	4	1	9½	4	2	4½
5d	0	0¾	5	0	7¾	5	1	2¾	5	1	9½	5	2	4½
6d	0	0¾	4/6	0	7¾	8/6	1	2¾	12/6	1	9¾	16/6	2	4¾
7d	0	1	7	0	8	7	1	3	7	1	10	7	2	4¾
8d	0	1¼	8	0	8	8	1	3	8	1	10	8	2	5
9d	0	1¼	9	0	8¼	9	1	3¼	9	1	10¼	9	2	5¼
10d	0	1½	10	0	8½	10	1	3¼	10	1	10¼	10	2	5¼
11d	0	1½	11	0	8½	11	1	3½	11	1	10½	11	2	5½
1/-	**0**	**1¾**	**5/-**	**0**	**8¾**	**9/-**	**1**	**3¾**	**13/-**	**1**	**10½**	**17/-**	**2**	**5½**
1/1	0	2	5/1	0	8¾	1	1	3¾	1	1	10¾	1	2	5¾
2	0	2	2	0	9	2	1	4	2	1	11	2	2	5¾
3	0	2¼	3	0	9¼	3	1	4	3	1	11	3	2	6
4	0	2¼	4	0	9¼	4	1	4¼	4	1	11¼	4	2	6¼
5	0	2½	5	0	9½	5	1	4½	5	1	11¼	5	2	6¼
1/6	0	2½	5/6	0	9½	9/6	1	4½	13/6	1	11½	17/6	2	6½
7	0	2¾	7	0	9¾	7	1	4¾	7	1	11¾	7	2	6½
8	0	3	8	0	9¾	8	1	4¾	8	1	11¾	8	2	6¾
9	0	3	9	0	10	9	1	5	9	2	0	9	2	7
10	0	3¼	10	0	10¼	10	1	5	10	2	0	10	2	7
11	0	3¼	11	0	10¼	11	1	5¼	11	2	0¼	11	2	7¼
2/-	**0**	**3½**	**6/-**	**0**	**10½**	**10/-**	**1**	**5½**	**14/-**	**2**	**0¼**	**18/-**	**2**	**7¼**
2/1	0	3¾	1	0	10½	10/1	1	5½	1	2	0½	1	2	7½
2	0	3¾	2	0	10¾	2	1	5¾	2	2	0¾	2	2	7½
3	0	4	3	0	11	3	1	5¾	3	2	0¾	3	2	7¾
4	0	4	4	0	11	4	1	6	4	2	1	4	2	8
5	0	4¼	5	0	11¼	5	1	6¼	5	2	1	5	2	8
2/6	0	4¼	6/6	0	11¼	10/6	1	6¼	14/6	2	1¼	18/6	2	8¼
7	0	4½	7	0	11½	7	1	6½	7	2	1½	7	2	8¼
8	0	4¾	8	0	11½	8	1	6½	8	2	1½	8	2	8½
9	0	4¾	9	0	11¾	9	1	6¾	9	2	1¾	9	2	8¾
10	0	5	10	1	0	10	1	6¾	10	2	1¾	10	2	8¾
11	0	5	11	1	0	11	1	7	11	2	2	11	2	9
3/-	**0**	**5¼**	**7/-**	**1**	**0¼**	**11/-**	**1**	**7¼**	**15/-**	**2**	**2**	**19/-**	**2**	**9**
3/1	0	5¼	1	1	0¼	1	1	7¼	15/1	2	2¼	1	2	9¼
2	0	5½	2	1	0½	2	1	7½	2	2	2½	2	2	9¼
3	0	5¾	3	1	0½	3	1	7½	3	2	2½	3	2	9½
4	0	5¾	4	1	0¾	4	1	7¾	4	2	2¾	4	2	9¾
5	0	6	5	1	1	5	1	7¾	5	2	2¾	5	2	9¾
3/6	0	6	7/6	1	1	11/6	1	8	15/6	2	3	19/6	2	10
7	0	6¼	7	1	1¼	7	1	8¼	7	2	3	7	2	10
8	0	6½	8	1	1¼	8	1	8¼	8	2	3¼	8	2	10¼
9	0	6½	9	1	1½	9	1	8½	9	2	3½	9	2	10¼
10	0	6¾	10	1	1¾	10	1	8½	10	2	3½	10	2	10½
11	0	6¾	11	1	1¾	11	1	8¾	11	2	3¾	11	2	10¾
4/-	**0**	**7**	**8/-**	**1**	**2**	**12/-**	**1**	**9**	**16/-**	**2**	**3¾**	**20/-**	**2**	**10¾**
20/6	2s	11¾	25/6	3s	8¼	31/-	4s	6	35/6	5s	1¾	Guineas.		
21/-	3	0½	26/-	3	9¼	31/6	4	6¾	36/-	5	2¾	1.	3s	0½
22/-	3	2¼	27/-	3	11	32/-	4	7¾	37/-	5	4½	2.	6	1
22/6	3	3¼	27/6	3	11¾	32/6	4	8½	37/6	5	5¼	3.	9	1½
23/-	3	4	28/-	4	0¾	33/-	4	9½	38/-	5	6	4.	12	2¼
24/-	3	5¾	29/-	4	2½	34/-	4	11¼	39/-	5	7¾	5.	15	2¾
25/-	3s	7½	**30/-**	4s	4¼	**35/-**	5s	1	**40/-**	5s	9½	6.	18	3¼

(=12$\frac{7}{10}$% on Gross Returns).

£	s. d.	£	s. d.	£	s. d.	£	s. d.
£1	£0 3s. 0	£51	£7 13s. 0	£101	£15 3s. 0	£151	£22 13s. 0
2	0 6 0	52	7 16 0	102	15 6 0	152	22 16 0
3	0 9 0	53	7 19 0	103	15 9 0	153	22 19 0
4	0 12 0	54	8 2 0	104	15 12 0	154	23 2 0
5	0 15 0	55	8 5 0	105	15 15 0	155	23 5 0
6	0 18 0	56	8 8 0	106	15 18 0	156	23 8 0
7	1 1 0	57	8 11 0	107	16 1 0	157	23 11 0
8	1 4 0	58	8 14 0	108	16 4 0	158	23 14 0
9	1 7 0	59	8 17 0	109	16 7 0	159	23 17 0
10	£1 10s. 0	60	£9 0s. 0	110	£16 10s. 0	160	£24 0s. 0
11	£1 13s. 0	61	£9 3s. 0	111	£16 13s. 0	161	£24 3s. 0
12	1 16 0	62	9 6 0	112	16 16 0	162	24 6 0
13	1 19 0	63	9 9 0	113	16 19 0	163	24 9 0
14	2 2 0	64	9 12 0	114	17 2 0	164	24 12 0
15	2 5 0	65	9 15 0	115	17 5 0	165	24 15 0
16	2 8 0	66	9 18 0	116	17 8 0	166	24 18 0
17	2 11 0	67	10 1 0	117	17 11 0	167	25 1 0
18	2 14 0	68	10 4 0	118	17 14 0	168	25 4 0
19	2 17 0	69	10 7 0	119	17 17 0	169	25 7 0
20	£3 0s. 0	70	10 10s. 0	120	£18 0s. 0	170	£25 10s. 0
21	£3 3s. 0	71	10 13s. 0	121	£18 3s. 0	171	£25 13s. 0
22	3 6 0	72	10 16 0	122	18 6 0	172	25 16 0
23	3 9 0	73	10 19 0	123	18 9 0	173	25 19 0
24	3 12 0	74	11 2 0	124	18 12 0	174	26 2 0
25	3 15 0	75	11 5 0	125	18 15 0	175	26 5 0
26	3 18 0	76	11 8 0	126	18 18 0	176	26 8 0
27	4 1 0	77	11 11 0	127	19 1 0	177	26 11 0
28	4 4 0	78	11 14 0	128	19 4 0	178	26 14 0
29	4 7 0	79	11 17 0	129	19 7 0	179	26 17 0
30	£4 10s. 0	80	12 0s. 0	130	£19 10s. 0	180	£27 0s. 0
31	£4 13s. 0	81	12 3s. 0	131	£19 13s. 0	181	£27 3s. 0
32	4 16 0	82	12 6 0	132	19 16 0	182	27 6 0
33	4 19 0	83	12 9 0	133	19 19 0	183	27 9 0
34	5 2 0	84	12 12 0	134	20 2 0	184	27 12 0
35	5 5 0	85	12 15 0	135	20 5 0	185	27 15 0
36	5 8 0	86	12 18 0	136	20 8 0	186	27 18 0
37	5 11 0	87	13 1 0	137	20 11 0	187	28 1 0
38	5 14 0	88	13 4 0	138	20 14 0	188	28 4 0
39	5 17 0	89	13 7 0	139	20 17 0	189	28 7 0
40	£6 0s. 0	90	13 10s. 0	140	£21 0s. 0	190	£28 10s. 0
41	£6 3s. 0	91	13 13s. 0	141	£21 3s. 0	191	£28 13s. 0
42	6 6 0	92	13 16 0	142	21 6 0	192	28 16 0
43	6 9 0	93	13 19 0	143	21 9 0	193	28 19 0
44	6 12 0	94	14 2 0	144	21 12 0	194	29 2 0
45	6 15 0	95	14 5 0	145	21 15 0	195	29 5 0
46	6 18 0	96	14 8 0	146	21 18 0	196	29 8 0
47	7 1 0	97	14 11 0	147	22 1 0	197	29 11 0
48	7 4 0	98	14 14 0	148	22 4 0	198	29 14 0
49	7 7 0	99	14 17 0	149	22 7 0	199	29 17 0
50	£7 10s. 0	100	15 0s. 0	150	£22 10s. 0	200	£30 0s. 0
250	£37 10s.0d	700	105 0s.0d	1200	180 0s.0d	2000	£300 0s. 0
300	45 0 0	750	112 10 0	1400	210 0 0	2500	375 0 0
400	60 0 0	800	120 0 0	1500	225 0 0	3000	450 0 0
500	75 0 0	900	135 0 0	1600	240 0 0	4000	600 0 0
600	£90 0s. 0d	1000	150 0s. 0d	1800	270 0s.0d	5000	£750 0s. 0

85% off.

15% FIFTEEN PER CENT. 15%

1d	0s. 0¼	4/1	0s. 7¼	8/1	1s. 2½	12/1	1s. 9¾	16/1	2s. 5
2d	0 0¼	2	0 7½	2	1 2¾	2	1 10	2	2 5
3d	0 0½	3	0 7¾	3	1 2¾	3	1 10	3	2 5¼
4d	0 0½	4	0 7¾	4	1 3	4	1 10¼	4	2 5½
5d	0 0¾	5	0 8	5	1 3¼	5	1 10¼	5	2 5½
6d	0 1	4/6	0 8	8/6	1 3¼	12/6	1 10½	16/6	2 5¾
7d	0 1	7	0 8¼	7	1 3½	7	1 10¾	7	2 5¾
8d	0 1¼	8	0 8½	8	1 3½	8	1 10¾	8	2 6
9d	0 1¼	9	0 8½	9	1 3¾	9	1 11	9	2 6¼
10d	0 1½	10	0 8¾	10	1 4	10	1 11	10	2 6¼
11d	0 1¾	11	0 8¾	11	1 4	11	1 11¼	11	2 6½
1/-	0s. 1¾	**5/-**	0s. 9	**9/-**	1s. 4¼	**13/-**	1s.11½	**17/-**	2s. 6½
1/1	0s. 2	5/1	0s. 9¼	9/1	1s. 4¼	13/1	1s.11½	17/1	2s. 6¾
2	0 2	2	0 9¼	2	1 4½	2	1 11¾	2	2 7
3	0 2¼	3	0 9½	3	1 4¾	3	1 11¾	3	2 7
4	0 2½	4	0 9½	4	1 4¾	4	2 0	4	2 7¼
5	0 2½	5	0 9¾	5	1 5	5	2 0¼	5	2 7¼
1/6	0 2¾	5/6	0 10	9/6	1 5	13/6	2 0¼	17/6	2 7½
7	0 2¾	7	0 10	7	1 5¼	7	2 0½	7	2 7¾
8	0 3	8	0 10¼	8	1 5½	8	2 0½	8	2 7¾
9	0 3¼	9	0 10¼	9	1 5½	9	2 0¾	9	2 8
10	0 3¼	10	0 10½	10	1 5¾	10	2 1	10	2 8
11	0 3½	11	0 10¾	11	1 5¾	11	2 1	11	2 8¼
2/-	0s. 3½	**6/-**	0s.10¾	**10/-**	1s. 6	**14/-**	2s. 1¼	**18/-**	2s. 8½
2/1	0s. 3¾	6/1	0s.11	10/1	1s. 6¼	14/1	2s. 1¼	18/1	2s. 8½
2	0 4	2	0 11	2	1 6¼	2	2 1½	2	2 8¾
3	0 4	3	0 11¼	3	1 6½	3	2 1¾	3	2 8¾
4	0 4¼	4	0 11½	4	1 6½	4	2 1¾	4	2 9
5	0 4¼	5	0 11½	5	1 6¾	5	2 2	5	2 9¼
2/6	0 4½	6/6	0 11¾	10/6	1 7	14/6	2 2	18/6	2 9¼
7	0 4¾	7	0 11¾	7	1 7	7	2 2¼	7	2 9½
8	0 4¾	8	1 0	8	1 7¼	8	2 2½	8	2 9½
9	0 5	9	1 0¼	9	1 7¼	9	2 2½	9	2 9¾
10	0 5	10	1 0¼	10	1 7½	10	2 2¾	10	2 10
11	0 5¼	11	1 0½	11	1 7¾	11	2 2¾	11	2 10
3/-	0s. 5½	**7/-**	1s. 0½	**11/-**	1s. 7¾	**15/-**	2s. 3	**19/-**	2s.10¼
3/1	0s. 5½	7/1	1s. 0¾	11/1	1s. 8	15/1	2s. 3¼	19/1	2s.10¼
2	0 5¾	2	1 1	2	1 8	2	2 3¼	2	2 10½
3	0 5¾	3	1 1	3	1 8¼	3	2 3½	3	2 10¾
4	0 6	4	1 1¼	4	1 8½	4	2 3½	4	2 10¾
5	0 6¼	5	1 1¼	5	1 8½	5	2 3¾	5	2 11
3/6	0 6¼	7/6	1 1½	11/6	1 8¾	15/6	2 4	19/6	2 11
7	0 6½	7	1 1¾	7	1 8¾	7	2 4	7	2 11¼
8	0 6½	8	1 1¾	8	1 9	8	2 4¼	8	2 11½
9	0 6¾	9	1 2	9	1 9¼	9	2 4¼	9	2 11½
10	0 7	10	1 2	10	1 9¼	10	2 4½	10	2 11¾
11	0 7	11	1 2¼	11	1 9½	11	2 4¾	11	2 11¾
4/-	0s. 7¼	**8/-**	1s. 2½	**12/-**	1s. 9½	**16/-**	2s. 4¾	**20/-**	3s. 0

20/6	3s. 1	25/6	3s.10	31/-	4s. 7¾	35/6	5s. 4	Guineas.	
21/-	3 1¾	26/-	3 10¾	31/6	4 8¾	36/-	5 4¾	1.	3s. 1¾
22/-	3 3½	27/-	4 0½	32/-	4 9½	37/-	5 6½	2.	6 3½
22/6	3 4½	27/6	4 1½	32/6	4 10½	37/6	5 7½	3.	9 5¼
23/-	3 5½	28/-	4 2½	33/-	4 11½	38/-	5 8½	4.	12 7¼
24/-	3 7¼	29/-	4 4¼	34/-	5 1¼	39/-	5 10¼	5.	15 9
25/-	3s. 9	**30/-**	4s. 6	**35/-**	5s. 3	**40/-**	6s. 0	6.	18s.10¾

(13%* on Gross Returns).

15½ Per Cent.

15½%

£1	£0	3s	1¼	£51	£7	18s	1¼	£101	15	13s	1¼	£151	23	8s	1¼
2	0	6	2½	52	8	1	2½	102	15	16	2½	152	23	11	2½
3	0	9	3½	53	8	4	3½	103	15	19	3½	153	23	14	3½
4	0	12	4¾	54	8	7	4¾	104	16	2	4¾	154	23	17	4¾
5	0	15	6	55	8	10	6	105	16	5	6	155	24	0	6
6	0	18	7¼	56	8	13	7¼	106	16	8	7¼	156	24	3	7¼
7	1	1	8½	57	8	16	8½	107	16	11	8½	157	24	6	8½
8	1	4	9½	58	8	19	9½	108	16	14	9½	158	24	9	9½
9	1	7	10¾	59	9	2	10¾	109	16	17	10¾	159	24	12	10¾
10	**1**	**11**	**0**	**60**	**9**	**6**	**0**	**110**	**17**	**1**	**0**	**160**	**24**	**16**	**0**
11	1	14	1¼	61	9	9	1¼	111	17	4	1¼	161	24	19	1¼
12	1	17	2½	62	9	12	2½	112	17	7	2½	162	25	2	2½
13	2	0	3½	63	9	15	3½	113	17	10	3½	163	25	5	3½
14	2	3	4¾	64	9	18	4¾	114	17	13	4¾	164	25	8	4¾
15	2	6	6	65	10	1	6	115	17	16	6	165	25	11	6
16	2	9	7¼	66	10	4	7¼	116	17	19	7¼	166	25	14	7¼
17	2	12	8½	67	10	7	8½	117	18	2	8½	167	25	17	8½
18	2	15	9½	68	10	10	9½	118	18	5	9½	168	26	0	9½
19	2	18	10¾	69	10	13	10¾	119	18	8	10¾	169	26	3	10¾
20	**3**	**2**	**0**	**70**	**10**	**17**	**0**	**120**	**18**	**12**	**0**	**170**	**26**	**7**	**0**
21	3	5	1¼	71	11	0	1¼	121	18	15	1¼	171	26	10	1¼
22	3	8	2½	72	11	3	2½	122	18	18	2½	172	26	13	2½
23	3	11	3½	73	11	6	3½	123	19	1	3½	173	26	16	3½
24	3	14	4¾	74	11	9	4¾	124	19	4	4¾	174	26	19	4¾
25	3	17	6	75	11	12	6	125	19	7	6	175	27	2	6
26	4	0	7¼	76	11	15	7¼	126	19	10	7¼	176	27	5	7¼
27	4	3	8½	77	11	18	8½	127	19	13	8½	177	27	8	8½
28	4	6	9½	78	12	1	9½	128	19	16	9½	178	27	11	9½
29	4	9	10¾	79	12	4	10¾	129	19	19	10¾	179	27	14	10¾
30	**4**	**13**	**0**	**80**	**12**	**8**	**0**	**130**	**20**	**3**	**0**	**180**	**27**	**18**	**0**
31	4	16	1¼	81	12	11	1¼	131	20	6	1¼	181	28	1	1¼
32	4	19	2½	82	12	14	2½	132	20	9	2½	182	28	4	2½
33	5	2	3½	83	12	17	3½	133	20	12	3½	183	28	7	3½
34	5	5	4¾	84	13	0	4¾	134	20	15	4¾	184	28	10	4¾
35	5	8	6	85	13	3	6	135	20	18	6	185	28	13	6
36	5	11	7¼	86	13	6	7¼	136	21	1	7¼	186	28	16	7¼
37	5	14	8½	87	13	9	8½	137	21	4	8½	187	28	19	8½
38	5	17	9½	88	13	12	9½	138	21	7	9½	188	29	2	9½
39	6	0	10¾	89	13	15	10¾	139	21	10	10¾	189	29	5	10¾
40	**6**	**4**	**0**	**90**	**13**	**19**	**0**	**140**	**21**	**14**	**0**	**190**	**29**	**9**	**0**
41	6	7	1¼	91	14	2	1¼	141	21	17	1¼	191	29	12	1¼
42	6	10	2½	92	14	5	2½	142	22	0	2½	192	29	15	2½
43	6	13	3½	93	14	8	3½	143	22	3	3½	193	29	18	3½
44	6	16	4¾	94	14	11	4¾	144	22	6	4¾	194	30	1	4¾
45	6	19	6	95	14	14	6	145	22	9	6	195	30	4	6
46	7	2	7¼	96	14	17	7¼	146	22	12	7¼	196	30	7	7¼
47	7	5	8½	97	15	0	8½	147	22	15	8½	197	30	10	8½
48	7	8	9½	98	15	3	9½	148	22	18	9½	198	30	13	9½
49	7	11	10¾	99	15	6	10¾	149	23	1	10¾	199	30	16	10¾
50	**7**	**15**	**0**	**100**	**15**	**10**	**0**	**150**	**23**	**5**	**0**	**200**	**31**	**0**	**0**

250	38	15s	0d	700	108	10s	0d	1200	186	0s	0d	2000	310	0s	0
300	46	10	0	750	116	5	0	1400	217	0	0	2500	387	10	0
400	62	0	0	800	124	0	0	1500	232	10	0	3000	465	0	0
500	77	10	0	900	139	10	0	1600	248	0	0	4000	620	0	0
600	93	0s	0d	1000	155	0s	0d	1800	279	0s	0d	5000	775	0s	0

84½% off

15½ Per Cent.

15½%

1d	0s	0¼	4/1	0s	7½	8/1	1s	3	12/1	1s	10½	16/1	2s	6
2d	0	0¼	2	0	7¾	2	1	3¼	2	1	10¾	2	2	6
3d	0	0½	3	0	8	3	1	3¼	3	1	10¾	3	2	6¼
4d	0	0½	4	0	8	4	1	3½	4	1	11	4	2	6½
5d	0	0¾	5	0	8¼	5	1	3¾	5	1	11	5	2	6½
6d	0	1	4/6	0	8¼	8/6	1	3¾	12/6	1	11¼	16/6	2	6¾
7d	0	1	7	0	8½	7	1	4	7	1	11½	7	2	6¾
8d	0	1¼	8	0	8¾	8	1	4	8	1	11½	8	2	7
9d	0	1½	9	0	8¾	9	1	4¼	9	1	11¾	9	2	7¼
10d	0	1½	10	0	9	10	1	4½	10	1	11¾	10	2	7¼
11d	0	1¾	11	0	9¼	11	1	4½	11	2	0	11	2	7½
1/-	**0**	**1¾**	**5/-**	**0**	**9¼**	**9/-**	**1**	**4¾**	**13/-**	**2**	**0¼**	**17/-**	**2**	**7½**
1/1	0	2	5/1	0	9½	1	1	5	1	2	0¼	1	2	7¾
2	0	2¼	2	0	9½	2	1	5	2	2	0½	2	2	8
3	0	2¼	3	0	9¾	3	1	5¼	3	2	0¾	3	2	8
4	0	2½	4	0	10	4	1	5¼	4	2	0¾	4	2	8¼
5	0	2¾	5	0	10	5	1	5½	5	2	1	5	2	8½
1/6	0	2¾	5/6	0	10¼	9/6	1	5¾	13/6	2	1	17/6	2	8½
7	0	3	7	0	10½	7	1	5¾	7	2	1¼	7	2	8¾
8	0	3	8	0	10½	8	1	6	8	2	1½	8	2	8¾
9	0	3¼	9	0	10¾	9	1	6¼	9	2	1½	9	2	9
10	0	3½	10	0	10¾	10	1	6¼	10	2	1¾	10	2	9¼
11	0	3½	11	0	11	11	1	6½	11	2	2	11	2	9¼
2/-	**0**	**3¾**	**6/-**	**0**	**11¼**	**10/-**	**1**	**6½**	**14/-**	**2**	**2**	**18/-**	**2**	**9½**
2/1	0	4	1	0	11¼	10/1	1	6¾	1	2	2¼	1	2	9¾
2	0	4	2	0	11½	2	1	7	2	2	2¼	2	2	9¾
3	0	4¼	3	0	11¾	3	1	7	3	2	2½	3	2	10
4	0	4¼	4	0	11¾	4	1	7¼	4	2	2¾	4	2	10
5	0	4½	5	1	0	5	1	7½	5	2	2¾	5	2	10¼
2/6	0	4¾	6/6	1	0	10/6	1	7½	14/6	2	3	18/6	2	10½
7	0	4¾	7	1	0¼	7	1	7¾	7	2	3¼	7	2	10½
8	0	5	8	1	0½	8	1	7¾	8	2	3¼	8	2	10¾
9	0	5	9	1	0½	9	1	8	9	2	3½	9	2	11
10	0	5¼	10	1	0¾	10	1	8¼	10	2	3½	10	2	11
11	0	5½	11	1	0¾	11	1	8¼	11	2	3¾	11	2	11¼
3/-	**0**	**5½**	**7/-**	**1**	**1**	**11/-**	**1**	**8½**	**15/-**	**2**	**4**	**19/-**	**2**	**11¼**
3/1	0	5¾	1	1	1¼	1	1	8½	15/1	2	4	1	2	11½
2	0	6	2	1	1¼	2	1	8¾	2	2	4¼	2	2	11¾
3	0	6	3	1	1½	3	1	9	3	2	4¼	3	2	11¾
4	0	6¼	4	1	1¾	4	1	9	4	2	4½	4	3	0
5	0	6¼	5	1	1¾	5	1	9¼	5	2	4¾	5	3	0
3/6	0	6½	7/6	1	2	11/6	1	9½	15/6	2	4¾	19/6	3	0¼
7	0	6¾	7	1	2	7	1	9½	7	2	5	7	3	0½
8	0	6¾	8	1	2¼	8	1	9¾	8	2	5¼	8	3	0½
9	0	7	9	1	2½	9	1	9¾	9	2	5¼	9	3	0¾
10	0	7¼	10	1	2½	10	1	10	10	2	5½	10	3	1
11	0	7¼	11	1	2¾	11	1	10¼	11	2	5½	11	3	1
4/-	**0**	**7½**	**8/-**	**1**	**3**	**12/-**	**1**	**10¼**	**16/-**	**2**	**5¾**	**20/-**	**3**	**1¼**

20/6	3s	2¼	25/6	3s	11½	31/-	4s	9¾	35/6	5s	6	Guineas.		
21/-	3	3	26/-	4	0¼	31/6	4	10½	36/-	5	7	1.	3s	3
22/-	3	5	27/-	4	2¼	32/-	4	11½	37/-	5	8¾	2.	6	6
22/6	3	5¾	27/6	4	3¼	32/6	5	0½	37/6	5	9¾	3.	9	9¼
23/-	3	6¾	28/-	4	4	33/-	5	1½	38/-	5	10¾	4.	13	0¼
24/-	3	8¾	29/-	4	6	34/-	5	3¼	39/-	6	0½	5.	16	3¼
25/-	3s	10½	**30/-**	4s	7¾	**35/-**	5s	5	**40/-**	6s	2½	6.	19s	6¼

(=13 4/10 % on Gross Returns).

£		s.	d.	£		s.	d.	£		s.	d.	£		s.	d.
£1	0	3s.	2½	£51	8	3s.	2½	£101	16	3s.	2½	£151	24	3s.	2½
2	0	6	4¾	52	8	6	4¾	102	16	6	4¾	152	24	6	4¾
3	0	9	7¼	53	8	9	7¼	103	16	9	7¼	153	24	9	7¼
4	0	12	9½	54	8	12	9½	104	16	12	9½	154	24	12	9½
5	0	16	0	55	8	16	0	105	16	16	0	155	24	16	0
6	0	19	2½	56	8	19	2½	106	16	19	2½	156	24	19	2½
7	1	2	4¾	57	9	2	4¾	107	17	2	4¾	157	25	2	4¾
8	1	5	7¼	58	9	5	7¼	108	17	5	7¼	158	25	5	7¼
9	1	8	9½	59	9	8	9½	109	17	8	9½	159	25	8	9½
10	1	12s.	0	60	9	12s.	0	110	17	12s.	0	160	25	12s.	0
11	1	15	2½	61	9	15	2½	111	17	15	2½	161	25	15	2½
12	1	18	4¾	62	9	18	4¾	112	17	18	4¾	162	25	18	4¾
13	2	1	7¼	63	10	1	7¼	113	18	1	7¼	163	26	1	7¼
14	2	4	9½	64	10	4	9½	114	18	4	9½	164	26	4	9½
15	2	8	0	65	10	8	0	115	18	8	0	165	26	8	0
16	2	11	2½	66	10	11	2½	116	18	11	2½	166	26	11	2½
17	2	14	4¾	67	10	14	4¾	117	18	14	4¾	167	26	14	4¾
18	2	17	7¼	68	10	17	7¼	118	18	17	7¼	168	26	17	7¼
19	3	0	9½	69	11	0	9½	119	19	0	9½	169	27	0	9½
20	3	4s.	0	70	11	4s.	0	120	19	4s.	0	170	27	4s.	0
21	3	7	2½	71	11	7	2½	121	19	7	2½	171	27	7	2½
22	3	10	4¾	72	11	10	4¾	122	19	10	4¾	172	27	10	4¾
23	3	13	7¼	73	11	13	7¼	123	19	13	7¼	173	27	13	7¼
24	3	16	9½	74	11	16	9½	124	19	16	9½	174	27	16	9½
25	4	0	0	75	12	0	0	125	20	0	0	175	28	0	0
26	4	3	2½	76	12	3	2½	126	20	3	2½	176	28	3	2½
27	4	6	4¾	77	12	6	4¾	127	20	6	4¾	177	28	6	4¾
28	4	9	7¼	78	12	9	7¼	128	20	9	7¼	178	28	9	7¼
29	4	12	9½	79	12	12	9½	129	20	12	9½	179	28	12	9½
30	4	16s.	0	80	12	16s.	0	130	20	16s.	0	180	28	16s.	0
31	4	19	2½	81	12	19	2½	131	20	19	2½	181	28	19	2½
32	5	2	4¾	82	13	2	4¾	132	21	2	4¾	182	29	2	4¾
33	5	5	7¼	83	13	5	7¼	133	21	5	7¼	183	29	5	7¼
34	5	8	9½	84	13	8	9½	134	21	8	9½	184	29	8	9½
35	5	12	0	85	13	12	0	135	21	12	0	185	29	12	0
36	5	15	2½	86	13	15	2½	136	21	15	2½	186	29	15	2½
37	5	18	4¾	87	13	18	4¾	137	21	18	4¾	187	29	18	4¾
38	6	1	7¼	88	14	1	7¼	138	22	1	7¼	188	30	1	7¼
39	6	4	9½	89	14	4	9½	139	22	4	9½	189	30	4	9½
40	6	8s.	0	90	14	8s.	0	140	22	8s.	0	190	30	8s.	0
41	6	11	2½	91	14	11	2½	141	22	11	2½	191	30	11	2½
42	6	14	4¾	92	14	14	4¾	142	22	14	4¾	192	30	14	4¾
43	6	17	7¼	93	14	17	7¼	143	22	17	7¼	193	30	17	7¼
44	7	0	9½	94	15	0	9½	144	23	0	9½	194	31	0	9½
45	7	4	0	95	15	4	0	145	23	4	0	195	31	4	0
46	7	7	2½	96	15	7	2½	146	23	7	2½	196	31	7	2½
47	7	10	4¾	97	15	10	4¾	147	23	10	4¾	197	31	10	4¾
48	7	13	7¼	98	15	13	7¼	148	23	13	7¼	198	31	13	7¼
49	7	16	9½	99	15	16	9½	149	23	16	9½	199	31	16	9½
50	8	0s.	0	100	16	0s.	0	150	24	0s.	0	200	32	0s.	0

250	£40	0	0	700	112	0	0	1200	192	0	0	2000	320	0	0
300	48	0	0	750	120	0	0	1400	224	0	0	2500	400	0	0
400	64	0	0	800	128	0	0	1500	240	0	0	3000	480	0	0
500	80	0	0	900	144	0	0	1600	256	0	0	4000	640	0	0
600	96	0	0	1000	160	0	0	1800	288	0	0	5000	800	0	0

84% off.

1d	0s. 0¼	4/1	0s. 7¾	8/1	1s. 3½	12/1	1s.11¼	16/1	2s. 7
2d	0 0¼	2	0 8	2	1 3¾	2	1 11¼	2	2 7
3d	0 0½	3	0 8¼	3	1 3¾	3	1 11½	3	2 7¼
4d	0 0¾	4	0 8¼	4	1 4	4	1 11¾	4	2 7¼
5d	0 0¾	5	0 8½	5	1 4¼	5	1 11¾	5	2 7½
6d	0 1	4/6	0 8¾	8/6	1 4¼	12/6	2 0	16/6	2 7¾
7d	0 1	7	0 8¾	7	1 4½	7	2 0¼	7	2 7¾
8d	0 1¼	8	0 9	8	1 4¾	8	2 0¼	8	2 8
9d	0 1½	9	0 9	9	1 4¾	9	2 0½	9	2 8¼
10d	0 1½	10	0 9¼	10	1 5	10	2 0¾	10	2 8¼
11d	0 1¾	11	0 9½	11	1 5	11	2 0¾	11	2 8½
1/-	0s. 2	**5/-**	0s. 9½	**9/-**	1s. 5¼	**13/-**	2s. 1	**17/-**	2s. 8¾
1/1	0 2	5/1	0 9¾	9/1	1 5½	13/1	2 1	17/1	2 8¾
2	0 2¼	2	0 10	2	1 5½	2	2 1¼	2	2 9
3	0 2½	3	0 10	3	1 5¾	3	2 1½	3	2 9
4	0 2½	4	0 10¼	4	1 6	4	2 1½	4	2 9¼
5	0 2¾	5	0 10½	5	1 6	5	2 1¾	5	2 9½
1/6	0 3	5/6	0 10½	9/6	1 6¼	13/6	2 2	17/6	2 9½
7	0 3	7	0 10¾	7	1 6½	7	2 2	7	2 9¾
8	0 3¼	8	0 11	8	1 6½	8	2 2¼	8	2 10
9	0 3¼	9	0 11	9	1 6¾	9	2 2½	9	2 10
10	0 3½	10	0 11¼	10	1 7	10	2 2½	10	2 10¼
11	0 3¾	11	0 11¼	11	1 7	11	2 2¾	11	2 10½
2/-	0s. 3¾	**6/-**	0s.11½	**10/-**	1s. 7¼	**14/-**	2s. 3	**18/-**	2s.10½
2/1	0 4	6/1	0 11¾	10/1	1 7¼	14/1	2 3	18/1	2 10¾
2	0 4¼	2	0 11¾	2	1 7½	2	2 3¼	2	2 11
3	0 4¼	3	1 0	3	1 7¾	3	2 3¼	3	2 11
4	0 4½	4	1 0¼	4	1 7¾	4	2 3½	4	2 11¼
5	0 4¾	5	1 0¼	5	1 8	5	2 3¾	5	2 11¼
2/6	0 4¾	6/6	1 0½	10/6	1 8¼	14/6	2 3¾	18/6	2 11½
7	0 5	7	1 0¾	7	1 8¼	7	2 4	7	2 11¾
8	0 5	8	1 0¾	8	1 8½	8	2 4¼	8	2 11¾
9	0 5¼	9	1 1	9	1 8¾	9	2 4¼	9	3 0
10	0 5½	10	1 1	10	1 8¾	10	2 4½	10	3 0¼
11	0 5½	11	1 1¼	11	1 9	11	2 4¾	11	3 0¼
3/-	0s. 5¾	**7/-**	1s. 1½	**11/-**	1s. 9	**15/-**	2s. 4¾	**19/-**	3s. 0½
3/1	0 6	7/1	1 1½	11/1	1 9¼	15/1	2 5	19/1	3 0¾
2	0 6	2	1 1¾	2	1 9½	2	2 5	2	3 0¾
3	0 6¼	3	1 2	3	1 9½	3	2 5¼	3	3 1
4	0 6½	4	1 2	4	1 9¾	4	2 5½	4	3 1
5	0 6½	5	1 2¼	5	1 10	5	2 5½	5	3 1¼
3/6	0 6¾	7/6	1 2½	11/6	1 10	15/6	2 5¾	19/6	3 1½
7	0 7	7	1 2½	7	1 10¼	7	2 6	7	3 1½
8	0 7	8	1 2¾	8	1 10½	8	2 6	8	3 1¾
9	0 7¼	9	1 3	9	1 10½	9	2 6¼	9	3 2
10	0 7¼	10	1 3	10	1 10¾	10	2 6½	10	3 2
11	0 7½	11	1 3¼	11	1 11	11	2 6½	11	3 2¼
4/-	0s. 7¾	**8/-**	1s. 3¼	**12/-**	1s.11	**16/-**	2s. 6¾	**20/-**	3s. 2½

								Guineas.	
20/6	3s. 3¼	25/6	4s. 1	31/-	4s. 11½	35/6	5s. 8¼		
21/-	3 4¼	26/-	4 2	31/6	5 0½	36/-	5 9	1.	3s. 4¼
22/-	3 6¼	27/-	4 3¾	32/-	5 1½	37/-	5 11	2.	6 8¾
22/6	3 7¼	27/6	4 4¾	32/6	5 2½	37/6	6 0	3.	10 1
23/-	3 8¼	28/-	4 5¾	33/-	5 3¼	38/-	6 1	4.	13 5¼
24/-	3 10	29/-	4 7¾	34/-	5 5¼	39/-	6 3	5.	16 9½
25/-	4s. 0	**30/-**	4s. 9½	**35/-**	5s. 7¼	**40/-**	6s. 4¾	6.	20s. 2

(=13$\frac{8}{10}$%* on Gross Returns.)

£	£ s. d.	£	£ s. d.	£	£ s. d.	£	£ s. d.
£1	0 3s. 3	£51	8 5s. 9	£101	16 8s. 3	£151	24 10s. 9
2	0 6 6	52	8 9 0	102	16 11 6	152	24 14 0
3	0 9 9	53	8 12 3	103	16 14 9	153	24 17 3
4	0 13 0	54	8 15 6	104	16 18 0	154	25 0 6
5	0 16 3	55	8 18 9	105	17 1 3	155	25 3 9
6	0 19 6	56	9 2 0	106	17 4 6	156	25 7 0
7	1 2 9	57	9 5 3	107	17 7 9	157	25 10 3
8	1 6 0	58	9 8 6	108	17 11 0	158	25 13 6
9	1 9 3	59	9 11 9	109	17 14 3	159	25 16 9
10	1 12s. 6	60	9 15s. 0	110	17 17s. 6	160	26 0s. 0
11	1 15 9	61	9 18 3	111	18 0 9	161	26 3 3
12	1 19 0	62	10 1 6	112	18 4 0	162	26 6 6
13	2 2 3	63	10 4 9	113	18 7 3	163	26 9 9
14	2 5 6	64	10 8 0	114	18 10 6	164	26 13 0
15	2 8 9	65	10 11 3	115	18 13 9	165	26 16 3
16	2 12 0	66	10 14 6	116	18 17 0	166	26 19 6
17	2 15 3	67	10 17 9	117	19 0 3	167	27 2 9
18	2 18 6	68	11 1 0	118	19 3 6	168	27 6 0
19	3 1 9	69	11 4 3	119	19 6 9	169	27 9 3
20	3 5s. 0	70	11 7s. 6	120	19 10s. 0	170	27 12s. 6
21	3 8 3	71	11 10 9	121	19 13 3	171	27 15 9
22	3 11 6	72	11 14 0	122	19 16 6	172	27 19 0
23	3 14 9	73	11 17 3	123	19 19 9	173	28 2 3
24	3 18 0	74	12 0 6	124	20 3 0	174	28 5 6
25	4 1 3	75	12 3 9	125	20 6 3	175	28 8 9
26	4 4 6	76	12 7 0	126	20 9 6	176	28 12 0
27	4 7 9	77	12 10 3	127	20 12 9	177	28 15 3
28	4 11 0	78	12 13 6	128	20 16 0	178	28 18 6
29	4 14 3	79	12 16 9	129	20 19 3	179	29 1 9
30	4 17s. 6	80	13 0s. 0	130	21 2s. 6	180	29 5s. 0
31	5 0 9	81	13 3 3	131	21 5 9	181	29 8 3
32	5 4 0	82	13 6 6	132	21 9 0	182	29 11 6
33	5 7 3	83	13 9 9	133	21 12 3	183	29 14 9
34	5 10 6	84	13 13 0	134	21 15 6	184	29 18 0
35	5 13 9	85	13 16 3	135	21 18 9	185	30 1 3
36	5 17 0	86	13 19 6	136	22 2 0	186	30 4 6
37	6 0 3	87	14 2 9	137	22 5 3	187	30 7 9
38	6 3 6	88	14 6 0	138	22 8 6	188	30 11 0
39	6 6 9	89	14 9 3	139	22 11 9	189	30 14 3
40	6 10s. 0	90	14 12s. 6	140	22 15s. 0	190	30 17s 0
41	6 13 3	91	14 15 9	141	22 18 3	191	31 0 9
42	6 16 6	92	14 19 0	142	23 1 6	192	31 4 0
43	6 19 9	93	15 2 3	143	23 4 9	193	31 7 3
44	7 3 0	94	15 5 6	144	23 8 0	194	31 10 6
45	7 6 3	95	15 8 9	145	23 11 3	195	31 13 9
46	7 9 6	96	15 12 0	146	23 14 6	196	31 17 0
47	7 12 9	97	15 15 3	147	23 17 9	197	32 0 3
48	7 16 0	98	15 18 6	148	24 1 0	198	32 3 6
49	7 19 3	99	16 1 9	149	24 4 3	199	32 6 9
50	8 2s. 6	100	16 5s. 0	150	24 7s. 6	200	32 10s. 0

£	£ s. d.	£	£ s. d.	£	£ s. d.	£	£ s. d.
250	£40 12 6	700	113 15 0	1200	195 0 0	2000	325 0 0
300	48 15 0	750	121 17 6	1400	227 10 0	2500	406 5 0
400	65 0 0	800	130 0 0	1500	243 15 0	3000	487 10 0
500	81 5 0	900	146 5 0	1600	260 0 0	4000	650 0 0
600	97 10 0	1000	162 10 0	1800	292 10 0	5000	812 10 0

83¾% off.

	s.	d.		s.	d.		s.	d.		s.	d.		s.	d.
1d	0s.	0¼	4/1	0s.	8	8/1	1s.	3¾	12/1	1s.	11½	16/1	2s.	7¼
2d	0	0¼	2	0	8¼	2	1	4	2	1	11¾	2	2	7½
3d	0	0½	3	0	8¼	3	1	4	3	2	0	3	2	7¾
4d	0	0¾	4	0	8½	4	1	4¼	4	2	0	4	2	7¾
5d	0	0¾	5	0	8½	5	1	4½	5	2	0¼	5	2	8
6d	0	1	4/6	0	8¾	8/6	1	4½	12/6	2	0½	16/6	2	8¼
7d	0	1¼	7	0	9	7	1	4¾	7	2	0½	7	2	8¼
8d	0	1¼	8	0	9	8	1	5	8	2	0¾	8	2	8½
9d	0	1½	9	0	9¼	9	1	5	9	2	0¾	9	2	8¾
10d	0	1¾	10	0	9½	10	1	5¼	10	2	1	10	2	8¾
11d	0	1¾	11	0	9½	11	1	5½	11	2	1¼	11	2	9
1/-	0s.	2	**5/-**	0s.	9¾	**9/-**	1s.	5½	**13/-**	2s.	1¼	**17/-**	2s.	9¼
1/1	0	2	5/1	0	10	9/1	1	5¾	13/1	2	1½	17/1	2	9¼
2	0	2¼	2	0	10	2	1	6	2	2	1¾	2	2	9½
3	0	2½	3	0	10¼	3	1	6	3	2	1¾	3	2	9¾
4	0	2½	4	0	10½	4	1	6¼	4	2	2	4	2	9¾
5	0	2¾	5	0	10½	5	1	6¼	5	2	2¼	5	2	10
1/6	0	3	5/6	0	10¾	9/6	1	6½	13/6	2	2¼	17/6	2	10¼
7	0	3	7	0	11	7	1	6¾	7	2	2½	7	2	10¼
8	0	3¼	8	0	11	8	1	6¾	8	2	2¾	8	2	10½
9	0	3½	9	0	11¼	9	1	7	9	2	2¾	9	2	10½
10	0	3½	10	0	11½	10	1	7¼	10	2	3	10	2	10¾
11	0	3¾	11	0	11½	11	1	7¼	11	2	3¼	11	2	11
2/-	0s.	4	**6/-**	0s.	11¾	**10/-**	1s.	7½	**14/-**	2s.	3¼	**18/-**	2s.	11
2/1	0	4	6/1	0	11¾	10/1	1	7¾	14/1	2	3½	18/1	2	11¼
2	0	4¼	2	1	0	2	1	7¾	2	2	3¾	2	2	11½
3	0	4½	3	1	0¼	3	1	8	3	2	3¾	3	2	11½
4	0	4½	4	1	0¼	4	1	8¼	4	2	4	4	2	11¾
5	0	4¾	5	1	0½	5	1	8¼	5	2	4	5	3	0
2/6	0	5	6/6	1	0¾	10/6	1	8½	14/6	2	4¼	18/6	3	0
7	0	5	7	1	0¾	7	1	8¾	7	2	4½	7	3	0¼
8	0	5¼	8	1	1	8	1	8¾	8	2	4½	8	3	0¼
9	0	5¼	9	1	1¼	9	1	9	9	2	4¾	9	3	0½
10	0	5½	10	1	1¼	10	1	9¼	10	2	5	10	3	0¾
11	0	5¾	11	1	1½	11	1	9¼	11	2	5	11	3	1
3/-	0s.	5¾	**7/-**	1s.	1¾	**11/-**	1s.	9½	**15/-**	2s.	5¼	**19/-**	3s.	1
3/1	0	6	7/1	1	1¾	11/1	1	9½	15/1	2	5½	19/1	3	1¼
2	0	6¼	2	1	2	2	1	9¾	2	2	5½	2	3	1½
3	0	6¼	3	1	2¼	3	1	10	3	2	5¾	3	3	1½
4	0	6½	4	1	2¼	4	1	10	4	2	6	4	3	1¾
5	0	6¾	5	1	2½	5	1	10¼	5	2	6	5	3	1¾
3/6	0	6¾	7/6	1	2¾	11/6	1	10½	15/6	2	6¼	19/6	3	2
7	0	7	7	1	2¾	7	1	10½	7	2	6½	7	3	2¼
8	0	7¼	8	1	3	8	1	10¾	8	2	6½	8	3	2¼
9	0	7¼	9	1	3	9	1	11	9	2	6¾	9	3	2½
10	0	7½	10	1	3¼	10	1	11	10	2	7	10	3	2¾
11	0	7¾	11	1	3½	11	1	11¼	11	2	7	11	3	2¾
4/-	0s.	7¾	**8/-**	1s.	3½	**12/-**	1s.	11½	**16/-**	2s.	7¼	**20/-**	3s.	3

	s.	d.		s.	d.		s.	d.		s.	d.	Guineas.	s.	d.
20/6	3s.	4	25/6	4s.	1¾	31/-	5s.	0½	35/6	5s.	9¼			
21/-	3	5	26/-	4	2¾	31/6	5	1½	36/-	5	10¼	1.	3s.	5
22/-	3	7	27/-	4	4¾	32/-	5	2½	37/-	6	0¼	2.	6	10
22/6	3	8	27/6	4	5¾	32/6	5	3½	37/6	6	1¼	3.	10	2¾
23/-	3	8¾	28/-	4	6½	33/-	5	4¼	38/-	6	2	4.	13	7¾
24/-	3	10¾	29/-	4	8½	34/-	5	6¼	39/-	6	4	5.	17	0¾
25/-	4s.	0¾	**30/-**	4s.	10½	**35/-**	5s.	8¼	**40/-**	6s.	6	6.	20s.	5¾

(=14%* on Gross Returns.)

£1	£0	3s	3½	£51	£8	8s	3½	£101	16	13s	3½	£151	24	18s	3½
2	0	6	7¼	52	8	11	7¼	102	16	16	7¼	152	25	1	7¼
3	0	9	10¾	53	8	14	10¾	103	16	19	10¾	153	25	4	10¾
4	0	13	2½	54	8	18	2½	104	17	3	2½	154	25	8	2½
5	0	16	6	55	9	1	6	105	17	6	6	155	25	11	6
6	0	19	9½	56	9	4	9½	106	17	9	9½	156	25	14	9½
7	1	3	1¼	57	9	8	1¼	107	17	13	1¼	157	25	18	1¼
8	1	6	4¾	58	9	11	4¾	108	17	16	4¾	158	26	1	4¾
9	1	9	8½	59	9	14	8½	109	17	19	8½	159	26	4	8½
10	1	13	0	60	9	18	0	110	18	3	0	160	26	8	0
11	1	16	3½	61	10	1	3½	111	18	6	3½	161	26	11	3½
12	1	19	7¼	62	10	4	7¼	112	18	9	7¼	162	26	14	7¼
13	2	2	10¾	63	10	7	10¾	113	18	12	10¾	163	26	17	10¾
14	2	6	2½	64	10	11	2½	114	18	16	2½	164	27	1	2½
15	2	9	6	65	10	14	6	115	18	19	6	165	27	4	6
16	2	12	9½	66	10	17	9½	116	19	2	9½	166	27	7	9½
17	2	16	1¼	67	11	1	1¼	117	19	6	1¼	167	27	11	1¼
18	2	19	4¾	68	11	4	4¾	118	19	9	4¾	168	27	14	4¾
19	3	2	8½	69	11	7	8½	119	19	12	8½	169	27	17	8½
20	3	6	0	70	11	11	0	120	19	16	0	170	28	1	0
21	3	9	3½	71	11	14	3½	121	19	19	3½	171	28	4	3½
22	3	12	7¼	72	11	17	7¼	122	20	2	7¼	172	28	7	7¼
23	3	15	10¾	73	12	0	10¾	123	20	5	10¾	173	28	10	10¾
24	3	19	2½	74	12	4	2½	124	20	9	2½	174	28	14	2½
25	4	2	6	75	12	7	6	125	20	12	6	175	28	17	6
26	4	5	9½	76	12	10	9½	126	20	15	9½	176	29	0	9½
27	4	9	1¼	77	12	14	1¼	127	20	19	1¼	177	29	4	1¼
28	4	12	4¾	78	12	17	4¾	128	21	2	4¾	178	29	7	4¾
29	4	15	8½	79	13	0	8½	129	21	5	8½	179	29	10	8½
30	4	19	0	80	13	4	0	130	21	9	0	180	29	14	0
31	5	2	3½	81	13	7	3½	131	21	12	3½	181	29	17	3½
32	5	5	7¼	82	13	10	7¼	132	21	15	7¼	182	30	0	7¼
33	5	8	10¾	83	13	13	10¾	133	21	18	10¾	183	30	3	10¾
34	5	12	2½	84	13	17	2½	134	22	2	2½	184	30	7	2½
35	5	15	6	85	14	0	6	135	22	5	6	185	30	10	6
36	5	18	9½	86	14	3	9½	136	22	8	9½	186	30	13	9½
37	6	2	1¼	87	14	7	1¼	137	22	12	1¼	187	30	17	1¼
38	6	5	4¾	88	14	10	4¾	138	22	15	4¾	188	31	0	4¾
39	6	8	8½	89	14	13	8½	139	22	18	8½	189	31	3	8½
40	6	12	0	90	14	17	0	140	23	2	0	190	31	7	0
41	6	15	3½	91	15	0	3½	141	23	5	3½	191	31	10	3½
42	6	18	7¼	92	15	3	7¼	142	23	8	7¼	192	31	13	7¼
43	7	1	10¾	93	15	6	10¾	143	23	11	10¾	193	31	16	10¾
44	7	5	2½	94	15	10	2½	144	23	15	2½	194	32	0	2½
45	7	8	6	95	15	13	6	145	23	18	6	195	32	3	6
46	7	11	9½	96	15	16	9½	146	24	1	9½	196	32	6	9½
47	7	15	1¼	97	16	0	1¼	147	24	5	1¼	197	32	10	1¼
48	7	18	4¾	98	16	3	4¾	148	24	8	4¾	198	32	13	4¾
49	8	1	8½	99	16	6	8½	149	24	11	8½	199	32	16	8½
50	8	5	0	100	16	10	0	150	24	15	0	200	33	0	0

250	41	5s	0d	700	115	10s	0d	1200	198	0s	0d	2000	330	0s	0
300	49	10	0	750	123	15	0	1400	231	0	0	2500	412	10	0
400	66	0	0	800	132	0	0	1500	247	10	0	3000	495	0	0
500	82	10	0	900	148	10	0	1600	264	0	0	4000	660	0	0
600	99	0s	0d	1000	165	0s	0d	1800	297	0s	0d	5000	825	0s	0

83½% off

1d	0s	0¼	4/1	0s	8	8/1	1s	4	12/1	2s	0	16/1	2s	7¾
2d	0	0¼	2	0	8¼	2	1	4¼	2	2	0	2	2	8
3d	0	0½	3	0	8½	3	1	4¼	3	2	0¼	3	2	8¼
4d	0	0¾	4	0	8½	4	1	4½	4	2	0½	4	2	8¼
5d	0	0¾	5	0	8¾	5	1	4¾	5	2	0½	5	2	8½
6d	0	1	4/6	0	9	8/6	1	4¾	12/6	2	0¾	16/6	2	8¾
7d	0	1¼	7	0	9	7	1	5	7	2	1	7	2	8¾
8d	0	1¼	8	0	9¼	8	1	5¼	8	2	1	8	2	9
9d	0	1½	9	0	9½	9	1	5¼	9	2	1¼	9	2	9¼
10d	0	1¾	10	0	9½	10	1	5½	10	2	1½	10	2	9¼
11d	0	1¾	11	0	9¾	11	1	5¾	11	2	1½	11	2	9½
1/-	**0**	**2**	**5/-**	**0**	**10**	**9/-**	**1**	**5¾**	**13/-**	**2**	**1¾**	**17/-**	**2**	**9¾**
1/1	0	2¼	5/1	0	10	1	1	6	1	2	2	1	2	9¾
2	0	2¼	2	0	10¼	2	1	6¼	2	2	2	2	2	10
3	0	2½	3	0	10½	3	1	6¼	3	2	2¼	3	2	10¼
4	0	2¾	4	0	10½	4	1	6½	4	2	2½	4	2	10¼
5	0	2¾	5	0	10¾	5	1	6¾	5	2	2½	5	2	10½
1/6	0	3	5/6	0	11	9/6	1	6¾	13/6	2	2¾	17/6	2	10¾
7	0	3¼	7	0	11	7	1	7	7	2	3	7	2	10¾
8	0	3¼	8	0	11¼	8	1	7¼	8	2	3	8	2	11
9	0	3½	9	0	11½	9	1	7¼	9	2	3¼	9	2	11¼
10	0	3¾	10	0	11½	10	1	7½	10	2	3½	10	2	11¼
11	0	3¾	11	0	11¾	11	1	7¾	11	2	3½	11	2	11½
2/-	**0**	**4**	**6/-**	**1**	**0**	**10/-**	**1**	**7¾**	**14/-**	**2**	**3¾**	**18/-**	**2**	**11¾**
2/1	0	4¼	1	1	0	10/1	1	8	1	2	4	1	2	11¾
2	0	4¼	2	1	0¼	2	1	8¼	2	2	4	2	3	0
3	0	4½	3	1	0½	3	1	8¼	3	2	4¼	3	3	0¼
4	0	4½	4	1	0½	4	1	8½	4	2	4½	4	3	0¼
5	0	4¾	5	1	0¾	5	1	8¾	5	2	4½	5	3	0½
2/6	0	5	6/6	1	0¾	10/6	1	8¾	14/6	2	4¾	18/6	3	0¾
7	0	5	7	1	1	7	1	9	7	2	5	7	3	0¾
8	0	5¼	8	1	1¼	8	1	9	8	2	5	8	3	1
9	0	5½	9	1	1¼	9	1	9¼	9	2	5¼	9	3	1¼
10	0	5½	10	1	1½	10	1	9½	10	2	5¼	10	3	1¼
11	0	5¾	11	1	1¾	11	1	9½	11	2	5½	11	3	1½
3/-	**0**	**6**	**7/-**	**1**	**1¾**	**11/-**	**1**	**9¾**	**15/-**	**2**	**5¾**	**19/-**	**3**	**1½**
3/1	0	6	1	1	2	1	1	10	15/1	2	5¾	1	3	1¾
2	0	6¼	2	1	2¼	2	1	10	2	2	6	2	3	2
3	0	6½	3	1	2¼	3	1	10¼	3	2	6¼	3	3	2
4	0	6½	4	1	2½	4	1	10½	4	2	6¼	4	3	2¼
5	0	6¾	5	1	2¾	5	1	10½	5	2	6½	5	3	2½
3/6	0	7	7/6	1	2¾	11/6	1	10¾	15/6	2	6¾	19/6	3	2½
7	0	7	7	1	3	7	1	11	7	2	6¾	7	3	2¾
8	0	7¼	8	1	3¼	8	1	11	8	2	7	8	3	3
9	0	7½	9	1	3¼	9	1	11¼	9	2	7¼	9	3	3
10	0	7½	10	1	3½	10	1	11½	10	2	7¼	10	3	3¼
11	0	7¾	11	1	3¾	11	1	11½	11	2	7½	11	3	3½
4/-	**0**	**8**	**8/-**	**1**	**3¾**	**12/-**	**1**	**11¾**	**16/-**	**2**	**7¾**	**20/-**	**3**	**3½**

20/6	3s	4½	25/6	4s	2½	31/-	5s	1½	35/6	5s	10¼	Guineas.		
21/-	3	5½	26/-	4	3½	31/6	5	2¼	36/-	5	11¼	1.	3s	5½
22/-	3	7½	27/-	4	5½	32/-	5	3¼	37/-	6	1¼	2.	6	11¼
22/6	3	8½	27/6	4	6½	32/6	5	4¼	37/6	6	2¼	3.	10	4¾
23/-	3	9½	28/-	4	7½	33/-	5	5¼	38/-	6	3¼	4.	13	10¼
24/-	3	11½	29/-	4	9½	34/-	5	7¼	39/-	6	5¼	5.	17	4
25/-	4s	1½	**30/-**	4s	11½	**35/-**	5s	9¼	**40/-**	6s	7¼	6.	20s	9½

(=14 2/10% on Gross Returns).

£1	£0 3s. 4	£51	£8 10s. 0	£101	£16 16s. 8	£151	£25 3s. 4
2	0 6 8	52	8 13 4	102	17 0 0	152	25 6 8
3	0 10 0	53	8 16 8	103	17 3 4	153	25 10 0
4	0 13 4	54	9 0 0	104	17 6 8	154	25 13 4
5	0 16 8	55	9 3 4	105	17 10 0	155	25 16 8
6	1 0 0	56	9 6 8	106	17 13 4	156	26 0 0
7	1 3 4	57	9 10 0	107	17 16 8	157	26 3 4
8	1 6 8	58	9 13 4	108	18 0 0	158	26 6 8
9	1 10 0	59	9 16 8	109	18 3 4	159	26 10 0
10	£1 13s. 4	60	10 0s. 0	110	£18 6s. 8	160	£26 13s. 4
11	£1 16s. 8	61	10 3s. 4	111	£18 10s. 0	161	£26 16s. 8
12	2 0 0	62	10 6 8	112	18 13 4	162	27 0 0
13	2 3 4	63	10 10 0	113	18 16 8	163	27 3 4
14	2 6 8	64	10 13 4	114	19 0 0	164	27 6 8
15	2 10 0	65	10 16 8	115	19 3 4	165	27 10 0
16	2 13 4	66	11 0 0	116	19 6 8	166	27 13 4
17	2 16 8	67	11 3 4	117	19 10 0	167	27 16 8
18	3 0 0	68	11 6 8	118	19 13 4	168	28 0 0
19	3 3 4	69	11 10 0	119	19 16 8	169	28 3 4
20	£3 6s. 8	70	11 13s. 4	120	£20 0s. 0	170	£28 6s. 8
21	£3 10s. 0	71	11 16s. 8	121	£20 3s. 4	171	£28 10s. 0
22	3 13 4	72	12 0 0	122	20 6 8	172	28 13 4
23	3 16 8	73	12 3 4	123	20 10 0	173	28 16 8
24	4 0 0	74	12 6 8	124	20 13 4	174	29 0 0
25	4 3 4	75	12 10 0	125	20 16 8	175	29 3 4
26	4 6 8	76	12 13 4	126	21 0 0	176	29 6 8
27	4 10 0	77	12 16 8	127	21 3 4	177	29 10 0
28	4 13 4	78	13 0 0	128	21 6 8	178	29 13 4
29	4 16 8	79	13 3 4	129	21 10 0	179	29 16 8
30	£5 0s. 0	80	13 6s. 8	130	£21 13s. 4	180	£30 0s. 0
31	£5 3s. 4	81	13 10s. 0	131	£21 16s. 8	181	£30 3s. 4
32	5 6 8	82	13 13 4	132	22 0 0	182	30 6 8
33	5 10 0	83	13 16 8	133	22 3 4	183	30 10 0
34	5 13 4	84	14 0 0	134	22 6 8	184	30 13 4
35	5 16 8	85	14 3 4	135	22 10 0	185	30 16 8
36	6 0 0	86	14 6 8	136	22 13 4	186	31 0 0
37	6 3 4	87	14 10 0	137	22 16 8	187	31 3 4
38	6 6 8	88	14 13 4	138	23 0 0	188	31 6 8
39	6 10 0	89	14 16 8	139	23 3 4	189	31 10 0
40	£6 13s. 4	90	15 0s. 0	140	£23 6s. 8	190	£31 13s. 4
41	£6 16s. 8	91	15 3s. 4	141	£23 10s. 0	191	£31 16s. 8
42	7 0 0	92	15 6 8	142	23 13 4	192	32 0 0
43	7 3 4	93	15 10 0	143	23 16 8	193	32 3 4
44	7 6 8	94	15 13 4	144	24 0 0	194	32 6 8
45	7 10 0	95	15 16 8	145	24 3 4	195	32 10 0
46	7 13 4	96	16 0 0	146	24 6 8	196	32 13 4
47	7 16 8	97	16 3 4	147	24 10 0	197	32 16 8
48	8 0 0	98	16 6 8	148	24 13 4	198	33 0 0
49	8 3 4	99	16 10 0	149	24 16 8	199	33 3 4
50	£8 6s. 8	100	16 13s. 4	150	£25 0s 0	200	£33 6s. 8

250	£41 13s. 4d	700	116 13s.4d	1200	200 0s.0d	2000	£333 6s. 8
300	50 0 0	750	125 0 0	1400	233 6 8	2500	416 13 4
400	66 13 4	800	133 6 8	1500	250 0 0	3000	500 0 0
500	83 6 8	900	150 0 0	1600	266 13 4	4000	666 13 4
600	100 0s.0d	1000	166 13s.4d	1800	300 0s.0d	5000	£833 6s. 8

83⅓% off.   (16⅔% = 1-6th)

1d	0s.	0¼	4/1	0s.	8¼	8/1	1s.	4¼	12/1	2s.	0¼	16/1	2s.	8¼
2d	0	0¼	2	0	8¼	2	1	4¼	2	2	0¼	2	2	8¼
3d	0	0½	3	0	8½	3	1	4½	3	2	0½	3	2	8½
4d	0	0¾	4	0	8¾	4	1	4¾	4	2	0¾	4	2	8¾
5d	0	0¾	5	0	8¾	5	1	4¾	5	2	0¾	5	2	8¾
6d	0	1	4/6	0	9	8/6	1	5	12/6	2	1	16/6	2	9
7d	0	1¼	7	0	9¼	7	1	5¼	7	2	1¼	7	2	9¼
8d	0	1¼	8	0	9¼	8	1	5¼	8	2	1¼	8	2	9¼
9d	0	1½	9	0	9½	9	1	5½	9	2	1½	9	2	9½
10d	0	1¾	10	0	9¾	10	1	5¾	10	2	1¾	10	2	9¾
11d	0	1¾	11	0	9¾	11	1	5¾	11	2	1¾	11	2	9¾
1/-	0s.	2	**5/-**	0s.	10	**9/-**	1s.	6	**13/-**	2s.	2	**17/-**	2s.	10
1/1	0s.	2¼	5/1	0s.	10¼	9/1	1s.	6¼	13/1	2s.	2¼	17/1	2s.	10¼
2	0	2¼	2	0	10¼	2	1	6¼	2	2	2¼	2	2	10¼
3	0	2½	3	0	10½	3	1	6½	3	2	2½	3	2	10½
4	0	2¾	4	0	10¾	4	1	6¾	4	2	2¾	4	2	10¾
5	0	2¾	5	0	10¾	5	1	6¾	5	2	2¾	5	2	10¾
1/6	0	3	5/6	0	11	9/6	1	7	13/6	2	3	17/6	2	11
7	0	3¼	7	0	11¼	7	1	7¼	7	2	3¼	7	2	11¼
8	0	3¼	8	0	11¼	8	1	7¼	8	2	3¼	8	2	11¼
9	0	3½	9	0	11½	9	1	7½	9	2	3½	9	2	11½
10	0	3¾	10	0	11¾	10	1	7¾	10	2	3¾	10	2	11¾
11	0	3¾	11	0	11¾	11	1	7¾	11	2	3¾	11	2	11¾
2/-	0s.	4	**6/-**	1s.	0	**10/-**	1s.	8	**14/-**	2s.	4	**18/-**	3s.	0
2/1	0s.	4¼	6/1	1s.	0¼	10/1	1s.	8¼	14/1	2s.	4¼	18/1	3s.	0¼
2	0	4¼	2	1	0¼	2	1	8¼	2	2	4¼	2	3	0¼
3	0	4½	3	1	0½	3	1	8½	3	2	4½	3	3	0½
4	0	4¾	4	1	0¾	4	1	8¾	4	2	4¾	4	3	0¾
5	0	4¾	5	1	0¾	5	1	8¾	5	2	4¾	5	3	0¾
2/6	0	5	6/6	1	1	10/6	1	9	14/6	2	5	18/6	3	1
7	0	5¼	7	1	1¼	7	1	9¼	7	2	5¼	7	3	1¼
8	0	5¼	8	1	1¼	8	1	9¼	8	2	5¼	8	3	1¼
9	0	5½	9	1	1½	9	1	9½	9	2	5½	9	3	1½
10	0	5¾	10	1	1¾	10	1	9¾	10	2	5¾	10	3	1¾
11	0	5¾	11	1	1¾	11	1	9¾	11	2	5¾	11	3	1¾
3/-	0s.	6	**7/-**	1s.	2	**11/-**	1s.	10	**15/-**	2s.	6	**19/-**	3s.	2
3/1	0s.	6¼	7/1	1s.	2¼	11/1	1s.	10¼	15/1	2s.	6¼	19/1	3s.	2¼
2	0	6¼	2	1	2¼	2	1	10¼	2	2	6¼	2	3	2¼
3	0	6½	3	1	2½	3	1	10½	3	2	6½	3	3	2½
4	0	6¾	4	1	2¾	4	1	10¾	4	2	6¾	4	3	2¾
5	0	6¾	5	1	2¾	5	1	10¾	5	2	6¾	5	3	2¾
3/6	0	7	7/6	1	3	11/6	1	11	15/6	2	7	19/6	3	3
7	0	7¼	7	1	3¼	7	1	11¼	7	2	7¼	7	3	3¼
8	0	7¼	8	1	3¼	8	1	11¼	8	2	7¼	8	3	3¼
9	0	7½	9	1	3½	9	1	11½	9	2	7½	9	3	3½
10	0	7¾	10	1	3¾	10	1	11¾	10	2	7¾	10	3	3¾
11	0	7¾	11	1	3¾	11	1	11¾	11	2	7¾	11	3	3¾
4/-	0s.	8	**8/-**	1s.	4	**12/-**	2s.	0	**16/-**	2s.	8	**20/-**	3s.	4

20/6	3s.	5	25/6	4s.	3	31/-	5s.	2	35/6	5s.	11	Guineas.			
21/-	3	6	26/-	4	4	31/6	5	3	36/-	6	0	1.	£0	3s.	6
22/-	3	8	27/-	4	6	32/-	5	4	37/-	6	2	2.	0	7	0
22/6	3	9	27/6	4	7	32/6	5	5	37/6	6	3	3.	0	10	6
23/-	3	10	28/-	4	8	33/-	5	6	38/-	6	4	4.	0	14	0
24/-	4	0	29/-	4	10	34/-	5	8	39/-	6	6	5.	0	17	6
25/-	4s.	2	**30/-**	5s.	0	**35/-**	5s.	10	**40/-**	6s.	8	6.	£1	1s.	0

(=14 3/10%* on Gross Returns).

17% 17 Per Cent. 17%

£1	0	3s.	4¾	£51	8	13s.	4¾	£101	17	3s.	4¾	£151	25	13s.	4¾
2	0	6	9½	52	8	16	9½	102	17	6	9½	152	25	16	9½
3	0	10	2½	53	9	0	2½	103	17	10	2½	153	26	0	2½
4	0	13	7¼	54	9	3	7¼	104	17	13	7¼	154	26	3	7¼
5	0	17	0	55	9	7	0	105	17	17	0	155	26	7	0
6	1	0	4¾	56	9	10	4¾	106	18	0	4¾	156	26	10	4¾
7	1	3	9½	57	9	13	9½	107	18	3	9½	157	26	13	9½
8	1	7	2½	58	9	17	2½	108	18	7	2½	158	26	17	2½
9	1	10	7¼	59	10	0	7¼	109	18	10	7¼	159	27	0	7¼
10	**1**	**14s.**	**0**	**60**	**10**	**4s.**	**0**	**110**	**18**	**14s.**	**0**	**160**	**27**	**4s.**	**0**
11	1	17	4¾	61	10	7	4¾	111	18	17	4¾	161	27	7	4¾
12	2	0	9½	62	10	10	9½	112	19	0	9½	162	27	10	9½
13	2	4	2½	63	10	14	2½	113	19	4	2½	163	27	14	2½
14	2	7	7¼	64	10	17	7¼	114	19	7	7¼	164	27	17	7¼
15	2	11	0	65	11	1	0	115	19	11	0	165	28	1	0
16	2	14	4¾	66	11	4	4¾	116	19	14	4¾	166	28	4	4¾
17	2	17	9½	67	11	7	9½	117	19	17	9½	167	28	7	9½
18	3	1	2½	68	11	11	2½	118	20	1	2½	168	28	11	2½
19	3	4	7¼	69	11	14	7¼	119	20	4	7¼	169	28	14	7¼
20	**3**	**8s.**	**0**	**70**	**11**	**18s.**	**0**	**120**	**20**	**8s.**	**0**	**170**	**28**	**18s.**	**0**
21	3	11	4¾	71	12	1	4¾	121	20	11	4¾	171	29	1	4¾
22	3	14	9½	72	12	4	9½	122	20	14	9½	172	29	4	9½
23	3	18	2½	73	12	8	2½	123	20	18	2½	173	29	8	2½
24	4	1	7¼	74	12	11	7¼	124	21	1	7¼	174	29	11	7¼
25	4	5	0	75	12	15	0	125	21	5	0	175	29	15	0
26	4	8	4¾	76	12	18	4¾	126	21	8	4¾	176	29	18	4¾
27	4	11	9½	77	13	1	9½	127	21	11	9½	177	30	1	9½
28	4	15	2½	78	13	5	2½	128	21	15	2½	178	30	5	2½
29	4	18	7¼	79	13	8	7¼	129	21	18	7¼	179	30	8	7¼
30	**5**	**2s.**	**0**	**80**	**13**	**12s.**	**0**	**130**	**22**	**2s.**	**0**	**180**	**30**	**12s.**	**0**
31	5	5	4¾	81	13	15	4¾	131	22	5	4¾	181	30	15	4¾
32	5	8	9½	82	13	18	9½	132	22	8	9½	182	30	18	9½
33	5	12	2½	83	14	2	2½	133	22	12	2½	183	31	2	2½
34	5	15	7¼	84	14	5	7¼	134	22	15	7¼	184	31	5	7¼
35	5	19	0	85	14	9	0	135	22	19	0	185	31	9	0
36	6	2	4¾	86	14	12	4¾	136	23	2	4¾	186	31	12	4¾
37	6	5	9½	87	14	15	9½	137	23	5	9½	187	31	15	9½
38	6	9	2½	88	14	19	2½	138	23	9	2½	188	31	19	2½
39	6	12	7¼	89	15	2	7¼	139	23	12	7¼	189	32	2	7¼
40	**6**	**16s.**	**0**	**90**	**15**	**6s.**	**0**	**140**	**23**	**16s.**	**0**	**190**	**32**	**6s**	**0**
41	6	19	4¾	91	15	9	4¾	141	23	19	4¾	191	32	9	4¾
42	7	2	9½	92	15	12	9½	142	24	2	9½	192	32	12	9½
43	7	6	2½	93	15	16	2½	143	24	6	2½	193	32	16	2½
44	7	9	7¼	94	15	19	7¼	144	24	9	7¼	194	32	19	7¼
45	7	13	0	95	16	3	0	145	24	13	0	195	33	3	0
46	7	16	4¾	96	16	6	4¾	146	24	16	4¾	196	33	6	4¾
47	7	19	9½	97	16	9	9½	147	24	19	9½	197	33	9	9½
48	8	3	2½	98	16	13	2½	148	25	3	2½	198	33	13	2½
49	8	6	7¼	99	16	16	7¼	149	25	6	7¼	199	33	16	7¼
50	**8**	**10s.**	**0**	**100**	**17**	**0s.**	**0**	**150**	**25**	**10s.**	**0**	**200**	**34**	**0s.**	**0**

250	£42	10	0	700	119	0	0	1200	204	0	0	2000	340	0	0
300	51	0	0	750	127	10	0	1400	238	0	0	2500	425	0	0
400	68	0	0	800	136	0	0	1500	255	0	0	3000	510	0	0
500	85	0	0	900	153	0	0	1600	272	0	0	4000	680	0	0
600	102	0	0	1000	170	0	0	1800	306	0	0	5000	850	0	0

83% off.

1d	0s. 0¼	4/1	0s. 8¼	8/1	1s. 4½	12/1	2s. 0¾	16/1	2s. 8¾
2d	0 0¼	2	0 8½	2	1 4¾	2	2 0¾	2	2 9
3d	0 0½	3	0 8¾	3	1 4¾	3	2 1	3	2 9¼
4d	0 0¾	4	0 8¾	4	1 5	4	2 1¼	4	2 9¼
5d	0 0¾	5	0 9	5	1 5¼	5	2 1¼	5	2 9½
6d	0 1	4/6	0 9¼	8/6	1 5¼	12/6	2 1½	16/6	2 9¾
7d	0 1¼	7	0 9¼	7	1 5½	7	2 1¾	7	2 9¾
8d	0 1¼	8	0 9½	8	1 5¾	8	2 1¾	8	2 10
9d	0 1½	9	0 9¾	9	1 5¾	9	2 2	9	2 10¼
10d	0 1¾	10	0 9¾	10	1 6	10	2 2¼	10	2 10¼
11d	0 1¾	11	0 10	11	1 6¼	11	2 2¼	11	2 10½
1/-	0s. 2	**5/-**	0s. 10¼	**9/-**	1s. 6¼	**13/-**	2s. 2½	**17/-**	2s. 10¾
1/1	0 2¼	5/1	0 10¼	9/1	1 6½	13/1	2 2¾	17/1	2 10¾
2	0 2½	2	0 10½	2	1 6¾	2	2 2¾	2	2 11
3	0 2½	3	0 10¾	3	1 6¾	3	2 3	3	2 11¼
4	0 2¾	4	0 11	4	1 7	4	2 3¼	4	2 11¼
5	0 3	5	0 11	5	1 7¼	5	2 3¼	5	2 11½
1/6	0 3	5/6	0 11¼	9/6	1 7½	13/6	2 3½	17/6	2 11¾
7	0 3¼	7	0 11½	7	1 7½	7	2 3¾	7	2 11¾
8	0 3½	8	0 11½	8	1 7¾	8	2 4	8	3 0
9	0 3½	9	0 11¾	9	1 8	9	2 4	9	3 0¼
10	0 3¾	10	1 0	10	1 8	10	2 4¼	10	3 0½
11	0 4	11	1 0	11	1 8¼	11	2 4½	11	3 0½
2/-	0s. 4	**6/-**	1s. 0¼	**10/-**	1s. 8½	**14/-**	2s. 4½	**18/-**	3s. 0¾
2/1	0 4¼	6/1	1 0½	10/1	1 8½	14/1	2 4¾	18/1	3 1
2	0 4½	2	1 0½	2	1 8¾	2	2 5	2	3 1
3	0 4½	3	1 0¾	3	1 9	3	2 5	3	3 1¼
4	0 4¾	4	1 1	4	1 9	4	2 5¼	4	3 1½
5	0 5	5	1 1	5	1 9¼	5	2 5½	5	3 1½
2/6	0 5	6/6	1 1¼	10/6	1 9½	14/6	2 5½	18/6	3 1¾
7	0 5¼	7	1 1½	7	1 9½	7	2 5¾	7	3 2
8	0 5½	8	1 1½	8	1 9¾	8	2 6	8	3 2
9	0 5½	9	1 1¾	9	1 10	9	2 6	9	3 2¼
10	0 5¾	10	1 2	10	1 10	10	2 6¼	10	3 2½
11	0 6	11	1 2	11	1 10¼	11	2 6½	11	3 2½
3/-	0s. 6	**7/-**	1s. 2¼	**11/-**	1s. 10½	**15/-**	2s. 6½	**19/-**	3s. 2¾
3/1	0 6¼	7/1	1 2½	11/1	1 10½	15/1	2 6¾	19/1	3 3
2	0 6½	2	1 2½	2	1 10¾	2	2 7	2	3 3
3	0 6¾	3	1 2¾	3	1 11	3	2 7	3	3 3¼
4	0 6¾	4	1 3	4	1 11	4	2 7¼	4	3 3½
5	0 7	5	1 3¼	5	1 11¼	5	2 7½	5	3 3½
3/6	0 7¼	7/6	1 3¼	11/6	1 11½	15/6	2 7½	19/6	3 3¾
7	0 7¼	7	1 3½	7	1 11¾	7	2 7¾	7	3 4
8	0 7½	8	1 3¾	8	1 11¾	8	2 8	8	3 4
9	0 7¾	9	1 3¾	9	2 0	9	2 8¼	9	3 4¼
10	0 7¾	10	1 4	10	2 0¼	10	2 8¼	10	3 4½
11	0 8	11	1 4¼	11	2 0¼	11	2 8½	11	3 4¾
4/-	0s 8¼	**8/-**	1s. 4¼	**12/-**	2s. 0½	**16/-**	2s. 8¾	**20/-**	3s. 4¾

20/6	3s. 5¾	25/6	4s. 4	31/-	5s. 3¼	35/6	6s. 0½	Guineas.	
21/-	3 6¾	26/-	4 5	31/6	5 4¼	36/-	6 1½	1.	3s. 6¾
22/-	3 9	27/-	4 7	32/-	5 5¼	37/-	6 3½	2.	7 1¾
22/6	3 10	27/6	4 8	32/6	5 6¼	37/6	6 4½	3.	10 8½
23/-	3 11	28/-	4 9	33/-	5 7¼	38/-	6 5½	4.	14 3¼
24/-	4 1	29/-	4 11¼	34/-	5 9¼	39/-	6 7½	5.	17 10¼
25/-	4s. 3	**30/-**	5s. 1¼	**35/-**	5s. 11½	**40/-**	6s. 9½	6.	21s. 5

(=14½%* on Gross Returns.)

£		£		£		£	
£1	£0 3s. 6	£51	£8 18s. 6	£101	£17 13s. 6	£151	£26 8s. 6
2	0 7 0	52	9 2 0	102	17 17 0	152	26 12 0
3	0 10 6	53	9 5 6	103	18 0 6	153	26 15 6
4	0 14 0	54	9 9 0	104	18 4 0	154	26 19 0
5	0 17 6	55	9 12 6	105	18 7 6	155	27 2 6
6	1 1 0	56	9 16 0	106	18 11 0	156	27 6 0
7	1 4 6	57	9 19 6	107	18 14 6	157	27 9 6
8	1 8 0	58	10 3 0	108	18 18 0	158	27 13 0
9	1 11 6	59	10 6 6	109	19 1 6	159	27 16 6
10	£1 15s. 0	60	10 10s. 0	110	£19 5s. 0	160	£28 0s. 0
11	£1 18s. 6	61	10 13s. 6	111	£19 8s. 6	161	£28 3s. 6
12	2 2 0	62	10 17 0	112	19 12 0	162	28 7 0
13	2 5 6	63	11 0 6	113	19 15 6	163	28 10 6
14	2 9 0	64	11 4 0	114	19 19 0	164	28 14 0
15	2 12 6	65	11 7 6	115	20 2 6	165	28 17 6
16	2 16 0	66	11 11 0	116	20 6 0	166	29 1 0
17	2 19 6	67	11 14 6	117	20 9 6	167	29 4 6
18	3 3 0	68	11 18 0	118	20 13 0	168	29 8 0
19	3 6 6	69	12 1 6	119	20 16 6	169	29 11 6
20	£3 10s. 0	70	12 5s. 0	120	£21 0s. 0	170	£29 15s. 0
21	£3 13s. 6	71	12 8s. 6	121	£21 3s. 6	171	£29 18s. 6
22	3 17 0	72	12 12 0	122	21 7 0	172	30 2 0
23	4 0 6	73	12 15 6	123	21 10 6	173	30 5 6
24	4 4 0	74	12 19 0	124	21 14 0	174	30 9 0
25	4 7 6	75	13 2 6	125	21 17 6	175	30 12 6
26	4 11 0	76	13 6 0	126	22 1 0	176	30 16 0
27	4 14 6	77	13 9 6	127	22 4 6	177	30 19 6
28	4 18 0	78	13 13 0	128	22 8 0	178	31 3 0
29	5 1 6	79	13 16 6	129	22 11 6	179	31 6 6
30	£5 5s. 0	80	14 0s. 0	130	£22 15s. 0	180	£31 10s. 0
31	£5 8s. 6	81	14 3s. 6	131	£22 18s. 6	181	£31 13s. 6
32	5 12 0	82	14 7 0	132	23 2 0	182	31 17 0
33	5 15 6	83	14 10 6	133	23 5 6	183	32 0 6
34	5 19 0	84	14 14 0	134	23 9 0	184	32 4 0
35	6 2 6	85	14 17 6	135	23 12 6	185	32 7 6
36	6 6 0	86	15 1 0	136	23 16 0	186	32 11 0
37	6 9 6	87	15 4 6	137	23 19 6	187	32 14 6
38	6 13 0	88	15 8 0	138	24 3 0	188	32 18 0
39	6 16 6	89	15 11 6	139	24 6 6	189	33 1 6
40	£7 0s. 0	90	15 15s. 0	140	£24 10s. 0	190	£33 5s. 0
41	£7 3s. 6	91	15 18s. 6	141	£24 13s. 6	191	£33 8s. 6
42	7 7 0	92	16 2 0	142	24 17 0	192	33 12 0
43	7 10 6	93	16 5 6	143	25 0 6	193	33 15 6
44	7 14 0	94	16 9 0	144	25 4 0	194	33 19 0
45	7 17 6	95	16 12 6	145	25 7 6	195	34 2 6
46	8 1 0	96	16 16 0	146	25 11 0	196	34 6 0
47	8 4 6	97	16 19 6	147	25 14 6	197	34 9 6
48	8 8 0	98	17 3 0	148	25 18 0	198	34 13 0
49	8 11 6	99	17 6 6	149	26 1 6	199	34 16 6
50	£8 15s. 0	100	17 10s. 0	150	£26 5s. 0	200	£35 0s. 0
250	£43 15s.0d	700	122 10s.d	1200	210 0s.0d	2000	£350 0s. 0
300	52 10 0	750	131 5 0	1400	245 0 0	2500	437 10 0
400	70 0 0	800	140 0 0	1500	262 10 0	3000	525 0 0
500	87 10 0	900	157 10 0	1600	280 0 0	4000	700 0 0
600	105 0s.0d	1000	175 0s.0d	1800	315 0s.0d	5000	£875 0s. 0

82½% off.

17½% 17½ Per Cent. 17½%

1d	0s.	0¼	4/1	0s.	8½	8/1	1s.	5	12/1	2s.	1½	16/1	2s.	9¾
2d	0	0¼	2	0	8¾	2	1	5¼	2	2	1½	2	2	10
3d	0	0½	3	0	9	3	1	5¼	3	2	1¾	3	2	10¼
4d	0	0¾	4	0	9	4	1	5½	4	2	2	4	2	10¼
5d	0	1	5	0	9¼	5	1	5¾	5	2	2	5	2	10½
6d	0	1	4/6	0	9½	8/6	1	5¾	12/6	2	2¼	16/6	2	10¾
7d	0	1¼	7	0	9¾	7	1	6	7	2	2½	7	2	10¾
8d	0	1½	8	0	9¾	8	1	6¼	8	2	2½	8	2	11
9d	0	1½	9	0	10	9	1	6½	9	2	2¾	9	2	11¼
10d	0	1¾	10	0	10¼	10	1	6½	10	2	3	10	2	11¼
11d	0	2	11	0	10¼	11	1	6¾	11	2	3¼	11	2	11½
1/-	0s.	2	**5/-**	0s.	10½	**9/-**	1s.	7	**13/-**	2s.	3¼	**17/-**	2s.	11¾
1/1	0s.	2¼	5/1	0s.	10¾	9/1	1s.	7	13/1	2s.	3½	17/1	3s.	0
2	0	2½	2	0	10¾	2	1	7¼	2	2	3¾	2	3	0
3	0	2¾	3	0	11	3	1	7½	3	2	3¾	3	3	0¼
4	0	2¾	4	0	11¼	4	1	7½	4	2	4	4	3	0½
5	0	3	5	0	11½	5	1	7¾	5	2	4¼	5	3	0½
1/6	0	3¼	5/6	0	11½	9/6	1	8	13/6	2	4¼	17/6	3	0¾
7	0	3¼	7	0	11¾	7	1	8¼	7	2	4½	7	3	1
8	0	3½	8	1	0	8	1	8¼	8	2	4¾	8	3	1
9	0	3¾	9	1	0	9	1	8½	9	2	5	9	3	1¼
10	0	3¾	10	1	0¼	10	1	8¾	10	2	5	10	3	1½
11	0	4	11	1	0½	11	1	8¾	11	2	5¼	11	3	1¾
2/-	0s.	4¼	**6/-**	1s.	0½	**10/-**	1s.	9	**14/-**	2s.	5½	**18/-**	3s.	1¾
2/1	0s.	4½	6/1	1s.	0¾	10/1	1s.	9¼	14/1	2s.	5½	18/1	3s.	2
2	0	4½	2	1	1	2	1	9¼	2	2	5¾	2	3	2¼
3	0	4¾	3	1	1¼	3	1	9½	3	2	6	3	3	2¼
4	0	5	4	1	1¼	4	1	9¾	4	2	6	4	3	2½
5	0	5	5	1	1½	5	1	10	5	2	6¼	5	3	2¾
2/6	0	5¼	6/6	1	1¾	10/6	1	10	14/6	2	6½	18/6	3	2¾
7	0	5½	7	1	1¾	7	1	10¼	7	2	6¾	7	3	3
8	0	5½	8	1	2	8	1	10½	8	2	6¾	8	3	3¼
9	0	5¾	9	1	2¼	9	1	10½	9	2	7	9	3	3½
10	0	6	10	1	2¼	10	1	10¾	10	2	7¼	10	3	3½
11	0	6¼	11	1	2½	11	1	11	11	2	7¼	11	3	3¾
3/-	0s.	6¼	**7/-**	1s.	2¾	**11/-**	1s.	11	**15/-**	2s.	7½	**19/-**	3s.	4
3/1	0s.	6½	7/1	1s.	3	11/1	1s.	11¼	15/1	2s.	7¾	19/1	3s.	4
2	0	6¾	2	1	3	2	1	11½	2	2	7¾	2	3	4¼
3	0	6¾	3	1	3¼	3	1	11¾	3	2	8	3	3	4½
4	0	7	4	1	3½	4	1	11¾	4	2	8¼	4	3	4½
5	0	7¼	5	1	3½	5	2	0	5	2	8½	5	3	4¾
3/6	0	7¼	7/6	1	3¾	11/6	2	0¼	15/6	2	8½	19/6	3	5
7	0	7½	7	1	4	7	2	0¼	7	2	8¾	7	3	5¼
8	0	7¾	8	1	4	8	2	0½	8	2	9	8	3	5¼
9	0	8	9	1	4¼	9	2	0¾	9	2	9	9	3	5½
10	0	8	10	1	4½	10	2	0¾	10	2	9¼	10	3	5¾
11	0	8¼	11	1	4¾	11	2	1	11	2	9½	11	3	5¾
4/-	0s.	8½	**8/-**	1s.	4¾	**12/-**	2s.	1¼	**16/-**	2s.	9½	**20/-**	3s.	6

												Guineas.			
20/6	3s.	7	25/6	4s.	5½	31/-	5s.	5	35/6	6s.	2½				
21/-	3	8	26/-	4	6½	31/6	5	6¼	36/-	6	3½	1.	£0	3s.	8
22/-	3	10¼	27/-	4	8¾	32/-	5	7¼	37/-	6	5¾	2.	0	7	4¼
22/6	3	11¼	27/6	4	9¾	32/6	5	8¼	37/6	6	6¾	3.	0	11	0¼
23/-	4	0¼	28/-	4	10¾	33/-	5	9¼	38/-	6	7¾	4.	0	14	8½
24/-	4	2½	29/-	5	1	34/-	5	11½	39/-	6	10	5.	0	18	4½
25/-	4s.	4½	**30/-**	5s.	3	**35/-**	6s.	1½	**40/-**	7s.	0	6.	£1	2s.	0½

(=14 9/10 %* on Gross Returns).

18 Per Cent.

£1	0	3s.	7¼	£51	9	3s.	7¼	£101	18	3s.	7¼	£151	27	3s.	7¼
2	0	7	2½	52	9	7	2½	102	18	7	2½	152	27	7	2½
3	0	10	9½	53	9	10	9½	103	18	10	9½	153	27	10	9½
4	0	14	4¾	54	9	14	4¾	104	18	14	4¾	154	27	14	4¾
5	0	18	0	55	9	18	0	105	18	18	0	155	27	18	0
6	1	1	7¼	56	10	1	7¼	106	19	1	7¼	156	28	1	7¼
7	1	5	2½	57	10	5	2½	107	19	5	2½	157	28	5	2½
8	1	8	9½	58	10	8	9½	108	19	8	9½	158	28	8	9½
9	1	12	4¾	59	10	12	4¾	109	19	12	4¾	159	28	12	4¾
10	1	16s.	0	**60**	10	16s.	0	**110**	19	16s.	0	**160**	28	16s.	0
11	1	19	7¼	61	10	19	7¼	111	19	19	7¼	161	28	19	7¼
12	2	3	2½	62	11	3	2½	112	20	3	2½	162	29	3	2½
13	2	6	9½	63	11	6	9½	113	20	6	9½	163	29	6	9½
14	2	10	4¾	64	11	10	4¾	114	20	10	4¾	164	29	10	4¾
15	2	14	0	65	11	14	0	115	20	14	0	165	29	14	0
16	2	17	7¼	66	11	17	7¼	116	20	17	7¼	166	29	17	7¼
17	3	1	2½	67	12	1	2½	117	21	1	2½	167	30	1	2½
18	3	4	9½	68	12	4	9½	118	21	4	9½	168	30	4	9½
19	3	8	4¾	69	12	8	4¾	119	21	8	4¾	169	30	8	4¾
20	3	12s.	0	**70**	12	12s.	0	**120**	21	12s.	0	**170**	30	12s.	0
21	3	15	7¼	71	12	15	7¼	121	21	15	7¼	171	30	15	7¼
22	3	19	2½	72	12	19	2½	122	21	19	2½	172	30	19	2½
23	4	2	9½	73	13	2	9½	123	22	2	9½	173	31	2	9½
24	4	6	4¾	74	13	6	4¾	124	22	6	4¾	174	31	6	4¾
25	4	10	0	75	13	10	0	125	22	10	0	175	31	10	0
26	4	13	7¼	76	13	13	7¼	126	22	13	7¼	176	31	13	7¼
27	4	17	2½	77	13	17	2½	127	22	17	2½	177	31	17	2½
28	5	0	9½	78	14	0	9½	128	23	0	9½	178	32	0	9½
29	5	4	4¾	79	14	4	4¾	129	23	4	4¾	179	32	4	4¾
30	5	8s.	0	**80**	14	8s.	0	**130**	23	8s.	0	**180**	32	8s.	0
31	5	11	7¼	81	14	11	7¼	131	23	11	7¼	181	32	11	7¼
32	5	15	2½	82	14	15	2½	132	23	15	2½	182	32	15	2½
33	5	18	9½	83	14	18	9½	133	23	18	9½	183	32	18	9½
34	6	2	4¾	84	15	2	4¾	134	24	2	4¾	184	33	2	4¾
35	6	6	0	85	15	6	0	135	24	6	0	185	33	6	0
36	6	9	7¼	86	15	9	7¼	136	24	9	7¼	186	33	9	7¼
37	6	13	2½	87	15	13	2½	137	24	13	2½	187	33	13	2½
38	6	16	9½	88	15	16	9½	138	24	16	9½	188	33	16	9½
39	7	0	4¾	89	16	0	4¾	139	25	0	4¾	189	34	0	4¾
40	7	4s.	0	**90**	16	4s.	0	**140**	25	4s.	0	**190**	34	4s	0
41	7	7	7¼	91	16	7	7¼	141	25	7	7¼	191	34	7	7¼
42	7	11	2½	92	16	11	2½	142	25	11	2½	192	34	11	2½
43	7	14	9½	93	16	14	9½	143	25	14	9½	193	34	14	9½
44	7	18	4¾	94	16	18	4¾	144	25	18	4¾	194	34	18	4¾
45	8	2	0	95	17	2	0	145	26	2	0	195	35	2	0
46	8	5	7¼	96	17	5	7¼	146	26	5	7¼	196	35	5	7¼
47	8	9	2½	97	17	9	2½	147	26	9	2½	197	35	9	2½
48	8	12	9½	98	17	12	9½	148	26	12	9½	198	35	12	9½
49	8	16	4¾	99	17	16	4¾	149	26	16	4¾	199	35	16	4¾
50	9	0s.	0	**100**	18	0s.	0	**150**	27	0s.	0	**200**	36	0s.	0
250	£45	0	0	700	126	0	0	1200	216	0	0	2000	360	0	0
300	54	0	0	750	135	0	0	1400	252	0	0	2500	450	0	0
400	72	0	0	800	144	0	0	1500	270	0	0	3000	540	0	0
500	90	0	0	900	162	0	0	1600	288	0	0	4000	720	0	0
600	108	0	0	1000	180	0	0	1800	324	0	0	5000	900	0	0

82% off.

18% 18 PER CENT. 18%

1d	0s.	0¼	4/1	0s.	8¾	8/1	1s.	5½	12/1	2s.	2	16/1	2s.	10¾
2d	0	0¼	2	0	9	2	1	5¾	2	2	2¼	2	2	11
3d	0	0½	3	0	9¼	3	1	5¾	3	2	2½	3	2	11
4d	0	0¾	4	0	9¼	4	1	6	4	2	2¾	4	2	11¼
5d	0	1	5	0	9½	5	1	6¼	5	2	2¾	5	2	11½
6d	0	1	4/6	0	9¾	8/6	1	6¼	12/6	2	3	16/6	2	11¾
7d	0	1¼	7	0	10	7	1	6½	7	2	3¼	7	2	11¾
8d	0	1½	8	0	10	8	1	6¾	8	2	3¼	8	3	0
9d	0	1½	9	0	10¼	9	1	7	9	2	3½	9	3	0¼
10d	0	1¾	10	0	10½	10	1	7	10	2	3¾	10	3	0¼
11d	0	2	11	0	10½	11	1	7¼	11	2	4	11	3	0½
1/-	0s.	2¼	**5/-**	0s.	10¾	**9/-**	1s.	7½	**13/-**	2s	4	**17/-**	3s.	0¾
1/1	0	2¼	5/1	0	11	9/1	1	7½	13/1	2	4¼	17/1	3	1
2	0	2½	2	0	11	2	1	7¾	2	2	4½	2	3	1
3	0	2¾	3	0	11¼	3	1	8	3	2	4½	3	3	1¼
4	0	3	4	0	11½	4	1	8¼	4	2	4¾	4	3	1½
5	0	3	5	0	11¾	5	1	8¼	5	2	5	5	3	1½
1/6	0	3¼	5/6	1	0	9/6	1	8½	13/6	2	5¼	17/6	3	1¾
7	0	3½	7	1	0	7	1	8¾	7	2	5¼	7	3	2
8	0	3½	8	1	0¼	8	1	9	8	2	5½	8	3	2¼
9	0	3¾	9	1	0½	9	1	9	9	2	5¾	9	3	2¼
10	0	4	10	1	0½	10	1	9¼	10	2	6	10	3	2½
11	0	4¼	11	1	0¾	11	1	9½	11	2	6	11	3	2¾
2/-	0s.	4¼	**6/-**	1s.	1	**10/-**	1s.	9½	**14/-**	2s.	6¼	**18/-**	3s.	3
2/1	0	4½	6/1	1	1¼	10/1	1	9¾	14/1	2	6½	18/1	3	3
2	0	4¾	2	1	1¼	2	1	10	2	2	6½	2	3	3¼
3	0	4¾	3	1	1½	3	1	10¼	3	2	6¾	3	3	3½
4	0	5	4	1	1¾	4	1	10¼	4	2	7	4	3	3½
5	0	5¼	5	1	1¾	5	1	10½	5	2	7¼	5	3	3¾
2/6	0	5½	6/6	1	2	10/6	1	10¾	14/6	2	7¼	18/6	3	4
7	0	5½	7	1	2¼	7	1	10¾	7	2	7½	7	3	4¼
8	0	5¾	8	1	2½	8	1	11	8	2	7¾	8	3	4¼
9	0	6	9	1	2½	9	1	11¼	9	2	7¾	9	3	4½
10	0	6	10	1	2¾	10	1	11½	10	2	8	10	3	4¾
11	0	6¼	11	1	3	11	1	11½	11	2	8¼	11	3	4¾
3/-	0s.	6½	**7/-**	1s.	3	**11/-**	1s.	11¾	**15/-**	2s.	8½	**19/-**	3s.	5
3/1	0	6¾	7/1	1	3¼	11/1	2	0	15/1	2	8½	19/1	3	5¼
2	0	6¾	2	1	3½	2	2	0	2	2	8¾	2	3	5¼
3	0	7	3	1	3¾	3	2	0¼	3	2	9	3	3	5½
4	0	7¼	4	1	3¾	4	2	0½	4	2	9	4	3	5¾
5	0	7½	5	1	4	5	2	0¾	5	2	9¼	5	3	6
3/6	0	7½	7/6	1	4¼	11/6	2	0¾	15/6	2	9½	19/6	3	6
7	0	7¾	7	1	4½	7	2	1	7	2	9¾	7	3	6¼
8	0	8	8	1	4½	8	2	1¼	8	2	9¾	8	3	6½
9	0	8	9	1	4¾	9	2	1½	9	2	10	9	3	6¾
10	0	8¼	10	1	5	10	2	1½	10	2	10¼	10	3	6¾
11	0	8½	11	1	5	11	2	1¾	11	2	10½	11	3	7
4/-	0s.	8¾	**8/-**	1s.	5¼	**12/-**	2s.	2	**16/-**	2s.	10½	**20/-**	3s.	7¼

20/6	3s.	8¼	25/6	4s.	7	31/-	5s.	7	35/6	6s.	4¾	Guineas.		
21/-	3	9¼	26/-	4	8¼	31/6	5	8	36/-	6	5¾	1.	3s.	9¼
22/-	3	11½	27/-	4	10¼	32/-	5	9	37/-	6	8	2.	7	6¾
22/6	4	0½	27/6	4	11½	32/6	5	10¼	37/6	6	9	3.	11	4
23/-	4	1¾	28/-	5	0½	33/-	5	11¼	38/-	6	10	4.	15	1½
24/-	4	3¾	29/-	5	2¾	34/-	6	1½	39/-	7	0¼	5.	18	10¾
25/-	4s.	6	**30/-**	5s.	4¾	**35/-**	6s.	3½	**40/-**	7s.	2½	6.	22s.	8¼

(=15$\frac{3}{10}$%* on Gross Returns.)

18½% — 18½ Per Cent. — 18½%

£1	£0 3s 8½	£51	£9 8s 8½	£101	18 13s 8½	£151	27 18s 8½
2	0 7 4¾	52	9 12 4¾	102	18 17 4¾	152	28 2 4¾
3	0 11 1¼	53	9 16 1¼	103	19 1 1¼	153	28 6 1¼
4	0 14 9½	54	9 19 9½	104	19 4 9½	154	28 9 9½
5	0 18 6	55	10 3 6	105	19 8 6	155	28 13 6
6	1 2 2½	56	10 7 2½	106	19 12 2½	156	28 17 2½
7	1 5 10¾	57	10 10 10¾	107	19 15 10¾	157	29 0 10¾
8	1 9 7¼	58	10 14 7¼	108	19 19 7¼	158	29 4 7¼
9	1 13 3½	59	10 18 3½	109	20 3 3½	159	29 8 3½
10	**1 17 0**	**60**	**11 2 0**	**110**	**20 7 0**	**160**	**29 12 0**
11	2 0 8½	61	11 5 8½	111	20 10 8½	161	29 15 8½
12	2 4 4¾	62	11 9 4¾	112	20 14 4¾	162	29 19 4¾
13	2 8 1¼	63	11 13 1¼	113	20 18 1¼	163	30 3 1¼
14	2 11 9½	64	11 16 9½	114	21 1 9½	164	30 6 9½
15	2 15 6	65	12 0 6	115	21 5 6	165	30 10 6
16	2 19 2½	66	12 4 2½	116	21 9 2½	166	30 14 2½
17	3 2 10¾	67	12 7 10¾	117	21 12 10¾	167	30 17 10¾
18	3 6 7¼	68	12 11 7¼	118	21 16 7¼	168	31 1 7¼
19	3 10 3½	69	12 15 3½	119	22 0 3½	169	31 5 3½
20	**3 14 0**	**70**	**12 19 0**	**120**	**22 4 0**	**170**	**31 9 0**
21	3 17 8½	71	13 2 8½	121	22 7 8½	171	31 12 8½
22	4 1 4¾	72	13 6 4¾	122	22 11 4¾	172	31 16 4¾
23	4 5 1¼	73	13 10 1¼	123	22 15 1¼	173	32 0 1¼
24	4 8 9½	74	13 13 9½	124	22 18 9½	174	32 3 9½
25	4 12 6	75	13 17 6	125	23 2 6	175	32 7 6
26	4 16 2½	76	14 1 2½	126	23 6 2½	176	32 11 2½
27	4 19 10¾	77	14 4 10¾	127	23 9 10¾	177	32 14 10¾
28	5 3 7¼	78	14 8 7¼	128	23 13 7¼	178	32 18 7¼
29	5 7 3½	79	14 12 3½	129	23 17 3½	179	33 2 3½
30	**5 11 0**	**80**	**14 16 0**	**130**	**24 1 0**	**180**	**33 6 0**
31	5 14 8½	81	14 19 8½	131	24 4 8½	181	33 9 8½
32	5 18 4¾	82	15 3 4¾	132	24 8 4¾	182	33 13 4¾
33	6 2 1¼	83	15 7 1¼	133	24 12 1¼	183	33 17 1¼
34	6 5 9½	84	15 10 9½	134	24 15 9½	184	34 0 9½
35	6 9 6	85	15 14 6	135	24 19 6	185	34 4 6
36	6 13 2½	86	15 18 2½	136	25 3 2½	186	34 8 2½
37	6 16 10¾	87	16 1 10¾	137	25 6 10¾	187	34 11 10¾
38	7 0 7¼	88	16 5 7¼	138	25 10 7¼	188	34 15 7¼
39	7 4 3½	89	16 9 3½	139	25 14 3½	189	34 19 3½
40	**7 8 0**	**90**	**16 13 0**	**140**	**25 18 0**	**190**	**35 3 0**
41	7 11 8½	91	16 16 8½	141	26 1 8½	191	35 6 8½
42	7 15 4¾	92	17 0 4¾	142	26 5 4¾	192	35 10 4¾
43	7 19 1¼	93	17 4 1¼	143	26 9 1¼	193	35 14 1½
44	8 2 9½	94	17 7 9½	144	26 12 9½	194	35 17 9½
45	8 6 6	95	17 11 6	145	26 16 6	195	36 1 6
46	8 10 2½	96	17 15 2½	146	27 0 2½	196	36 5 2½
47	8 13 10¾	97	17 18 10¾	147	27 3 10¾	197	36 8 10¾
48	8 17 7¼	98	18 2 7¼	148	27 7 7¼	198	36 12 7¼
49	9 1 3½	99	18 6 3½	149	27 11 3½	199	36 16 3½
50	**9 5 0**	**100**	**18 10 0**	**150**	**27 15 0**	**200**	**37 0 0**

250	46 5s 0d	700	129 10s 0d	1200	222 0s 0d	2000	370 0s 0
300	55 10 0	750	138 15 0	1400	259 0 0	2500	462 10 0
400	74 0 0	800	148 0 0	1500	277 10 0	3000	555 0 0
500	92 10 0	900	166 10 0	1600	296 0 0	4000	740 0 0
600	111 0s 0d	1000	185 0s 0d	1800	333 0s 0d	5000	925 0s 0

81½% off

18½% 18½ Per Cent. 18½%

1d	0s	0¼	4/1	0s	9	8/1	1s	6	12/1	2s	2¾	16/1	2s	11¾
2d	0	0¼	2	0	9¼	2	1	6¼	2	2	3	2	3	0
3d	0	0½	3	0	9½	3	1	6¼	3	2	3¼	3	3	0
4d	0	0¾	4	0	9½	4	1	6½	4	2	3½	4	3	0¼
5d	0	1	5	0	9¾	5	1	6¾	5	2	3½	5	3	0½
6d	0	1	4/6	0	10	8/6	1	6¾	12/6	2	3¾	16/6	3	0¾
7d	0	1¼	7	0	10¼	7	1	7	7	2	4	7	3	0¾
8d	0	1½	8	0	10¼	8	1	7¼	8	2	4	8	3	1
9d	0	1¾	9	0	10½	9	1	7½	9	2	4¼	9	3	1¼
10d	0	1¾	10	0	10¾	10	1	7½	10	2	4½	10	3	1¼
11d	0	2	11	0	11	11	1	7¾	11	2	4¾	11	3	1½
1/-	0	2¼	**5/-**	0	11	**9/-**	1	8	**13/-**	2	4¾	**17/-**	3	1¾
1/1	0	2½	5/1	0	11¼	1	1	8¼	1	2	5	1	3	2
2	0	2½	2	0	11½	2	1	8¼	2	2	5¼	2	3	2
3	0	2¾	3	0	11¾	3	1	8½	3	2	5½	3	3	2¼
4	0	3	4	0	11¾	4	1	8¾	4	2	5½	4	3	2½
5	0	3¼	5	1	0	5	1	9	5	2	5¾	5	3	2¾
1/6	0	3¼	5/6	1	0¼	9/6	1	9	13/6	2	6	17/6	3	2¾
7	0	3½	7	1	0½	7	1	9¼	7	2	6¼	7	3	3
8	0	3¾	8	1	0½	8	1	9½	8	2	6¼	8	3	3¼
9	0	4	9	1	0¾	9	1	9¾	9	2	6½	9	3	3½
10	0	4	10	1	1	10	1	9¾	10	2	6¾	10	3	3½
11	0	4¼	11	1	1¼	11	1	10	11	2	7	11	3	3¾
2/-	0	4½	**6/-**	1	1¼	**10/-**	1	10¼	**14/-**	2	7	**18/-**	3	4
2/1	0	4¾	1	1	1½	10/1	1	10½	1	2	7¼	1	3	4¼
2	0	4¾	2	1	1¾	2	1	10½	2	2	7½	2	3	4¼
3	0	5	3	1	2	3	1	10¾	3	2	7¾	3	3	4½
4	0	5¼	4	1	2	4	1	11	4	2	7¾	4	3	4¾
5	0	5¼	5	1	2¼	5	1	11¼	5	2	8	5	3	5
2/6	0	5½	6/6	1	2½	10/6	1	11¼	14/6	2	8¼	18/6	3	5
7	0	5¾	7	1	2½	7	1	11½	7	2	8½	7	3	5¼
8	0	6	8	1	2¾	8	1	11¾	8	2	8½	8	3	5½
9	0	6	9	1	3	9	1	11¾	9	2	8¾	9	3	5¾
10	0	6¼	10	1	3¼	10	2	0	10	2	9	10	3	5¾
11	0	6½	11	1	3¼	11	2	0¼	11	2	9	11	3	6
3/-	0	6¾	**7/-**	1	3½	**11/-**	2	0½	**15/-**	2	9¼	**19/-**	3	6¼
3/1	0	6¾	1	1	3¾	1	2	0½	15/1	2	9½	1	3	6¼
2	0	7	2	1	4	2	2	0¾	2	2	9¾	2	3	6½
3	0	7¼	3	1	4	3	2	1	3	2	9¾	3	3	6¾
4	0	7½	4	1	4¼	4	2	1¼	4	2	10	4	3	7
5	0	7½	5	1	4½	5	2	1¼	5	2	10¼	5	3	7
3/6	0	7¾	7/6	1	4¾	11/6	2	1½	15/6	2	10½	19/6	3	7¼
7	0	8	7	1	4¾	7	2	1¾	7	2	10½	7	3	7½
8	0	8¼	8	1	5	8	2	2	8	2	10¾	8	3	7¾
9	0	8¼	9	1	5¼	9	2	2	9	2	11	9	3	7¾
10	0	8½	10	1	5½	10	2	2¼	10	2	11¼	10	3	8
11	0	8¾	11	1	5½	11	2	2½	11	2	11¼	11	3	8¼
4/-	0	9	**8/-**	1	5¾	**12/-**	2	2¾	**16/-**	2	11½	**20/-**	3	8½

20/6	3s	9½	25/6	4s	8½	31/-	5s	8¾	35/6	6s	6¾	Guineas.	
21/-	3	10½	26/-	4	9¾	31/6	5	10	36/-	6	8	1.	3s 10½
22/-	4	0¾	27/-	5	0	32/-	5	11	37/-	6	10¼	2.	7 9¼
22/6	4	2	27/6	5	1	32/6	6	0¼	37/6	6	11¼	3.	11 7¾
23/-	4	3	28/-	5	2¼	33/-	6	1¼	38/-	7	0¼	4.	15 6½
24/-	4	5¼	29/-	5	4½	34/-	6	3½	39/-	7	2½	5.	19 5
25/-	4s	7½	**30/-**	5s	6½	**35/-**	6s	5¾	**40/-**	7s	4¾	6.	23s 3¾

(=$15\frac{6}{10}$% on Gross Returns).

£	£ s. d.	£	£ s. d.	£	£ s. d.	£	£ s. d.
£1	0 0 3 9	£51	9 11s. 3	£101	18 18s. 9	£151	28 6s. 3
2	0 7 6	52	9 15 0	102	19 2 6	152	28 10 0
3	0 11 3	53	9 18 9	103	19 6 3	153	28 13 9
4	0 15 0	54	10 2 6	104	19 10 0	154	28 17 6
5	0 18 9	55	10 6 3	105	19 13 9	155	29 1 3
6	1 2 6	56	10 10 0	106	19 17 6	156	29 5 0
7	1 6 3	57	10 13 9	107	20 1 3	157	29 8 9
8	1 10 0	58	10 17 6	108	20 5 0	158	29 12 6
9	1 13 9	59	11 1 3	109	20 8 9	159	29 16 3
10	1 17s. 6	60	11 5s. 0	110	20 12s. 6	160	30 0s. 0
11	2 1 3	61	11 8 9	111	20 16 3	161	30 3 9
12	2 5 0	62	11 12 6	112	21 0 0	162	30 7 6
13	2 8 9	63	11 16 3	113	21 3 9	163	30 11 3
14	2 12 6	64	12 0 0	114	21 7 6	164	30 15 0
15	2 16 3	65	12 3 9	115	21 11 3	165	30 18 9
16	3 0 0	66	12 7 6	116	21 15 0	166	31 2 6
17	3 3 9	67	12 11 3	117	21 18 9	167	31 6 3
18	3 7 6	68	12 15 0	118	22 2 6	168	31 10 0
19	3 11 3	69	12 18 9	119	22 6 3	169	31 13 9
20	3 15s. 0	70	13 2s. 6	120	22 10s. 0	170	31 17s. 6
21	3 18 9	71	13 6 3	121	22 13 9	171	32 1 3
22	4 2 6	72	13 10 0	122	22 17 6	172	32 5 0
23	4 6 3	73	13 13 9	123	23 1 3	173	32 8 9
24	4 10 0	74	13 17 6	124	23 5 0	174	32 12 6
25	4 13 9	75	14 1 3	125	23 8 9	175	32 16 3
26	4 17 6	76	14 5 0	126	23 12 6	176	33 0 0
27	5 1 3	77	14 8 9	127	23 16 3	177	33 3 9
28	5 5 0	78	14 12 6	128	24 0 0	178	33 7 6
29	5 8 9	79	14 16 3	129	24 3 9	179	33 11 3
30	5 12s. 6	80	15 0s. 0	130	24 7s. 6	180	33 15s. 0
31	5 16 3	81	15 3 9	131	24 11 3	181	33 18 9
32	6 0 0	82	15 7 6	132	24 15 0	182	34 2 6
33	6 3 9	83	15 11 3	133	24 18 9	183	34 6 3
34	6 7 6	84	15 15 0	134	25 2 6	184	34 10 0
35	6 11 3	85	15 18 9	135	25 6 3	185	34 13 9
36	6 15 0	86	16 2 6	136	25 10 0	186	34 17 6
37	6 18 9	87	16 6 3	137	25 13 9	187	35 1 3
38	7 2 6	88	16 10 0	138	25 17 6	188	35 5 0
39	7 6 3	89	16 13 9	139	26 1 3	189	35 8 9
40	7 10s. 0	90	16 17s. 6	140	26 5s. 0	190	35 12s. 6
41	7 13 9	91	17 1 3	141	26 8 9	191	35 16 3
42	7 17 6	92	17 5 0	142	26 12 6	192	36 0 0
43	8 1 3	93	17 8 9	143	26 16 3	193	36 3 9
44	8 5 0	94	17 12 6	144	27 0 0	194	36 7 6
45	8 8 9	95	17 16 3	145	27 3 9	195	36 11 3
46	8 12 6	96	18 0 0	146	27 7 6	196	36 15 0
47	8 16 3	97	18 3 9	147	27 11 3	197	36 18 9
48	9 0 0	98	18 7 6	148	27 15 0	198	37 2 6
49	9 3 9	99	18 11 3	149	27 18 9	199	37 6 3
50	9 7s. 6	100	18 15s. 0	150	28 2s. 6	200	37 10s. 0

£	£ s. d.	£	£ s. d.	£	£ s. d.	£	£ s. d.
250	£46 17 6	700	131 5 0	1200	225 0 0	2000	375 0 0
300	56 5 0	750	140 12 6	1400	262 10 0	2500	468 15 0
400	75 0 0	800	150 0 0	1500	281 5 0	3000	562 10 0
500	93 15 0	900	168 15 0	1600	300 0 0	4000	750 0 0
600	112 10 0	1000	187 10 0	1800	337 10 0	5000	937 10 0

81¼% off.   (18¾% = 3-16ths)

18¾ Per Cent.

18¾%

1d	0s.	0¼	4/1	0s.	9¼	8/1	1s.	6¼	12/1	2s.	3¼	16/1	3s.	0¼
2d	0	0½	2	0	9½	2	1	6½	2	2	3½	2	3	0½
3d	0	0½	3	0	9½	3	1	6½	3	2	3½	3	3	0½
4d	0	0¾	4	0	9¾	4	1	6¾	4	2	3¾	4	3	0¾
5d	0	1	5	0	10	5	1	7	5	2	4	5	3	1
6d	0	1¼	4/6	0	10¼	8/6	1	7¼	12/6	2	4¼	16/6	3	1¼
7d	0	1¼	7	0	10¼	7	1	7¼	7	2	4¼	7	3	1¼
8d	0	1½	8	0	10½	8	1	7½	8	2	4½	8	3	1½
9d	0	1¾	9	0	10¾	9	1	7¾	9	2	4¾	9	3	1¾
10d	0	2	10	0	11	10	1	8	10	2	5	10	3	2
11d	0	2	11	0	11	11	1	8	11	2	5	11	3	2
1/-	0s.	2¼	**5/-**	0s.	11¼	**9/-**	1s.	8¼	**13/-**	2s	5¼	**17/-**	3s.	2¼
1/1	0	2½	5/1	0	11½	9/1	1	8½	13/1	2	5½	17/1	3	2½
2	0	2¾	2	0	11¾	2	1	8¾	2	2	5¾	2	3	2¾
3	0	2¾	3	0	11¾	3	1	8¾	3	2	5¾	3	3	2¾
4	0	3	4	1	0	4	1	9	4	2	6	4	3	3
5	0	3¼	5	1	0¼	5	1	9¼	5	2	6¼	5	3	3¼
1/6	0	3½	5/6	1	0½	9/6	1	9½	13/6	2	6½	17/6	3	3½
7	0	3½	7	1	0½	7	1	9½	7	2	6½	7	3	3½
8	0	3¾	8	1	0¾	8	1	9¾	8	2	6¾	8	3	3¾
9	0	4	9	1	1	9	1	10	9	2	7	9	3	4
10	0	4¼	10	1	1¼	10	1	10¼	10	2	7¼	10	3	4¼
11	0	4¼	11	1	1¼	11	1	10¼	11	2	7¼	11	3	4¼
2/-	0s.	4½	**6/-**	1s.	1½	**10/-**	1s.	10½	**14/-**	2s.	7½	**18/-**	3s.	4½
2/1	0	4¾	6/1	1	1¾	10/1	1	10¾	14/1	2	7¾	18/1	3	4¾
2	0	5	2	1	2	2	1	11	2	2	8	2	3	5
3	0	5	3	1	2	3	1	11	3	2	8	3	3	5
4	0	5¼	4	1	2¼	4	1	11¼	4	2	8¼	4	3	5¼
5	0	5½	5	1	2½	5	1	11½	5	2	8½	5	3	5½
2/6	0	5¾	6/6	1	2¾	10/6	1	11¾	14/6	2	8¾	18/6	3	5¾
7	0	5¾	7	1	2¾	7	1	11¾	7	2	8¾	7	3	5¾
8	0	6	8	1	3	8	2	0	8	2	9	8	3	6
9	0	6¼	9	1	3¼	9	2	0¼	9	2	9¼	9	3	6¼
10	0	6½	10	1	3½	10	2	0½	10	2	9½	10	3	6½
11	0	6½	11	1	3½	11	2	0½	11	2	9½	11	3	6½
3/-	0s.	6¾	**7/-**	1s.	3¾	**11/-**	2s.	0¾	**15/-**	2s.	9¾	**19/-**	3s.	6¾
3/1	0	7	7/1	1	4	11/1	2	1	15/1	2	10	19/1	3	7
2	0	7¼	2	1	4¼	2	2	1¼	2	2	10¼	2	3	7¼
3	0	7¼	3	1	4¼	3	2	1¼	3	2	10¼	3	3	7¼
4	0	7½	4	1	4½	4	2	1½	4	2	10½	4	3	7½
5	0	7¾	5	1	4¾	5	2	1¾	5	2	10¾	5	3	7¾
3/6	0	8	7/6	1	5	11/6	2	2	15/6	2	11	19/6	3	8
7	0	8	7	1	5	7	2	2	7	2	11	7	3	8
8	0	8¼	8	1	5¼	8	2	2¼	8	2	11¼	8	3	8¼
9	0	8½	9	1	5½	9	2	2½	9	2	11½	9	3	8½
10	0	8¾	10	1	5¾	10	2	2¾	10	2	11¾	10	3	8¾
11	0	8¾	11	1	5¾	11	2	2¾	11	2	11¾	11	3	8¾
4/-	0s.	9	**8/-**	1s.	6	**12/-**	2s.	3	**16/-**	3s.	0	**20/-**	3s.	9

20/6	3s.	10¼	25/6	4s.	9½	31/-	5s.	9¾	35/6	6s.	8	Guineas.		
21/-	3	11¼	26/-	4	10½	31/6	5	11	36/-	6	9	1.	3s.	11¼
22/-	4	1½	27/-	5	0¾	32/-	6	0	37/-	6	11¼	2.	7	10½
22/6	4	2¾	27/6	5	2	32/6	6	1¼	37/6	7	0½	3.	11	9¾
23/-	4	3¾	28/-	5	3	33/-	6	2¼	38/-	7	1½	4.	15	9
24/-	4	6	29/-	5	5¼	34/-	6	4½	39/-	7	3¾	5.	19	8¼
25/-	4s.	8¼	**30/-**	5s.	7½	**35/-**	6s.	6¾	**40/-**	7s.	6	6.	23s.	7½

(=15$\frac{8}{10}$%* on Gross Returns.)

19% 19 PER CENT. 19%

£1	0	3s.	9½	£51	9	13s.	9½	£101	19	3s.	9½	£151	28	13s.	9½
2	0	7	7¼	52	9	17	7¼	102	19	7	7¼	152	28	17	7¼
3	0	11	4¾	53	10	1	4¾	103	19	11	4¾	153	29	1	4¾
4	0	15	2½	54	10	5	2½	104	19	15	2½	154	29	5	2½
5	0	19	0	55	10	9	0	105	19	19	0	155	29	9	0
6	1	2	9½	56	10	12	9½	106	20	2	9½	156	29	12	9½
7	1	6	7¼	57	10	16	7¼	107	20	6	7¼	157	29	16	7¼
8	1	10	4¾	58	11	0	4¾	108	20	10	4¾	158	30	0	4¾
9	1	14	2½	59	11	4	2½	109	20	14	2½	159	30	4	2½
10	**1**	**18s.**	**0**	**60**	**11**	**8s.**	**0**	**110**	**20**	**18s.**	**0**	**160**	**30**	**8s.**	**0**
11	2	1	9½	61	11	11	9½	111	21	1	9½	161	30	11	9½
12	2	5	7¼	62	11	15	7¼	112	21	5	7¼	162	30	15	7¼
13	2	9	4¾	63	11	19	4¾	113	21	9	4¾	163	30	19	4¾
14	2	13	2½	64	12	3	2½	114	21	13	2½	164	31	3	2½
15	2	17	0	65	12	7	0	115	21	17	0	165	31	7	0
16	3	0	9½	66	12	10	9½	116	22	0	9½	166	31	10	9½
17	3	4	7¼	67	12	14	7¼	117	22	4	7¼	167	31	14	7¼
18	3	8	4¾	68	12	18	4¾	118	22	8	4¾	168	31	18	4¾
19	3	12	2½	69	13	2	2½	119	22	12	2½	169	32	2	2½
20	**3**	**16s.**	**0**	**70**	**13**	**6s.**	**0**	**120**	**22**	**16s.**	**0**	**170**	**32**	**6s.**	**0**
21	3	19	9½	71	13	9	9½	121	22	19	9½	171	32	9	9½
22	4	3	7¼	72	13	13	7¼	122	23	3	7¼	172	32	13	7¼
23	4	7	4¾	73	13	17	4¾	123	23	7	4¾	173	32	17	4¾
24	4	11	2½	74	14	1	2½	124	23	11	2½	174	33	1	2½
25	4	15	0	75	14	5	0	125	23	15	0	175	33	5	0
26	4	18	9½	76	14	8	9½	126	23	18	9½	176	33	8	9½
27	5	2	7¼	77	14	12	7¼	127	24	2	7¼	177	33	12	7¼
28	5	6	4¾	78	14	16	4¾	128	24	6	4¾	178	33	16	4¾
29	5	10	2½	79	15	0	2½	129	24	10	2½	179	34	0	2½
30	**5**	**14s.**	**0**	**80**	**15**	**4s.**	**0**	**130**	**24**	**14s.**	**0**	**180**	**34**	**4s.**	**0**
31	5	17	9½	81	15	7	9½	131	24	17	9½	181	34	7	9½
32	6	1	7¼	82	15	11	7¼	132	25	1	7¼	182	34	11	7¼
33	6	5	4¾	83	15	15	4¾	133	25	5	4¾	183	34	15	4¾
34	6	9	2½	84	15	19	2½	134	25	9	2½	184	34	19	2½
35	6	13	0	85	16	3	0	135	25	13	0	185	35	3	0
36	6	16	9½	86	16	6	9½	136	25	16	9½	186	35	6	9½
37	7	0	7¼	87	16	10	7¼	137	26	0	7¼	187	35	10	7¼
38	7	4	4¾	88	16	14	4¾	138	26	4	4¾	188	35	14	4¾
39	7	8	2½	89	16	18	2½	139	26	8	2½	189	35	18	2½
40	**7**	**12s.**	**0**	**90**	**17**	**2s.**	**0**	**140**	**26**	**12s.**	**0**	**190**	**36**	**2s**	**0**
41	7	15	9½	91	17	5	9½	141	26	15	9½	191	36	5	9½
42	7	19	7¼	92	17	9	7¼	142	26	19	7¼	192	36	9	7¼
43	8	3	4¾	93	17	13	4¾	143	27	3	4¾	193	36	13	4¾
44	8	7	2½	94	17	17	2½	144	27	7	2½	194	36	17	2½
45	8	11	0	95	18	1	0	145	27	11	0	195	37	1	0
46	8	14	9½	96	18	4	9½	146	27	14	9½	196	37	4	9½
47	8	18	7¼	97	18	8	7¼	147	27	18	7¼	197	37	8	7¼
48	9	2	4¾	98	18	12	4¾	148	28	2	4¾	198	37	12	4¾
49	9	6	2½	99	18	16	2½	149	28	6	2½	199	37	16	2½
50	**9**	**10s.**	**0**	**100**	**19**	**0s.**	**0**	**150**	**28**	**10s.**	**0**	**200**	**38**	**0s.**	**0**

250	£47	10	0	700	133	0	0	1200	228	0	0	2000	380	0	0
300	57	0	0	750	142	10	0	1400	266	0	0	2500	475	0	0
400	76	0	0	800	152	0	0	1500	285	0	0	3000	570	0	0
500	95	0	0	900	171	0	0	1600	304	0	0	4000	760	0	0
600	114	0	0	1000	190	0	0	1800	342	0	0	5000	950	0	0

81% off.

1d	0s.	0¼	4/1	0s.	9¼	8/1	1s.	6½	12/1	2s.	3½	16/1	3s.	0¾
2d	0	0½	2	0	9½	2	1	6½	2	2	3¾	2	3	0¾
3d	0	0½	3	0	9¾	3	1	6¾	3	2	4	3	3	1
4d	0	0¾	4	0	10	4	1	7	4	2	4	4	3	1¼
5d	0	1	5	0	10	5	1	7¼	5	2	4¼	5	3	1½
6d	0	1¼	4/6	0	10¼	8/6	1	7½	12/6	2	4½	16/6	3	1½
7d	0	1¼	7	0	10½	7	1	7½	7	2	4¾	7	3	1¾
8d	0	1½	8	0	10¾	8	1	7¾	8	2	5	8	3	2
9d	0	1¾	9	0	10¾	9	1	8	9	2	5	9	3	2¼
10d	0	2	10	0	11	10	1	8¼	10	2	5¼	10	3	2½
11d	0	2	11	0	11¼	11	1	8¼	11	2	5½	11	3	2½
1/-	0s.	2¼	**5/-**	0s.	11½	**9/-**	1s.	8½	**13/-**	2s	5¾	**17/-**	3s.	2¾
1/1	0	2½	5/1	0	11½	9/1	1	8¾	13/1	2	5¾	17/1	3	3
2	0	2¾	2	0	11¾	2	1	9	2	2	6	2	3	3¼
3	0	2¾	3	1	0	3	1	9	3	2	6¼	3	3	3¼
4	0	3	4	1	0¼	4	1	9¼	4	2	6½	4	3	3½
5	0	3¼	5	1	0¼	5	1	9½	5	2	6½	5	3	3¾
1/6	0	3½	5/6	1	0½	9/6	1	9¾	13/6	2	6¾	17/6	3	4
7	0	3½	7	1	0¾	7	1	9¾	7	2	7	7	3	4
8	0	3¾	8	1	1	8	1	10	8	2	7¼	8	3	4¼
9	0	4	9	1	1	9	1	10¼	9	2	7¼	9	3	4½
10	0	4¼	10	1	1¼	10	1	10½	10	2	7½	10	3	4¾
11	0	4¼	11	1	1½	11	1	10½	11	2	7¾	11	3	4¾
2/-	0s.	4½	**6/-**	1s.	1¾	**10/-**	1s.	10¾	**14/-**	2s.	8	**18/-**	3s.	5
2/1	0	4¾	6/1	1	1¾	10/1	1	11	14/1	2	8	18/1	3	5¼
2	0	5	2	1	2	2	1	11¼	2	2	8¼	2	3	5½
3	0	5¼	3	1	2¼	3	1	11¼	3	2	8½	3	3	5½
4	0	5¼	4	1	2½	4	1	11½	4	2	8¾	4	3	5¾
5	0	5½	5	1	2¾	5	1	11¾	5	2	8¾	5	3	6
2/6	0	5¾	6/6	1	2¾	10/6	2	0	14/6	2	9	18/6	3	6¼
7	0	6	7	1	3	7	2	0¼	7	2	9¼	7	3	6¼
8	0	6	8	1	3¼	8	2	0¼	8	2	9½	8	3	6½
9	0	6¼	9	1	3½	9	2	0½	9	2	9¾	9	3	6¾
10	0	6½	10	1	3½	10	2	0¾	10	2	9¾	10	3	7
11	0	6¾	11	1	3¾	11	2	1	11	2	10	11	3	7¼
3/-	0s.	6¾	**7/-**	1s.	4	**11/-**	2s.	1	**15/-**	2s.	10¼	**19/-**	3s.	7¼
3/1	0	7	7/1	1	4¼	11/1	2	1¼	15/1	2	10½	19/1	3	7½
2	0	7¼	2	1	4¼	2	2	1½	2	2	10½	2	3	7¾
3	0	7½	3	1	4½	3	2	1¾	3	2	10¾	3	3	8
4	0	7½	4	1	4¾	4	2	1¾	4	2	11	4	3	8
5	0	7¾	5	1	5	5	2	2	5	2	11¼	5	3	8¼
3/6	0	8	7/6	1	5	11/6	2	2¼	15/6	2	11¼	19/6	3	8½
7	0	8¼	7	1	5¼	7	2	2½	7	2	11½	7	3	8¾
8	0	8¼	8	1	5½	8	2	2½	8	2	11¾	8	3	8¾
9	0	8½	9	1	5¾	9	2	2¾	9	3	0	9	3	9
10	0	8¾	10	1	5¾	10	2	3	10	3	0	10	3	9¼
11	0	9	11	1	6	11	2	3¼	11	3	0¼	11	3	9½
4/-	0s	9	**8/-**	1s.	6¼	**12/-**	2s.	3¼	**16/-**	3s.	0½	**20/-**	3s.	9½

20/6	3s.	10¾	25/6	4s.	10¼	31/-	5s.	10¾	35/6	6s.	9	Guineas.		
21/-	4	0	26/-	4	11¼	31/6	5	11¾	36/-	6	10	1.	4s.	0
22/-	4	2¼	27/-	5	1½	32/-	6	1	37/-	7	0¼	2.	7	11¾
22/6	4	3¼	27/6	5	2¾	32/6	6	2	37/6	7	1½	3.	11	11¾
23/-	4	4½	28/-	5	3¾	33/-	6	3¼	38/-	7	2¾	4.	15	11½
24/-	4	6¾	29/-	5	6	34/-	6	5½	39/-	7	5	5.	19	11½
25/-	4s.	9	**30/-**	5s.	8½	**35/-**	6s.	7¾	**40/-**	7s.	7¼	6.	23s.	11¼

(=16%* on Gross Returns.)

£1	£0	3s 10¾	£51	£9	18s 10¾	£101	19	13s 10¾	£151	29	8s 10¾
2	0	7 9½	52	10	2 9½	102	19	17 9½	152	29	12 9½
3	0	11 8½	53	10	6 8½	103	20	1 8½	153	29	16 8½
4	0	15 7¼	54	10	10 7¼	104	20	5 7¼	154	30	0 7¼
5	0	19 6	55	10	14 6	105	20	9 6	155	30	4 6
6	1	3 4¾	56	10	18 4¾	106	20	13 4¾	156	30	8 4¾
7	1	7 3½	57	11	2 3½	107	20	17 3½	157	30	12 3½
8	1	11 2½	58	11	6 2½	108	21	1 2½	158	30	16 2½
9	1	15 1¼	59	11	10 1¼	109	21	5 1¼	159	31	0 1¼
10	1	19 0	60	11	14 0	110	21	9 0	160	31	4 0
11	2	2 10¾	61	11	17 10¾	111	21	12 10¾	161	31	7 10¾
12	2	6 9½	62	12	1 9½	112	21	16 9½	162	31	11 9½
13	2	10 8½	63	12	5 8½	113	22	0 8½	163	31	15 8½
14	2	14 7¼	64	12	9 7¼	114	22	4 7¼	164	31	19 7¼
15	2	18 6	65	12	13 6	115	22	8 6	165	32	3 6
16	3	2 4¾	66	12	17 4¾	116	22	12 4¾	166	32	7 4¾
17	3	6 3½	67	13	1 3½	117	22	16 3½	167	32	11 3½
18	3	10 2½	68	13	5 2½	118	23	0 2½	168	32	15 2½
19	3	14 1¼	69	13	9 1¼	119	23	4 1¼	169	32	19 1¼
20	3	18 0	70	13	13 0	120	23	8 0	170	33	3 0
21	4	1 10¾	71	13	16 10¾	121	23	11 10¾	171	33	6 10¾
22	4	5 9½	72	14	0 9½	122	23	15 9½	172	33	10 9½
23	4	9 8½	73	14	4 8½	123	23	19 8½	173	33	14 8½
24	4	13 7¼	74	14	8 7¼	124	24	3 7¼	174	33	18 7¼
25	4	17 6	75	14	12 6	125	24	7 6	175	34	2 6
26	5	1 4¾	76	14	16 4¾	126	24	11 4¾	176	34	6 4¾
27	5	5 3½	77	15	0 3½	127	24	15 3½	177	34	10 3½
28	5	9 2½	78	15	4 2½	128	24	19 2½	178	34	14 2½
29	5	13 1¼	79	15	8 1¼	129	25	3 1¼	179	34	18 1¼
30	5	17 0	80	15	12 0	130	25	7 0	180	35	2 0
31	6	0 10¾	81	15	15 10¾	131	25	10 10¾	181	35	5 10¾
32	6	4 9½	82	15	19 9½	132	25	14 9½	182	35	9 9½
33	6	8 8½	83	16	3 8½	133	25	18 8½	183	35	13 8½
34	6	12 7¼	84	16	7 7¼	134	26	2 7¼	184	35	17 7¼
35	6	16 6	85	16	11 6	135	26	6 6	185	36	1 6
36	7	0 4¾	86	16	15 4¾	136	26	10 4¾	186	36	5 4¾
37	7	4 3½	87	16	19 3½	137	26	14 3½	187	36	9 3½
38	7	8 2½	88	17	3 2½	138	26	18 2½	188	36	13 2½
39	7	12 1¼	89	17	7 1¼	139	27	2 1¼	189	36	17 1¼
40	7	16 0	90	17	11 0	140	27	6 0	190	37	1 0
41	7	19 10¾	91	17	14 10¾	141	27	9 10¾	191	37	4 10¾
42	8	3 9½	92	17	18 9½	142	27	13 9½	192	37	8 9½
43	8	7 8½	93	18	2 8½	143	27	17 8½	193	37	12 8½
44	8	11 7¼	94	18	6 7¼	144	28	1 7¼	194	37	16 7¼
45	8	15 6	95	18	10 6	145	28	5 6	195	38	0 6
46	8	19 4¾	96	18	14 4¾	146	28	9 4¾	196	38	4 4¾
47	9	3 3½	97	18	18 3½	147	28	13 3½	197	38	8 3½
48	9	7 2½	98	19	2 2½	148	28	17 2½	198	38	12 2½
49	9	11 1¼	99	19	6 1¼	149	29	1 1¼	199	38	16 1¼
50	9	15 0	100	19	10 0	150	29	5 0	200	39	0 0

250	48 15s 0d	700	136 10s 0d	1200	234 0s 0d	2000	390 0s 0
300	58 10 0	750	146 5 0	1400	273 0 0	2500	487 10 0
400	78 0 0	800	156 0 0	1500	292 10 0	3000	585 0 0
500	97 10 0	900	175 10 0	1600	312 0 0	4000	780 0 0
600	117 0s 0d	1000	195 0s 0d	1800	351 0s 0d	5000	975 0s 0

80½% off

1d	0s	0¼	4/1	0s	9½	8/1	1s	7	12/1	2s	4¼	16/1	3s	1¾
2d	0	0½	2	0	9¾	2	1	7	2	2	4½	2	3	1¾
3d	0	0½	3	0	10	3	1	7¼	3	2	4¾	3	3	2
4d	0	0¾	4	0	10¼	4	1	7½	4	2	4¾	4	3	2¼
5d	0	1	5	0	10¼	5	1	7¾	5	2	5	5	3	2½
6d	0	1¼	4/6	0	10½	8/6	1	8	12/6	2	5¼	16/6	3	2½
7d	0	1¼	7	0	10¾	7	1	8	7	2	5½	7	3	2¾
8d	0	1½	8	0	11	8	1	8¼	8	2	5¾	8	3	3
9d	0	1¾	9	0	11	9	1	8½	9	2	5¾	9	3	3¼
10d	0	2	10	0	11¼	10	1	8¾	10	2	6	10	3	3½
11d	0	2¼	11	0	11½	11	1	8¾	11	2	6¼	11	3	3½
1/-	**0**	**2¼**	**5/-**	**0**	**11¾**	**9/-**	**1**	**9**	**13/-**	**2**	**6½**	**17/-**	**3**	**3¾**
1/1	0	2½	5/1	1	0	1	1	9¼	1	2	6½	1	3	4
2	0	2¾	2	1	0	2	1	9½	2	2	6¾	2	3	4¼
3	0	3	3	1	0¼	3	1	9¾	3	2	7	3	3	4¼
4	0	3	4	1	0½	4	1	9¾	4	2	7¼	4	3	4½
5	0	3¼	5	1	0¾	5	1	10	5	2	7½	5	3	4¾
1/6	0	3½	5/6	1	0¾	9/6	1	10¼	13/6	2	7½	17/6	3	5
7	0	3¾	7	1	1	7	1	10½	7	2	7¾	7	3	5¼
8	0	4	8	1	1¼	8	1	10½	8	2	8	8	3	5¼
9	0	4	9	1	1½	9	1	10¾	9	2	8¼	9	3	5½
10	0	4¼	10	1	1¾	10	1	11	10	2	8¼	10	3	5¾
11	0	4½	11	1	1¾	11	1	11¼	11	2	8½	11	3	6
2/-	**0**	**4¾**	**6/-**	**1**	**2**	**10/-**	**1**	**11½**	**14/-**	**2**	**8¾**	**18/-**	**3**	**6**
2/1	0	5	1	1	2¼	10/1	1	11½	1	2	9	1	3	6¼
2	0	5	2	1	2½	2	1	11¾	2	2	9¼	2	3	6½
3	0	5¼	3	1	2¾	3	2	0	3	2	9¼	3	3	6¾
4	0	5½	4	1	2¾	4	2	0¼	4	2	9½	4	3	7
5	0	5¾	5	1	3	5	2	0½	5	2	9¾	5	3	7
2/6	0	5¾	6/6	1	3¼	10/6	2	0½	14/6	2	10	18/6	3	7¼
7	0	6	7	1	3½	7	2	0¾	7	2	10¼	7	3	7½
8	0	6¼	8	1	3½	8	2	1	8	2	10¼	8	3	7¾
9	0	6½	9	1	3¾	9	2	1¼	9	2	10½	9	3	8
10	0	6¾	10	1	4	10	2	1¼	10	2	10¾	10	3	8
11	0	6¾	11	1	4¼	11	2	1½	11	2	11	11	3	8¼
3/-	**0**	**7**	**7/-**	**1**	**4½**	**11/-**	**2**	**1¾**	**15/-**	**2**	**11**	**19/-**	**3**	**8½**
3/1	0	7¼	1	1	4½	1	2	2	15/1	2	11¼	1	3	8¾
2	0	7½	2	1	4¾	2	2	2¼	2	2	11½	2	3	8¾
3	0	7½	3	1	5	3	2	2¼	3	2	11¾	3	3	9
4	0	7¾	4	1	5¼	4	2	2½	4	3	0	4	3	9¼
5	0	8	5	1	5¼	5	2	2¾	5	3	0	5	3	9½
3/6	0	8¼	7/6	1	5½	11/6	2	3	15/6	3	0¼	19/6	3	9¾
7	0	8½	7	1	5¾	7	2	3	7	3	0½	7	3	9¾
8	0	8½	8	1	6	8	2	3¼	8	3	0¾	8	3	10
9	0	8¾	9	1	6¼	9	2	3½	9	3	0¾	9	3	10¼
10	0	9	10	1	6¼	10	2	3¾	10	3	1	10	3	10½
11	0	9¼	11	1	6½	11	2	4	11	3	1¼	11	3	10½
4/-	**0**	**9¼**	**8/-**	**1**	**6¾**	**12/-**	**2**	**4**	**16/-**	**3**	**1½**	**20/-**	**3**	**10¾**

20/6	4s	0	25/6	4s	11¾	31/-	6s	0½	35/6	6s	11	Guineas.		
21/-	4	1¼	26/-	5	0¾	31/6	6	1¾	36/-	7	0¼	1.	4s	1¼
22/-	4	3½	27/-	5	3¼	32/-	6	3	37/-	7	2½	2.	8	2¼
22/6	4	4¾	27/6	5	4¼	32/6	6	4	37/6	7	3¾	3.	12	3½
23/-	4	5¾	28/-	5	5½	33/-	6	5¼	38/-	7	5	4.	16	4½
24/-	4	8¼	29/-	5	7¾	34/-	6	7½	39/-	7	7¼	5.	20	5¾
25/-	4s	10½	**30/-**	5s	10¼	**35/-**	6s	10	**40/-**	7s	9½	**6.**	24s	6¾

(=16 3/10% on Gross Returns).

£1	£0 4s. 0	£51	10 4s. 0	£101	£20 4s. 0	£151	£30 4s. 0
2	0 8 0	52	10 8 0	102	20 8 0	152	30 8 0
3	0 12 0	53	10 12 0	103	20 12 0	153	30 12 0
4	0 16 0	54	10 16 0	104	20 16 0	154	30 16 0
5	1 0 0	55	11 0 0	105	21 0 0	155	31 0 0
6	1 4 0	56	11 4 0	106	21 4 0	156	31 4 0
7	1 8 0	57	11 8 0	107	21 8 0	157	31 8 0
8	1 12 0	58	11 12 0	108	21 12 0	158	31 12 0
9	1 16 0	59	11 16 0	109	21 16 0	159	31 16 0
10	£2 0s. 0	60	12 0s. 0	110	£22 0s. 0	160	£32 0s. 0
11	£2 4s. 0	61	12 4s. 0	111	£22 4s. 0	161	£32 4s. 0
12	2 8 0	62	12 8 0	112	22 8 0	162	32 8 0
13	2 12 0	63	12 12 0	113	22 12 0	163	32 12 0
14	2 16 0	64	12 16 0	114	22 16 0	164	32 16 0
15	3 0 0	65	13 0 0	115	23 0 0	165	33 0 0
16	3 4 0	66	13 4 0	116	23 4 0	166	33 4 0
17	3 8 0	67	13 8 0	117	23 8 0	167	33 8 0
18	3 12 0	68	13 12 0	118	23 12 0	168	33 12 0
19	3 16 0	69	13 16 0	119	23 16 0	169	33 16 0
20	£4 0s. 0	70	14 0s. 0	120	£24 0s. 0	170	£34 0s. 0
21	£4 4s. 0	71	14 4s. 0	121	£24 4s. 0	171	£34 4s. 0
22	4 8 0	72	14 8 0	122	24 8 0	172	34 8 0
23	4 12 0	73	14 12 0	123	24 12 0	173	34 12 0
24	4 16 0	74	14 16 0	124	24 16 0	174	34 16 0
25	5 0 0	75	15 0 0	125	25 0 0	175	35 0 0
26	5 4 0	76	15 4 0	126	25 4 0	176	35 4 0
27	5 8 0	77	15 8 0	127	25 8 0	177	35 8 0
28	5 12 0	78	15 12 0	128	25 12 0	178	35 12 0
29	5 16 0	79	15 16 0	129	25 16 0	179	35 16 0
30	£6 0s. 0	80	16 0s. 0	130	£26 0s. 0	180	£36 0s. 0
31	£6 4s. 0	81	16 4s. 0	131	£26 4s. 0	181	£36 4s. 0
32	6 8 0	82	16 8 0	132	26 8 0	182	36 8 0
33	6 12 0	83	16 12 0	133	26 12 0	183	36 12 0
34	6 16 0	84	16 16 0	134	26 16 0	184	36 16 0
35	7 0 0	85	17 0 0	135	27 0 0	185	37 0 0
36	7 4 0	86	17 4 0	136	27 4 0	186	37 4 0
37	7 8 0	87	17 8 0	137	27 8 0	187	37 8 0
38	7 12 0	88	17 12 0	138	27 12 0	188	37 12 0
39	7 16 0	89	17 16 0	139	27 16 0	189	37 16 0
40	£8 0s. 0	90	18 0s. 0	140	£28 0s. 0	190	£38 0s. 0
41	£8 4s. 0	91	18 4s. 0	141	£28 4s. 0	191	£38 4s. 0
42	8 8 0	92	18 8 0	142	28 8 0	192	38 8 0
43	8 12 0	93	18 12 0	143	28 12 0	193	38 12 0
44	8 16 0	94	18 16 0	144	28 16 0	194	38 16 0
45	9 0 0	95	19 0 0	145	29 0 0	195	39 0 0
46	9 4 0	96	19 4 0	146	29 4 0	196	39 4 0
47	9 8 0	97	19 8 0	147	29 8 0	197	39 8 0
48	9 12 0	98	19 12 0	148	29 12 0	198	39 12 0
49	9 16 0	99	19 16 0	149	29 16 0	199	39 16 0
50	10 0s. 0	100	20 0s. 0	150	£30 0s. 0	200	£40 0s. 0

250	£50 0s. 0d	700	140 0s.0d	1200	240 0s.0d	2000	£400 0s. 0
300	60 0 0	750	150 0 0	1400	280 0 0	2500	500 0 0
400	80 0 0	800	160 0 0	1500	300 0 0	3000	600 0 0
500	100 0 0	900	180 0 0	1600	320 0 0	4000	800 0 0
600	120 0s. 0d	1000	200 0s.0d	1800	360 0s.0d	5000	£1000 0s. 0

80% off.   (20%=1-5th)

20% Twenty Per Cent. 20%

1d	0s. 0¼	4/1	0s. 9¾	8/1	1s. 7½	12/1	2s. 5	16/1	3s. 2½
2d	0 0½	2	0 10	2	1 7½	2	2 5¼	2	3 2¾
3d	0 0½	3	0 10¼	3	1 7¾	3	2 5½	3	3 3
4d	0 0¾	4	0 10½	4	1 8	4	2 5½	4	3 3¼
5d	0 1	5	0 10½	5	1 8¼	5	2 5¾	5	3 3½
6d	0 1¼	4/6	0 10¾	8/6	1 8½	12/6	2 6	16/6	3 3½
7d	0 1½	7	0 11	7	1 8½	7	2 6¼	7	3 3¾
8d	0 1½	8	0 11¼	8	1 8¾	8	2 6½	8	3 4
9d	0 1¾	9	0 11½	9	1 9	9	2 6½	9	3 4¼
10d	0 2	10	0 11½	10	1 9¼	10	2 6¾	10	3 4½
11d	0 2¼	11	0 11¾	11	1 9½	11	2 7	11	3 4½
1/-	0s. 2½	**5/-**	1s. 0	**9/-**	1s. 9½	**13/-**	2s. 7¼	**17/-**	3s. 4¾
1/1	0s. 2½	5/1	1s. 0¼	9/1	1s. 9¾	13/1	2s. 7½	17/1	3s. 5
2	0 2¾	2	1 0½	2	1 10	2	2 7½	2	3 5¼
3	0 3	3	1 0½	3	1 10¼	3	2 7¾	3	3 5½
4	0 3¼	4	1 0¾	4	1 10½	4	2 8	4	3 5½
5	0 3½	5	1 1	5	1 10½	5	2 8¼	5	3 5¾
1/6	0 3½	5/6	1 1¼	9/6	1 10¾	13/6	2 8½	17/6	3 6
7	0 3¾	7	1 1½	7	1 11	7	2 8½	7	3 6¼
8	0 4	8	1 1½	8	1 11¼	8	2 8¾	8	3 6½
9	0 4¼	9	1 1¾	9	1 11½	9	2 9	9	3 6½
10	0 4½	10	1 2	10	1 11½	10	2 9¼	10	3 6¾
11	0 4½	11	1 2¼	11	1 11¾	11	2 9½	11	3 7
2/-	0s. 4¾	**6/-**	1s. 2½	**10/-**	2s. 0	**14/-**	2s. 9½	**18/-**	3s. 7¼
2/1	0s. 5	6/1	1s. 2½	10/1	2s. 0¼	14/1	2s. 9¾	18/1	3s. 7½
2	0 5¼	2	1 2¾	2	2 0½	2	2 10	2	3 7½
3	0 5½	3	1 3	3	2 0½	3	2 10¼	3	3 7¾
4	0 5½	4	1 3¼	4	2 0¾	4	2 10½	4	3 8
5	0 5¾	5	1 3½	5	2 1	5	2 10½	5	3 8¼
2/6	0 6	6/6	1 3½	10/6	2 1¼	14/6	2 10¾	18/6	3 8½
7	0 6¼	7	1 3¾	7	2 1½	7	2 11	7	3 8½
8	0 6½	8	1 4	8	2 1½	8	2 11¼	8	3 8¾
9	0 6½	9	1 4¼	9	2 1¾	9	2 11½	9	3 9
10	0 6¾	10	1 4½	10	2 2	10	2 11½	10	3 9¼
11	0 7	11	1 4½	11	2 2¼	11	2 11¾	11	3 9½
3/-	0s. 7¼	**7/-**	1s. 4¾	**11/-**	2s. 2½	**15/-**	3s. 0	**19/-**	3s. 9½
3/1	0s. 7½	7/1	1s. 5	11/1	2s. 2½	15/1	3s. 0¼	19/1	3s. 9¾
2	0 7½	2	1 5¼	2	2 2¾	2	3 0½	2	3 10
3	0 7¾	3	1 5½	3	2 3	3	3 0½	3	3 10¼
4	0 8	4	1 5½	4	2 3¼	4	3 0¾	4	3 10½
5	0 8¼	5	1 5¾	5	2 3½	5	3 1	5	3 10½
3/6	0 8½	7/6	1 6	11/6	2 3½	15/6	3 1¼	19/6	3 10¾
7	0 8½	7	1 6¼	7	2 3¾	7	3 1½	7	3 11
8	0 8¾	8	1 6½	8	2 4	8	3 1½	8	3 11¼
9	0 9	9	1 6½	9	2 4¼	9	3 1¾	9	3 11½
10	0 9¼	10	1 6¾	10	2 4½	10	3 2	10	3 11½
11	0 9½	11	1 7	11	2 4½	11	3 2¼	11	3 11¾
4/-	0s. 9½	**8/-**	1s. 7¼	**12/-**	2s. 4¾	**16/-**	3s. 2½	**20/-**	4s. 0

20/6	4s. 1¼	25/6	5s. 1¼	31/-	6s. 2½	35/6	7s. 1¼	Guineas.	
21/-	4 2½	26/-	5 2½	31/6	6 3½	36/-	7 2½	1.	£0 4s. 2½
22/-	4 4¾	27/-	5 4¾	32/-	6 4¾	37/-	7 4¾	2.	0 8 4¾
22/6	4 6	27/6	5 6	32/6	6 6	37/6	7 6	3.	0 12 7¼
23/-	4 7¼	28/-	5 7¼	33/-	6 7¼	38/-	7 7¼	4.	0 16 9½
24/-	4 9½	29/-	5 9½	34/-	6 9½	39/-	7 9½	5.	1 1 0
25/-	5s. 0	**30/-**	6s. 0	**35/-**	7s. 0	**40/-**	8s. 0	6.	£1 5s. 2½

(16⅔% on Gross Returns).

£1	£0 4s 2½	£51	10 14s 2½	£101	21 4s 2½	£151	31 14s 2½
2	0 8 4¾	52	10 18 4¾	102	21 8 4¾	152	31 18 4¾
3	0 12 7¼	53	11 2 7¼	103	21 12 7¼	153	32 2 7¼
4	0 16 9½	54	11 6 9½	104	21 16 9½	154	32 6 9½
5	1 1 0	55	11 11 0	105	22 1 0	155	32 11 0
6	1 5 2½	56	11 15 2½	106	22 5 2½	156	32 15 2½
7	1 9 4¾	57	11 19 4¾	107	22 9 4¾	157	32 19 4¾
8	1 13 7¼	58	12 3 7¼	108	22 13 7¼	158	33 3 7¼
9	1 17 9½	59	12 7 9½	109	22 17 9½	159	33 7 9½
10	2 2 0	**60**	12 12 0	**110**	23 2 0	**160**	33 12 0
11	2 6 2½	61	12 16 2½	111	23 6 2½	161	33 16 2½
12	2 10 4¾	62	13 0 4¾	112	23 10 4¾	162	34 0 4¾
13	2 14 7¼	63	13 4 7¼	113	23 14 7¼	163	34 4 7¼
14	2 18 9½	64	13 8 9½	114	23 18 9½	164	34 8 9½
15	3 3 0	65	13 13 0	115	24 3 0	165	34 13 0
16	3 7 2½	66	13 17 2½	116	24 7 2½	166	34 17 2½
17	3 11 4¾	67	14 1 4¾	117	24 11 4¾	167	35 1 4¾
18	3 15 7¼	68	14 5 7¼	118	24 15 7¼	168	35 5 7¼
19	3 19 9½	69	14 9 9½	119	24 19 9½	169	35 9 9½
20	4 4 0	**70**	14 14 0	**120**	25 4 0	**170**	35 14 0
21	4 8 2½	71	14 18 2½	121	25 8 2½	171	35 18 2½
22	4 12 4¾	72	15 2 4¾	122	25 12 4¾	172	36 2 4¾
23	4 16 7¼	73	15 6 7¼	123	25 16 7¼	173	36 6 7¼
24	5 0 9½	74	15 10 9½	124	26 0 9½	174	36 10 9½
25	5 5 0	75	15 15 0	125	26 5 0	175	36 15 0
26	5 9 2½	76	15 19 2½	126	26 9 2½	176	36 19 2½
27	5 13 4¾	77	16 3 4¾	127	26 13 4¾	177	37 3 4¾
28	5 17 7¼	78	16 7 7¼	128	26 17 7¼	178	37 7 7¼
29	6 1 9½	79	16 11 9½	129	27 1 9½	179	37 11 9½
30	6 6 0	**80**	16 16 0	**130**	27 6 0	**180**	37 16 0
31	6 10 2½	81	17 0 2½	131	27 10 2½	181	38 0 2½
32	6 14 4¾	82	17 4 4¾	132	27 14 4¾	182	38 4 4¾
33	6 18 7¼	83	17 8 7¼	133	27 18 7¼	183	38 8 7¼
34	7 2 9½	84	17 12 9½	134	28 2 9½	184	38 12 9½
35	7 7 0	85	17 17 0	135	28 7 0	185	38 17 0
36	7 11 2½	86	18 1 2½	136	28 11 2½	186	39 1 2½
37	7 15 4¾	87	18 5 4¾	137	28 15 4¾	187	39 5 4¾
38	7 19 7¼	88	18 9 7¼	138	28 19 7¼	188	39 9 7¼
39	8 3 9½	89	18 13 9½	139	29 3 9½	189	39 13 9½
40	8 8 0	**90**	18 18 0	**140**	29 8 0	**190**	39 18 0
41	8 12 2½	91	19 2 2½	141	29 12 2½	191	40 2 2½
42	8 16 4¾	92	19 6 4¾	142	29 16 4¾	192	40 6 4¾
43	9 0 7¼	93	19 10 7¼	143	30 0 7¼	193	40 10 7¼
44	9 4 9½	94	19 14 9½	144	30 4 9½	194	40 14 9½
45	9 9 0	95	19 19 0	145	30 9 0	195	40 19 0
46	9 13 2½	96	20 3 2½	146	30 13 2½	196	41 3 2½
47	9 17 4¾	97	20 7 4¾	147	30 17 4¾	197	41 7 4¾
48	10 1 7¼	98	20 11 7¼	148	31 1 7¼	198	41 11 7¼
49	10 5 9½	99	20 15 9½	149	31 5 9½	199	41 15 9½
50	10 10 0	**100**	21 0 0	**150**	31 10 0	**200**	42 0 0

250	52 10s 0d	700	147 0s 0d	1200	252 0s 0d	2000	420 0s 0d
300	63 0 0	750	157 10 0	1400	294 0 0	2500	525 0 0
400	84 0 0	800	168 0 0	1500	315 0 0	3000	630 0 0
500	105 0 0	900	189 0 0	1600	336 0 0	4000	840 0 0
600	126 0s 0d	1000	210 0s 0d	1800	378 0s 0d	5000	1050 0s 0

79% off

21% **21 PER CENT.** 21%

1d	0s	0¼	4/1	0s	10¼	8/1	1s	8¼	12/1	2s	6½	16/1	3s	4½
2d	0	0½	2	0	10½	2	1	8½	2	2	6¾	2	3	4¾
3d	0	0¾	3	0	10¾	3	1	8¾	3	2	6¾	3	3	5
4d	0	0¾	4	0	11	4	1	9	4	2	7	4	3	5¼
5d	0	1	5	0	11¼	5	1	9¼	5	2	7¼	5	3	5¼
6d	0	1¼	4/6	0	11¼	8/6	1	9½	12/6	2	7½	16/6	3	5½
7d	0	1½	7	0	11½	7	1	9¾	7	2	7¾	7	3	5¾
8d	0	1¾	8	0	11¾	8	1	9¾	8	2	8	8	3	6
9d	0	2	9	1	0	9	1	10	9	2	8¼	9	3	6¼
10d	0	2	10	1	0¼	10	1	10¼	10	2	8¼	10	3	6½
11d	0	2¼	11	1	0½	11	1	10½	11	2	8½	11	3	6¾
1/-	**0**	**2½**	**5/-**	**1**	**0½**	**9/-**	**1**	**10¾**	**13/-**	**2**	**8¾**	**17/-**	**3**	**6¾**
1/1	0	2¾	5/1	1	0¾	9/1	1	11	13/1	2	9	17/1	3	7
2	0	3	2	1	1	2	1	11	2	2	9¼	2	3	7¼
3	0	3¼	3	1	1¼	3	1	11¼	3	2	9½	3	3	7½
4	0	3¼	4	1	1½	4	1	11½	4	2	9½	4	3	7¾
5	0	3½	5	1	1¾	5	1	11¾	5	2	9¾	5	3	8
1/6	0	3¾	5/6	1	1¾	9/6	2	0	13/6	2	10	17/6	3	8
7	0	4	7	1	2	7	2	0¼	7	2	10¼	7	3	8¼
8	0	4¼	8	1	2¼	8	2	0¼	8	2	10½	8	3	8½
9	0	4½	9	1	2½	9	2	0½	9	2	10¾	9	3	8¾
10	0	4½	10	1	2¾	10	2	0¾	10	2	10¾	10	3	9
11	0	4¾	11	1	3	11	2	1	11	2	11	11	3	9¼
2/-	**0**	**5**	**6/-**	**1**	**3**	**10/-**	**2**	**1¼**	**14/-**	**2**	**11¼**	**18/-**	**3**	**9¼**
2/1	0	5¼	6/1	1	3¼	10/1	2	1½	14/1	2	11½	18/1	3	9½
2	0	5½	2	1	3½	2	2	1½	2	2	11¾	2	3	9¾
3	0	5¾	3	1	3¾	3	2	1¾	3	3	0	3	3	10
4	0	6	4	1	4	4	2	2	4	3	0	4	3	10¼
5	0	6	5	1	4¼	5	2	2¼	5	3	0¼	5	3	10½
2/6	0	6¼	6/6	1	4½	10/6	2	2½	14/6	3	0½	18/6	3	10½
7	0	6½	7	1	4½	7	2	2¾	7	3	0¾	7	3	10¾
8	0	6¾	8	1	4¾	8	2	3	8	3	1	8	3	11
9	0	7	9	1	5	9	2	3	9	3	1¼	9	3	11¼
10	0	7¼	10	1	5¼	10	2	3¼	10	3	1½	10	3	11½
11	0	7¼	11	1	5½	11	2	3½	11	3	1½	11	3	11¾
3/-	**0**	**7½**	**7/-**	**1**	**5¾**	**11/-**	**2**	**3¾**	**15/-**	**3**	**1¾**	**19/-**	**4**	**0**
3/1	0	7¾	7/1	1	5¾	11/1	2	4	15/1	3	2	19/1	4	0
2	0	8	2	1	6	2	2	4¼	2	3	2¼	2	4	0¼
3	0	8¼	3	1	6¼	3	2	4¼	3	3	2½	3	4	0½
4	0	8½	4	1	6½	4	2	4½	4	3	2¾	4	4	0¾
5	0	8½	5	1	6¾	5	2	4¾	5	3	2¾	5	4	1
3/6	0	8¾	7/6	1	7	11/6	2	5	15/6	3	3	19/6	4	1¼
7	0	9	7	1	7	7	2	5¼	7	3	3¼	7	4	1¼
8	0	9¼	8	1	7¼	8	2	5½	8	3	3½	8	4	1½
9	0	9½	9	1	7½	9	2	5½	9	3	3¾	9	4	1¾
10	0	9¾	10	1	7¾	10	2	5¾	10	3	4	10	4	2
11	0	9¾	11	1	8	11	2	6	11	3	4	11	4	2¼
4/-	**0**	**10**	**8/-**	**1**	**8¼**	**12/-**	**2**	**6¼**	**16/-**	**3**	**4¼**	**20/-**	**4**	**2½**

20/6	4s	3¾	25/6	5s	4¼	31/-	6s	6	35/6	7s	5½	Guineas			
21/-	4	5	26/-	5	5½	31/6	6	7½	36/-	7	6¾	1.	£0	4	5
22/-	4	7½	27/-	5	8	32/-	6	8¾	37/-	7	9¼	2.	0	8	9¾
22/6	4	8¾	27/6	5	9¼	32/6	6	10	37/6	7	10½	3.	0	13	2¾
23/-	4	10	28/-	5	10½	33/-	6	11¼	38/-	7	11¾	4.	0	17	7¾
24/-	5	0½	29/-	6	1	34/-	7	1¾	39/-	8	2¼	5.	1	2	0½
25/-	5s	3	**30/-**	6s	3½	**35/-**	7s	4¼	**40/-**	8s	4¾	6.	£1	6	5½

(=17 4/10% on Gross Returns).

£1	£0	4s	4¾	£51	11	4s	4¾	£101	22	4s	4¾	£151	33	4s	4¾
2	0	8	9½	52	11	8	9½	102	22	8	9½	152	33	8	9½
3	0	13	2½	53	11	13	2½	103	22	13	2½	153	33	13	2½
4	0	17	7¼	54	11	17	7¼	104	22	17	7¼	154	33	17	7¼
5	1	2	0	55	12	2	0	105	23	2	0	155	34	2	0
6	1	6	4¾	56	12	6	4¾	106	23	6	4¾	156	34	6	4¾
7	1	10	9½	57	12	10	9½	107	23	10	9½	157	34	10	9½
8	1	15	2½	58	12	15	2½	108	23	15	2½	158	34	15	2½
9	1	19	7¼	59	12	19	7¼	109	23	19	7¼	159	34	19	7¼
10	**2**	**4**	**0**	**60**	**13**	**4**	**0**	**110**	**24**	**4**	**0**	**160**	**35**	**4**	**0**
11	2	8	4¾	61	13	8	4¾	111	24	8	4¾	161	35	8	4¾
12	2	12	9½	62	13	12	9½	112	24	12	9½	162	35	12	9½
13	2	17	2½	63	13	17	2½	113	24	17	2½	163	35	17	2½
14	3	1	7¼	64	14	1	7¼	114	25	1	7¼	164	36	1	7¼
15	3	6	0	65	14	6	0	115	25	6	0	165	36	6	0
16	3	10	4¾	66	14	10	4¾	116	25	10	4¾	166	36	10	4¾
17	3	14	9½	67	14	14	9½	117	25	14	9½	167	36	14	9½
18	3	19	2½	68	14	19	2½	118	25	19	2½	168	36	19	2½
19	4	3	7¼	69	15	3	7¼	119	26	3	7¼	169	37	3	7¼
20	**4**	**8**	**0**	**70**	**15**	**8**	**0**	**120**	**26**	**8**	**0**	**170**	**37**	**8**	**0**
21	4	12	4¾	71	15	12	4¾	121	26	12	4¾	171	37	12	4¾
22	4	16	9½	72	15	16	9½	122	26	16	9½	172	37	16	9½
23	5	1	2½	73	16	1	2½	123	27	1	2½	173	38	1	2½
24	5	5	7¼	74	16	5	7¼	124	27	5	7¼	174	38	5	7¼
25	5	10	0	75	16	10	0	125	27	10	0	175	38	10	0
26	5	14	4¾	76	16	14	4¾	126	27	14	4¾	176	38	14	4¾
27	5	18	9½	77	16	18	9½	127	27	18	9½	177	38	18	9½
28	6	3	2½	78	17	3	2½	128	28	3	2½	178	39	3	2½
29	6	7	7¼	79	17	7	7¼	129	28	7	7¼	179	39	7	7¼
30	**6**	**12**	**0**	**80**	**17**	**12**	**0**	**130**	**28**	**12**	**0**	**180**	**39**	**12**	**0**
31	6	16	4¾	81	17	16	4¾	131	28	16	4¾	181	39	16	4¾
32	7	0	9½	82	18	0	9½	132	29	0	9½	182	40	0	9½
33	7	5	2½	83	18	5	2½	133	29	5	2½	183	40	5	2½
34	7	9	7¼	84	18	9	7¼	134	29	9	7¼	184	40	9	7¼
35	7	14	0	85	18	14	0	135	29	14	0	185	40	14	0
36	7	18	4¾	86	18	18	4¾	136	29	18	4¾	186	40	18	4¾
37	8	2	9½	87	19	2	9½	137	30	2	9½	187	41	2	9½
38	8	7	2½	88	19	7	2½	138	30	7	2½	188	41	7	2½
39	8	11	7¼	89	19	11	7¼	139	30	11	7¼	189	41	11	7¼
40	**8**	**16**	**0**	**90**	**19**	**16**	**0**	**140**	**30**	**16**	**0**	**190**	**41**	**16**	**0**
41	9	0	4¾	91	20	0	4¾	141	31	0	4¾	191	42	0	4¾
42	9	4	9½	92	20	4	9½	142	31	4	9½	192	42	4	9½
43	9	9	2½	93	20	9	2½	143	31	9	2½	193	42	9	2½
44	9	13	7¼	94	20	13	7¼	144	31	13	7¼	194	42	13	7¼
45	9	18	0	95	20	18	0	145	31	18	0	195	42	18	0
46	10	2	4¾	96	21	2	4¾	146	32	2	4¾	196	43	2	4¾
47	10	6	9½	97	21	6	9½	147	32	6	9½	197	43	6	9½
48	10	11	2½	98	21	11	2½	148	32	11	2½	198	43	11	2½
49	10	15	7¼	99	21	15	7¼	149	32	15	7¼	199	43	15	7¼
50	**11**	**0**	**0**	**100**	**22**	**0**	**0**	**150**	**33**	**0**	**0**	**200**	**44**	**0**	**0**

250	55	0s	0d	700	154	0s	0d	1200	264	0s	0d	2000	440	0s	0
300	66	0	0	750	165	0	0	1400	308	0	0	2500	550	0	0
400	88	0	0	800	176	0	0	1500	330	0	0	3000	660	0	0
500	110	0	0	900	198	0	0	1600	352	0	0	4000	880	0	0
600	132	0s	0d	1000	220	0s	0d	1800	396	0s	0d	5000	1100	0s	0

78% off

22 Per Cent.

1d	0s	0¼	4/1	0s	10¾	8/1	1s	9¼	12/1	2s	8	16/1	3s	6½
2d	0	0½	2	0	11	2	1	9½	2	2	8	2	3	6¾
3d	0	0¾	3	0	11¼	3	1	9¾	3	2	8¼	3	3	7
4d	0	1	4	0	11½	4	1	10	4	2	8½	4	3	7
5d	0	1	5	0	11¾	5	1	10¼	5	2	8¾	5	3	7¼
6d	0	1¼	4/6	1	0	8/6	1	10½	12/6	2	9	16/6	3	7½
7d	0	1½	7	1	0	7	1	10¾	7	2	9¼	7	3	7¾
8d	0	1¾	8	1	0¼	8	1	11	8	2	9½	8	3	8
9d	0	2	9	1	0½	9	1	11	9	2	9¾	9	3	8¼
10d	0	2¼	10	1	0¾	10	1	11¼	10	2	10	10	3	8½
11d	0	2½	11	1	1	11	1	11½	11	2	10	11	3	8¾
1/-	**0**	**2¾**	**5/-**	**1**	**1¼**	**9/-**	**1**	**11¾**	**13/-**	**2**	**10¼**	**17/-**	**3**	**9**
1/1	0	2¾	5/1	1	1½	9/1	2	0	13/1	2	10½	17/1	3	9
2	0	3	2	1	1¾	2	2	0¼	2	2	10¾	2	3	9¼
3	0	3¼	3	1	1¾	3	2	0½	3	2	11	3	3	9½
4	0	3½	4	1	2	4	2	0¾	4	2	11¼	4	3	9¾
5	0	3¾	5	1	2¼	5	2	0¾	5	2	11½	5	3	10
1/6	0	4	5/6	1	2½	9/6	2	1	13/6	2	11¾	17/6	3	10¼
7	0	4¼	7	1	2¾	7	2	1¼	7	2	11¾	7	3	10½
8	0	4½	8	1	3	8	2	1½	8	3	0	8	3	10¾
9	0	4½	9	1	3¼	9	2	1¾	9	3	0¼	9	3	10¾
10	0	4¾	10	1	3½	10	2	2	10	3	0½	10	3	11
11	0	5	11	1	3½	11	2	2¼	11	3	0¾	11	3	11¼
2/-	**0**	**5¼**	**6/-**	**1**	**3¾**	**10/-**	**2**	**2½**	**14/-**	**3**	**1**	**18/-**	**3**	**11½**
2/1	0	5½	6/1	1	4	10/1	2	2½	14/1	3	1¼	18/1	3	11¾
2	0	5¾	2	1	4¼	2	2	2¾	2	3	1½	2	4	0
3	0	6	3	1	4½	3	2	3	3	3	1½	3	4	0¼
4	0	6¼	4	1	4¾	4	2	3¼	4	3	1¾	4	4	0½
5	0	6½	5	1	5	5	2	3½	5	3	2	5	4	0½
2/6	0	6½	6/6	1	5¼	10/6	2	3¾	14/6	3	2¼	18/6	4	0¾
7	0	6¾	7	1	5½	7	2	4	7	3	2½	7	4	1
8	0	7	8	1	5½	8	2	4¼	8	3	2¾	8	4	1¼
9	0	7¼	9	1	5¾	9	2	4½	9	3	3	9	4	1½
10	0	7½	10	1	6	10	2	4½	10	3	3¼	10	4	1¾
11	0	7¾	11	1	6¼	11	2	4¾	11	3	3½	11	4	2
3/-	**0**	**8**	**7/-**	**1**	**6½**	**11/-**	**2**	**5**	**15/-**	**3**	**3½**	**19/-**	**4**	**2¼**
3/1	0	8¼	7/1	1	6¾	11/1	2	5¼	15/1	3	3¾	19/1	4	2½
2	0	8¼	2	1	7	2	2	5½	2	3	4	2	4	2½
3	0	8½	3	1	7¼	3	2	5¾	3	3	4¼	3	4	2¾
4	0	8¾	4	1	7¼	4	2	6	4	3	4½	4	4	3
5	0	9	5	1	7½	5	2	6¼	5	3	4¾	5	4	3¼
3/6	0	9¼	7/6	1	7¾	11/6	2	6¼	15/6	3	5	19/6	4	3½
7	0	9½	7	1	8	7	2	6½	7	3	5¼	7	4	3¾
8	0	9¾	8	1	8¼	8	2	6¾	8	3	5¼	8	4	4
9	0	10	9	1	8½	9	2	7	9	3	5½	9	4	4¼
10	0	10	10	1	8¾	10	2	7¼	10	3	5¾	10	4	4¼
11	0	10¼	11	1	9	11	2	7½	11	3	6	11	4	4½
4/-	**0**	**10½**	**8/-**	**1**	**9**	**12/-**	**2**	**7¾**	**16/-**	**3**	**6¼**	**20/-**	**4**	**4¾**

20/6	4s	6	25/6	5s	7¼	31/-	6s	9¾	35/6	7s	9¾	Guineas		
21/-	4	7½	26/-	5	8¾	31/6	6	11¼	36/-	7	11	1. £0	4	7½
22/-	4	10	27/-	5	11¼	32/-	7	0½	37/-	8	1¾	2. 0	9	3
22/6	4	11½	27/6	6	0½	32/6	7	1¾	37/6	8	3	3. 0	13	10¼
23/-	5	0¾	28/-	6	2	33/-	7	3	38/-	8	4¼	4. 0	18	5¾
24/-	5	3¼	29/-	6	4½	34/-	7	5¾	39/-	8	7	5. 1	3	1¼
25/-	5s	6	**30/-**	6s	7¼	**35/-**	7s	8½	**40/-**	8s	9½	6. £1	7	8¾

(=18% on Gross Returns).

£		s.	d.	£		s.	d.	£		s.	d.	£		s.	d.
£1	£0	4s.	6	£51	11	9s.	6	£101	£22	14s.	6	£151	£33	19s.	6
2	0	9	0	52	11	14	0	102	22	19	0	152	34	4	0
3	0	13	6	53	11	18	6	103	23	3	6	153	34	8	6
4	0	18	0	54	12	3	0	104	23	8	0	154	34	13	0
5	1	2	6	55	12	7	6	105	23	12	6	155	34	17	6
6	1	7	0	56	12	12	0	106	23	17	0	156	35	2	0
7	1	11	6	57	12	16	6	107	24	1	6	157	35	6	6
8	1	16	0	58	13	1	0	108	24	6	0	158	35	11	0
9	2	0	6	59	13	5	6	109	24	10	6	159	35	15	6
10	£2	5s.	0	60	13	10s.	0	110	£24	15s.	0	160	£36	0s.	0
11	£2	9s.	6	61	13	14s.	6	111	£24	19s.	6	161	£36	4s.	6
12	2	14	0	62	13	19	0	112	25	4	0	162	36	9	0
13	2	18	6	63	14	3	6	113	25	8	6	163	36	13	6
14	3	3	0	64	14	8	0	114	25	13	0	164	36	18	0
15	3	7	6	65	14	12	6	115	25	17	6	165	37	2	6
16	3	12	0	66	14	17	0	116	26	2	0	166	37	7	0
17	3	16	6	67	15	1	6	117	26	6	6	167	37	11	6
18	4	1	0	68	15	6	0	118	26	11	0	168	37	16	0
19	4	5	6	69	15	10	6	119	26	15	6	169	38	0	6
20	£4	10s.	0	70	15	15s.	0	120	£27	0s.	0	170	£38	5s.	0
21	£4	14s.	6	71	15	19s.	6	121	£27	4s.	6	171	£38	9s.	6
22	4	19	0	72	16	4	0	122	27	9	0	172	38	14	0
23	5	3	6	73	16	8	6	123	27	13	6	173	38	18	6
24	5	8	0	74	16	13	0	124	27	18	0	174	39	3	0
25	5	12	6	75	16	17	6	125	28	2	6	175	39	7	6
26	5	17	0	76	17	2	0	126	28	7	0	176	39	12	0
27	6	1	6	77	17	6	6	127	28	11	6	177	39	16	6
28	6	6	0	78	17	11	0	128	28	16	0	178	40	1	0
29	6	10	6	79	17	15	6	129	29	0	6	179	40	5	6
30	£6	15s.	0	80	18	0s.	0	130	£29	5s.	0	180	£40	10s.	0
31	£6	19s.	6	81	18	4s.	6	131	£29	9s.	6	181	£40	14s.	6
32	7	4	0	82	18	9	0	132	29	14	0	182	40	19	0
33	7	8	6	83	18	13	6	133	29	18	6	183	41	3	6
34	7	13	0	84	18	18	0	134	30	3	0	184	41	8	0
35	7	17	6	85	19	2	6	135	30	7	6	185	41	12	6
36	8	2	0	86	19	7	0	136	30	12	0	186	41	17	0
37	8	6	6	87	19	11	6	137	30	16	6	187	42	1	6
38	8	11	0	88	19	16	0	138	31	1	0	188	42	6	0
39	8	15	6	89	20	0	6	139	31	5	6	189	42	10	6
40	£9	0s.	0	90	20	5s.	0	140	£31	10s.	0	190	£42	15s.	0
41	£9	4s.	6	91	20	9s.	6	141	£31	14s.	6	191	£42	19s.	6
42	9	9	0	92	20	14	0	142	31	19	0	192	43	4	0
43	9	13	6	93	20	18	6	143	32	3	6	193	43	8	6
44	9	18	0	94	21	3	0	144	32	8	0	194	43	13	0
45	10	2	6	95	21	7	6	145	32	12	6	195	43	17	6
46	10	7	0	96	21	12	0	146	32	17	0	196	44	2	0
47	10	11	6	97	21	16	6	147	33	1	6	197	44	6	6
48	10	16	0	98	22	1	0	148	33	6	0	198	44	11	0
49	11	0	6	99	22	5	6	149	33	10	6	199	44	15	6
50	11	5s.	0	100	22	10s.	0	150	£33	15s.	0	200	£45	0s.	0

250	£56 5s. 0d	700	157 10s.0d	1200	270 0s.0d	2000	£450 0s. 0
300	67 10 0	750	168 15 0	1400	315 0 0	2500	562 10 0
400	90 0 0	800	180 0 0	1500	337 10 0	3000	675 0 0
500	112 10 0	900	202 10 0	1600	360 0 0	4000	900 0 0
600	135 0s.0d	1000	225 0s.0d	1800	405 0s.0d	5000	£1125 0s. 0

77½% off.

1d	0s. 0¼	4/1	0s.11	8/1	1s. 9¾	12/1	2s. 8¾	16/1	3s. 7½
2d	0 0½	2	0 11¼	2	1 10	2	2 8¾	2	3 7¾
3d	0 0¾	3	0 11½	3	1 10¼	3	2 9	3	3 8
4d	0 1	4	0 11¾	4	1 10½	4	2 9¼	4	3 8
5d	0 1¼	5	1 0	5	1 10¾	5	2 9½	5	3 8¼
6d	0 1¼	4/6	1 0¼	8/6	1 11	12/6	2 9¾	16/6	3 8½
7d	0 1½	7	1 0½	7	1 11¼	7	2 10	7	3 8¾
8d	0 1¾	8	1 0½	8	1 11½	8	2 10¼	8	3 9
9d	0 2	9	1 0¾	9	1 11¾	9	2 10½	9	3 9¼
10d	0 2¼	10	1 1	10	1 11¾	10	2 10¾	10	3 9½
11d	0 2½	11	1 1¼	11	2 0	11	2 11	11	3 9¾
1/-	0s. 2¾	**5/-**	1s. 1½	**9/-**	2s. 0¼	**13/-**	2s.11	**17/-**	3s.10
1/1	0s. 3	5/1	1s. 1¾	9/1	2s. 0½	13/1	2s.11¼	17/1	3s.10¼
2	0 3¼	2	1 2	2	2 0¾	2	2 11½	2	3 10¼
3	0 3½	3	1 2¼	3	2 1	3	2 11¾	3	3 10½
4	0 3½	4	1 2½	4	2 1¼	4	3 0	4	3 10¾
5	0 3¾	5	1 2¾	5	2 1½	5	3 0¼	5	3 11
1/6	0 4	5/6	1 2¾	9/6	2 1¾	13/6	3 0½	17/6	3 11¼
7	0 4¼	7	1 3	7	2 2	7	3 0¾	7	3 11½
8	0 4½	8	1 3¼	8	2 2	8	3 1	8	3 11¾
9	0 4¾	9	1 3½	9	2 2¼	9	3 1¼	9	4 0
10	0 5	10	1 3¾	10	2 2½	10	3 1¼	10	4 0¼
11	0 5¼	11	1 4	11	2 2¾	11	3 1½	11	4 0½
2/-	0s. 5½	**6/-**	1s. 4¼	**10/-**	2s. 3	**14/-**	3s. 1¾	**18/-**	4s. 0½
2/1	0s. 5¾	6/1	1s. 4½	10/1	2s. 3¼	14/1	3s. 2	18/1	4s. 0¾
2	0 5¾	2	1 4¾	2	2 3½	2	3 2¼	2	4 1
3	0 6	3	1 5	3	2 3¾	3	3 2½	3	4 1¼
4	0 6¼	4	1 5	4	2 4	4	3 2¾	4	4 1½
5	0 6½	5	1 5¼	5	2 4¼	5	3 3	5	4 1¾
2/6	0 6¾	6/6	1 5½	10/6	2 4¼	14/6	3 3¼	18/6	4 2
7	0 7	7	1 5¾	7	2 4½	7	3 3½	7	4 2¼
8	0 7¼	8	1 6	8	2 4¾	8	3 3½	8	4 2½
9	0 7½	9	1 6¼	9	2 5	9	3 3¾	9	4 2¾
10	0 7¾	10	1 6½	10	2 5¼	10	3 4	10	4 2¾
11	0 8	11	1 6¾	11	2 5½	11	3 4¼	11	4 3
3/-	0s. 8	**7/-**	1s. 7	**11/-**	2s. 5¾	**15/-**	3s. 4½	**19/-**	4s. 3¼
3/1	0s. 8¼	7/1	1s. 7¼	11/1	2s. 6	15/1	3s. 4¾	19/1	4s. 3½
2	0 8½	2	1 7¼	2	2 6¼	2	3 5	2	4 3¾
3	0 8¾	3	1 7½	3	2 6½	3	3 5¼	3	4 4
4	0 9	4	1 7¾	4	2 6½	4	3 5½	4	4 4¼
5	0 9¼	5	1 8	5	2 6¾	5	3 5¾	5	4 4½
3/6	0 9½	7/6	1 8¼	11/6	2 7	15/6	3 5¾	19/6	4 4¾
7	0 9¾	7	1 8½	7	2 7¼	7	3 6	7	4 5
8	0 10	8	1 8¾	8	2 7½	8	3 6¼	8	4 5
9	0 10¼	9	1 9	9	2 7¾	9	3 6½	9	4 5¼
10	0 10¼	10	1 9¼	10	2 8	10	3 6¾	10	4 5½
11	0 10½	11	1 9½	11	2 8¼	11	3 7	11	4 5¾
4/-	0s.10¾	**8/-**	1s. 9½	**12/-**	2s. 8½	**16/-**	3s. 7¼	**20/-**	4s. 6

20/6	4s. 7¼	25/6	5s. 8¾	31/-	6s. 11¾	35/6	7s.11¾	Guineas.	
21/-	4 8¾	26/-	5 10¼	31/6	7 1	36/-	8 1¼	1.	£0 4s. 8¾
22/-	4 11½	27/-	6 1	32/-	7 2½	37/-	8 4	2.	0 9 5½
22/6	5 0¾	27/6	6 2¼	32/6	7 3¾	37/6	8 5¼	3.	0 14 2
23/-	5 2	28/-	6 3½	33/-	7 5	38/-	8 6½	4.	0 18 10¾
24/-	5 4¾	29/-	6 6¼	34/-	7 7¾	39/-	8 9¼	5.	1 3 7½
25/-	5s. 7½	**30/-**	6s. 9	**35/-**	7s. 10½	**40/-**	9s. 0	6.	£1 8s. 4¼

(=18$\frac{4}{10}$%* on Gross Returns).

£		£		£		£	
£1	£0 4s 7¼	£51	11 14s 7¼	£101	23 4s 7¼	£151	34 14s 7¼
2	0 9 2½	52	11 19 2½	102	23 9 2½	152	34 19 2½
3	0 13 9½	53	12 3 9½	103	23 13 9½	153	35 3 9½
4	0 18 4¾	54	12 8 4¾	104	23 18 4¾	154	35 8 4¾
5	1 3 0	55	12 13 0	105	24 3 0	155	35 13 0
6	1 7 7¼	56	12 17 7¼	106	24 7 7¼	156	35 17 7¼
7	1 12 2½	57	13 2 2½	107	24 12 2½	157	36 2 2½
8	1 16 9½	58	13 6 9½	108	24 16 9½	158	36 6 9½
9	2 1 4¾	59	13 11 4¾	109	25 1 4¾	159	36 11 4¾
10	2 6 0	60	13 16 0	110	25 6 0	160	36 16 0
11	2 10 7¼	61	14 0 7¼	111	25 10 7¼	161	37 0 7¼
12	2 15 2½	62	14 5 2½	112	25 15 2½	162	37 5 2½
13	2 19 9½	63	14 9 9½	113	25 19 9½	163	37 9 9½
14	3 4 4¾	64	14 14 4¾	114	26 4 4¾	164	37 14 4¾
15	3 9 0	65	14 19 0	115	26 9 0	165	37 19 0
16	3 13 7¼	66	15 3 7¼	116	26 13 7¼	166	38 3 7¼
17	3 18 2½	67	15 8 2½	117	26 18 2½	167	38 8 2½
18	4 2 9½	68	15 12 9½	118	27 2 9½	168	38 12 9½
19	4 7 4¾	69	15 17 4¾	119	27 7 4¾	169	38 17 4¾
20	4 12 0	70	16 2 0	120	27 12 0	170	39 2 0
21	4 16 7¼	71	16 6 7¼	121	27 16 7¼	171	39 6 7¼
22	5 1 2½	72	16 11 2½	122	28 1 2½	172	39 11 2½
23	5 5 9½	73	16 15 9½	123	28 5 9½	173	39 15 9½
24	5 10 4¾	74	17 0 4¾	124	28 10 4¾	174	40 0 4¾
25	5 15 0	75	17 5 0	125	28 15 0	175	40 5 0
26	5 19 7¼	76	17 9 7¼	126	28 19 7¼	176	40 9 7¼
27	6 4 2½	77	17 14 2½	127	29 4 2½	177	40 14 2½
28	6 8 9½	78	17 18 9½	128	29 8 9½	178	40 18 9½
29	6 13 4¾	79	18 3 4¾	129	29 13 4¾	179	41 3 4¾
30	6 18 0	80	18 8 0	130	29 18 0	180	41 8 0
31	7 2 7¼	81	18 12 7¼	131	30 2 7¼	181	41 12 7¼
32	7 7 2½	82	18 17 2½	132	30 7 2½	182	41 17 2½
33	7 11 9½	83	19 1 9½	133	30 11 9½	183	42 1 9½
34	7 16 4¾	84	19 6 4¾	134	30 16 4¾	184	42 6 4¾
35	8 1 0	85	19 11 0	135	31 1 0	185	42 11 0
36	8 5 7¼	86	19 15 7¼	136	31 5 7¼	186	42 15 7¼
37	8 10 2½	87	20 0 2½	137	31 10 2½	187	43 0 2½
38	8 14 9½	88	20 4 9½	138	31 14 9½	188	43 4 9½
39	8 19 4¾	89	20 9 4¾	139	31 19 4¾	189	43 9 4¾
40	9 4 0	90	20 14 0	140	32 4 0	190	43 14 0
41	9 8 7¼	91	20 18 7¼	141	32 8 7¼	191	43 18 7¼
42	9 13 2½	92	21 3 2½	142	32 13 2½	192	44 3 2½
43	9 17 9½	93	21 7 9½	143	32 17 9½	193	44 7 9½
44	10 2 4¾	94	21 12 4¾	144	33 2 4¾	194	44 12 4¾
45	10 7 0	95	21 17 0	145	33 7 0	195	44 17 0
46	10 11 7¼	96	22 1 7¼	146	33 11 7¼	196	45 1 7¼
47	10 16 2½	97	22 6 2½	147	33 16 2½	197	45 6 2½
48	11 0 9½	98	22 10 9½	148	34 0 9½	198	45 10 9½
49	11 5 4¾	99	22 15 4¾	149	34 5 4¾	199	45 15 4¾
50	11 10 0	100	23 0 0	150	34 10 0	200	46 0 0

£		£		£		£	
250	57 10s 0d	700	161 0s 0d	1200	276 0s 0d	2000	460 0s 0d
300	69 0 0	750	172 10 0	1400	322 0 0	2500	575 0 0
400	92 0 0	800	184 0 0	1500	345 0 0	3000	690 0 0
500	115 0 0	900	207 0 0	1600	368 0 0	4000	920 0 0
600	138 0s 0d	1000	230 0s 0d	1800	414 0s 0d	5000	1150 0s 0

77% off

23% — 23 Per Cent. — 23%

1d	0s	0¼	4/1	0s	11¼	8/1	1s	10¼	12/1	2s	9¼	16/1	3s	8½
2d	0	0½	2	0	11½	2	1	10½	2	2	9½	2	3	8½
3d	0	0¾	3	0	11¾	3	1	10¾	3	2	9¾	3	3	8¾
4d	0	1	4	1	0	4	1	11	4	2	10	4	3	9
5d	0	1¼	5	1	0¼	5	1	11¼	5	2	10¼	5	3	9¼
6d	0	1½	4/6	1	0½	8/6	1	11½	12/6	2	10½	16/6	3	9½
7d	0	1½	7	1	0¾	7	1	11¾	7	2	10¾	7	3	9¾
8d	0	1¾	8	1	1	8	2	0	8	2	11	8	3	10
9d	0	2	9	1	1	9	2	0¼	9	2	11¼	9	3	10¼
10d	0	2¼	10	1	1¼	10	2	0½	10	2	11½	10	3	10½
11d	0	2½	11	1	1½	11	2	0½	11	2	11¾	11	3	10¾
1/-	**0**	**2¾**	**5/-**	**1**	**1¾**	**9/-**	**2**	**0¾**	**13/-**	**3**	**0**	**17/-**	**3**	**11**
1/1	0	3	5/1	1	2	9/1	2	1	13/1	3	0	17/1	3	11¼
2	0	3¼	2	1	2¼	2	2	1¼	2	3	0¼	2	3	11½
3	0	3½	3	1	2½	3	2	1½	3	3	0½	3	3	11½
4	0	3¾	4	1	2¾	4	2	1¾	4	3	0¾	4	3	11¾
5	0	4	5	1	3	5	2	2	5	3	1	5	4	0
1/6	0	4¼	5/6	1	3¼	9/6	2	2¼	13/6	3	1¼	17/6	4	0¼
7	0	4¼	7	1	3½	7	2	2½	7	3	1½	7	4	0½
8	0	4½	8	1	3¾	8	2	2¾	8	3	1¾	8	4	0¾
9	0	4¾	9	1	3¾	9	2	3	9	3	2	9	4	1
10	0	5	10	1	4	10	2	3¼	10	3	2¼	10	4	1¼
11	0	5¼	11	1	4¼	11	2	3¼	11	3	2½	11	4	1½
2/-	**0**	**5½**	**6/-**	**1**	**4½**	**10/-**	**2**	**3½**	**14/-**	**3**	**2¾**	**18/-**	**4**	**1¾**
2/1	0	5¾	6/1	1	4¾	10/1	2	3¾	14/1	3	2¾	18/1	4	2
2	0	6	2	1	5	2	2	4	2	3	3	2	4	2¼
3	0	6¼	3	1	5¼	3	2	4¼	3	3	3¼	3	4	2½
4	0	6½	4	1	5½	4	2	4½	4	3	3½	4	4	2¾
5	0	6¾	5	1	5¾	5	2	4¾	5	3	3¾	5	4	2¾
2/6	0	7	6/6	1	6	10/6	2	5	14/6	3	4	18/6	4	3
7	0	7¼	7	1	6¼	7	2	5¼	7	3	4¼	7	4	3¼
8	0	7¼	8	1	6½	8	2	5½	8	3	4½	8	4	3½
9	0	7½	9	1	6¾	9	2	5¾	9	3	4¾	9	4	3¾
10	0	7¾	10	1	6¾	10	2	6	10	3	5	10	4	4
11	0	8	11	1	7	11	2	6¼	11	3	5¼	11	4	4¼
3/-	**0**	**8¼**	**7/-**	**1**	**7¼**	**11/-**	**2**	**6½**	**15/-**	**3**	**5½**	**19/-**	**4**	**4½**
3/1	0	8½	7/1	1	7½	11/1	2	6½	15/1	3	5¾	19/1	4	4¾
2	0	8¾	2	1	7¾	2	2	6¾	2	3	5¾	2	4	5
3	0	9	3	1	8	3	2	7	3	3	6	3	4	5¼
4	0	9¼	4	1	8¼	4	2	7¼	4	3	6¼	4	4	5¼
5	0	9½	5	1	8½	5	2	7½	5	3	6½	5	4	5½
3/6	0	9¾	7/6	1	8¾	11/6	2	7¾	15/6	3	6¾	19/6	4	5¾
7	0	10	7	1	9	7	2	8	7	3	7	7	4	6
8	0	10	8	1	9¼	8	2	8¼	8	3	7¼	8	4	6¼
9	0	10¼	9	1	9½	9	2	8½	9	3	7½	9	4	6½
10	0	10½	10	1	9½	10	2	8¾	10	3	7¾	10	4	6¾
11	0	10¾	11	1	9¾	11	2	9	11	3	8	11	4	7
4/-	**0**	**11**	**8/-**	**1**	**10**	**12/-**	**2**	**9**	**16/-**	**3**	**8¼**	**20/-**	**4**	**7¼**

20/6	4s	8½	25/6	5s	10½	31/-	7s	1½	35/6	8s	2	Guineas			
21/-	4	10	26/-	5	11¾	31/6	7	3	36/-	8	3¼	1.	£0	4	10
22/-	5	0¾	27/-	6	2½	32/-	7	4¼	37/-	8	6	2.	0	9	8
22/6	5	2	27/6	6	4	32/6	7	5¾	37/6	8	7½	3.	0	14	6
23/-	5	3½	28/-	6	5¼	33/-	7	7	38/-	8	9	4.	0	19	3¾
24/-	5	6¼	29/-	6	8	34/-	7	9¾	39/-	8	11¾	5.	1	4	1¾
25/-	5s	9	**30/-**	6s	10¾	**35/-**	8s	0½	**40/-**	9s	2½	6.	£1	8	11¾

(=$18\frac{7}{10}$% on Gross Returns).

£	£	s	d	£	£	s	d	£	£	s	d	£	£	s	d
1	0	4	9½	51	12	4	9½	101	24	4	9½	151	36	4	9½
2	0	9	7¼	52	12	9	7¼	102	24	9	7¼	152	36	9	7¼
3	0	14	4¾	53	12	14	4¾	103	24	14	4¾	153	36	14	4¾
4	0	19	2½	54	12	19	2½	104	24	19	2½	154	36	19	2½
5	1	4	0	55	13	4	0	105	25	4	0	155	37	4	0
6	1	8	9½	56	13	8	9½	106	25	8	9½	156	37	8	9½
7	1	13	7¼	57	13	13	7¼	107	25	13	7¼	157	37	13	7¼
8	1	18	4¾	58	13	18	4¾	108	25	18	4¾	158	37	18	4¾
9	2	3	2½	59	14	3	2½	109	26	3	2½	159	38	3	2½
10	2	8	0	60	14	8	0	110	26	8	0	160	38	8	0
11	2	12	9½	61	14	12	9½	111	26	12	9½	161	38	12	9½
12	2	17	7¼	62	14	17	7¼	112	26	17	7¼	162	38	17	7¼
13	3	2	4¾	63	15	2	4¾	113	27	2	4¾	163	39	2	4¾
14	3	7	2½	64	15	7	2½	114	27	7	2½	164	39	7	2½
15	3	12	0	65	15	12	0	115	27	12	0	165	39	12	0
16	3	16	9½	66	15	16	9½	116	27	16	9½	166	39	16	9½
17	4	1	7¼	67	16	1	7¼	117	28	1	7¼	167	40	1	7¼
18	4	6	4¾	68	16	6	4¾	118	28	6	4¾	168	40	6	4¾
19	4	11	2½	69	16	11	2½	119	28	11	2½	169	40	11	2½
20	4	16	0	70	16	16	0	120	28	16	0	170	40	16	0
21	5	0	9½	71	17	0	9½	121	29	0	9½	171	41	0	9½
22	5	5	7¼	72	17	5	7¼	122	29	5	7¼	172	41	5	7¼
23	5	10	4¾	73	17	10	4¾	123	29	10	4¾	173	41	10	4¾
24	5	15	2½	74	17	15	2½	124	29	15	2½	174	41	15	2½
25	6	0	0	75	18	0	0	125	30	0	0	175	42	0	0
26	6	4	9½	76	18	4	9½	126	30	4	9½	176	42	4	9½
27	6	9	7¼	77	18	9	7¼	127	30	9	7¼	177	42	9	7¼
28	6	14	4¾	78	18	14	4¾	128	30	14	4¾	178	42	14	4¾
29	6	19	2½	79	18	19	2½	129	30	19	2½	179	42	19	2½
30	7	4	0	80	19	4	0	130	31	4	0	180	43	4	0
31	7	8	9½	81	19	8	9½	131	31	8	9½	181	43	8	9½
32	7	13	7¼	82	19	13	7¼	132	31	13	7¼	182	43	13	7¼
33	7	18	4¾	83	19	18	4¾	133	31	18	4¾	183	43	18	4¾
34	8	3	2½	84	20	3	2½	134	32	3	2½	184	44	3	2½
35	8	8	0	85	20	8	0	135	32	8	0	185	44	8	0
36	8	12	9½	86	20	12	9½	136	32	12	9½	186	44	12	9½
37	8	17	7¼	87	20	17	7¼	137	32	17	7¼	187	44	17	7¼
38	9	2	4¾	88	21	2	4¾	138	33	2	4¾	188	45	2	4¾
39	9	7	2½	89	21	7	2½	139	33	7	2½	189	45	7	2½
40	9	12	0	90	21	12	0	140	33	12	0	190	45	12	0
41	9	16	9½	91	21	16	9½	141	33	16	9½	191	45	16	9½
42	10	1	7¼	92	22	1	7¼	142	34	1	7¼	192	46	1	7¼
43	10	6	4¾	93	22	6	4¾	143	34	6	4¾	193	46	6	4¾
44	10	11	2½	94	22	11	2½	144	34	11	2½	194	46	11	2½
45	10	16	0	95	22	16	0	145	34	16	0	195	46	16	0
46	11	0	9½	96	23	0	9½	146	35	0	9½	196	47	0	9½
47	11	5	7¼	97	23	5	7¼	147	35	5	7¼	197	47	5	7¼
48	11	10	4¾	98	23	10	4¾	148	35	10	4¾	198	47	10	4¾
49	11	15	2½	99	23	15	2½	149	35	15	2½	199	47	15	2½
50	12	0	0	100	24	0	0	150	36	0	0	200	48	0	0

£	£	s	d	£	£	s	d	£	£	s	d	£	£	s	d
250	60	0s	0d	700	168	0s	0d	1200	288	0s	0d	2000	480	0s	0
300	72	0	0	750	180	0	0	1400	336	0	0	2500	600	0	0
400	96	0	0	800	192	0	0	1500	360	0	0	3000	720	0	0
500	120	0	0	900	216	0	0	1600	384	0	0	4000	960	0	0
600	144	0s	0d	1000	240	0s	0d	1800	432	0s	0d	5000	1200	0s	0

76% off

24% 24 PER CENT. 24%

1d	0s	0¼	4/1	0s	11¾	8/1	1s	11¼	12/1	2s	10¾	16/1	3s	10¼
2d	0	0½	2	1	0	2	1	11½	2	2	11	2	3	10½
3d	0	0¾	3	1	0¼	3	1	11¾	3	2	11¼	3	3	10¾
4d	0	1	4	1	0½	4	2	0	4	2	11½	4	3	11
5d	0	1¼	5	1	0¾	5	2	0¼	5	2	11¾	5	3	11¼
6d	0	1½	4/6	1	1	8/6	2	0½	12/6	3	0	16/6	3	11½
7d	0	1¾	7	1	1¼	7	2	0¾	7	3	0¼	7	3	11¾
8d	0	2	8	1	1½	8	2	1	8	3	0½	8	4	0
9d	0	2¼	9	1	1¾	9	2	1¼	9	3	0¾	9	4	0¼
10d	0	2½	10	1	2	10	2	1½	10	3	1	10	4	0½
11d	0	2¾	11	1	2¼	11	2	1¾	11	3	1¼	11	4	0¾
1/-	**0**	**3**	**5/-**	**1**	**2½**	**9/-**	**2**	**2**	**13/-**	**3**	**1½**	**17/-**	**4**	**1**
1/1	0	3	5/1	1	2¾	9/1	2	2¼	13/1	3	1¾	17/1	4	1¼
2	0	3¼	2	1	3	2	2	2½	2	3	2	2	4	1½
3	0	3½	3	1	3	3	2	2¾	3	3	2¼	3	4	1¾
4	0	3¾	4	1	3¼	4	2	3	4	3	2½	4	4	2
5	0	4	5	1	3½	5	2	3	5	3	2¾	5	4	2¼
1/6	0	4¼	5/6	1	3¾	9/6	2	3¼	13/6	3	3	17/6	4	2½
7	0	4½	7	1	4	7	2	3½	7	3	3	7	4	2¾
8	0	4¾	8	1	4¼	8	2	3¾	8	3	3¼	8	4	3
9	0	5	9	1	4½	9	2	4	9	3	3½	9	4	3
10	0	5¼	10	1	4¾	10	2	4¼	10	3	3¾	10	4	3¼
11	0	5½	11	1	5	11	2	4½	11	3	4	11	4	3½
2/-	**0**	**5¾**	**6/-**	**1**	**5¼**	**10/-**	**2**	**4¾**	**14/-**	**3**	**4¼**	**18/-**	**4**	**3¾**
2/1	0	6	6/1	1	5½	10/1	2	5	14/1	3	4½	18/1	4	4
2	0	6¼	2	1	5¾	2	2	5¼	2	3	4¾	2	4	4¼
3	0	6½	3	1	6	3	2	5½	3	3	5	3	4	4½
4	0	6¾	4	1	6¼	4	2	5¾	4	3	5¼	4	4	4¾
5	0	7	5	1	6½	5	2	6	5	3	5½	5	4	5
2/6	0	7¼	6/6	1	6¾	10/6	2	6¼	14/6	3	5¾	18/6	4	5¼
7	0	7½	7	1	7	7	2	6½	7	3	6	7	4	5½
8	0	7¾	8	1	7¼	8	2	6¾	8	3	6¼	8	4	5¾
9	0	8	9	1	7½	9	2	7	9	3	6½	9	4	6
10	0	8¼	10	1	7¾	10	2	7¼	10	3	6¾	10	4	6¼
11	0	8½	11	1	8	11	2	7½	11	3	7	11	4	6½
3/-	**0**	**8¾**	**7/-**	**1**	**8¼**	**11/-**	**2**	**7¾**	**15/-**	**3**	**7¼**	**19/-**	**4**	**6¾**
3/1	0	9	7/1	1	8½	11/1	2	8	15/1	3	7½	19/1	4	7
2	0	9	2	1	8¾	2	2	8¼	2	3	7¾	2	4	7¼
3	0	9¼	3	1	9	3	2	8½	3	3	8	3	4	7½
4	0	9½	4	1	9	4	2	8¾	4	3	8¼	4	4	7¾
5	0	9¾	5	1	9¼	5	2	9	5	3	8½	5	4	8
3/6	0	10	7/6	1	9½	11/6	2	9	15/6	3	8¾	19/6	4	8¼
7	0	10¼	7	1	9¾	7	2	9¼	7	3	9	7	4	8½
8	0	10½	8	1	10	8	2	9½	8	3	9	8	4	8¾
9	0	10¾	9	1	10¼	9	2	9¾	9	3	9¼	9	4	9
10	0	11	10	1	10½	10	2	10	10	3	9½	10	4	9
11	0	11¼	11	1	10¾	11	2	10¼	11	3	9¾	11	4	9¼
4/-	**0**	**11½**	**8/-**	**1**	**11**	**12/-**	**2**	**10½**	**16/-**	**3**	**10**	**20/-**	**4**	**9½**

20/6	4s	11	25/6	6s	1½	31/-	7s	5¼	35/6	8s	6¼	Guineas			
21/-	5	0½	26/-	6	3	31/6	7	6¾	36/-	8	7¾	1.	£0	5	0½
22/-	5	3¼	27/-	6	5¾	32/-	7	8¼	37/-	8	10½	2.	0	10	1
22/6	5	4¾	27/6	6	7¼	32/6	7	9½	37/6	9	0	3.	0	15	1½
23/-	5	6¼	28/-	6	8¾	33/-	7	11	38/-	9	1½	4.	1	0	2
24/-	5	9	29/-	6	11½	34/-	8	2	39/-	9	4¼	5.	1	5	2½
25/-	6s	0	**30/-**	7s	2½	**35/-**	8s	4¾	**40/-**	9s	7¼	6.	£1	10	3

(=19$\frac{4}{10}$% on Gross Returns).

£				£				£				£			
£1	£0	5s.	0	£51	12	15s.	0	£101	£25	5s.	0	£151	£37	15s.	0
2	0	10	0	52	13	0	0	102	25	10	0	152	38	0	0
3	0	15	0	53	13	5	0	103	25	15	0	153	38	5	0
4	1	0	0	54	13	10	0	104	26	0	0	154	38	10	0
5	1	5	0	55	13	15	0	105	26	5	0	155	38	15	0
6	1	10	0	56	14	0	0	106	26	10	0	156	39	0	0
7	1	15	0	57	14	5	0	107	26	15	0	157	39	5	0
8	2	0	0	58	14	10	0	108	27	0	0	158	39	10	0
9	2	5	0	59	14	15	0	109	27	5	0	159	39	15	0
10	£2	10s.	0	60	15	0s.	0	110	£27	10s.	0	160	£40	0s.	0
11	£2	15s.	0	61	15	5s.	0	111	£27	15s.	0	161	£40	5s.	0
12	3	0	0	62	15	10	0	112	28	0	0	162	40	10	0
13	3	5	0	63	15	15	0	113	28	5	0	163	40	15	0
14	3	10	0	64	16	0	0	114	28	10	0	164	41	0	0
15	3	15	0	65	16	5	0	115	28	15	0	165	41	5	0
16	4	0	0	66	16	10	0	116	29	0	0	166	41	10	0
17	4	5	0	67	16	15	0	117	29	5	0	167	41	15	0
18	4	10	0	68	17	0	0	118	29	10	0	168	42	0	0
19	4	15	0	69	17	5	0	119	29	15	0	169	42	5	0
20	£5	0s.	0	70	17	10s.	0	120	£30	0s.	0	170	£42	10s.	0
21	£5	5s.	0	71	17	15s.	0	121	£30	5s.	0	171	£42	15s.	0
22	5	10	0	72	18	0	0	122	30	10	0	172	43	0	0
23	5	15	0	73	18	5	0	123	30	15	0	173	43	5	0
24	6	0	0	74	18	10	0	124	31	0	0	174	43	10	0
25	6	5	0	75	18	15	0	125	31	5	0	175	43	15	0
26	6	10	0	76	19	0	0	126	31	10	0	176	44	0	0
27	6	15	0	77	19	5	0	127	31	15	0	177	44	5	0
28	7	0	0	78	19	10	0	128	32	0	0	178	44	10	0
29	7	5	0	79	19	15	0	129	32	5	0	179	44	15	0
30	£7	10s.	0	80	20	0s.	0	130	£32	10s.	0	180	£45	0s.	0
31	£7	15s.	0	81	20	5s.	0	131	£32	15s.	0	181	£45	5s.	0
32	8	0	0	82	20	10	0	132	33	0	0	182	45	10	0
33	8	5	0	83	20	15	0	133	33	5	0	183	45	15	0
34	8	10	0	84	21	0	0	134	33	10	0	184	46	0	0
35	8	15	0	85	21	5	0	135	33	15	0	185	46	5	0
36	9	0	0	86	21	10	0	136	34	0	0	186	46	10	0
37	9	5	0	87	21	15	0	137	34	5	0	187	46	15	0
38	9	10	0	88	22	0	0	138	34	10	0	188	47	0	0
39	9	15	0	89	22	5	0	139	34	15	0	189	47	5	0
40	10	0s.	0	90	22	10s.	0	140	£35	0s.	0	190	£47	10s.	0
41	10	5s.	0	91	22	15s.	0	141	£35	5s.	0	191	£47	15s.	0
42	10	10	0	92	23	0	0	142	35	10	0	192	48	0	0
43	10	15	0	93	23	5	0	143	35	15	0	193	48	5	0
44	11	0	0	94	23	10	0	144	36	0	0	194	48	10	0
45	11	5	0	95	23	15	0	145	36	5	0	195	48	15	0
46	11	10	0	96	24	0	0	146	36	10	0	196	49	0	0
47	11	15	0	97	24	5	0	147	36	15	0	197	49	5	0
48	12	0	0	98	24	10	0	148	37	0	0	198	49	10	0
49	12	5	0	99	24	15	0	149	37	5	0	199	49	15	0
50	12	10s.	0	100	25	0s.	0	150	£37	10s.	0	200	£50	0s.	0

£				£				£				£			
250	£62	10s.	0d	700	175	0s.	d	1200	300	0s.	d	2000	£500	0s.	0
300	75	0	0	750	187	10	0	1400	350	0	0	2500	625	0	0
400	100	0	0	800	200	0	0	1500	375	0	0	3000	750	0	0
500	125	0	0	900	225	0	0	1600	400	0	0	4000	1000	0	0
600	150	0s.	0d	1000	250	0s.	d	1800	450	0s.	d	5000	£1250	0s.	0

75% off.

1d	0s. 0¼	4/1	1s. 0¼	8/1	2s. 0¼	12/1	3s. 0¼	16/1	4s. 0¼
2d	0 0½	2	1 0½	2	2 0½	2	3 0½	2	4 0½
3d	0 0¾	3	1 0¾	3	2 0¾	3	3 0¾	3	4 0¾
4d	0 1	4	1 1	4	2 1	4	3 1	4	4 1
5d	0 1¼	5	1 1¼	5	2 1¼	5	3 1¼	5	4 1¼
6d	0 1½	4/6	1 1½	8/6	2 1½	12/6	3 1½	16/6	4 1½
7d	0 1¾	7	1 1¾	7	2 1¾	7	3 1¾	7	4 1¾
8d	0 2	8	1 2	8	2 2	8	3 2	8	4 2
9d	0 2¼	9	1 2¼	9	2 2¼	9	3 2¼	9	4 2¼
10d	0 2½	10	1 2½	10	2 2½	10	3 2½	10	4 2½
11d	0 2¾	11	1 2¾	11	2 2¾	11	3 2¾	11	4 2¾
1/-	0s. 3	5/-	1s. 3	9/-	2s. 3	13/-	3s. 3	17/-	4s. 3
1/1	0s. 3¼	5/1	1s. 3¼	9/1	2s. 3¼	13/1	3s. 3¼	17/1	4s. 3¼
2	0 3½	2	1 3½	2	2 3½	2	3 3½	2	4 3½
3	0 3¾	3	1 3¾	3	2 3¾	3	3 3¾	3	4 3¾
4	0 4	4	1 4	4	2 4	4	3 4	4	4 4
5	0 4¼	5	1 4¼	5	2 4¼	5	3 4¼	5	4 4¼
1/6	0 4½	5/6	1 4½	9/6	2 4½	13/6	3 4½	17/6	4 4½
7	0 4¾	7	1 4¾	7	2 4¾	7	3 4¾	7	4 4¾
8	0 5	8	1 5	8	2 5	8	3 5	8	4 5
9	0 5¼	9	1 5¼	9	2 5¼	9	3 5¼	9	4 5¼
10	0 5½	10	1 5½	10	2 5½	10	3 5½	10	4 5½
11	0 5¾	11	1 5¾	11	2 5¾	11	3 5¾	11	4 5¾
2/-	0s. 6	6/-	1s. 6	10/-	2s. 6	14/-	3s. 6	18/-	4s. 6
2/1	0s. 6¼	6/1	1s. 6¼	10/1	2s. 6¼	14/1	3s. 6¼	18/1	4s. 6¼
2	0 6½	2	1 6½	2	2 6½	2	3 6½	2	4 6½
3	0 6¾	3	1 6¾	3	2 6¾	3	3 6¾	3	4 6¾
4	0 7	4	1 7	4	2 7	4	3 7	4	4 7
5	0 7¼	5	1 7¼	5	2 7¼	5	3 7¼	5	4 7¼
2/6	0 7½	6/6	1 7½	10/6	2 7½	14/6	3 7½	18/6	4 7½
7	0 7¾	7	1 7¾	7	2 7¾	7	3 7¾	7	4 7¾
8	0 8	8	1 8	8	2 8	8	3 8	8	4 8
9	0 8¼	9	1 8¼	9	2 8¼	9	3 8¼	9	4 8¼
10	0 8½	10	1 8½	10	2 8½	10	3 8½	10	4 8½
11	0 8¾	11	1 8¾	11	2 8¾	11	3 8¾	11	4 8¾
3/-	0s. 9	7/-	1s. 9	11/-	2s. 9	15/-	3s. 9	19/-	4s. 9
3/1	0s. 9¼	7/1	1s. 9¼	11/1	2s. 9¼	15/1	3s. 9¼	19/1	4s. 9¼
2	0 9½	2	1 9½	2	2 9½	2	3 9½	2	4 9½
3	0 9¾	3	1 9¾	3	2 9¾	3	3 9¾	3	4 9¾
4	0 10	4	1 10	4	2 10	4	3 10	4	4 10
5	0 10¼	5	1 10¼	5	2 10¼	5	3 10¼	5	4 10¼
3/6	0 10½	7/6	1 10½	11/6	2 10½	15/6	3 10½	19/6	4 10½
7	0 10¾	7	1 10¾	7	2 10¾	7	3 10¾	7	4 10¾
8	0 11	8	1 11	8	2 11	8	3 11	8	4 11
9	0 11¼	9	1 11¼	9	2 11¼	9	3 11¼	9	4 11¼
10	0 11½	10	1 11½	10	2 11½	10	3 11½	10	4 11½
11	0 11¾	11	1 11¾	11	2 11¾	11	3 11¾	11	4 11¾
4/-	1s. 0	8/-	2s. 0	12/-	3s. 0	16/-	4s. 0	20/-	5s. 0

20/6	5s. 1½	25/6	6s. 4½	31/-	7s. 9	35/6	8s.10½	Guineas.	
21/-	5 3	26/-	6 6	31/6	7 10½	36/-	9 0	1.	£0 5s. 3
22/-	5 6	27/-	6 9	32/-	8 0	37/-	9 3	2.	0 10 6
22/6	5 7½	27/6	6 10½	32/6	8 1½	37/6	9 4½	3.	0 15 9
23/-	5 9	28/-	7 0	33/-	8 3	38/-	9 6	4.	1 1 0
24/-	6 0	29/-	7 3	34/-	8 6	39/-	9 9	5.	1 6 3
25/-	6s. 3	30/-	7s. 6	35/-	8s. 9	40/-	10s. 0	6.	£1 11s. 6

(20% on Gross Returns).

£	£	s	d	£	£	s	d	£	£	s	d	£	£	s	d
1	0	5	2½	51	13	5	2½	101	26	5	2½	151	39	5	2½
2	0	10	4¾	52	13	10	4¾	102	26	10	4¾	152	39	10	4¾
3	0	15	7¼	53	13	15	7¼	103	26	15	7¼	153	39	15	7¼
4	1	0	9½	54	14	0	9½	104	27	0	9½	154	40	0	9½
5	1	6	0	55	14	6	0	105	27	6	0	155	40	6	0
6	1	11	2½	56	14	11	2½	106	27	11	2½	156	40	11	2½
7	1	16	4¾	57	14	16	4¾	107	27	16	4¾	157	40	16	4¾
8	2	1	7¼	58	15	1	7¼	108	28	1	7¼	158	41	1	7¼
9	2	6	9½	59	15	6	9½	109	28	6	9½	159	41	6	9½
10	2	12	0	60	15	12	0	110	28	12	0	160	41	12	0
11	2	17	2½	61	15	17	2½	111	28	17	2½	161	41	17	2½
12	3	2	4¾	62	16	2	4¾	112	29	2	4¾	162	42	2	4¾
13	3	7	7¼	63	16	7	7¼	113	29	7	7¼	163	42	7	7¼
14	3	12	9½	64	16	12	9½	114	29	12	9½	164	42	12	9½
15	3	18	0	65	16	18	0	115	29	18	0	165	42	18	0
16	4	3	2½	66	17	3	2½	116	30	3	2½	166	43	3	2½
17	4	8	4¾	67	17	8	4¾	117	30	8	4¾	167	43	8	4¾
18	4	13	7¼	68	17	13	7¼	118	30	13	7¼	168	43	13	7¼
19	4	18	9½	69	17	18	9½	119	30	18	9½	169	43	18	9½
20	5	4	0	70	18	4	0	120	31	4	0	170	44	4	0
21	5	9	2½	71	18	9	2½	121	31	9	2½	171	44	9	2½
22	5	14	4¾	72	18	14	4¾	122	31	14	4¾	172	44	14	4¾
23	5	19	7¼	73	18	19	7¼	123	31	19	7¼	173	44	19	7¼
24	6	4	9½	74	19	4	9½	124	32	4	9½	174	45	4	9½
25	6	10	0	75	19	10	0	125	32	10	0	175	45	10	0
26	6	15	2½	76	19	15	2½	126	32	15	2½	176	45	15	2½
27	7	0	4¾	77	20	0	4¾	127	33	0	4¾	177	46	0	4¾
28	7	5	7¼	78	20	5	7¼	128	33	5	7¼	178	46	5	7¼
29	7	10	9½	79	20	10	9½	129	33	10	9½	179	46	10	9½
30	7	16	0	80	20	16	0	130	33	16	0	180	46	16	0
31	8	1	2½	81	21	1	2½	131	34	1	2½	181	47	1	2½
32	8	6	4¾	82	21	6	4¾	132	34	6	4¾	182	47	6	4¾
33	8	11	7¼	83	21	11	7¼	133	34	11	7¼	183	47	11	7¼
34	8	16	9½	84	21	16	9½	134	34	16	9½	184	47	16	9½
35	9	2	0	85	22	2	0	135	35	2	0	185	48	2	0
36	9	7	2½	86	22	7	2½	136	35	7	2½	186	48	7	2½
37	9	12	4¾	87	22	12	4¾	137	35	12	4¾	187	48	12	4¾
38	9	17	7¼	88	22	17	7¼	138	35	17	7¼	188	48	17	7¼
39	10	2	9½	89	23	2	9½	139	36	2	9½	189	49	2	9½
40	10	8	0	90	23	8	0	140	36	8	0	190	49	8	0
41	10	13	2½	91	23	13	2½	141	36	13	2½	191	49	13	2½
42	10	18	4¾	92	23	18	4¾	142	36	18	4¾	192	49	18	4¾
43	11	3	7¼	93	24	3	7¼	143	37	3	7¼	193	50	3	7¼
44	11	8	9½	94	24	8	9½	144	37	8	9½	194	50	8	9½
45	11	14	0	95	24	14	0	145	37	14	0	195	50	14	0
46	11	19	2½	96	24	19	2½	146	37	19	2½	196	50	19	2½
47	12	4	4¾	97	25	4	4¾	147	38	4	4¾	197	51	4	4¾
48	12	9	7¼	98	25	9	7¼	148	38	9	7¼	198	51	9	7¼
49	12	14	9½	99	25	14	9½	149	38	14	9½	199	51	14	9½
50	13	0	0	100	26	0	0	150	39	0	0	200	52	0	0

£	£ s d	£	£ s d	£	£ s d	£	£ s d
250	65 0s 0d	700	182 0s 0d	1200	312 0s 0d	2000	520 0s 0d
300	78 0 0	750	195 0 0	1400	364 0 0	2500	650 0 0
400	104 0 0	800	208 0 0	1500	390 0 0	3000	780 0 0
500	130 0 0	900	234 0 0	1600	416 0 0	4000	1040 0 0
600	156 0s 0d	1000	260 0s 0d	1800	468 0s 0d	5000	1300 0s 0

74% off

26 Per Cent.

26%

1d	0s	0¼	4/1	1s	0¾	8/1	2s	1¼	12/1	3s	1¾	16/1	4s	2¼
2d	0	0½	2	1	1	2	2	1½	2	3	2	2	4	2½
3d	0	0¾	3	1	1¼	3	2	1¾	3	3	2¼	3	4	2¾
4d	0	1	4	1	1½	4	2	2	4	3	2½	4	4	3
5d	0	1¼	5	1	1¾	5	2	2¼	5	3	2¾	5	4	3¼
6d	0	1½	4/6	1	2	8/6	2	2½	12/6	3	3	16/6	4	3½
7d	0	1¾	7	1	2¼	7	2	2¾	7	3	3¼	7	4	3¾
8d	0	2	8	1	2½	8	2	3	8	3	3½	8	4	4
9d	0	2¼	9	1	2¾	9	2	3¼	9	3	3¾	9	4	4¼
10d	0	2½	10	1	3	10	2	3½	10	3	4	10	4	4½
11d	0	2¾	11	1	3¼	11	2	3¾	11	3	4¼	11	4	4¾
1/-	**0**	**3**	**5/-**	**1**	**3½**	**9/-**	**2**	**4**	**13/-**	**3**	**4½**	**17/-**	**4**	**5**
1/1	0	3½	5/1	1	3¾	9/1	2	4¼	13/1	3	4¾	17/1	4	5¼
2	0	3¾	2	1	4	2	2	4½	2	3	5	2	4	5½
3	0	4	3	1	4½	3	2	4¾	3	3	5¼	3	4	5¾
4	0	4¼	4	1	4¾	4	2	5	4	3	5½	4	4	6
5	0	4½	5	1	5	5	2	5½	5	3	5¾	5	4	6¼
1/6	0	4¾	5/6	1	5¼	9/6	2	5¾	13/6	3	6	17/6	4	6½
7	0	5	7	1	5½	7	2	6	7	3	6½	7	4	6¾
8	0	5¼	8	1	5¾	8	2	6¼	8	3	6¾	8	4	7
9	0	5½	9	1	6	9	2	6½	9	3	7	9	4	7½
10	0	5¾	10	1	6¼	10	2	6¾	10	3	7¼	10	4	7¾
11	0	6	11	1	6½	11	2	7	11	3	7½	11	4	8
2/-	**0**	**6¼**	**6/-**	**1**	**6¾**	**10/-**	**2**	**7¼**	**14/-**	**3**	**7¾**	**18/-**	**4**	**8¼**
2/1	0	6½	6/1	1	7	10/1	2	7½	14/1	3	8	18/1	4	8½
2	0	6¾	2	1	7¼	2	2	7¾	2	3	8¼	2	4	8¾
3	0	7	3	1	7½	3	2	8	3	3	8½	3	4	9
4	0	7¼	4	1	7¾	4	2	8¼	4	3	8¾	4	4	9¼
5	0	7½	5	1	8	5	2	8½	5	3	9	5	4	9½
2/6	0	7¾	6/6	1	8¼	10/6	2	8¾	14/6	3	9¼	18/6	4	9¾
7	0	8	7	1	8½	7	2	9	7	3	9½	7	4	10
8	0	8¼	8	1	8¾	8	2	9¼	8	3	9¾	8	4	10¼
9	0	8½	9	1	9	9	2	9½	9	3	10	9	4	10½
10	0	8¾	10	1	9¼	10	2	9¾	10	3	10¼	10	4	10¾
11	0	9	11	1	9½	11	2	10	11	3	10½	11	4	11
3/-	**0**	**9¼**	**7/-**	**1**	**9¾**	**11/-**	**2**	**10¼**	**15/-**	**3**	**10¾**	**19/-**	**4**	**11¼**
3/1	0	9½	7/1	1	10	11/1	2	10½	15/1	3	11	19/1	4	11½
2	0	10	2	1	10¼	2	2	10¾	2	3	11¼	2	4	11¾
3	0	10¼	3	1	10½	3	2	11	3	3	11½	3	5	0
4	0	10½	4	1	11	4	2	11¼	4	3	11¾	4	5	0¼
5	0	10¾	5	1	11¼	5	2	11½	5	4	0	5	5	0½
3/6	0	11	7/6	1	11½	11/6	3	0	15/6	4	0¼	19/6	5	0¾
7	0	11¼	7	1	11¾	7	3	0¼	7	4	0½	7	5	1
8	0	11½	8	2	0	8	3	0½	8	4	1	8	5	1¼
9	0	11¾	9	2	0¼	9	3	0¾	9	4	1¼	9	5	1½
10	1	0	10	2	0½	10	3	1	10	4	1½	10	5	2
11	1	0¼	11	2	0¾	11	3	1¼	11	4	1¾	11	5	2¼
4/-	**1**	**0½**	**8/-**	**2**	**1**	**12/-**	**3**	**1½**	**16/-**	**4**	**2**	**20/-**	**5**	**2½**

20/6	5s	4	25/6	6s	7½	31/-	8s	0¾	35/6	9s	2¾	Guineas	
21/-	5	5½	26/-	6	9	31/6	8	2¼	36/-	9	4¼	1.	£0 5 5½
22/-	5	8¾	27/-	7	0¼	32/-	8	3¾	37/-	9	7½	2.	0 10 11
22/6	5	10¼	27/6	7	1¾	32/6	8	5½	37/6	9	9	3.	0 16 4½
23/-	5	11¾	28/-	7	3¼	33/-	8	7	38/-	9	10½	4.	1 1 10
24/-	6	3	29/-	7	6½	34/-	8	10	39/-	10	1¾	5.	1 7 3½
25/-	6s	6	**30/-**	7s	9½	**35/-**	9s	1¼	**40/-**	10s	4¾	6.	£1 12 9

(=20 6/10 % on Gross Returns).

£	£ s d	£	£ s d	£	£ s d	£	£ s d
£1	£0 5s 4¾	£51	13 15s 4¾	£101	27 5s 4¾	£151	40 15s 4¾
2	0 10 9½	52	14 0 9½	102	27 10 9½	152	41 0 9½
3	0 16 2½	53	14 6 2½	103	27 16 2½	153	41 6 2½
4	1 1 7¼	54	14 11 7¼	104	28 1 7¼	154	41 11 7¼
5	1 7 0	55	14 17 0	105	28 7 0	155	41 17 0
6	1 12 4¾	56	15 2 4¾	106	28 12 4¾	156	42 2 4¾
7	1 17 9½	57	15 7 9½	107	28 17 9½	157	42 7 9½
8	2 3 2½	58	15 13 2½	108	29 3 2½	158	42 13 2½
9	2 8 7¼	59	15 18 7¼	109	29 8 7¼	159	42 18 7¼
10	2 14 0	60	16 4 0	110	29 14 0	160	43 4 0
11	2 19 4¾	61	16 9 4¾	111	29 19 4¾	161	43 9 4¾
12	3 4 9½	62	16 14 9½	112	30 4 9½	162	43 14 9½
13	3 10 2½	63	17 0 2½	113	30 10 2½	163	44 0 2½
14	3 15 7¼	64	17 5 7¼	114	30 15 7¼	164	44 5 7¼
15	4 1 0	65	17 11 0	115	31 1 0	165	44 11 0
16	4 6 4¾	66	17 16 4¾	116	31 6 4¾	166	44 16 4¾
17	4 11 9½	67	18 1 9½	117	31 11 9½	167	45 1 9½
18	4 17 2½	68	18 7 2½	118	31 17 2½	168	45 7 2½
19	5 2 7¼	69	18 12 7¼	119	32 2 7¼	169	45 12 7¼
20	5 8 0	70	18 18 0	120	32 8 0	170	45 18 0
21	5 13 4¾	71	19 3 4¾	121	32 13 4¾	171	46 3 4¾
22	5 18 9½	72	19 8 9½	122	32 18 9½	172	46 8 9½
23	6 4 2½	73	19 14 2½	123	33 4 2½	173	46 14 2½
24	6 9 7¼	74	19 19 7¼	124	33 9 7¼	174	46 19 7¼
25	6 15 0	75	20 5 0	125	33 15 0	175	47 5 0
26	7 0 4¾	76	20 10 4¾	126	34 0 4¾	176	47 10 4¾
27	7 5 9½	77	20 15 9½	127	34 5 9½	177	47 15 9½
28	7 11 2½	78	21 1 2½	128	34 11 2½	178	48 1 2½
29	7 16 7¼	79	21 6 7¼	129	34 16 7¼	179	48 6 7¼
30	8 2 0	80	21 12 0	130	35 2 0	180	48 12 0
31	8 7 4¾	81	21 17 4¾	131	35 7 4¾	181	48 17 4¾
32	8 12 9½	82	22 2 9½	132	35 12 9½	182	49 2 9½
33	8 18 2½	83	22 8 2½	133	35 18 2½	183	49 8 2½
34	9 3 7¼	84	22 13 7¼	134	36 3 7¼	184	49 13 7¼
35	9 9 0	85	22 19 0	135	36 9 0	185	49 19 0
36	9 14 4¾	86	23 4 4¾	136	36 14 4¾	186	50 4 4¾
37	9 19 9½	87	23 9 9½	137	36 19 9½	187	50 9 9½
38	10 5 2½	88	23 15 2½	138	37 5 2½	188	50 15 2½
39	10 10 7¼	89	24 0 7¼	139	37 10 7¼	189	51 0 7¼
40	10 16 0	90	24 6 0	140	37 16 0	190	51 6 0
41	11 1 4¾	91	24 11 4¾	141	38 1 4¾	191	51 11 4¾
42	11 6 9½	92	24 16 9½	142	38 6 9½	192	51 16 9½
43	11 12 2½	93	25 2 2½	143	38 12 2½	193	52 2 2½
44	11 17 7¼	94	25 7 7¼	144	38 17 7¼	194	52 7 7¼
45	12 3 0	95	25 13 0	145	39 3 0	195	52 13 0
46	12 8 4¾	96	25 18 4¾	146	39 8 4¾	196	52 18 4¾
47	12 13 9½	97	26 3 9½	147	39 13 9½	197	53 3 9½
48	12 19 2½	98	26 9 2½	148	39 19 2½	198	53 9 2½
49	13 4 7¼	99	26 14 7¼	149	40 4 7¼	199	53 14 7¼
50	13 10 0	100	27 0 0	150	40 10 0	200	54 0 0

£	£ s d	£	£ s d	£	£ s d	£	£ s d
250	67 10s 0d	700	189 0s 0d	1200	324 0s 0d	2000	540 0s 0
300	81 0 0	750	202 10 0	1400	378 0 0	2500	675 0 0
400	108 0 0	800	216 0 0	1500	405 0 0	3000	810 0 0
500	135 0 0	900	243 0 0	1600	432 0 0	4000	1080 0 0
600	162 0s 0d	1000	270 0s 0d	1800	486 0s 0d	5000	1350 0s 0

73% off

1d	0s	0¼	4/1	1s	1¼	8/1	2s	2¼	12/1	3s	3¼	16/1	4s	4
2d	0	0½	2	1	1½	2	2	2½	2	3	3½	2	4	4½
3d	0	0¾	3	1	1¾	3	2	2¾	3	3	3¾	3	4	4¾
4d	0	1	4	1	2	4	2	3	4	3	4	4	4	5
5d	0	1¼	5	1	2¼	5	2	3¼	5	3	4¼	5	4	5¼
6d	0	1½	4/6	1	2½	8/6	2	3½	12/6	3	4½	16/6	4	5½
7d	0	2	7	1	2¾	7	2	3¾	7	3	4¾	7	4	5¾
8d	0	2¼	8	1	3	8	2	4	8	3	5	8	4	6
9d	0	2½	9	1	3½	9	2	4¼	9	3	5¼	9	4	6¼
10d	0	2¾	10	1	3¾	10	2	4½	10	3	5½	10	4	6½
11d	0	3	11	1	4	11	2	5	11	3	5¾	11	4	6¾
1/-	**0**	**3¼**	**5/-**	**1**	**4¼**	**9/-**	**2**	**5¼**	**13/-**	**3**	**6**	**17/-**	**4**	**7**
1/1	0	3½	5/1	1	4½	9/1	2	5½	13/1	3	6¼	17/1	4	7¼
2	0	3¾	2	1	4¾	2	2	5¾	2	3	6¾	2	4	7½
3	0	4	3	1	5	3	2	6	3	3	7	3	4	8
4	0	4¼	4	1	5¼	4	2	6¼	4	3	7¼	4	4	8¼
5	0	4½	5	1	5½	5	2	6½	5	3	7½	5	4	8½
1/6	0	4¾	5/6	1	5¾	9/6	2	6¾	13/6	3	7¾	17/6	4	8¾
7	0	5¼	7	1	6	7	2	7	7	3	8	7	4	9
8	0	5½	8	1	6¼	8	2	7¼	8	3	8¼	8	4	9¼
9	0	5¾	9	1	6¾	9	2	7½	9	3	8½	9	4	9½
10	0	6	10	1	7	10	2	7¾	10	3	8¾	10	4	9¾
11	0	6¼	11	1	7¼	11	2	8¼	11	3	9	11	4	10
2/-	**0**	**6½**	**6/-**	**1**	**7½**	**10/-**	**2**	**8½**	**14/-**	**3**	**9¼**	**18/-**	**4**	**10¼**
2/1	0	6¾	6/1	1	7¾	10/1	2	8¾	14/1	3	9¾	18/1	4	10½
2	0	7	2	1	8	2	2	9	2	3	10	2	4	10¾
3	0	7¼	3	1	8¼	3	2	9¼	3	3	10¼	3	4	11¼
4	0	7½	4	1	8½	4	2	9½	4	3	10½	4	4	11½
5	0	7¾	5	1	8¾	5	2	9¾	5	3	10¾	5	4	11¾
2/6	0	8	6/6	1	9	10/6	2	10	14/6	3	11	18/6	5	0
7	0	8¼	7	1	9¼	7	2	10¼	7	3	11¼	7	5	0¼
8	0	8¾	8	1	9½	8	2	10½	8	3	11½	8	5	0½
9	0	9	9	1	9¾	9	2	10¾	9	3	11¾	9	5	0¾
10	0	9¼	10	1	10¼	10	2	11	10	4	0	10	5	1
11	0	9½	11	1	10½	11	2	11¼	11	4	0¼	11	5	1¼
3/-	**0**	**9¾**	**7/-**	**1**	**10¾**	**11/-**	**2**	**11¾**	**15/-**	**4**	**0½**	**19/-**	**5**	**1½**
3/1	0	10	7/1	1	11	11/1	3	0	15/1	4	0¾	19/1	5	1¾
2	0	10¼	2	1	11¼	2	3	0¼	2	4	1¼	2	5	2
3	0	10½	3	1	11½	3	3	0½	3	4	1½	3	5	2¼
4	0	10¾	4	1	11¾	4	3	0¾	4	4	1¾	4	5	2¾
5	0	11	5	2	0	5	3	1	5	4	2	5	5	3
3/6	0	11¼	7/6	2	0¼	11/6	3	1¼	15/6	4	2¼	19/6	5	3¼
7	0	11½	7	2	0½	7	3	1½	7	4	2½	7	5	3½
8	1	0	8	2	0¾	8	3	1¾	8	4	2¾	8	5	3¾
9	1	0¼	9	2	1	9	3	2	9	4	3	9	5	4
10	1	0½	10	2	1½	10	3	2¼	10	4	3¼	10	5	4¼
11	1	0¾	11	2	1¾	11	3	2½	11	4	3½	11	5	4½
4/-	**1**	**1**	**8/-**	**2**	**2**	**12/-**	**3**	**3**	**16/-**	**4**	**3¾**	**20/-**	**5**	**4¾**

20/6	5s	6½	25/6	6s	10½	31/-	8s	4½	35/6	9s	7	Guineas			
21/-	5	8	26/-	7	0¼	31/6	8	6	36/-	9	8¾	1.	£0	5	8
22/-	5	11¼	27/-	7	3½	32/-	8	7¾	37/-	10	0	2.	0	11	4
22/6	6	1	27/6	7	5	32/6	8	9¼	37/6	10	1½	3.	0	17	0
23/-	6	2½	28/-	7	6¾	33/-	8	11	38/-	10	3	4.	1	2	8¼
24/-	6	5¾	29/-	7	10	34/-	9	2¼	39/-	10	6¼	5.	1	8	4¼
25/-	6s	9	**30/-**	8s	1¼	**35/-**	9s	5½	**40/-**	10s	9½	6.	£1	14	0¼

(=21$\frac{3}{10}$% on Gross Returns).

£				£				£				£			
£1	£0	5s.	6	£51	14	0s.	6	£101	£27	15s.	6	£151	£41	10s.	6
2	0	11	0	52	14	6	0	102	28	1	0	152	41	16	0
3	0	16	6	53	14	11	6	103	28	6	6	153	42	1	6
4	1	2	0	54	14	17	0	104	28	12	0	154	42	7	0
5	1	7	6	55	15	2	6	105	28	17	6	155	42	12	6
6	1	13	0	56	15	8	0	106	29	3	0	156	42	18	0
7	1	18	6	57	15	13	6	107	29	8	6	157	43	3	6
8	2	4	0	58	15	19	0	108	29	14	0	158	43	9	0
9	2	9	6	59	16	4	6	109	29	19	6	159	43	14	6
10	£2	15s.	0	60	16	10s.	0	110	£30	5s.	0	160	£44	0s.	0
11	£3	0s.	6	61	16	15s.	6	111	£30	10s.	6	161	£44	5s.	6
12	3	6	0	62	17	1	0	112	30	16	0	162	44	11	0
13	3	11	6	63	17	6	6	113	31	1	6	163	44	16	6
14	3	17	0	64	17	12	0	114	31	7	0	164	45	2	0
15	4	2	6	65	17	17	6	115	31	12	6	165	45	7	6
16	4	8	0	66	18	3	0	116	31	18	0	166	45	13	0
17	4	13	6	67	18	8	6	117	32	3	6	167	45	18	6
18	4	19	0	68	18	14	0	118	32	9	0	168	46	4	0
19	5	4	6	69	18	19	6	119	32	14	6	169	46	9	6
20	£5	10s.	0	70	19	5s.	0	120	£33	0s.	0	170	£46	15s.	0
21	£5	15s.	6	71	19	10s.	6	121	£33	5s.	6	171	£47	0s.	6
22	6	1	0	72	19	16	0	122	33	11	0	172	47	6	0
23	6	6	6	73	20	1	6	123	33	16	6	173	47	11	6
24	6	12	0	74	20	7	0	124	34	2	0	174	47	17	0
25	6	17	6	75	20	12	6	125	34	7	6	175	48	2	6
26	7	3	0	76	20	18	0	126	34	13	0	176	48	8	0
27	7	8	6	77	21	3	6	127	34	18	6	177	48	13	6
28	7	14	0	78	21	9	0	128	35	4	0	178	48	19	0
29	7	19	6	79	21	14	6	129	35	9	6	179	49	4	6
30	£8	5s.	0	80	22	0s.	0	130	£35	15s.	0	180	£49	10s.	0
31	£8	10s.	6	81	22	5s.	6	131	£36	0s.	6	181	£49	15s.	6
32	8	16	0	82	22	11	0	132	36	6	0	182	50	1	0
33	9	1	6	83	22	16	6	133	36	11	6	183	50	6	6
34	9	7	0	84	23	2	0	134	36	17	0	184	50	12	0
35	9	12	6	85	23	7	6	135	37	2	6	185	50	17	6
36	9	18	0	86	23	13	0	136	37	8	0	186	51	3	0
37	10	3	6	87	23	18	6	137	37	13	6	187	51	8	6
38	10	9	0	88	24	4	0	138	37	19	0	188	51	14	0
39	10	14	6	89	24	9	6	139	38	4	6	189	51	19	6
40	11	0s.	0	90	24	15s.	0	140	£38	10s.	0	190	£52	5s.	0
41	11	5s.	6	91	25	0s.	6	141	£38	15s.	6	191	£52	10s.	6
42	11	11	0	92	25	6	0	142	39	1	0	192	52	16	0
43	11	16	6	93	25	11	6	143	39	6	6	193	53	1	6
44	12	2	0	94	25	17	0	144	39	12	0	194	53	7	0
45	12	7	6	95	26	2	6	145	39	17	6	195	53	12	6
46	12	13	0	96	26	8	0	146	40	3	0	196	53	18	0
47	12	18	6	97	26	13	6	147	40	8	6	197	54	3	6
48	13	4	0	98	26	19	0	148	40	14	0	198	54	9	0
49	13	9	6	99	27	4	6	149	40	19	6	199	54	14	6
50	13	15s.	0	100	27	10s.	0	150	£41	5s.	0	200	£55	0s.	0

250	£68	15s.	0d	700	192	10s.	0d	1200	330	0s.	0d	2000	£550	0s.	0
300	82	10	0	750	206	5	0	1400	385	0	0	2500	687	10	0
400	110	0	0	800	220	0	0	1500	412	10	0	3000	825	0	0
500	137	10	0	900	247	10	0	1600	440	0	0	4000	1100	0	0
600	165	0s.	0d	1000	275	0s.	0d	1800	495	0s.	0d	5000	£1375	0s.	0

72½% off.

1d	0s.	0¼	4/1	1s.	1½	8/1	2s.	2¾	12/1	3s.	4	16/1	4s.	5
2d	0	0½	2	1	1¾	2	2	3	2	3	4¼	2	4	5¼
3d	0	0¾	3	1	2	3	2	3¼	3	3	4½	3	4	5¾
4d	0	1	4	1	2¼	4	2	3½	4	3	4¾	4	4	6
5d	0	1½	5	1	2½	5	2	3¾	5	3	5	5	4	6¼
6d	0	1¾	4/6	1	2¾	8/6	2	4	12/6	3	5¼	16/6	4	6½
7d	0	2	7	1	3¼	7	2	4¼	7	3	5½	7	4	6¾
8d	0	2¼	8	1	3½	8	2	4½	8	3	5¾	8	4	7
9d	0	2½	9	1	3¾	9	2	5	9	3	6	9	4	7¼
10d	0	2¾	10	1	4	10	2	5¼	10	3	6¼	10	4	7½
11d	0	3	11	1	4¼	11	2	5½	11	3	6¾	11	4	7¾
1/-	0s.	3¼	**5/-**	1s.	4½	**9/-**	2s.	5¾	**13/-**	3s.	7	**17/-**	4s.	8
1/1	0s.	3½	5/1	1s.	4¾	9/1	2s.	6	13/1	3s.	7¼	17/1	4s.	8½
2	0	3¾	2	1	5	2	2	6¼	2	3	7½	2	4	8¾
3	0	4¼	3	1	5¼	3	2	6½	3	3	7¾	3	4	9
4	0	4½	4	1	5½	4	2	6¾	4	3	8	4	4	9¼
5	0	4¾	5	1	6	5	2	7	5	3	8¼	5	4	9½
1/6	0	5	5/6	1	6¼	9/6	2	7¼	13/6	3	8½	17/6	4	9¾
7	0	5¼	7	1	6½	7	2	7¾	7	3	8¾	7	4	10
8	0	5½	8	1	6¾	8	2	8	8	3	9	8	4	10¼
9	0	5¾	9	1	7	9	2	8¼	9	3	9½	9	4	10½
10	0	6	10	1	7¼	10	2	8½	10	3	9¾	10	4	10¾
11	0	6¼	11	1	7½	11	2	8¾	11	3	10	11	4	11¼
2/-	0s.	6½	**6/-**	1s.	7¾	**10/-**	2s.	9	**14/-**	3s.	10¼	**18/-**	4s.	11½
2/1	0s.	7	6/1	1s.	8	10/1	2s.	9¼	14/1	3s.	10½	18/1	4s.	11¾
2	0	7¼	2	1	8¼	2	2	9½	2	3	10¾	2	5	0
3	0	7½	3	1	8¾	3	2	9¾	3	3	11	3	5	0¼
4	0	7¾	4	1	9	4	2	10	4	3	11¼	4	5	0½
5	0	8	5	1	9¼	5	2	10½	5	3	11½	5	5	0¾
2/6	0	8¼	6/6	1	9½	10/6	2	10¾	14/6	3	11¾	18/6	5	1
7	0	8½	7	1	9¾	7	2	11	7	4	0¼	7	5	1¼
8	0	8¾	8	1	10	8	2	11¼	8	4	0½	8	5	1½
9	0	9	9	1	10¼	9	2	11½	9	4	0¾	9	5	2
10	0	9¼	10	1	10½	10	2	11¾	10	4	1	10	5	2¼
11	0	9¾	11	1	10¾	11	3	0	11	4	1¼	11	5	2½
3/-	0s.	10	**7/-**	1s.	11	**11/-**	3s.	0¼	**15/-**	4s.	1½	**19/-**	5s.	2¾
3/1	0s.	10¼	7/1	1s.	11½	11/1	3s.	0½	15/1	4s.	1¾	19/1	5s.	3
2	0	10½	2	1	11¾	2	3	0¾	2	4	2	2	5	3¼
3	0	10¾	3	2	0	3	3	1¼	3	4	2¼	3	5	3½
4	0	11	4	2	0¼	4	3	1½	4	4	2½	4	5	3¾
5	0	11¼	5	2	0½	5	3	1¾	5	4	3	5	5	4
3/6	0	11½	7/6	2	0¾	11/6	3	2	15/6	4	3¼	19/6	5	4¼
7	0	11¾	7	2	1	7	3	2¼	7	4	3½	7	5	4¾
8	1	0	8	2	1¼	8	3	2½	8	4	3¾	8	5	5
9	1	0½	9	2	1½	9	3	2¾	9	4	4	9	5	5¼
10	1	0¾	10	2	1¾	10	3	3	10	4	4¼	10	5	5½
11	1	1	11	2	2¼	11	3	3¼	11	4	4½	11	5	5¾
4/-	1s.	1¼	**8/-**	2s.	2½	**12/-**	3s.	3½	**16/-**	4s.	4¾	**20/-**	5s.	6

20/6	5s.	7¾	25/6	7s.	0¼	31/-	8s.	6¼	35/6	9s.	9¼	Guineas.			
21/-	5	9¼	26/-	7	1¾	31/6	8	8	36/-	9	10¾	1.	£0	5s.	9¼
22/-	6	0½	27/-	7	5	32/-	8	9½	37/-	10	2	2.	0	11	6½
22/6	6	2¼	27/6	7	6¾	32/6	8	11¼	37/6	10	3¾	3.	0	17	4
23/-	6	4	28/-	7	8½	33/-	9	1	38/-	10	5½	4.	1	3	1¼
24/-	6	7¼	29/-	7	11¾	34/-	9	4¼	39/-	10	8¾	5.	1	8	10½
25/-	6s.	10½	**30/-**	8s.	3	**35/-**	9s.	7½	**40/-**	11s.	0	6.	£1	14s.	7¾

(=21$\frac{6}{10}$%* on Gross Returns).

£	value			£	value			£	value			£	value		
£1	£0	5s	7¼	£51	14	5s	7¼	£101	28	5s	7¼	£151	42	5s	7¼
2	0	11	2½	52	14	11	2½	102	28	11	2½	152	42	11	2½
3	0	16	9½	53	14	16	9½	103	28	16	9½	153	42	16	9½
4	1	2	4¾	54	15	2	4¾	104	29	2	4¾	154	43	2	4¾
5	1	8	0	55	15	8	0	105	29	8	0	155	43	8	0
6	1	13	7¼	56	15	13	7¼	106	29	13	7¼	156	43	13	7¼
7	1	19	2½	57	15	19	2½	107	29	19	2½	157	43	19	2½
8	2	4	9½	58	16	4	9½	108	30	4	9½	158	44	4	9½
9	2	10	4¾	59	16	10	4¾	109	30	10	4¾	159	44	10	4¾
10	2	16	0	60	16	16	0	110	30	16	0	160	44	16	0
11	3	1	7¼	61	17	1	7¼	111	31	1	7¼	161	45	1	7¼
12	3	7	2½	62	17	7	2½	112	31	7	2½	162	45	7	2½
13	3	12	9½	63	17	12	9½	113	31	12	9½	163	45	12	9½
14	3	18	4¾	64	17	18	4¾	114	31	18	4¾	164	45	18	4¾
15	4	4	0	65	18	4	0	115	32	4	0	165	46	4	0
16	4	9	7¼	66	18	9	7¼	116	32	9	7¼	166	46	9	7¼
17	4	15	2½	67	18	15	2½	117	32	15	2½	167	46	15	2½
18	5	0	9½	68	19	0	9½	118	33	0	9½	168	47	0	9½
19	5	6	4¾	69	19	6	4¾	119	33	6	4¾	169	47	6	4¾
20	5	12	0	70	19	12	0	120	33	12	0	170	47	12	0
21	5	17	7¼	71	19	17	7¼	121	33	17	7¼	171	47	17	7¼
22	6	3	2½	72	20	3	2½	122	34	3	2½	172	48	3	2½
23	6	8	9½	73	20	8	9½	123	34	8	9½	173	48	8	9½
24	6	14	4¾	74	20	14	4¾	124	34	14	4¾	174	48	14	4¾
25	7	0	0	75	21	0	0	125	35	0	0	175	49	0	0
26	7	5	7¼	76	21	5	7¼	126	35	5	7¼	176	49	5	7¼
27	7	11	2½	77	21	11	2½	127	35	11	2½	177	49	11	2½
28	7	16	9½	78	21	16	9½	128	35	16	9½	178	49	16	9½
29	8	2	4¾	79	22	2	4¾	129	36	2	4¾	179	50	2	4¾
30	8	8	0	80	22	8	0	130	36	8	0	180	50	8	0
31	8	13	7¼	81	22	13	7¼	131	36	13	7¼	181	50	13	7¼
32	8	19	2½	82	22	19	2½	132	36	19	2½	182	50	19	2½
33	9	4	9½	83	23	4	9½	133	37	4	9½	183	51	4	9½
34	9	10	4¾	84	23	10	4¾	134	37	10	4¾	184	51	10	4¾
35	9	16	0	85	23	16	0	135	37	16	0	185	51	16	0
36	10	1	7¼	86	24	1	7¼	136	38	1	7¼	186	52	1	7¼
37	10	7	2½	87	24	7	2½	137	38	7	2½	187	52	7	2½
38	10	12	9½	88	24	12	9½	138	38	12	9½	188	52	12	9½
39	10	18	4¾	89	24	18	4¾	139	38	18	4¾	189	52	18	4¾
40	11	4	0	90	25	4	0	140	39	4	0	190	53	4	0
41	11	9	7¼	91	25	9	7¼	141	39	9	7¼	191	53	9	7¼
42	11	15	2½	92	25	15	2½	142	39	15	2½	192	53	15	2½
43	12	0	9½	93	26	0	9½	143	40	0	9½	193	54	0	9½
44	12	6	4¾	94	26	6	4¾	144	40	6	4¾	194	54	6	4¾
45	12	12	0	95	26	12	0	145	40	12	0	195	54	12	0
46	12	17	7¼	96	26	17	7¼	146	40	17	7¼	196	54	17	7¼
47	13	3	2½	97	27	3	2½	147	41	3	2½	197	55	3	2½
48	13	8	9½	98	27	8	9½	148	41	8	9½	198	55	8	9½
49	13	14	4¾	99	27	14	4¾	149	41	14	4¾	199	55	14	4¾
50	14	0	0	100	28	0	0	150	42	0	0	200	56	0	0

£	value			£	value			£	value			£	value		
250	70	0s	0d	700	196	0s	0d	1200	336	0s	0d	2000	560	0s	0d
300	84	0	0	750	210	0	0	1400	392	0	0	2500	700	0	0
400	112	0	0	800	224	0	0	1500	420	0	0	3000	840	0	0
500	140	0	0	900	252	0	0	1600	448	0	0	4000	1120	0	0
600	168	0s	0d	1000	280	0s	0d	1800	504	0s	0d	5000	1400	0s	0

72% off

28% 28 Per Cent. 28%

1d	0s	0¼	4/1	1s	1¾	8/1	2s	3¼	12/1	3s	4½	16/1	4s	6
2d	0	0½	2	1	2	2	2	3½	2	3	5	2	4	6¼
3d	0	0¾	3	1	2¼	3	2	3¾	3	3	5¼	3	4	6½
4d	0	1	4	1	2½	4	2	4	4	3	5½	4	4	7
5d	0	1½	5	1	2¾	5	2	4¼	5	3	5¾	5	4	7¼
6d	0	1¾	4/6	1	3	8/6	2	4½	12/6	3	6	16/6	4	7½
7d	0	2	7	1	3½	7	2	4¾	7	3	6¼	7	4	7¾
8d	0	2¼	8	1	3¾	8	2	5	8	3	6½	8	4	8
9d	0	2½	9	1	4	9	2	5½	9	3	6¾	9	4	8¼
10d	0	2¾	10	1	4¼	10	2	5¾	10	3	7	10	4	8½
11d	0	3	11	1	4½	11	2	6	11	3	7½	11	4	8¾
1/-	**0**	**3¼**	**5/-**	**1**	**4¾**	**9/-**	**2**	**6¼**	**13/-**	**3**	**7¾**	**17/-**	**4**	**9**
1/1	0	3¾	5/1	1	5	9/1	2	6½	13/1	3	8	17/1	4	9½
2	0	4	2	1	5¼	2	2	6¾	2	3	8¼	2	4	9¾
3	0	4¼	3	1	5¾	3	2	7	3	3	8½	3	4	10
4	0	4½	4	1	6	4	2	7¼	4	3	8¾	4	4	10¼
5	0	4¾	5	1	6¼	5	2	7¾	5	3	9	5	4	10½
1/6	0	5	5/6	1	6½	9/6	2	8	13/6	3	9¼	17/6	4	10¾
7	0	5¼	7	1	6¾	7	2	8¼	7	3	9¾	7	4	11
8	0	5½	8	1	7	8	2	8½	8	3	10	8	4	11¼
9	0	6	9	1	7¼	9	2	8¾	9	3	10¼	9	4	11¾
10	0	6¼	10	1	7½	10	2	9	10	3	10½	10	5	0
11	0	6½	11	1	8	11	2	9¼	11	3	10¾	11	5	0¼
2/-	**0**	**6¾**	**6/-**	**1**	**8¼**	**10/-**	**2**	**9½**	**14/-**	**3**	**11**	**18/-**	**5**	**0½**
2/1	0	7	6/1	1	8½	10/1	2	10	14/1	3	11¼	18/1	5	0¾
2	0	7¼	2	1	8¾	2	2	10¼	2	3	11½	2	5	1
3	0	7½	3	1	9	3	2	10½	3	4	0	3	5	1¼
4	0	7¾	4	1	9¼	4	2	10¾	4	4	0¼	4	5	1½
5	0	8	5	1	9½	5	2	11	5	4	0½	5	5	2
2/6	0	8½	6/6	1	9¾	10/6	2	11¼	14/6	4	0¾	18/6	5	2¼
7	0	8¾	7	1	10	7	2	11½	7	4	1	7	5	2½
8	0	9	8	1	10½	8	2	11¾	8	4	1¼	8	5	2¾
9	0	9¼	9	1	10¾	9	3	0	9	4	1½	9	5	3
10	0	9½	10	1	11	10	3	0½	10	4	1¾	10	5	3¼
11	0	9¾	11	1	11¼	11	3	0¾	11	4	2	11	5	3½
3/-	**0**	**10**	**7/-**	**1**	**11½**	**11/-**	**3**	**1**	**15/-**	**4**	**2½**	**19/-**	**5**	**3¾**
3/1	0	10¼	7/1	1	11¾	11/1	3	1¼	15/1	4	2¾	19/1	5	4
2	0	10¾	2	2	0	2	3	1½	2	4	3	2	5	4½
3	0	11	3	2	0¼	3	3	1¾	3	4	3¼	3	5	4¾
4	0	11¼	4	2	0¾	4	3	2	4	4	3½	4	5	5
5	0	11½	5	2	1	5	3	2¼	5	4	3¾	5	5	5¼
3/6	0	11¾	7/6	2	1¼	11/6	3	2¾	15/6	4	4	19/6	5	5½
7	1	0	7	2	1½	7	3	3	7	4	4¼	7	5	5¾
8	1	0¼	8	2	1¾	8	3	3¼	8	4	4¾	8	5	6
9	1	0½	9	2	2	9	3	3½	9	4	5	9	5	6¼
10	1	1	10	2	2¼	10	3	3¾	10	4	5¼	10	5	6¾
11	1	1¼	11	2	2½	11	3	4	11	4	5½	11	5	7
4/-	**1**	**1½**	**8/-**	**2**	**3**	**12/-**	**3**	**4¼**	**16/-**	**4**	**5¾**	**20/-**	**5**	**7¼**

20/6	5s	9	25/6	7s	1¾	31/-	8s	8¼	35/6	9s	11¼	Guineas	
21/-	5	10½	26/-	7	3¼	31/6	8	9¾	36/-	10	1	1.	£0 5 10½
22/-	6	2	27/-	7	6¾	32/-	8	11½	37/-	10	4¼	2.	0 11 9
22/6	6	3½	27/6	7	8½	32/6	9	1¼	37/6	10	6	3.	0 17 7¾
23/-	6	5¼	28/-	7	10	33/-	9	3	38/-	10	7¾	4.	1 3 6¼
24/-	6	8¾	29/-	8	1½	34/-	9	6¼	39/-	10	11	5.	1 9 4¾
25/-	7s	0	**30/-**	8s	4¾	**35/-**	9s	9½	**40/-**	11s	2½	6.	£1 15 3¼

(=21$\frac{9}{10}$% on Gross Returns).

29 Per Cent.

£1	£0	5s	9½	£51	14	15s	9½	£101	29	5s	9½	£151	43	15s	9½
2	0	11	7¼	52	15	1	7¼	102	29	11	7¼	152	44	1	7¼
3	0	17	4¾	53	15	7	4¾	103	29	17	4¾	153	44	7	4¾
4	1	3	2½	54	15	13	2½	104	30	3	2½	154	44	13	2½
5	1	9	0	55	15	19	0	105	30	9	0	155	44	19	0
6	1	14	9½	56	16	4	9½	106	30	14	9½	156	45	4	9½
7	2	0	7¼	57	16	10	7¼	107	31	0	7¼	157	45	10	7¼
8	2	6	4¾	58	16	16	4¾	108	31	6	4¾	158	45	16	4¾
9	2	12	2½	59	17	2	2½	109	31	12	2½	159	46	2	2½
10	**2**	**18**	**0**	**60**	**17**	**8**	**0**	**110**	**31**	**18**	**0**	**160**	**46**	**8**	**0**
11	3	3	9½	61	17	13	9½	111	32	3	9½	161	46	13	9½
12	3	9	7¼	62	17	19	7¼	112	32	9	7¼	162	46	19	7¼
13	3	15	4¾	63	18	5	4¾	113	32	15	4¾	163	47	5	4¾
14	4	1	2½	64	18	11	2½	114	33	1	2½	164	47	11	2½
15	4	7	0	65	18	17	0	115	33	7	0	165	47	17	0
16	4	12	9½	66	19	2	9½	116	33	12	9½	166	48	2	9½
17	4	18	7¼	67	19	8	7¼	117	33	18	7¼	167	48	8	7¼
18	5	4	4¾	68	19	14	4¾	118	34	4	4¾	168	48	14	4¾
19	5	10	2½	69	20	0	2½	119	34	10	2½	169	49	0	2½
20	**5**	**16**	**0**	**70**	**20**	**6**	**0**	**120**	**34**	**16**	**0**	**170**	**49**	**6**	**0**
21	6	1	9½	71	20	11	9½	121	35	1	9½	171	49	11	9½
22	6	7	7¼	72	20	17	7¼	122	35	7	7¼	172	49	17	7¼
23	6	13	4¾	73	21	3	4¾	123	35	13	4¾	173	50	3	4¾
24	6	19	2½	74	21	9	2½	124	35	19	2½	174	50	9	2½
25	7	5	0	75	21	15	0	125	36	5	0	175	50	15	0
26	7	10	9½	76	22	0	9½	126	36	10	9½	176	51	0	9½
27	7	16	7¼	77	22	6	7¼	127	36	16	7¼	177	51	6	7¼
28	8	2	4¾	78	22	12	4¾	128	37	2	4¾	178	51	12	4¾
29	8	8	2½	79	22	18	2½	129	37	8	2½	179	51	18	2½
30	**8**	**14**	**0**	**80**	**23**	**4**	**0**	**130**	**37**	**14**	**0**	**180**	**52**	**4**	**0**
31	8	19	9½	81	23	9	9½	131	37	19	9½	181	52	9	9½
32	9	5	7¼	82	23	15	7¼	132	38	5	7¼	182	52	15	7¼
33	9	11	4¾	83	24	1	4¾	133	38	11	4¾	183	53	1	4¾
34	9	17	2½	84	24	7	2½	134	38	17	2½	184	53	7	2½
35	10	3	0	85	24	13	0	135	39	3	0	185	53	13	0
36	10	8	9½	86	24	18	9½	136	39	8	9½	186	53	18	9½
37	10	14	7¼	87	25	4	7¼	137	39	14	7¼	187	54	4	7¼
38	11	0	4¾	88	25	10	4¾	138	40	0	4¾	188	54	10	4¾
39	11	6	2½	89	25	16	2½	139	40	6	2½	189	54	16	2½
40	**11**	**12**	**0**	**90**	**26**	**2**	**0**	**140**	**40**	**12**	**0**	**190**	**55**	**2**	**0**
41	11	17	9½	91	26	7	9½	141	40	17	9½	191	55	7	9½
42	12	3	7¼	92	26	13	7¼	142	41	3	7¼	192	55	13	7¼
43	12	9	4¾	93	26	19	4¾	143	41	9	4¾	193	55	19	4¾
44	12	15	2½	94	27	5	2½	144	41	15	2½	194	56	5	2½
45	13	1	0	95	27	11	0	145	42	1	0	195	56	11	0
46	13	6	9½	96	27	16	9½	146	42	6	9½	196	56	16	9½
47	13	12	7¼	97	28	2	7¼	147	42	12	7¼	197	57	2	7¼
48	13	18	4¾	98	28	8	4¾	148	42	18	4¾	198	57	8	4¾
49	14	4	2½	99	28	14	2½	149	43	4	2½	199	57	14	2½
50	**14**	**10**	**0**	**100**	**29**	**0**	**0**	**150**	**43**	**10**	**0**	**200**	**58**	**-**	**0**

250	72	10s	0d	700	203	0s	0d	1200	348	0s	0d	2000	580	0s	0
300	87	0	0	750	217	10	0	1400	406	0	0	2500	725	0	0
400	116	0	0	800	232	0	0	1500	435	0	0	3000	870	0	0
500	145	0	0	900	261	0	0	1600	464	0	0	4000	1160	0	0
600	174	0s	0d	1000	290	0s	0d	1800	522	0s	0d	5000	1450	0s	0

71% off

29% 29 Per Cent. 29%

1d	0s	0¼	4/1	1s	2¼	8/1	2s	4¼	12/1	3s	6	16/1	4s	8
2d	0	0½	2	1	2½	2	2	4½	2	3	6¼	2	4	8¼
3d	0	0¾	3	1	2¾	3	2	4¾	3	3	6¾	3	4	8½
4d	0	1¼	4	1	3	4	2	5	4	3	7	4	4	8¾
5d	0	1½	5	1	3¼	5	2	5¼	5	3	7¼	5	4	9¼
6d	0	1¾	4/6	1	3¾	8/6	2	5½	12/6	3	7½	16/6	4	9½
7d	0	2	7	1	4	7	2	5¾	7	3	7¾	7	4	9¾
8d	0	2¼	8	1	4¼	8	2	6¼	8	3	8	8	4	10
9d	0	2½	9	1	4½	9	2	6½	9	3	8¼	9	4	10¼
10d	0	3	10	1	4¾	10	2	6¾	10	3	8¾	10	4	10½
11d	0	3¼	11	1	5	11	2	7	11	3	9	11	4	10¾
1/-	**0**	**3½**	**5/-**	**1**	**5½**	**9/-**	**2**	**7¼**	**13/-**	**3**	**9¼**	**17/-**	**4**	**11¼**
1/1	0	3¾	5/1	1	5¾	9/1	2	7½	13/1	3	9½	17/1	4	11½
2	0	4	2	1	6	2	2	8	2	3	9¾	2	4	11¾
3	0	4¼	3	1	6¼	3	2	8¼	3	3	10	3	5	0
4	0	4¾	4	1	6½	4	2	8½	4	3	10½	4	5	0¼
5	0	5	5	1	6¾	5	2	8¾	5	3	10¾	5	5	0½
1/6	0	5¼	5/6	1	7¼	9/6	2	9	13/6	3	11	17/6	5	1
7	0	5½	7	1	7½	7	2	9¼	7	3	11¼	7	5	1¼
8	0	5¾	8	1	7¾	8	2	9¾	8	3	11½	8	5	1½
9	0	6	9	1	8	9	2	10	9	3	11¾	9	5	1¾
10	0	6½	10	1	8¼	10	2	10¼	10	4	0¼	10	5	2
11	0	6¾	11	1	8½	11	2	10½	11	4	0½	11	5	2¼
2/-	**0**	**7**	**6/-**	**1**	**9**	**10/-**	**2**	**10¾**	**14/-**	**4**	**0¾**	**18/-**	**5**	**2¾**
2/1	0	7¼	6/1	1	9¼	10/1	2	11	14/1	4	1	18/1	5	3
2	0	7½	2	1	9½	2	2	11½	2	4	1¼	2	5	3¼
3	0	7¾	3	1	9¾	3	2	11¾	3	4	1½	3	5	3½
4	0	8	4	1	10	4	3	0	4	4	2	4	5	3¾
5	0	8½	5	1	10¼	5	3	0¼	5	4	2¼	5	5	4
2/6	0	8¾	6/6	1	10½	10/6	3	0½	14/6	4	2½	18/6	5	4½
7	0	9	7	1	11	7	3	0¾	7	4	2¾	7	5	4¾
8	0	9¼	8	1	11¼	8	3	1	8	4	3	8	5	5
9	0	9½	9	1	11½	9	3	1½	9	4	3¼	9	5	5¼
10	0	9¾	10	1	11¾	10	3	1¾	10	4	3½	10	5	5½
11	0	10¼	11	2	0	11	3	2	11	4	4	11	5	5¾
3/-	**0**	**10½**	**7/-**	**2**	**0¼**	**11/-**	**3**	**2¼**	**15/-**	**4**	**4¼**	**19/-**	**5**	**6**
3/1	0	10¾	7/1	2	0¾	11/1	3	2½	15/1	4	4½	19/1	5	6¼
2	0	11	2	2	1	2	3	2¾	2	4	4¾	2	5	6¾
3	0	11¼	3	2	1¼	3	3	3¼	3	4	5	3	5	7
4	0	11½	4	2	1½	4	3	3½	4	4	5¼	4	5	7¼
5	1	0	5	2	1¾	5	3	3¾	5	4	5¾	5	5	7½
3/6	1	0¼	7/6	2	2	11/6	3	4	15/6	4	6	19/6	5	7¾
7	1	0½	7	2	2½	7	3	4¼	7	4	6¼	7	5	8¼
8	1	0¾	8	2	2¾	8	3	4½	8	4	6½	8	5	8½
9	1	1	9	2	3	9	3	5	9	4	6¾	9	5	8¾
10	1	1¼	10	2	3¼	10	3	5¼	10	4	7	10	5	9
11	1	1¾	11	2	3½	11	3	5½	11	4	7½	11	5	9¼
4/-	**1**	**2**	**8/-**	**2**	**3¾**	**12/-**	**3**	**5¾**	**16/-**	**4**	**7¾**	**20/-**	**5**	**9½**

												Guineas			
20/6	5s	11¼	25/6	7s	4¾	31/-	9s	0	35/6	10s	3½				
21/-	6	1	26/-	7	6½	31/6	9	1½	36/-	10	5¼	1.	£0	6	1
22/-	6	4½	27/-	7	10	32/-	9	3¼	37/-	10	8¾	2.	0	12	2¼
22/6	6	6¼	27/6	7	11¾	32/6	9	5	37/6	10	10½	3.	0	18	3¼
23/-	6	8	28/-	8	1½	33/-	9	6¾	38/-	11	0¼	4.	1	4	4¼
24/-	6	11½	29/-	8	5	34/-	9	10¼	39/-	11	3¾	5.	1	10	5½
25/-	7s	3	**30/-**	8s	8½	**35/-**	10s	1¾	**40/-**	11s	7¼	6.	£1	16	6½

(=22½% on Gross Returns).

	£ s. d		£ s. d		£ s. d		£ s. d
£1	£0 6s. 0	£51	15 6s. 0	£101	£30 6s. 0	£151	£45 6s. 0
2	0 12 0	52	15 12 0	102	30 12 0	152	45 12 0
3	0 18 0	53	15 18 0	103	30 18 0	153	45 18 0
4	1 4 0	54	16 4 0	104	31 4 0	154	46 4 0
5	1 10 0	55	16 10 0	105	31 10 0	155	46 10 0
6	1 16 0	56	16 16 0	106	31 16 0	156	46 16 0
7	2 2 0	57	17 2 0	107	32 2 0	157	47 2 0
8	2 8 0	58	17 8 0	108	32 8 0	158	47 8 0
9	2 14 0	59	17 14 0	109	32 14 0	159	47 14 0
10	£3 0s. 0	60	18 0s. 0	110	£33 0s. 0	160	£48 0s. 0
11	£3 6s. 0	61	18 6s. 0	111	£33 6s. 0	161	£48 6s. 0
12	3 12 0	62	18 12 0	112	33 12 0	162	48 12 0
13	3 18 0	63	18 18 0	113	33 18 0	163	48 18 0
14	4 4 0	64	19 4 0	114	34 4 0	164	49 4 0
15	4 10 0	65	19 10 0	115	34 10 0	165	49 10 0
16	4 16 0	66	19 16 0	116	34 16 0	166	49 16 0
17	5 2 0	67	20 2 0	117	35 2 0	167	50 2 0
18	5 8 0	68	20 8 0	118	35 8 0	168	50 8 0
19	5 14 0	69	20 14 0	119	35 14 0	169	50 14 0
20	£6 0s. 0	70	21 0s. 0	120	£36 0s. 0	170	£51 0s. 0
21	£6 6s. 0	71	21 6s. 0	121	£36 6s. 0	171	£51 6s. 0
22	6 12 0	72	21 12 0	122	36 12 0	172	51 12 0
23	6 18 0	73	21 18 0	123	36 18 0	173	51 18 0
24	7 4 0	74	22 4 0	124	37 4 0	174	52 4 0
25	7 10 0	75	22 10 0	125	37 10 0	175	52 10 0
26	7 16 0	76	22 16 0	126	37 16 0	176	52 16 0
27	8 2 0	77	23 2 0	127	38 2 0	177	53 2 0
28	8 8 0	78	23 8 0	128	38 8 0	178	53 8 0
29	8 14 0	79	23 14 0	129	38 14 0	179	53 14 0
30	£9 0s. 0	80	24 0s. 0	130	£39 0s. 0	180	£54 0s. 0
31	£9 6s. 0	81	24 6s. 0	131	£39 6s. 0	181	£54 6s. 0
32	9 12 0	82	24 12 0	132	39 12 0	182	54 12 0
33	9 18 0	83	24 18 0	133	39 18 0	183	54 18 0
34	10 4 0	84	25 4 0	134	40 4 0	184	55 4 0
35	10 10 0	85	25 10 0	135	40 10 0	185	55 10 0
36	10 16 0	86	25 16 0	136	40 16 0	186	55 16 0
37	11 2 0	87	26 2 0	137	41 2 0	187	56 2 0
38	11 8 0	88	26 8 0	138	41 8 0	188	56 8 0
39	11 14 0	89	26 14 0	139	41 14 0	189	56 14 0
40	12 0s. 0	90	27 0s. 0	140	£42 0s. 0	190	£57 0s. 0
41	12 6s. 0	91	27 6s. 0	141	£42 6s. 0	191	£57 6s. 0
42	12 12 0	92	27 12 0	142	42 12 0	192	57 12 0
43	12 18 0	93	27 18 0	143	42 18 0	193	57 18 0
44	13 4 0	94	28 4 0	144	43 4 0	194	58 4 0
45	13 10 0	95	28 10 0	145	43 10 0	195	58 10 0
46	13 16 0	96	28 16 0	146	43 16 0	196	58 16 0
47	14 2 0	97	29 2 0	147	44 2 0	197	59 2 0
48	14 8 0	98	29 8 0	148	44 8 0	198	59 8 0
49	14 14 0	99	29 14 0	149	44 14 0	199	59 14 0
50	15 0s. 0	100	30 0s. 0	150	£45 0s. 0	200	£60 0s. 0

	£ s. d		£ s. d		£ s. d		£ s. d
250	£75 0s. 0	700	210 0s.0d	1200	360 0s.0d	2000	£600 0s. 0
300	90 0 0	750	225 0 0	1400	420 0 0	2500	750 0 0
400	120 0 0	800	240 0 0	1500	450 0 0	3000	900 0 0
500	150 0 0	900	270 0 0	1600	480 0 0	4000	1200 0 0
600	180 0s.0d	1000	300 0s.0d	1800	540 0s.0d	5000	£1500 0s. 0

70% off.

1d	0s. 0¼	4/1	1s. 2¾	8/1	2s. 5	12/1	3s. 7½	16/1	4s.10
2d	0 0½	2	1 3	2	2 5½	2	3 7¾	2	4 10¼
3d	0 1	3	1 3¼	3	2 5¾	3	3 8	3	4 10½
4d	0 1¼	4	1 3½	4	2 6	4	3 8½	4	4 10¾
5d	0 1½	5	1 4	5	2 6¼	5	3 8¾	5	4 11
6d	0 1¾	4/6	1 4¼	8/6	2 6½	12/6	3 9	16/6	4 11½
7d	0 2	7	1 4½	7	2 7	7	3 9¼	7	4 11¾
8d	0 2¼	8	1 4¾	8	2 7¼	8	3 9½	8	5 0
9d	0 2¾	9	1 5	9	2 7½	9	3 10	9	5 0¼
10d	0 3	10	1 5½	10	2 7¾	10	3 10¼	10	5 0½
11d	0 3¼	11	1 5¾	11	2 8	11	3 10½	11	5 1
1/-	**0s. 3½**	**5/-**	**1s. 6**	**9/-**	**2s. 8½**	**13/-**	**3s.10¾**	**17/-**	**5s. 1¼**
1/1	0s. 4	5/1	1s. 6¼	9/1	2s. 8¾	13/1	3s.11	17/1	5s. 1½
2	0 4¼	2	1 6½	2	2 9	2	3 11½	2	5 1¾
3	0 4½	3	1 7	3	2 9¼	3	3 11¾	3	5 2
4	0 4¾	4	1 7¼	4	2 9½	4	4 0	4	5 2½
5	0 5	5	1 7½	5	2 10	5	4 0¼	5	5 2¾
1/6	0 5½	5/6	1 7¾	9/6	2 10¼	13/6	4 0½	17/6	5 3
7	0 5¾	7	1 8	7	2 10½	7	4 1	7	5 3¼
8	0 6	8	1 8½	8	2 10¾	8	4 1¼	8	5 3½
9	0 6¼	9	1 8¾	9	2 11	9	4 1½	9	5 4
10	0 6½	10	1 9	10	2 11½	10	4 1¾	10	5 4¼
11	0 7	11	1 9¼	11	2 11¾	11	4 2	11	5 4½
2/-	**0s. 7¼**	**6/-**	**1s. 9½**	**10/-**	**3s. 0**	**14/-**	**4s. 2½**	**18/-**	**5s. 4¾**
2/1	0s. 7½	6/1	1s.10	10/1	3s. 0¼	14/1	4s. 2¾	18/1	5s. 5
2	0 7¾	2	1 10¼	2	3 0½	2	4 3	2	5 5½
3	0 8	3	1 10½	3	3 1	3	4 3¼	3	5 5¾
4	0 8½	4	1 10¾	4	3 1¼	4	4 3½	4	5 6
5	0 8¾	5	1 11	5	3 1½	5	4 4	5	5 6¼
2/6	0 9	6/6	1 11½	10/6	3 1¾	14/6	4 4¼	18/6	5 6½
7	0 9¼	7	1 11¾	7	3 2	7	4 4½	7	5 7
8	0 9½	8	2 0	8	3 2½	8	4 4¾	8	5 7¼
9	0 10	9	2 0¼	9	3 2¾	9	4 5	9	5 7½
10	0 10¼	10	2 0½	10	3 3	10	4 5½	10	5 7¾
11	0 10½	11	2 1	11	3 3¼	11	4 5¾	11	5 8
3/-	**0s.10¾**	**7/-**	**2s. 1¼**	**11/-**	**3s. 3½**	**15/-**	**4s. 6**	**19/-**	**5s. 8½**
3/1	0s.11	7/1	2s. 1½	11/1	3s. 4	15/1	4s. 6¼	19/1	5s. 8¾
2	0 11½	2	2 1¾	2	3 4¼	2	4 6½	2	5 9
3	0 11¾	3	2 2	3	3 4½	3	4 7	3	5 9¼
4	1 0	4	2 2½	4	3 4¾	4	4 7¼	4	5 9½
5	1 0¼	5	2 2¾	5	3 5	5	4 7½	5	5 10
3/6	1 0½	7/6	2 3	11/6	3 5½	15/6	4 7¾	19/6	5 10¼
7	1 1	7	2 3¼	7	3 5¾	7	4 8	7	5 10½
8	1 1¼	8	2 3½	8	3 6	8	4 8½	8	5 10¾
9	1 1½	9	2 4	9	3 6¼	9	4 8¾	9	5 11
10	1 1¾	10	2 4¼	10	3 6½	10	4 9	10	5 11½
11	1 2	11	2 4½	11	3 7	11	4 9¼	11	5 11¾
4/-	**1s. 2½**	**8/-**	**2s. 4¾**	**12/-**	**3s. 7¼**	**16/-**	**4s. 9½**	**20/-**	**6s. 0**

20/6	6s. 1¾	25/6	7s. 7¾	31/-	9s. 3½	35/6	10s. 7¾	Guineas.	
21/-	6 3½	26/-	7 9½	31/6	9 5½	36/-	10 9½	1.	£0 6s. 3½
22/-	6 7¼	27/-	8 1¼	32/-	9 7¼	37/-	11 1¼	2.	0 12 7¼
22/6	6 9	27/6	8 3	32/6	9 9	37/6	11 3	3.	0 18 10¾
23/-	6 10¾	28/-	8 4¾	33/-	9 10¾	38/-	11 4¾	4.	1 5 2½
24/-	7 2½	29/-	8 8½	34/-	10 2½	39/-	11 8½	5.	1 11 6
25/-	**7s. 6**	**30/-**	**9s. 0**	**35/-**	**10s. 6**	**40/-**	**12s. 0**	6.	£1 17s. 9½

(=23 1/10 %* on Gross Returns).

£1	£0	6s	2½	£51	15	16s	2½	£101	31	6s	2½	£151	46	16s	2½
2	0	12	4¾	52	16	2	4¾	102	31	12	4¾	152	47	2	4¾
3	0	18	7¼	53	16	8	7¼	103	31	18	7¼	153	47	8	7¼
4	1	4	9½	54	16	14	9½	104	32	4	9½	154	47	14	9½
5	1	11	0	55	17	1	0	105	32	11	0	155	48	1	0
6	1	17	2½	56	17	7	2½	106	32	17	2½	156	48	7	2½
7	2	3	4¾	57	17	13	4¾	107	33	3	4¾	157	48	13	4¾
8	2	9	7¼	58	17	19	7¼	108	33	9	7¼	158	48	19	7¼
9	2	15	9½	59	18	5	9½	109	33	15	9½	159	49	5	9½
10	**3**	**2**	**0**	**60**	**18**	**12**	**0**	**110**	**34**	**2**	**0**	**160**	**49**	**12**	**0**
11	3	8	2½	61	18	18	2½	111	34	8	2½	161	49	18	2½
12	3	14	4¾	62	19	4	4¾	112	34	14	4¾	162	50	4	4¾
13	4	0	7¼	63	19	10	7¼	113	35	0	7¼	163	50	10	7¼
14	4	6	9½	64	19	16	9½	114	35	6	9½	164	50	16	9½
15	4	13	0	65	20	3	0	115	35	13	0	165	51	3	0
16	4	19	2½	66	20	9	2½	116	35	19	2½	166	51	9	2½
17	5	5	4¾	67	20	15	4¾	117	36	5	4¾	167	51	15	4¾
18	5	11	7¼	68	21	1	7¼	118	36	11	7¼	168	52	1	7¼
19	5	17	9½	69	21	7	9½	119	36	17	9½	169	52	7	9½
20	**6**	**4**	**0**	**70**	**21**	**14**	**0**	**120**	**37**	**4**	**0**	**170**	**52**	**14**	**0**
21	6	10	2½	71	22	0	2½	121	37	10	2½	171	53	0	2½
22	6	16	4¾	72	22	6	4¾	122	37	16	4¾	172	53	6	4¾
23	7	2	7¼	73	22	12	7¼	123	38	2	7¼	173	53	12	7¼
24	7	8	9½	74	22	18	9½	124	38	8	9½	174	53	18	9½
25	7	15	0	75	23	5	0	125	38	15	0	175	54	5	0
26	8	1	2½	76	23	11	2½	126	39	1	2½	176	54	11	2½
27	8	7	4¾	77	23	17	4¾	127	39	7	4¾	177	54	17	4¾
28	8	13	7¼	78	24	3	7¼	128	39	13	7¼	178	55	3	7¼
29	8	19	9½	79	24	9	9½	129	39	19	9½	179	55	9	9½
30	**9**	**6**	**0**	**80**	**24**	**16**	**0**	**130**	**40**	**6**	**0**	**180**	**55**	**16**	**0**
31	9	12	2½	81	25	2	2½	131	40	12	2½	181	56	2	2½
32	9	18	4¾	82	25	8	4¾	132	40	18	4¾	182	56	8	4¾
33	10	4	7¼	83	25	14	7¼	133	41	4	7¼	183	56	14	7¼
34	10	10	9½	84	26	0	9½	134	41	10	9½	184	57	0	9½
35	10	17	0	85	26	7	0	135	41	17	0	185	57	7	0
36	11	3	2½	86	26	13	2½	136	42	3	2½	186	57	13	2½
37	11	9	4¾	87	26	19	4¾	137	42	9	4¾	187	57	19	4¾
38	11	15	7¼	88	27	5	7¼	138	42	15	7¼	188	58	5	7¼
39	12	1	9½	89	27	11	9½	139	43	1	9½	189	58	11	9½
40	**12**	**8**	**0**	**90**	**27**	**18**	**0**	**140**	**43**	**8**	**0**	**190**	**58**	**18**	**0**
41	12	14	2½	91	28	4	2½	141	43	14	2½	191	59	4	2½
42	13	0	4¾	92	28	10	4¾	142	44	0	4¾	192	59	10	4¾
43	13	6	7¼	93	28	16	7¼	143	44	6	7¼	193	59	16	7¼
44	13	12	9½	94	29	2	9½	144	44	12	9½	194	60	2	9½
45	13	19	0	95	29	9	0	145	44	19	0	195	60	9	0
46	14	5	2½	96	29	15	2½	146	45	5	2½	196	60	15	2½
47	14	11	4¾	97	30	1	4¾	147	45	11	4¾	197	61	1	4¾
48	14	17	7¼	98	30	7	7¼	148	45	17	7¼	198	61	7	7¼
49	15	3	9½	99	30	13	9½	149	46	3	9½	199	61	13	9½
50	**15**	**10**	**0**	**100**	**31**	**0**	**0**	**150**	**46**	**10**	**0**	**200**	**62**	**0**	**0**

250	77	10s	0d	700	217	0s	0d	1200	372	0s	0d	2000	620	0s	0
300	93	0	0	750	232	10	0	1400	434	0	0	2500	775	0	0
400	124	0	0	800	248	0	0	1500	465	0	0	3000	930	0	0
500	155	0	0	900	279	0	0	1600	496	0	0	4000	1240	0	0
600	186	0s	0d	1000	310	0s	0d	1800	558	0s	0d	5000	1550	0s	0

69% off

1d	0s	0¼	4/1	1s	3¼	8/1	2s	6	12/1	3s	9	16/1	4s	11¾
2d	0	0½	2	1	3½	2	2	6½	2	3	9¼	2	5	0¼
3d	0	1	3	1	3¾	3	2	6¾	3	3	9½	3	5	0½
4d	0	1¼	4	1	4	4	2	7	4	3	10	4	5	0¾
5d	0	1½	5	1	4½	5	2	7¼	5	3	10¼	5	5	1
6d	0	1¾	4/6	1	4¾	8/6	2	7½	12/6	3	10½	16/6	5	1½
7d	0	2¼	7	1	5	7	2	8	7	3	10¾	7	5	1¾
8d	0	2½	8	1	5¼	8	2	8¼	8	3	11	8	5	2
9d	0	2¾	9	1	5¾	9	2	8½	9	3	11½	9	5	2¼
10d	0	3	10	1	6	10	2	8¾	10	3	11¾	10	5	2½
11d	0	3½	11	1	6¼	11	2	9¼	11	4	0	11	5	3
1/-	**0**	**3¾**	**5/-**	**1**	**6½**	**9/-**	**2**	**9½**	**13/-**	**4**	**0¼**	**17/-**	**5**	**3¼**
1/1	0	4	5/1	1	7	9/1	2	9¾	13/1	4	0¾	17/1	5	3½
2	0	4¼	2	1	7¼	2	2	10	2	4	1	2	5	3¾
3	0	4¾	3	1	7½	3	2	10½	3	4	1¼	3	5	4¼
4	0	5	4	1	7¾	4	2	10¾	4	4	1½	4	5	4½
5	0	5¼	5	1	8¼	5	2	11	5	4	2	5	5	4¾
1/6	0	5½	5/6	1	8½	9/6	2	11¼	13/6	4	2¼	17/6	5	5
7	0	6	7	1	8¾	7	2	11¾	7	4	2½	7	5	5½
8	0	6¼	8	1	9	8	3	0	8	4	2¾	8	5	5¾
9	0	6½	9	1	9½	9	3	0¼	9	4	3¼	9	5	6
10	0	6¾	10	1	9¾	10	3	0½	10	4	3½	10	5	6¼
11	0	7¼	11	1	10	11	3	1	11	4	3¾	11	5	6¾
2/-	**0**	**7½**	**6/-**	**1**	**10¼**	**10/-**	**3**	**1¼**	**14/-**	**4**	**4**	**18/-**	**5**	**7**
2/1	0	7¾	6/1	1	10¾	10/1	3	1½	14/1	4	4½	18/1	5	7¼
2	0	8	2	1	11	2	3	1¾	2	4	4¾	2	5	7½
3	0	8¼	3	1	11¼	3	3	2¼	3	4	5	3	5	8
4	0	8¾	4	1	11½	4	3	2½	4	4	5¼	4	5	8¼
5	0	9	5	1	11¾	5	3	2¾	5	4	5¾	5	5	8½
2/6	0	9¼	6/6	2	0¼	10/6	3	3	14/6	4	6	18/6	5	8¾
7	0	9½	7	2	0½	7	3	3¼	7	4	6¼	7	5	9¼
8	0	10	8	2	0¾	8	3	3¾	8	4	6½	8	5	9½
9	0	10¼	9	2	1	9	3	4	9	4	6¾	9	5	9¾
10	0	10½	10	2	1½	10	3	4¼	10	4	7¼	10	5	10
11	0	10¾	11	2	1¾	11	3	4½	11	4	7½	11	5	10¼
3/-	**0**	**11¼**	**7/-**	**2**	**2**	**11/-**	**3**	**5**	**15/-**	**4**	**7¾**	**19/-**	**5**	**10¾**
3/1	0	11½	7/1	2	2¼	11/1	3	5¼	15/1	4	8	19/1	5	11
2	0	11¾	2	2	2¾	2	3	5½	2	4	8½	2	5	11¼
3	1	0	3	2	3	3	3	5¾	3	4	8¾	3	5	11½
4	1	0½	4	2	3¼	4	3	6¼	4	4	9	4	6	0
5	1	0¾	5	2	3½	5	3	6½	5	4	9¼	5	6	0¼
3/6	1	1	7/6	2	4	11/6	3	6¾	15/6	4	9¾	19/6	6	0½
7	1	1¼	7	2	4¼	7	3	7	7	4	10	7	6	0¾
8	1	1¾	8	2	4½	8	3	7½	8	4	10¼	8	6	1¼
9	1	2	9	2	4¾	9	3	7¾	9	4	10½	9	6	1½
10	1	2¼	10	2	5¼	10	3	8	10	4	11	10	6	1¾
11	1	2½	11	2	5½	11	3	8¼	11	4	11¼	11	6	2
4/-	**1**	**3**	**8/-**	**2**	**5¾**	**12/-**	**3**	**8¾**	**16/-**	**4**	**11½**	**20/-**	**6**	**2½**

20/6	6s	4¼	25/6	7s	10¾	31/-	9s	7¼	35/6	11s	0	Guineas			
21/-	6	6	26/-	8	0¾	31/6	9	9¼	36/-	11	2	1.	£0	6	6
22/-	6	9¾	27/-	8	4½	32/-	9	11	37/-	11	5¾	2.	0	13	0¼
22/6	6	11¾	27/6	8	6¼	32/6	10	1	37/6	11	7½	3.	0	19	6¼
23/-	7	1½	28/-	8	8¼	33/-	10	2¾	38/-	11	9¼	4.	1	6	0½
24/-	7	5¼	29/-	9	0	34/-	10	6½	39/-	12	1	5.	1	12	6½
25/-	7s	9	**30/-**	9s	3½	**35/-**	10s	10¼	**40/-**	12s	4¾	6.	£1	19	0¾

(=23$\frac{7}{10}$% on Gross Returns).

£	£	s	d	£		s	d	£		s	d	£		s	d
1	0	6s	3	51	15	18s	9	101	31	11s	3	151	47	3s	9
2	0	12	6	52	16	5	0	102	31	17	6	152	47	10	0
3	0	18	9	53	16	11	3	103	32	3	9	153	47	16	3
4	1	5	0	54	16	17	6	104	32	10	0	154	48	2	6
5	1	11	3	55	17	3	9	105	32	16	3	155	48	8	9
6	1	17	6	56	17	10	0	106	33	2	6	156	48	15	0
7	2	3	9	57	17	16	3	107	33	8	9	157	49	1	3
8	2	10	0	58	18	2	6	108	33	15	0	158	49	7	6
9	2	16	3	59	18	8	9	109	34	1	3	159	49	13	9
10	3	2	6	60	18	15	0	110	34	7	6	160	50	0	0
11	3	8	9	61	19	1	3	111	34	13	9	161	50	6	3
12	3	15	0	62	19	7	6	112	35	0	0	162	50	12	6
13	4	1	3	63	19	13	9	113	35	6	3	163	50	18	9
14	4	7	6	64	20	0	0	114	35	12	6	164	51	5	0
15	4	13	9	65	20	6	3	115	35	18	9	165	51	11	3
16	5	0	0	66	20	12	6	116	36	5	0	166	51	17	6
17	5	6	3	67	20	18	9	117	36	11	3	167	52	3	9
18	5	12	6	68	21	5	0	118	36	17	6	168	52	10	0
19	5	18	9	69	21	11	3	119	37	3	9	169	52	16	3
20	6	5	0	70	21	17	6	120	37	10	0	170	53	2	6
21	6	11	3	71	22	3	9	121	37	16	3	171	53	8	9
22	6	17	6	72	22	10	0	122	38	2	6	172	53	15	0
23	7	3	9	73	22	16	3	123	38	8	9	173	54	1	3
24	7	10	0	74	23	2	6	124	38	15	0	174	54	7	6
25	7	16	3	75	23	8	9	125	39	1	3	175	54	13	9
26	8	2	6	76	23	15	0	126	39	7	6	176	55	0	0
27	8	8	9	77	24	1	3	127	39	13	9	177	55	6	3
28	8	15	0	78	24	7	6	128	40	0	0	178	55	12	6
29	9	1	3	79	24	13	9	129	40	6	3	179	55	18	9
30	9	7	6	80	25	0	0	130	40	12	6	180	56	5	0
31	9	13	9	81	25	6	3	131	40	18	9	181	56	11	3
32	10	0	0	82	25	12	6	132	41	5	0	182	56	17	6
33	10	6	3	83	25	18	9	133	41	11	3	183	57	3	9
34	10	12	6	84	26	5	0	134	41	17	6	184	57	10	0
35	10	18	9	85	26	11	3	135	42	3	9	185	57	16	3
36	11	5	0	86	26	17	6	136	42	10	0	186	58	2	6
37	11	11	3	87	27	3	9	137	42	16	3	187	58	8	9
38	11	17	6	88	27	10	0	138	43	2	6	188	58	15	0
39	12	3	9	89	27	16	3	139	43	8	9	189	59	1	3
40	12	10	0	90	28	2	6	140	43	15	0	190	59	7	6
41	12	16	3	91	28	8	9	141	44	1	3	191	59	13	9
42	13	2	6	92	28	15	0	142	44	7	6	192	60	0	0
43	13	8	9	93	29	1	3	143	44	13	9	193	60	6	3
44	13	15	0	94	29	7	6	144	45	0	0	194	60	12	6
45	14	1	3	95	29	13	9	145	45	6	3	195	60	18	9
46	14	7	6	96	30	0	0	146	45	12	6	196	61	5	0
47	14	13	9	97	30	6	3	147	45	18	9	197	61	11	3
48	15	0	0	98	30	12	6	148	46	5	0	198	61	17	6
49	15	6	3	99	30	18	9	149	46	11	3	199	62	3	9
50	15	12	6	100	31	5	0	150	46	17	6	200	62	10	0

£		s	d	£		s	d	£		s	d	£		s	d
250	78	2s	6d	700	218	15s	0d	1200	375	0s	0d	2000	625	0s	0d
300	93	15	0	750	234	7	6	1400	437	10	0	2500	781	5	0
400	125	0	0	800	250	0	0	1500	468	15	0	3000	937	10	0
500	156	5	0	900	281	5	0	1600	500	0	0	4000	1250	0	0
600	187	10s	0d	1000	312	10s	0d	1800	562	10s	0d	5000	1562	10s	0d

68¾% off.

1d	0s	0¼	4/1	1s	3¼	8/1	2s	6¼	12/1	3s	9¼	16/1	5s	0¼
2d	0	0¾	2	1	3¾	2	2	6¾	2	3	9¾	2	5	0¾
3d	0	1	3	1	4	3	2	7	3	3	10	3	5	1
4d	0	1¼	4	1	4¼	4	2	7¼	4	3	10¼	4	5	1¼
5d	0	1½	5	1	4½	5	2	7½	5	3	10½	5	5	1½
6d	0	2	4/6	1	5	8/6	2	8	12/6	3	11	16/6	5	2
7d	0	2¼	7	1	5¼	7	2	8¼	7	3	11¼	7	5	2¼
8d	0	2½	8	1	5½	8	2	8½	8	3	11½	8	5	2½
9d	0	2¾	9	1	5¾	9	2	8¾	9	3	11¾	9	5	2¾
10d	0	3¼	10	1	6¼	10	2	9¼	10	4	0¼	10	5	3¼
11d	0	3½	11	1	6½	11	2	9½	11	4	0½	11	5	3½
1/-	**0**	**3¾**	**5/-**	**1**	**6¾**	**9/-**	**2**	**9¾**	**13/-**	**4**	**0¾**	**17/-**	**5**	**3¾**
1/1	0	4	5/1	1	7	9/1	2	10	13/1	4	1	17/1	5	4
2	0	4½	2	1	7½	2	2	10½	2	4	1½	2	5	4½
3	0	4¾	3	1	7¾	3	2	10¾	3	4	1¾	3	5	4¾
4	0	5	4	1	8	4	2	11	4	4	2	4	5	5
5	0	5¼	5	1	8¼	5	2	11¼	5	4	2¼	5	5	5¼
1/6	0	5¾	5/6	1	8¾	9/6	2	11¾	13/6	4	2¾	17/6	5	5¾
7	0	6	7	1	9	7	3	0	7	4	3	7	5	6
8	0	6¼	8	1	9¼	8	3	0¼	8	4	3¼	8	5	6¼
9	0	6½	9	1	9½	9	3	0½	9	4	3½	9	5	6½
10	0	7	10	1	10	10	3	1	10	4	4	10	5	7
11	0	7¼	11	1	10¼	11	3	1¼	11	4	4¼	11	5	7¼
2/-	**0**	**7½**	**6/-**	**1**	**10½**	**10/-**	**3**	**1½**	**14/-**	**4**	**4½**	**18/-**	**5**	**7½**
2/1	0	7¾	6/1	1	10¾	10/1	3	1¾	14/1	4	4¾	18/1	5	7¾
2	0	8¼	2	1	11¼	2	3	2¼	2	4	5¼	2	5	8¼
3	0	8½	3	1	11½	3	3	2½	3	4	5½	3	5	8½
4	0	8¾	4	1	11¾	4	3	2¾	4	4	5¾	4	5	8¾
5	0	9	5	2	0	5	3	3	5	4	6	5	5	9
2/6	0	9½	6/6	2	0½	10/6	3	3½	14/6	4	6½	18/6	5	9½
7	0	9¾	7	2	0¾	7	3	3¾	7	4	6¾	7	5	9¾
8	0	10	8	2	1	8	3	4	8	4	7	8	5	10
9	0	10¼	9	2	1¼	9	3	4¼	9	4	7¼	9	5	10¼
10	0	10¾	10	2	1¾	10	3	4¾	10	4	7¾	10	5	10¾
11	0	11	11	2	2	11	3	5	11	4	8	11	5	11
3/-	**0**	**11¼**	**7/-**	**2**	**2¼**	**11/-**	**3**	**5¼**	**15/-**	**4**	**8¼**	**19/-**	**5**	**11¼**
3/1	0	11½	7/1	2	2½	11/1	3	5½	15/1	4	8½	19/1	5	11½
2	1	0	2	2	3	2	3	6	2	4	9	2	6	0
3	1	0¼	3	2	3¼	3	3	6¼	3	4	9¼	3	6	0¼
4	1	0½	4	2	3½	4	3	6½	4	4	9½	4	6	0½
5	1	0¾	5	2	3¾	5	3	6¾	5	4	9¾	5	6	0¾
3/6	1	1¼	7/6	2	4¼	11/6	3	7¼	15/6	4	10¼	19/6	6	1¼
7	1	1½	7	2	4½	7	3	7½	7	4	10½	7	6	1½
8	1	1¾	8	2	4¾	8	3	7¾	8	4	10¾	8	6	1¾
9	1	2	9	2	5	9	3	8	9	4	11	9	6	2
10	1	2½	10	2	5½	10	3	8½	10	4	11½	10	6	2½
11	1	2¾	11	2	5¾	11	3	8¾	11	4	11¾	11	6	2¾
4/-	**1**	**3**	**8/-**	**2**	**6**	**12/-**	**3**	**9**	**16/-**	**5**	**0**	**20/-**	**6**	**3**

20/6	6s	5	25/6	7s	11¾	31/-	9s	8¼	35/6	11s	1¼	Guineas.		
21/-	6	6¾	26/-	8	1½	31/6	9	10¼	36/-	11	3	1.	£0 6	6¾
22/-	6	10½	27/-	8	5¼	32/-	10	0	37/-	11	6¾	2.	0 13	1½
22/6	7	0½	27/6	8	7¼	32/6	10	2	37/6	11	8¾	3.	0 19	8¼
23/-	7	2¼	28/-	8	9	33/-	10	3¾	38/-	11	10½	4.	1 6	3
24/-	7	6	29/-	9	0¾	34/-	10	7½	39/-	12	2¼	5.	1 12	9¾
25/-	7	9¾	**30/-**	9	4½	**35/-**	10	11¼	**40/-**	12	6	6.	£1 19	4½

(23$\frac{13}{16}$%* on Gross Returns).

£1	£0	6s	4¾	£51	16	6s	4¾	£101	32	6s	4¾	£151	48	6s	4¾
2	0	12	9½	52	16	12	9½	102	32	12	9½	152	48	12	9½
3	0	19	2½	53	16	19	2½	103	32	19	2½	153	48	19	2½
4	1	5	7¼	54	17	5	7¼	104	33	5	7¼	154	49	5	7¼
5	1	12	0	55	17	12	0	105	33	12	0	155	49	12	0
6	1	18	4¾	56	17	18	4¾	106	33	18	4¾	156	49	18	4¾
7	2	4	9½	57	18	4	9½	107	34	4	9½	157	50	4	9½
8	2	11	2½	58	18	11	2½	108	34	11	2½	158	50	11	2½
9	2	17	7¼	59	18	17	7¼	109	34	17	7¼	159	50	17	7¼
10	**3**	**4**	**0**	**60**	**19**	**4**	**0**	**110**	**35**	**4**	**0**	**160**	**51**	**4**	**0**
11	3	10	4¾	61	19	10	4¾	111	35	10	4¾	161	51	10	4¾
12	3	16	9½	62	19	16	9½	112	35	16	9½	162	51	16	9½
13	4	3	2½	63	20	3	2½	113	36	3	2½	163	52	3	2½
14	4	9	7¼	64	20	9	7¼	114	36	9	7¼	164	52	9	7¼
15	4	16	0	65	20	16	0	115	36	16	0	165	52	16	0
16	5	2	4¾	66	21	2	4¾	116	37	2	4¾	166	53	2	4¾
17	5	8	9½	67	21	8	9½	117	37	8	9½	167	53	8	9½
18	5	15	2½	68	21	15	2½	118	37	15	2½	168	53	15	2½
19	6	1	7¼	69	22	1	7¼	119	38	1	7¼	169	54	1	7¼
20	**6**	**8**	**0**	**70**	**22**	**8**	**0**	**120**	**38**	**8**	**0**	**170**	**54**	**8**	**0**
21	6	14	4¾	71	22	14	4¾	121	38	14	4¾	171	54	14	4¾
22	7	0	9½	72	23	0	9½	122	39	0	9½	172	55	0	9½
23	7	7	2½	73	23	7	2½	123	39	7	2½	173	55	7	2½
24	7	13	7¼	74	23	13	7¼	124	39	13	7¼	174	55	13	7¼
25	8	0	0	75	24	0	0	125	40	0	0	175	56	0	0
26	8	6	4¾	76	24	6	4¾	126	40	6	4¾	176	56	6	4¾
27	8	12	9½	77	24	12	9½	127	40	12	9½	177	56	12	9½
28	8	19	2½	78	24	19	2½	128	40	19	2½	178	56	19	2½
29	9	5	7¼	79	25	5	7¼	129	41	5	7¼	179	57	5	7¼
30	**9**	**12**	**0**	**80**	**25**	**12**	**0**	**130**	**41**	**12**	**0**	**180**	**57**	**12**	**0**
31	9	18	4¾	81	25	18	4¾	131	41	18	4¾	181	57	18	4¾
32	10	4	9½	82	26	4	9½	132	42	4	9½	182	58	4	9½
33	10	11	2½	83	26	11	2½	133	42	11	2½	183	58	11	2½
34	10	17	7¼	84	26	17	7¼	134	42	17	7¼	184	58	17	7¼
35	11	4	0	85	27	4	0	135	43	4	0	185	59	4	0
36	11	10	4¾	86	27	10	4¾	136	43	10	4¾	186	59	10	4¾
37	11	16	9½	87	27	16	9½	137	43	16	9½	187	59	16	9½
38	12	3	2½	88	28	3	2½	138	44	3	2½	188	60	3	2½
39	12	9	7¼	89	28	9	7¼	139	44	9	7¼	189	60	9	7¼
40	**12**	**16**	**0**	**90**	**28**	**16**	**0**	**140**	**44**	**16**	**0**	**190**	**60**	**16**	**0**
41	13	2	4¾	91	29	2	4¾	141	45	2	4¾	191	61	2	4¾
42	13	8	9½	92	29	8	9½	142	45	8	9½	192	61	8	9½
43	13	15	2½	93	29	15	2½	143	45	15	2½	193	61	15	2½
44	14	1	7¼	94	30	1	7¼	144	46	1	7¼	194	62	1	7¼
45	14	8	0	95	30	8	0	145	46	8	0	195	62	8	0
46	14	14	4¾	96	30	14	4¾	146	46	14	4¾	196	62	14	4¾
47	15	0	9½	97	31	0	9½	147	47	0	9½	197	63	0	9½
48	15	7	2½	98	31	7	2½	148	47	7	2½	198	63	7	2½
49	15	13	7¼	99	31	13	7¼	149	47	13	7¼	199	63	13	7¼
50	**16**	**0**	**0**	**100**	**32**	**0**	**0**	**150**	**48**	**0**	**0**	**200**	**64**	**0**	**0**

250	80	0s	0d	700	224	0s	0d	1200	384	0s	0d	2000	640	0s	0
300	96	0	0	750	240	0	0	1400	448	0	0	2500	800	0	0
400	128	0	0	800	256	0	0	1500	480	0	0	3000	960	0	0
500	160	0	0	900	288	0	0	1600	512	0	0	4000	1280	0	0
600	192	0s	0d	1000	320	0s	0d	1800	576	0s	0d	5000	1600	0s	0

68% off

1d	0s	0¼	4/1	1s	3¾	8/1	2s	7	12/1	3s	10½	16/1	5s	1¾
2d	0	0¾	2	1	4	2	2	7¼	2	3	10¾	2	5	2
3d	0	1	3	1	4¼	3	2	7¾	3	3	11	3	5	2¼
4d	0	1¼	4	1	4¾	4	2	8	4	3	11¼	4	5	2¾
5d	0	1½	5	1	5	5	2	8¼	5	3	11¾	5	5	3
6d	0	2	4/6	1	5¼	8/6	2	8¾	12/6	4	0	16/6	5	3¼
7d	0	2¼	7	1	5½	7	2	9	7	4	0¼	7	5	3¾
8d	0	2½	8	1	6	8	2	9¼	8	4	0¾	8	5	4
9d	0	3	9	1	6¼	9	2	9½	9	4	1	9	5	4¼
10d	0	3¼	10	1	6½	10	2	10	10	4	1¼	10	5	4¾
11d	0	3½	11	1	7	11	2	10¼	11	4	1½	11	5	5
1/-	**0**	**3¾**	**5/-**	**1**	**7¼**	**9/-**	**2**	**10½**	**13/-**	**4**	**2**	**17/-**	**5**	**5¼**
1/1	0	4¼	5/1	1	7½	9/1	2	11	13/1	4	2¼	17/1	5	5½
2	0	4½	2	1	7¾	2	2	11¼	2	4	2½	2	5	6
3	0	4¾	3	1	8¼	3	2	11½	3	4	3	3	5	6¼
4	0	5	4	1	8½	4	2	11¾	4	4	3¼	4	5	6½
5	0	5½	5	1	8¾	5	3	0¼	5	4	3½	5	5	7
1/6	0	5¾	5/6	1	9	9/6	3	0½	13/6	4	3¾	17/6	5	7¼
7	0	6	7	1	9½	7	3	0¾	7	4	4¼	7	5	7½
8	0	6½	8	1	9¾	8	3	1	8	4	4½	8	5	7¾
9	0	6¾	9	1	10	9	3	1½	9	4	4¾	9	5	8¼
10	0	7	10	1	10½	10	3	1¾	10	4	5	10	5	8½
11	0	7¼	11	1	10¾	11	3	2	11	4	5½	11	5	8¾
2/-	**0**	**7¾**	**6/-**	**1**	**11**	**10/-**	**3**	**2½**	**14/-**	**4**	**5¾**	**18/-**	**5**	**9**
2/1	0	8	6/1	1	11¼	10/1	3	2¾	14/1	4	6	18/1	5	9½
2	0	8¼	2	1	11¾	2	3	3	2	4	6½	2	5	9¾
3	0	8¾	3	2	0	3	3	3¼	3	4	6¾	3	5	10
4	0	9	4	2	0¼	4	3	3¾	4	4	7	4	5	10¼
5	0	9¼	5	2	0¾	5	3	4	5	4	7¼	5	5	10¾
2/6	0	9½	6/6	2	1	10/6	3	4¼	14/6	4	7¾	18/6	5	11
7	0	10	7	2	1¼	7	3	4¾	7	4	8	7	5	11¼
8	0	10¼	8	2	1½	8	3	5	8	4	8¼	8	5	11¾
9	0	10½	9	2	2	9	3	5¼	9	4	8¾	9	6	0
10	0	11	10	2	2¼	10	3	5½	10	4	9	10	6	0¼
11	0	11¼	11	2	2½	11	3	6	11	4	9¼	11	6	0¾
3/-	**0**	**11½**	**7/-**	**2**	**3**	**11/-**	**3**	**6¼**	**15/-**	**4**	**9½**	**19/-**	**6**	**1**
3/1	0	11¾	7/1	2	3¼	11/1	3	6½	15/1	4	10	19/1	6	1¼
2	1	0¼	2	2	3½	2	3	7	2	4	10¼	2	6	1½
3	1	0½	3	2	3¾	3	3	7¼	3	4	10½	3	6	2
4	1	0¾	4	2	4	4	3	7½	4	4	11	4	6	2¼
5	1	1	5	2	4½	5	3	7¾	5	4	11¼	5	6	2½
3/6	1	1½	7/6	2	4¾	11/6	3	8¼	15/6	4	11½	19/6	6	3
7	1	1¾	7	2	5	7	3	8½	7	4	11¾	7	6	3¼
8	1	2	8	2	5½	8	3	8¾	8	5	0¼	8	6	3½
9	1	2¼	9	2	5¾	9	3	9	9	5	0½	9	6	3¾
10	1	2¾	10	2	6	10	3	9½	10	5	0¾	10	6	4¼
11	1	3	11	2	6½	11	3	9¾	11	5	1	11	6	4½
4/-	**1**	**3¼**	**8/-**	**2**	**6¾**	**12/-**	**3**	**10**	**16/-**	**5**	**1½**	**20/-**	**6**	**4¾**

20/6	6s	6¾	25/6	8s	2	31/-	9s	11	35/6	11s	4¼	Guineas		
21/-	6	8¾	26/-	8	3¾	31/6	10	1	36/-	11	6¼	1.	£0 6	8¾
22/-	7	0½	27/-	8	7¼	32/-	10	3	37/-	11	10	2.	0 13	5¼
22/6	7	2½	27/6	8	9½	32/6	10	4¾	37/6	12	0	3.	1 0	2
23/-	7	4¼	28/-	8	11½	33/-	10	6¾	38/-	12	2	4.	1 6	10½
24/-	7	8¼	29/-	9	3¼	34/-	10	10½	39/-	12	5¾	5.	1 13	7¼
25/-	8s	0	**30/-**	9s	7¼	**35/-**	11s	2½	**40/-**	12s	9½	6.	£2 0	3¾

(=24$\frac{2}{10}$% on Gross Returns).

£				£				£				£			
1	£0	6s.	6	51	16	11s.	6	101	£32	16s.	6	151	£49	1s.	6
2	0	13	0	52	16	18	0	102	33	3	0	152	49	8	0
3	0	19	6	53	17	4	6	103	33	9	6	153	49	14	6
4	1	6	0	54	17	11	0	104	33	16	0	154	50	1	0
5	1	12	6	55	17	17	6	105	34	2	6	155	50	7	6
6	1	19	0	56	18	4	0	106	34	9	0	156	50	14	0
7	2	5	6	57	18	10	6	107	34	15	6	157	51	0	6
8	2	12	0	58	18	17	0	108	35	2	0	158	51	7	0
9	2	18	6	59	19	3	6	109	35	8	6	159	51	13	6
10	£3	5s.	0	60	19	10s.	0	110	£35	15s.	0	160	£52	0s.	0
11	£3	11s.	6	61	19	16s.	6	111	£36	1s.	6	161	£52	6s.	6
12	3	18	0	62	20	3	0	112	36	8	0	162	52	13	0
13	4	4	6	63	20	9	6	113	36	14	6	163	52	19	6
14	4	11	0	64	20	16	0	114	37	1	0	164	53	6	0
15	4	17	6	65	21	2	6	115	37	7	6	165	53	12	6
16	5	4	0	66	21	9	0	116	37	14	0	166	53	19	0
17	5	10	6	67	21	15	6	117	38	0	6	167	54	5	6
18	5	17	0	68	22	2	0	118	38	7	0	168	54	12	0
19	6	3	6	69	22	8	6	119	38	13	6	169	54	18	6
20	£6	10s.	0	70	22	15s.	0	120	£39	0s.	0	170	£55	5s.	0
21	£6	16s.	6	71	23	1s.	6	121	£39	6s.	6	171	£55	11s.	6
22	7	3	0	72	23	8	0	122	39	13	0	172	55	18	0
23	7	9	6	73	23	14	6	123	39	19	6	173	56	4	6
24	7	16	0	74	24	1	0	124	40	6	0	174	56	11	0
25	8	2	6	75	24	7	6	125	40	12	6	175	56	17	6
26	8	9	0	76	24	14	0	126	40	19	0	176	57	4	0
27	8	15	6	77	25	0	6	127	41	5	6	177	57	10	6
28	9	2	0	78	25	7	0	128	41	12	0	178	57	17	0
29	9	8	6	79	25	13	6	129	41	18	6	179	58	3	6
30	£9	15s.	0	80	26	0s.	0	130	£42	5s.	0	180	£58	10s.	0
31	10	1s.	6	81	26	6s.	6	131	£42	11s.	6	181	£58	16s.	6
32	10	8	0	82	26	13	0	132	42	18	0	182	59	3	0
33	10	14	6	83	26	19	6	133	43	4	6	183	59	9	6
34	11	1	0	84	27	6	0	134	43	11	0	184	59	16	0
35	11	7	6	85	27	12	6	135	43	17	6	185	60	2	6
36	11	14	0	86	27	19	0	136	44	4	0	186	60	9	0
37	12	0	6	87	28	5	6	137	44	10	6	187	60	15	6
38	12	7	0	88	28	12	0	138	44	17	0	188	61	2	0
39	12	13	6	89	28	18	6	139	45	3	6	189	61	8	6
40	13	0s.	0	90	29	5s.	0	140	£45	10s.	0	190	£61	15s.	0
41	13	6s.	6	91	29	11s.	6	141	£45	16s.	6	191	£62	1s.	6
42	13	13	0	92	29	18	0	142	46	3	0	192	62	8	0
43	13	19	6	93	30	4	6	143	46	9	6	193	62	14	6
44	14	6	0	94	30	11	0	144	46	16	0	194	63	1	0
45	14	12	6	95	30	17	6	145	47	2	6	195	63	7	6
46	14	19	0	96	31	4	0	146	47	9	0	196	63	14	0
47	15	5	6	97	31	10	6	147	47	15	6	197	64	0	6
48	15	12	0	98	31	17	0	148	48	2	0	198	64	7	0
49	15	18	6	99	32	3	6	149	48	8	6	199	64	13	6
50	16	5s.	0	100	32	10s.	0	150	£48	15s.	0	200	£65	0s.	0

250	£81	5s.	0d	700	227	10s.	0d	1200	390	0s.	0d	2000	£650	0s.	0
300	97	10	0	750	243	15	0	1400	455	0	0	2500	812	10	0
400	130	0	0	800	260	0	0	1500	487	10	0	3000	975	0	0
500	162	10	0	900	292	10	0	1600	520	0	0	4000	1300	0	0
600	195	0s.	0d	1000	325	0s.	0d	1800	585	0s.	0d	5000	£1625	0s.	0

67½% off.

32½% **32½ Per Cent.** 32½%

1d	0s. 0¼	4/1	1s. 4	8/1	2s. 7½	12/1	3s.11¼	16/1	5s. 2¾
2d	0 0¾	2	1 4¼	2	2 7¾	2	3 11½	2	5 3
3d	0 1	3	1 4½	3	2 8¼	3	3 11¾	3	5 3½
4d	0 1¼	4	1 5	4	2 8½	4	4 0	4	5 3¾
5d	0 1¾	5	1 5¼	5	2 8¾	5	4 0½	5	5 4
6d	0 2	4/6	1 5½	8/6	2 9¼	12/6	4 0¾	16/6	5 4¼
7d	0 2¼	7	1 6	7	2 9½	7	4 1	7	5 4¾
8d	0 2½	8	1 6¼	8	2 9¾	8	4 1½	8	5 5
9d	0 3	9	1 6½	9	2 10¼	9	4 1¾	9	5 5¼
10d	0 3¼	10	1 6¾	10	2 10½	10	4 2	10	5 5¾
11d	0 3½	11	1 7¼	11	2 10¾	11	4 2½	11	5 6
1/-	0s. 4	**5/-**	1s. 7½	**9/-**	2s.11	**13/-**	4s. 2¾	**17/-**	5s. 6½
1/1	0s. 4¼	5/1	1s. 7¾	9/1	2s.11½	13/1	4s. 3	17/1	5s. 6¾
2	0 4½	2	1 8¼	2	2 11¾	2	4 3¼	2	5 7
3	0 5	3	1 8½	3	3 0	3	4 3¾	3	5 7¼
4	0 5¼	4	1 8¾	4	3 0½	4	4 4	4	5 7½
5	0 5½	5	1 9¼	5	3 0¾	5	4 4¼	5	5 8
1/6	0 5¾	5/6	1 9½	9/6	3 1	13/6	4 4¾	17/6	5 8¼
7	0 6¼	7	1 9¾	7	3 1½	7	4 5	7	5 8½
8	0 6½	8	1 10	8	3 1¾	8	4 5¼	8	5 9
9	0 6¾	9	1 10½	9	3 2	9	4 5¾	9	5 9¼
10	0 7¼	10	1 10¾	10	3 2¼	10	4 6	10	5 9½
11	0 7½	11	1 11	11	3 2¾	11	4 6¼	11	5 10
2/-	0s. 7¾	**6/-**	1s.11½	**10/-**	3s. 3	**14/-**	4s. 6½	**18/-**	5s.10¼
2/1	0s. 8¼	6/1	1s.11¾	10/1	3s. 3¼	14/1	4s. 7	18/1	5s.10½
2	0 8½	2	2 0	2	3 3¾	2	4 7¼	2	5 10¾
3	0 8¾	3	2 0½	3	3 4	3	4 7½	3	5 11¼
4	0 9	4	2 0¾	4	3 4¼	4	4 8	4	5 11½
5	0 9½	5	2 1	5	3 4¾	5	4 8¼	5	5 11¾
2/6	0 9¾	6/6	2 1¼	10/6	3 5	14/6	4 8½	18/6	6 0¼
7	0 10	7	2 1¾	7	3 5¼	7	4 9	7	6 0½
8	0 10½	8	2 2	8	3 5½	8	4 9¼	8	6 0¾
9	0 10¾	9	2 2¼	9	3 6	9	4 9½	9	6 1¼
10	0 11	10	2 2¾	10	3 6¼	10	4 9¾	10	6 1½
11	0 11½	11	2 3	11	3 6½	11	4 10¼	11	6 1¾
3/-	0s.11¾	**7/-**	2s. 3¼	**11/-**	3s. 7	**15/-**	4s.10½	**19/-**	6s. 2
3/1	1s. 0	7/1	2s. 3¾	11/1	3s. 7¼	15/1	4s.10¾	19/1	6s. 2½
2	1 0¼	2	2 4	2	3 7½	2	4 11¼	2	6 2¾
3	1 0¾	3	2 4¼	3	3 8	3	4 11½	3	6 3
4	1 1	4	2 4½	4	3 8¼	4	4 11¾	4	6 3¼
5	1 1¼	5	2 5	5	3 8½	5	5 0¼	5	6 3¾
3/6	1 1¾	7/6	2 5¼	11/6	3 8¾	15/6	5 0½	19/6	6 4
7	1 2	7	2 5½	7	3 9¼	7	5 0¾	7	6 4½
8	1 2¼	8	2 6	8	3 9½	8	5 1	8	6 4¾
9	1 2¾	9	2 6¼	9	3 9¾	9	5 1½	9	6 5
10	1 3	10	2 6½	10	3 10¼	10	5 1¾	10	6 5¼
11	1 3¼	11	2 7	11	3 10½	11	5 2	11	6 5¾
4/-	1s. 3½	**8/-**	2s. 7¼	**12/-**	3s.10¾	**16/-**	5s. 2½	**20/-**	6s. 6

20/6	6s. 8	25/6	8s. 3½	31/-	10s. 1	35/6	11s. 6½	Guineas.	
21/-	6 10	26/-	8 5½	31/6	10 2¾	36/-	11 8½	1.	£0 6s.10
22/-	7 1¾	27/-	8 9¼	32/-	10 4¾	37/-	12 0¼	2.	0 13 7¾
22/6	7 3¾	27/6	8 11¼	32/6	10 6¾	37/6	12 2¼	3.	1 0 5¾
23/-	7 5¾	28/-	9 1¼	33/-	10 8¾	38/-	12 4¼	4.	1 7 3½
24/-	7 9½	29/-	9 5	34/-	11 0½	39/-	12 8	5.	1 14 1½
25/-	8s. 1½	**30/-**	9s. 9	**35/-**	11s. 4½	**40/-**	13s. 0	6.	£2 0s. 11½

(24½%* on Gross Returns).

£	£ s. d.	£	£ s. d.	£	£ s. d.	£	£ s. d.
1	0 6s 7¼	51	16 16s 7¼	101	33 6s 7¼	151	49 16s 7¼
2	0 13 2½	52	17 3 2½	102	33 13 2½	152	50 3 2½
3	0 19 9½	53	17 9 9½	103	33 19 9½	153	50 9 9½
4	1 6 4¾	54	17 16 4¾	104	34 6 4¾	154	50 16 4¾
5	1 13 0	55	18 3 0	105	34 13 0	155	51 3 0
6	1 19 7¼	56	18 9 7¼	106	34 19 7¼	156	51 9 7¼
7	2 6 2½	57	18 16 2½	107	35 6 2½	157	51 16 2½
8	2 12 9½	58	19 2 9½	108	35 12 9½	158	52 2 9½
9	2 19 4¾	59	19 9 4¾	109	35 19 4¾	159	52 9 4¾
10	3 6 0	60	19 16 0	110	36 6 0	160	52 16 0
11	3 12 7¼	61	20 2 7¼	111	36 12 7¼	161	53 2 7¼
12	3 19 2½	62	20 9 2½	112	36 19 2½	162	53 9 2½
13	4 5 9½	63	20 15 9½	113	37 5 9½	163	53 15 9½
14	4 12 4¾	64	21 2 4¾	114	37 12 4¾	164	54 2 4¾
15	4 19 0	65	21 9 0	115	37 19 0	165	54 9 0
16	5 5 7¼	66	21 15 7¼	116	38 5 7¼	166	54 15 7¼
17	5 12 2½	67	22 2 2½	117	38 12 2½	167	55 2 2½
18	5 18 9½	68	22 8 9½	118	38 18 9½	168	55 8 9½
19	6 5 4¾	69	22 15 4¾	119	39 5 4¾	169	55 15 4¾
20	6 12 0	70	23 2 0	120	39 12 0	170	56 2 0
21	6 18 7¼	71	23 8 7¼	121	39 18 7¼	171	56 8 7¼
22	7 5 2½	72	23 15 2½	122	40 5 2½	172	56 15 2½
23	7 11 9½	73	24 1 9½	123	40 11 9½	173	57 1 9½
24	7 18 4¾	74	24 8 4¾	124	40 18 4¾	174	57 8 4¾
25	8 5 0	75	24 15 0	125	41 5 0	175	57 15 0
26	8 11 7¼	76	25 1 7¼	126	41 11 7¼	176	58 1 7¼
27	8 18 2½	77	25 8 2½	127	41 18 2½	177	58 8 2½
28	9 4 9½	78	25 14 9½	128	42 4 9½	178	58 14 9½
29	9 11 4¾	79	26 1 4¾	129	42 11 4¾	179	59 1 4¾
30	9 18 0	80	26 8 0	130	42 18 0	180	59 8 0
31	10 4 7¼	81	26 14 7¼	131	43 4 7¼	181	59 14 7¼
32	10 11 2½	82	27 1 2½	132	43 11 2½	182	60 1 2½
33	10 17 9½	83	27 7 9½	133	43 17 9½	183	60 7 9½
34	11 4 4¾	84	27 14 4¾	134	44 4 4¾	184	60 14 4¾
35	11 11 0	85	28 1 0	135	44 11 0	185	61 1 0
36	11 17 7¼	86	28 7 7¼	136	44 17 7¼	186	61 7 7¼
37	12 4 2½	87	28 14 2½	137	45 4 2½	187	61 14 2½
38	12 10 9½	88	29 0 9½	138	45 10 9½	188	62 0 9½
39	12 17 4¾	89	29 7 4¾	139	45 17 4¾	189	62 7 4¾
40	13 4 0	90	29 14 0	140	46 4 0	190	62 14 0
41	13 10 7¼	91	30 0 7¼	141	46 10 7¼	191	63 0 7¼
42	13 17 2½	92	30 7 2½	142	46 17 2½	192	63 7 2½
43	14 3 9½	93	30 13 9½	143	47 3 9½	193	63 13 9½
44	14 10 4¾	94	31 0 4¾	144	47 10 4¾	194	64 0 4¾
45	14 17 0	95	31 7 0	145	47 17 0	195	64 7 0
46	15 3 7¼	96	31 13 7¼	146	48 3 7¼	196	64 13 7¼
47	15 10 2½	97	32 0 2½	147	48 10 2½	197	65 0 2½
48	15 16 9½	98	32 6 9½	148	48 16 9½	198	65 6 9½
49	16 3 4¾	99	32 13 4¾	149	49 3 4¾	199	65 13 4¾
50	16 10 0	100	33 0 0	150	49 10 0	200	66 0 0

£	£ s. d.	£	£ s. d.	£	£ s. d.	£	£ s. d.
250	82 10s 0d	700	231 0s 0d	1200	396 0s 0d	2000	660 0s 0
300	99 0 0	750	247 10 0	1400	462 0 0	2500	825 0 0
400	132 0 0	800	264 0 0	1500	495 0 0	3000	990 0 0
500	165 0 0	900	297 0 0	1600	528 0 0	4000	1320 0 0
600	198 0s 0d	1000	330 0s 0d	1800	594 0s 0d	5000	1650 0s 0

67% off

1d	0s	0¼	4/1	1s	4¼	8/1	2s	8	12/1	3s	11¾	16/1	5s	3¾
2d	0	0¾	2	1	4½	2	2	8¼	2	4	0¼	2	5	4
3d	0	1	3	1	4¾	3	2	8¾	3	4	0½	3	5	4¼
4d	0	1¼	4	1	5¼	4	2	9	4	4	0¾	4	5	4¾
5d	0	1¾	5	1	5½	5	2	9¼	5	4	1¼	5	5	5
6d	0	2	4/6	1	5¾	8/6	2	9¾	12/6	4	1½	16/6	5	5¼
7d	0	2¼	7	1	6¼	7	2	10	7	4	1¾	7	5	5¾
8d	0	2¾	8	1	6½	8	2	10¼	8	4	2¼	8	5	6
9d	0	3	9	1	6¾	9	2	10¾	9	4	2½	9	5	6¼
10d	0	3¼	10	1	7¼	10	2	11	10	4	2¾	10	5	6¾
11d	0	3¾	11	1	7½	11	2	11¼	11	4	3¼	11	5	7
1/-	**0**	**4**	**5/-**	**1**	**7¾**	**9/-**	**2**	**11¾**	**13/-**	**4**	**3½**	**17/-**	**5**	**7¼**
1/1	0	4¼	5/1	1	8¼	1	3	0	1	4	3¾	1	5	7¾
2	0	4½	2	1	8½	2	3	0¼	2	4	4¼	2	5	8
3	0	5	3	1	8¾	3	3	0¾	3	4	4½	3	5	8¼
4	0	5¼	4	1	9	4	3	1	4	4	4¾	4	5	8¾
5	0	5½	5	1	9½	5	3	1¼	5	4	5¼	5	5	9
1/6	0	6	5/6	1	9¾	9/6	3	1½	13/6	4	5½	17/6	5	9¼
7	0	6¼	7	1	10	7	3	2	7	4	5¾	7	5	9¾
8	0	6½	8	1	10½	8	3	2¼	8	4	6	8	5	10
9	0	7	9	1	10¾	9	3	2½	9	4	6½	9	5	10¼
10	0	7¼	10	1	11	10	3	3	10	4	6¾	10	5	10½
11	0	7½	11	1	11½	11	3	3¼	11	4	7	11	5	11
2/-	**0**	**8**	**6/-**	**1**	**11¾**	**10/-**	**3**	**3½**	**14/-**	**4**	**7½**	**18/-**	**5**	**11¼**
2/1	0	8¼	1	2	0	10/1	3	4	1	4	7¾	1	5	11½
2	0	8½	2	2	0½	2	3	4¼	2	4	8	2	6	0
3	0	9	3	2	0¾	3	3	4½	3	4	8½	3	6	0¼
4	0	9¼	4	2	1	4	3	5	4	4	8¾	4	6	0½
5	0	9½	5	2	1½	5	3	5¼	5	4	9	5	6	1
2/6	0	10	6/6	2	1¾	10/6	3	5½	14/6	4	9½	18/6	6	1¼
7	0	10¼	7	2	2	7	3	6	7	4	9¾	7	6	1½
8	0	10½	8	2	2½	8	3	6¼	8	4	10	8	6	2
9	0	11	9	2	2¾	9	3	6½	9	4	10½	9	6	2¼
10	0	11¼	10	2	3	10	3	7	10	4	10¾	10	6	2½
11	0	11½	11	2	3½	11	3	7¼	11	4	11	11	6	3
3/-	**1**	**0**	**7/-**	**2**	**3¾**	**11/-**	**3**	**7½**	**15/-**	**4**	**11½**	**19/-**	**6**	**3¼**
3/1	1	0¼	1	2	4	1	3	8	15/1	4	11¾	1	6	3½
2	1	0½	2	2	4½	2	3	8¼	2	5	0	2	6	4
3	1	0¾	3	2	4¾	3	3	8½	3	5	0½	3	6	4¼
4	1	1¼	4	2	5	4	3	9	4	5	0¾	4	6	4½
5	1	1½	5	2	5¼	5	3	9¼	5	5	1	5	6	5
3/6	1	1¾	7/6	2	5¾	11/6	3	9½	15/6	5	1½	19/6	6	5¼
7	1	2¼	7	2	6	7	3	9¾	7	5	1¾	7	6	5½
8	1	2½	8	2	6¼	8	3	10¼	8	5	2	8	6	6
9	1	2¾	9	2	6¾	9	3	10½	9	5	2¼	9	6	6¼
10	1	3¼	10	2	7	10	3	10¾	10	5	2¾	10	6	6½
11	1	3½	11	2	7¼	11	3	11¼	11	5	3	11	6	6¾
4/-	**1**	**3¾**	**8/-**	**2**	**7¾**	**12/-**	**3**	**11½**	**16/-**	**5**	**3¼**	**20/-**	**6**	**7¼**

20/6	6s	9¼	25/6	8s	5	31/-	10s	2¾	35/6	11s	8½	Guineas.		
21/-	6	11¼	26/-	8	7	31/6	10	4¾	36/-	11	10½	1. £0	6	11¼
22/-	7	3	27/-	8	11	32/-	10	6¾	37/-	12	2½	2. 0	13	10¼
22/6	7	5	27/6	9	1	32/6	10	8¾	37/6	12	4½	3. 1	0	9½
23/-	7	7	28/-	9	3	33/-	10	10¾	38/-	12	6½	4. 1	7	8¾
24/-	7	11	29/-	9	6¾	34/-	11	2¾	39/-	12	10½	5. 1	14	7¾
25/-	8s	3	**30/-**	9s	10¾	**35/-**	11s	6½	**40/-**	13s	2½	6. £2	1	7

(=24 8/10% on Gross Returns).

£	Value	£	Value	£	Value	£	Value
£1	£0 6s. 8	£51	17 0s. 0	£101	£33 13s. 4	£151	£50 6s. 8
2	0 13 4	52	17 6 8	102	34 0 0	152	50 13 4
3	1 0 0	53	17 13 4	103	34 6 8	153	51 0 0
4	1 6 8	54	18 0 0	104	34 13 4	154	51 6 8
5	1 13 4	55	18 6 8	105	35 0 0	155	51 13 4
6	2 0 0	56	18 13 4	106	35 6 8	156	52 0 0
7	2 6 8	57	19 0 0	107	35 13 4	157	52 6 8
8	2 13 4	58	19 6 8	108	36 0 0	158	52 13 4
9	3 0 0	59	19 13 4	109	36 6 8	159	53 0 0
10	£3 6s. 8	60	20 0s. 0	110	£36 13s. 4	160	£53 6s. 8
11	£3 13s. 4	61	20 6s. 8	111	£37 0s. 0	161	£53 13s. 4
12	4 0 0	62	20 13 4	112	37 6 8	162	54 0 0
13	4 6 8	63	21 0 0	113	37 13 4	163	54 6 8
14	4 13 4	64	21 6 8	114	38 0 0	164	54 13 4
15	5 0 0	65	21 13 4	115	38 6 8	165	55 0 0
16	5 6 8	66	22 0 0	116	38 13 4	166	55 6 8
17	5 13 4	67	22 6 8	117	39 0 0	167	55 13 4
18	6 0 0	68	22 13 4	118	39 6 8	168	56 0 0
19	6 6 8	69	23 0 0	119	39 13 4	169	56 6 8
20	£6 13s. 4	70	23 6s. 8	120	£40 0s. 0	170	£56 13s. 4
21	£7 0s. 0	71	23 13s. 4	121	£40 6s. 8	171	£57 0s. 0
22	7 6 8	72	24 0 0	122	40 13 4	172	57 6 8
23	7 13 4	73	24 6 8	123	41 0 0	173	57 13 4
24	8 0 0	74	24 13 4	124	41 6 8	174	58 0 0
25	8 6 8	75	25 0 0	125	41 13 4	175	58 6 8
26	8 13 4	76	25 6 8	126	42 0 0	176	58 13 4
27	9 0 0	77	25 13 4	127	42 6 8	177	59 0 0
28	9 6 8	78	26 0 0	128	42 13 4	178	59 6 8
29	9 13 4	79	26 6 8	129	43 0 0	179	59 13 4
30	10 0s. 0	80	26 13s. 4	130	£43 6s. 8	180	£60 0s. 0
31	10 6s. 8	81	27 0s. 0	131	£43 13s. 4	181	£60 6s. 8
32	10 13 4	82	27 6 8	132	44 0 0	182	60 13 4
33	11 0 0	83	27 13 4	133	44 6 8	183	61 0 0
34	11 6 8	84	28 0 0	134	44 13 4	184	61 6 8
35	11 13 4	85	28 6 8	135	45 0 0	185	61 13 4
36	12 0 0	86	28 13 4	136	45 6 8	186	62 0 0
37	12 6 8	87	29 0 0	137	45 13 4	187	62 6 8
38	12 13 4	88	29 6 8	138	46 0 0	188	62 13 4
39	13 0 0	89	29 13 4	139	46 6 8	189	63 0 0
40	13 6s. 8	90	30 0s. 0	140	£46 13s. 4	190	£63 6s. 8
41	13 13s. 4	91	30 6s. 8	141	£47 0s. 0	191	£63 13s. 4
42	14 0 0	92	30 13 4	142	47 6 8	192	64 0 0
43	14 6 8	93	31 0 0	143	47 13 4	193	64 6 8
44	14 13 4	94	31 6 8	144	48 0 0	194	64 13 4
45	15 0 0	95	31 13 4	145	48 6 8	195	65 0 0
46	15 6 8	96	32 0 0	146	48 13 4	196	65 6 8
47	15 13 4	97	32 6 8	147	49 0 0	197	65 13 4
48	16 0 0	98	32 13 4	148	49 6 8	198	66 0 0
49	16 6 8	99	33 0 0	149	49 13 4	199	66 6 8
50	16 13s. 4	100	33 6s. 8	150	£50 0s. 0	200	£66 13s. 4
250	83 6s.8d	700	233 6s.8d	1200	400 0s.0d	2000	£666 13s. 4
300	100 0 0	750	250 0 0	1400	466 13 4	2500	833 6 8
400	133 6 8	800	266 13 4	1500	500 0 0	3000	1000 0 0
500	166 13 4	900	300 0 0	1600	533 6 8	4000	1333 6 8
600	200 0s. 0d	1000	333 6s.8d	1800	600 0s.0d	5000	£1666 13s. 4

66⅔% off.   (33⅓%=1-3rd)

33⅓ Per Cent.

1d	0s. 0¼	4/1	1s. 4¼	8/1	2s. 8¼	12/1	4s. 0¼	16/1	5s. 4¼
2d	0 0¾	2	1 4¾	2	2 8¾	2	4 0¾	2	5 4¾
3d	0 1	3	1 5	3	2 9	3	4 1	3	5 5
4d	0 1¼	4	1 5¼	4	2 9¼	4	4 1¼	4	5 5¼
5d	0 1¾	5	1 5¾	5	2 9¾	5	4 1¾	5	5 5¾
6d	0 2	4/6	1 6	8/6	2 10	12/6	4 2	16/6	5 6
7d	0 2¼	7	1 6¼	7	2 10¼	7	4 2¼	7	5 6¼
8d	0 2¾	8	1 6¾	8	2 10¾	8	4 2¾	8	5 6¾
9d	0 3	9	1 7	9	2 11	9	4 3	9	5 7
10d	0 3¼	10	1 7¼	10	2 11¼	10	4 3¼	10	5 7¼
11d	0 3¾	11	1 7¾	11	2 11¾	11	4 3¾	11	5 7¾
1/-	**0s. 4**	**5/-**	**1s. 8**	**9/-**	**3s. 0**	**13/-**	**4s. 4**	**17/-**	**5s. 8**
1/1	0s. 4¼	5/1	1s. 8¼	9/1	3s. 0¼	13/1	4s. 4¼	17/1	5s. 8¼
2	0 4¾	2	1 8¾	2	3 0¾	2	4 4¾	2	5 8¾
3	0 5	3	1 9	3	3 1	3	4 5	3	5 9
4	0 5¼	4	1 9¼	4	3 1¼	4	4 5¼	4	5 9¼
5	0 5¾	5	1 9¾	5	3 1¾	5	4 5¾	5	5 9¾
1/6	0 6	5/6	1 10	9/6	3 2	13/6	4 6	17/6	5 10
7	0 6¼	7	1 10¼	7	3 2¼	7	4 6¼	7	5 10¼
8	0 6¾	8	1 10¾	8	3 2¾	8	4 6¾	8	5 10¾
9	0 7	9	1 11	9	3 3	9	4 7	9	5 11
10	0 7¼	10	1 11¼	10	3 3¼	10	4 7¼	10	5 11¼
11	0 7¾	11	1 11¾	11	3 3¾	11	4 7¾	11	5 11¾
2/-	**0s. 8**	**6/-**	**2s. 0**	**10/-**	**3s. 4**	**14/-**	**4s. 8**	**18/-**	**6s. 0**
2/1	0s. 8¼	6/1	2s. 0¼	10/1	3s. 4¼	14/1	4s. 8¼	18/1	6s. 0¼
2	0 8¾	2	2 0¾	2	3 4¾	2	4 8¾	2	6 0¾
3	0 9	3	2 1	3	3 5	3	4 9	3	6 1
4	0 9¼	4	2 1¼	4	3 5¼	4	4 9¼	4	6 1¼
5	0 9¾	5	2 1¾	5	3 5¾	5	4 9¾	5	6 1¾
2/6	0 10	6/6	2 2	10/6	3 6	14/6	4 10	18/6	6 2
7	0 10¼	7	2 2¼	7	3 6¼	7	4 10¼	7	6 2¼
8	0 10¾	8	2 2¾	8	3 6¾	8	4 10¾	8	6 2¾
9	0 11	9	2 3	9	3 7	9	4 11	9	6 3
10	0 11¼	10	2 3¼	10	3 7¼	10	4 11¼	10	6 3¼
11	0 11¾	11	2 3¾	11	3 7¾	11	4 11¾	11	6 3¾
3/-	**1s. 0**	**7/-**	**2s. 4**	**11/-**	**3s. 8**	**15/-**	**5s. 0**	**19/-**	**6s. 4**
3/1	1s. 0¼	7/1	2s. 4¼	11/1	3s. 8¼	15/1	5s. 0¼	19/1	6s. 4¼
2	1 0¾	2	2 4¾	2	3 8¾	2	5 0¾	2	6 4¾
3	1 1	3	2 5	3	3 9	3	5 1	3	6 5
4	1 1¼	4	2 5¼	4	3 9¼	4	5 1¼	4	6 5¼
5	1 1¾	5	2 5¾	5	3 9¾	5	5 1¾	5	6 5¾
3/6	1 2	7/6	2 6	11/6	3 10	15/6	5 2	19/6	6 6
7	1 2¼	7	2 6¼	7	3 10¼	7	5 2¼	7	6 6¼
8	1 2¾	8	2 6¾	8	3 10¾	8	5 2¾	8	6 6¾
9	1 3	9	2 7	9	3 11	9	5 3	9	6 7
10	1 3¼	10	2 7¼	10	3 11¼	10	5 3¼	10	6 7¼
11	1 3¾	11	2 7¾	11	3 11¾	11	5 3¾	11	6 7¾
4/-	**1s. 4**	**8/-**	**2s. 8**	**12/-**	**4s. 0**	**16/-**	**5s. 4**	**20/-**	**6s. 8**

								Guineas.	
20/6	6s.10	25/6	8s. 6	31/-	10s. 4	35/6	11s.10		
21/-	7 0	26/-	8 8	31/6	10 6	36/-	12 0	1.	£0 7s. 0
22/-	7 4	27/-	9 0	32/-	10 8	37/-	12 4	2.	0 14 0
22/6	7 6	27/6	9 2	32/6	10 10	37/6	12 6	3.	1 1 0
23/-	7 8	28/-	9 4	33/-	11 0	38/-	12 8	4.	1 8 0
24/-	8 0	29/-	9 8	34/-	11 4	39/-	13 0	5.	1 15 0
25/-	**8s. 4**	**30/-**	**10s. 0**	**35/-**	**11s. 8**	**40/-**	**13s. 4**	6.	£2 2s. 0

(25% on Gross Returns).

34 Per Cent.

£1	£0	6s	9½	£51	17	6s	9½	£101	34	6s	9½	£151	51	6s	9½
2	0	13	7¼	52	17	13	7¼	102	34	13	7¼	152	51	13	7¼
3	1	0	4¾	53	18	0	4¾	103	35	0	4¾	153	52	0	4¾
4	1	7	2½	54	18	7	2½	104	35	7	2½	154	52	7	2½
5	1	14	0	55	18	14	0	105	35	14	0	155	52	14	0
6	2	0	9½	56	19	0	9½	106	36	0	9½	156	53	0	9½
7	2	7	7¼	57	19	7	7¼	107	36	7	7¼	157	53	7	7¼
8	2	14	4¾	58	19	14	4¾	108	36	14	4¾	158	53	14	4¾
9	3	1	2½	59	20	1	2½	109	37	1	2½	159	54	1	2½
10	**3**	**8**	**0**	**60**	**20**	**8**	**0**	**110**	**37**	**8**	**0**	**160**	**54**	**8**	**0**
11	3	14	9½	61	20	14	9½	111	37	14	9½	161	54	14	9½
12	4	1	7¼	62	21	1	7¼	112	38	1	7¼	162	55	1	7¼
13	4	8	4¾	63	21	8	4¾	113	38	8	4¾	163	55	8	4¾
14	4	15	2½	64	21	15	2½	114	38	15	2½	164	55	15	2½
15	5	2	0	65	22	2	0	115	39	2	0	165	56	2	0
16	5	8	9½	66	22	8	9½	116	39	8	9½	166	56	8	9½
17	5	15	7¼	67	22	15	7¼	117	39	15	7¼	167	56	15	7¼
18	6	2	4¾	68	23	2	4¾	118	40	2	4¾	168	57	2	4¾
19	6	9	2½	69	23	9	2½	119	40	9	2½	169	57	9	2½
20	**6**	**16**	**0**	**70**	**23**	**16**	**0**	**120**	**40**	**16**	**0**	**170**	**57**	**16**	**0**
21	7	2	9½	71	24	2	9½	121	41	2	9½	171	58	2	9½
22	7	9	7¼	72	24	9	7¼	122	41	9	7¼	172	58	9	7¼
23	7	16	4¾	73	24	16	4¾	123	41	16	4¾	173	58	16	4¾
24	8	3	2½	74	25	3	2½	124	42	3	2½	174	59	3	2½
25	8	10	0	75	25	10	0	125	42	10	0	175	59	10	0
26	8	16	9½	76	25	16	9½	126	42	16	9½	176	59	16	9½
27	9	3	7¼	77	26	3	7¼	127	43	3	7¼	177	60	3	7¼
28	9	10	4¾	78	26	10	4¾	128	43	10	4¾	178	60	10	4¾
29	9	17	2½	79	26	17	2½	129	43	17	2½	179	60	17	2½
30	**10**	**4**	**0**	**80**	**27**	**4**	**0**	**130**	**44**	**4**	**0**	**180**	**61**	**4**	**0**
31	10	10	9½	81	27	10	9½	131	44	10	9½	181	61	10	9½
32	10	17	7¼	82	27	17	7¼	132	44	17	7¼	182	61	17	7¼
33	11	4	4¾	83	28	4	4¾	133	45	4	4¾	183	62	4	4¾
34	11	11	2½	84	28	11	2½	134	45	11	2½	184	62	11	2½
35	11	18	0	85	28	18	0	135	45	18	0	185	62	18	0
36	12	4	9½	86	29	4	9½	136	46	4	9½	186	63	4	9½
37	12	11	7¼	87	29	11	7¼	137	46	11	7¼	187	63	11	7¼
38	12	18	4¾	88	29	18	4¾	138	46	18	4¾	188	63	18	4¾
39	13	5	2½	89	30	5	2½	139	47	5	2½	189	64	5	2½
40	**13**	**12**	**0**	**90**	**30**	**12**	**0**	**140**	**47**	**12**	**0**	**190**	**64**	**12**	**0**
41	13	18	9½	91	30	18	9½	141	47	18	9½	191	64	18	9½
42	14	5	7¼	92	31	5	7¼	142	48	5	7¼	192	65	5	7¼
43	14	12	4¾	93	31	12	4¾	143	48	12	4¾	193	65	12	4¾
44	14	19	2½	94	31	19	2½	144	48	19	2½	194	65	19	2½
45	15	6	0	95	32	6	0	145	49	6	0	195	66	6	0
46	15	12	9½	96	32	12	9½	146	49	12	9½	196	66	12	9½
47	15	19	7¼	97	32	19	7¼	147	49	19	7¼	197	66	19	7¼
48	16	6	4¾	98	33	6	4¾	148	50	6	4¾	198	67	6	4¾
49	16	13	2½	99	33	13	2½	149	50	13	2½	199	67	13	2½
50	**17**	**0**	**0**	**100**	**34**	**0**	**0**	**150**	**51**	**0**	**0**	**200**	**68**	**0**	**0**

250	85	0s	0d	700	238	0s	0d	1200	408	0s	0d	2000	680	0s	0
300	102	0	0	750	255	0	0	1400	476	0	0	2500	850	0	0
400	136	0	0	800	272	0	0	1500	510	0	0	3000	1020	0	0
500	170	0	0	900	306	0	0	1600	544	0	0	4000	1360	0	0
600	204	0s	0d	1000	340	0s	0d	1800	612	0s	0d	5000	1700	0s	0

66% off

34 Per Cent.

34%

1d	0s	0¼	4/1	1s	4¾	8/1	2s	9	12/1	4s	1¼	16/1	5s	5½
2d	0	0¾	2	1	5	2	2	9¼	2	4	1¾	2	5	6
3d	0	1	3	1	5¼	3	2	9¾	3	4	2	3	5	6¼
4d	0	1¼	4	1	5¾	4	2	10	4	4	2¼	4	5	6¾
5d	0	1¾	5	1	6	5	2	10¼	5	4	2¾	5	5	7
6d	0	2	4/6	1	6¼	8/6	2	10¾	12/6	4	3	16/6	5	7¼
7d	0	2½	7	1	6¾	7	2	11	7	4	3¼	7	5	7¾
8d	0	2¾	8	1	7	8	2	11¼	8	4	3¾	8	5	8
9d	0	3	9	1	7½	9	2	11¾	9	4	4	9	5	8¼
10d	0	3½	10	1	7¾	10	3	0	10	4	4¼	10	5	8¾
11d	0	3¾	11	1	8	11	3	0½	11	4	4¾	11	5	9
1/-	**0**	**4**	**5/-**	**1**	**8½**	**9/-**	**3**	**0¾**	**13/-**	**4**	**5**	**17/-**	**5**	**9¼**
1/1	0	4½	5/1	1	8¾	9/1	3	1	13/1	4	5½	17/1	5	9¾
2	0	4¾	2	1	9	2	3	1½	2	4	5¾	2	5	10
3	0	5	3	1	9½	3	3	1¾	3	4	6	3	5	10½
4	0	5½	4	1	9¾	4	3	2	4	4	6½	4	5	10¾
5	0	5¾	5	1	10	5	3	2½	5	4	6¾	5	5	11
1/6	0	6	5/6	1	10½	9/6	3	2¾	13/6	4	7	17/6	5	11½
7	0	6½	7	1	10¾	7	3	3	7	4	7½	7	5	11¾
8	0	6¾	8	1	11	8	3	3½	8	4	7¾	8	6	0
9	0	7¼	9	1	11½	9	3	3¾	9	4	8	9	6	0½
10	0	7½	10	1	11¾	10	3	4	10	4	8½	10	6	0¾
11	0	7¾	11	2	0¼	11	3	4½	11	4	8¾	11	6	1
2/-	**0**	**8¼**	**6/-**	**2**	**0½**	**10/-**	**3**	**4¾**	**14/-**	**4**	**9**	**18/-**	**6**	**1½**
2/1	0	8½	6/1	2	0¾	10/1	3	5¼	14/1	4	9½	18/1	6	1¾
2	0	8¾	2	2	1¼	2	3	5½	2	4	9¾	2	6	2
3	0	9¼	3	2	1½	3	3	5¾	3	4	10¼	3	6	2½
4	0	9½	4	2	1¾	4	3	6¼	4	4	10½	4	6	2¾
5	0	9¾	5	2	2¼	5	3	6½	5	4	10¾	5	6	3¼
2/6	0	10¼	6/6	2	2½	10/6	3	6¾	14/6	4	11¼	18/6	6	3½
7	0	10½	7	2	2¾	7	3	7¼	7	4	11½	7	6	3¾
8	0	11	8	2	3¼	8	3	7½	8	4	11¾	8	6	4¼
9	0	11¼	9	2	3½	9	3	7¾	9	5	0¼	9	6	4½
10	0	11½	10	2	4	10	3	8¼	10	5	0½	10	6	4¾
11	1	0	11	2	4¼	11	3	8½	11	5	0¾	11	6	5¼
3/-	**1**	**0¼**	**7/-**	**2**	**4½**	**11/-**	**3**	**9**	**15/-**	**5**	**1¼**	**19/-**	**6**	**5½**
3/1	1	0½	7/1	2	5	11/1	3	9¼	15/1	5	1½	19/1	6	5¾
2	1	1	2	2	5¼	2	3	9½	2	5	2	2	6	6¼
3	1	1¼	3	2	5½	3	3	10	3	5	2¼	3	6	6½
4	1	1½	4	2	6	4	3	10¼	4	5	2½	4	6	7
5	1	2	5	2	6¼	5	3	10½	5	5	3	5	6	7¼
3/6	1	2¼	7/6	2	6½	11/6	3	11	15/6	5	3¼	19/6	6	7½
7	1	2½	7	2	7	7	3	11¼	7	5	3½	7	6	8
8	1	3	8	2	7¼	8	3	11½	8	5	4	8	6	8¼
9	1	3¼	9	2	7½	9	4	0	9	5	4¼	9	6	8½
10	1	3¾	10	2	8	10	4	0¼	10	5	4½	10	6	9
11	1	4	11	2	8¼	11	4	0½	11	5	5	11	6	9¼
4/-	**1**	**4¼**	**8/-**	**2**	**8¾**	**12/-**	**4**	**1**	**16/-**	**5**	**5¼**	**20/-**	**6**	**9½**

20/6	6s	11¾	25/6	8s	8	31/-	10s	6½	35/6	12s	0¾	**Guineas**		
21/-	7	1¾	26/-	8	10	31/6	10	8½	36/-	12	3	**1.** £0	7	1¾
22/-	7	5¾	27/-	9	2¼	32/-	10	10½	37/-	12	7	**2.** 0	14	3¼
22/6	7	7¾	27/6	9	4¼	32/6	11	0½	37/6	12	9	**3.** 1	1	5
23/-	7	9¾	28/-	9	6¼	33/-	11	2¾	38/-	12	11	**4.** 1	8	6¾
24/-	8	2	29/-	9	10¼	34/-	11	6¾	39/-	13	3	**5.** 1	15	8½
25/-	8s	6	**30/-**	10s	2½	**35/-**	11s	10¾	**40/-**	13s	7¼	**6.** £2	2	10

(=$25\frac{4}{10}$% on Gross Returns).

No.	£ s. d.	No.	£ s. d.	No.	£ s. d.	No.	£ s. d.
£1	£0 7s. 0	£51	17 17s. 0	£101	£35 7s. 0	£151	£52 17s. 0
2	0 14 0	52	18 4 0	102	35 14 0	152	53 4 0
3	1 1 0	53	18 11 0	103	36 1 0	153	53 11 0
4	1 8 0	54	18 18 0	104	36 8 0	154	53 18 0
5	1 15 0	55	19 5 0	105	36 15 0	155	54 5 0
6	2 2 0	56	19 12 0	106	37 2 0	156	54 12 0
7	2 9 0	57	19 19 0	107	37 9 0	157	54 19 0
8	2 16 0	58	20 6 0	108	37 16 0	158	55 6 0
9	3 3 0	59	20 13 0	109	38 3 0	159	55 13 0
10	£3 10s. 0	60	21 0s. 0	110	£38 10s. 0	160	£56 0s. 0
11	£3 17s. 0	61	21 7s. 0	111	£38 17s. 0	161	£56 7s. 0
12	4 4 0	62	21 14 0	112	39 4 0	162	56 14 0
13	4 11 0	63	22 1 0	113	39 11 0	163	57 1 0
14	4 18 0	64	22 8 0	114	39 18 0	164	57 8 0
15	5 5 0	65	22 15 0	115	40 5 0	165	57 15 0
16	5 12 0	66	23 2 0	116	40 12 0	166	58 2 0
17	5 19 0	67	23 9 0	117	40 19 0	167	58 9 0
18	6 6 0	68	23 16 0	118	41 6 0	168	58 16 0
19	6 13 0	69	24 3 0	119	41 13 0	169	59 3 0
20	£7 0s. 0	70	24 10s. 0	120	£42 0s. 0	170	£59 10s. 0
21	£7 7s. 0	71	24 17s. 0	121	£42 7s. 0	171	£59 17s. 0
22	7 14 0	72	25 4 0	122	42 14 0	172	60 4 0
23	8 1 0	73	25 11 0	123	43 1 0	173	60 11 0
24	8 8 0	74	25 18 0	124	43 8 0	174	60 18 0
25	8 15 0	75	26 5 0	125	43 15 0	175	61 5 0
26	9 2 0	76	26 12 0	126	44 2 0	176	61 12 0
27	9 9 0	77	26 19 0	127	44 9 0	177	61 19 0
28	9 16 0	78	27 6 0	128	44 16 0	178	62 6 0
29	10 3 0	79	27 13 0	129	45 3 0	179	62 13 0
30	10 10s. 0	80	28 0s. 0	130	£45 10s. 0	180	£63 0s. 0
31	10 17s. 0	81	28 7s. 0	131	£45 17s. 0	181	£63 7s. 0
32	11 4 0	82	28 14 0	132	46 4 0	182	63 14 0
33	11 11 0	83	29 1 0	133	46 11 0	183	64 1 0
34	11 18 0	84	29 8 0	134	46 18 0	184	64 8 0
35	12 5 0	85	29 15 0	135	47 5 0	185	64 15 0
36	12 12 0	86	30 2 0	136	47 12 0	186	65 2 0
37	12 19 0	87	30 9 0	137	47 19 0	187	65 9 0
38	13 6 0	88	30 16 0	138	48 6 0	188	65 16 0
39	13 13 0	89	31 3 0	139	48 13 0	189	66 3 0
40	14 0s. 0	90	31 10s. 0	140	£49 0s. 0	190	£66 10s. 0
41	14 7s. 0	91	31 17s. 0	141	£49 7s. 0	191	£66 17s. 0
42	14 14 0	92	32 4 0	142	49 14 0	192	67 4 0
43	15 1 0	93	32 11 0	143	50 1 0	193	67 11 0
44	15 8 0	94	32 18 0	144	50 8 0	194	67 18 0
45	15 15 0	95	33 5 0	145	50 15 0	195	68 5 0
46	16 2 0	96	33 12 0	146	51 2 0	196	68 12 0
47	16 9 0	97	33 19 0	147	51 9 0	197	68 19 0
48	16 16 0	98	34 6 0	148	51 16 0	198	69 6 0
49	17 3 0	99	34 13 0	149	52 3 0	199	69 13 0
50	17 10s. 0	100	35 0s. 0	150	£52 10s. 0	200	£70 0s. 0
250	£87 10s. 0d	700	245 0s.0d	1200	420 0s.0d	2000	£700 0s. 0
300	105 0 0	750	262 10 0	1400	490 0 0	2500	875 0 0
400	140 0 0	800	280 0 0	1500	525 0 0	3000	1050 0 0
500	175 0 0	900	315 0 0	1600	560 0 0	4000	1400 0 0
600	210 0s. 0d	1000	350 0s.0d	1800	630 0s.0d	5000	£1750 0s. 0

65% off.

35% THIRTY-FIVE PER CENT. 35%

1d	0s. 0¼	4/1	1s. 5¼	8/1	2s.10	12/1	4s. 2¾	16/1	5s. 7½
2d	0 0¾	2	1 5½	2	2 10¼	2	4 3	2	5 8
3d	0 1	3	1 5¾	3	2 10¾	3	4 3½	3	5 8¼
4d	0 1½	4	1 6¼	4	2 11	4	4 3¾	4	5 8½
5d	0 1¾	5	1 6½	5	2 11¼	5	4 4¼	5	5 9
6d	0 2	4/6	1 7	8/6	2 11¾	12/6	4 4½	16/6	5 9¼
7d	0 2½	7	1 7¼	7	3 0	7	4 4¾	7	5 9¾
8d	0 2¾	8	1 7½	8	3 0½	8	4 5¼	8	5 10
9d	0 3¼	9	1 8	9	3 0¾	9	4 5½	9	5 10¼
10d	0 3½	10	1 8¼	10	3 1	10	4 6	10	5 10¾
11d	0 3¾	11	1 8¾	11	3 1½	11	4 6¼	11	5 11
1/-	0s. 4¼	**5/-**	1s. 9	**9/-**	3s. 1¾	**13/-**	4s. 6½	**17/-**	5s.11½
1/1	0s. 4½	5/1	1s. 9¼	9/1	3s. 2¼	13/1	4s. 7	17/1	5s.11¾
2	0 5	2	1 9¾	2	3 2½	2	4 7¼	2	6 0
3	0 5¼	3	1 10	3	3 2¾	3	4 7¾	3	6 0½
4	0 5½	4	1 10½	4	3 3¼	4	4 8	4	6 0¾
5	0 6	5	1 10¾	5	3 3½	5	4 8¼	5	6 1¼
1/6	0 6¼	5/6	1 11	9/6	3 4	13/6	4 8¾	17/6	6 1½
7	0 6¾	7	1 11½	7	3 4¼	7	4 9	7	6 1¾
8	0 7	8	1 11¾	8	3 4½	8	4 9½	8	6 2¼
9	0 7¼	9	2 0¼	9	3 5	9	4 9¾	9	6 2½
10	0 7¾	10	2 0½	10	3 5¼	10	4 10	10	6 3
11	0 8	11	2 0¾	11	3 5¾	11	4 10½	11	6 3¼
2/-	0s. 8½	**6/-**	2s. 1¼	**10/-**	3s. 6	**14/-**	4s.10¾	**18/-**	6s. 3½
2/1	0s. 8¾	6/1	2s. 1½	10/1	3s. 6¼	14/1	4s.11¼	18/1	6s. 4
2	0 9	2	2 2	2	3 6¾	2	4 11½	2	6 4¼
3	0 9½	3	2 2¼	3	3 7	3	4 11¾	3	6 4¾
4	0 9¾	4	2 2½	4	3 7½	4	5 0¼	4	6 5
5	0 10¼	5	2 3	5	3 7¾	5	5 0½	5	6 5¼
2/6	0 10½	6/6	2 3¼	10/6	3 8	14/6	5 1	18/6	6 5¾
7	0 10¾	7	2 3¾	7	3 8½	7	5 1¼	7	6 6
8	0 11¼	8	2 4	8	3 8¾	8	5 1½	8	6 6½
9	0 11½	9	2 4¼	9	3 9¼	9	5 2	9	6 6¾
10	1 0	10	2 4¾	10	3 9½	10	5 2¼	10	6 7
11	1 0¼	11	2 5	11	3 9¾	11	5 2¾	11	6 7½
3/-	1s. 0½	**7/-**	2s. 5½	**11/-**	3s.10¼	**15/-**	5s. 3	**19/-**	6s. 7¾
3/1	1s. 1	7/1	2s. 5¾	11/1	3s.10½	15/1	5s. 3¼	19/1	6s. 8¼
2	1 1¼	2	2 6	2	3 11	2	5 3¾	2	6 8½
3	1 1¾	3	2 6½	3	3 11¼	3	5 4	3	6 8¾
4	1 2	4	2 6¾	4	3 11½	4	5 4½	4	6 9¼
5	1 2¼	5	2 7¼	5	4 0	5	5 4¾	5	6 9½
3/6	1 2¾	7/6	2 7½	11/6	4 0¼	15/6	5 5	19/6	6 10
7	1 3	7	2 7¾	7	4 0¾	7	5 5½	7	6 10¼
8	1 3½	8	2 8¼	8	4 1	8	5 5¾	8	6 10½
9	1 3¾	9	2 8½	9	4 1¼	9	5 6¼	9	6 11
10	1 4	10	2 9	10	4 1¾	10	5 6½	10	6 11¼
11	1 4½	11	2 9¼	11	4 2	11	5 6¾	11	6 11¾
4/-	1s. 4¾	**8/-**	2s. 9½	**12/-**	4s. 2½	**16/-**	5s. 7¼	**20/-**	7s. 0

20/6	7s. 2	25/6	8s.11	31/-	10s.10¼	35/6	12s. 5	Guineas.	
21/-	7 4¼	26/-	9 1¼	31/6	11 0¼	36/-	12 7¼	1.	£0 7s. 4¼
22/-	7 8½	27/-	9 5½	32/-	11 2½	37/-	12 11½	2.	0 14 8½
22/6	7 10½	27/6	9 7½	32/6	11 4½	37/6	13 1½	3.	1 2 0½
23/-	8 0½	28/-	9 9½	33/-	11 6½	38/-	13 3½	4.	1 9 4¾
24/-	8 4¾	29/-	10 1¾	34/-	11 10¾	39/-	13 7¾	5.	1 16 9
25/-	8s. 9	**30/-**	10s. 6	**35/-**	12s. 3	**40/-**	14s. 0	6.	£2 4s. 1½

(=25 9/10 %* on Gross Returns).

£			£			£			£		
1	£0	7s 4	£51	18	14s 0	£101	37	0s 8	£151	55	7s 4
2	0	14 8	52	19	1 4	102	37	8 0	152	55	14 8
3	1	2 0	53	19	8 8	103	37	15 4	153	56	2 0
4	1	9 4	54	19	16 0	104	38	2 8	154	56	9 4
5	1	16 8	55	20	3 4	105	38	10 0	155	56	16 8
6	2	4 0	56	20	10 8	106	38	17 4	156	57	4 0
7	2	11 4	57	20	18 0	107	39	4 8	157	57	11 4
8	2	18 8	58	21	5 4	108	39	12 0	158	57	18 8
9	3	6 0	59	21	12 8	109	39	19 4	159	58	6 0
10	3	13 4	60	22	0 0	110	40	6 8	160	58	13 4
11	4	0 8	61	22	7 4	111	40	14 0	161	59	0 8
12	4	8 0	62	22	14 8	112	41	1 4	162	59	8 0
13	4	15 4	63	23	2 0	113	41	8 8	163	59	15 4
14	5	2 8	64	23	9 4	114	41	16 0	164	60	2 8
15	5	10 0	65	23	16 8	115	42	3 4	165	60	10 0
16	5	17 4	66	24	4 0	116	42	10 8	166	60	17 4
17	6	4 8	67	24	11 4	117	42	18 0	167	61	4 8
18	6	12 0	68	24	18 8	118	43	5 4	168	61	12 0
19	6	19 4	69	25	6 0	119	43	12 8	169	61	19 4
20	7	6 8	70	25	13 4	120	44	0 0	170	62	6 8
21	7	14 0	71	26	0 8	121	44	7 4	171	62	14 0
22	8	1 4	72	26	8 0	122	44	14 8	172	63	1 4
23	8	8 8	73	26	15 4	123	45	2 0	173	63	8 8
24	8	16 0	74	27	2 8	124	45	9 4	174	63	16 0
25	9	3 4	75	27	10 0	125	45	16 8	175	64	3 4
26	9	10 8	76	27	17 4	126	46	4 0	176	64	10 8
27	9	18 0	77	28	4 8	127	46	11 4	177	64	18 0
28	10	5 4	78	28	12 0	128	46	18 8	178	65	5 4
29	10	12 8	79	28	19 4	129	47	6 0	179	65	12 8
30	11	0 0	80	29	6 8	130	47	13 4	180	66	0 0
31	11	7 4	81	29	14 0	131	48	0 8	181	66	7 4
32	11	14 8	82	30	1 4	132	48	8 0	182	66	14 8
33	12	2 0	83	30	8 8	133	48	15 4	183	67	2 0
34	12	9 4	84	30	16 0	134	49	2 8	184	67	9 4
35	12	16 8	85	31	3 4	135	49	10 0	185	67	16 8
36	13	4 0	86	31	10 8	136	49	17 4	186	68	4 0
37	13	11 4	87	31	18 0	137	50	4 8	187	68	11 4
38	13	18 8	88	32	5 4	138	50	12 0	188	68	18 8
39	14	6 0	89	32	12 8	139	50	19 4	189	69	6 0
40	14	13 4	90	33	0 0	140	51	6 8	190	69	13 4
41	15	0 8	91	33	7 4	141	51	14 0	191	70	0 8
42	15	8 0	92	33	14 8	142	52	1 4	192	70	8 0
43	15	15 4	93	34	2 0	143	52	8 8	193	70	15 4
44	16	2 8	94	34	9 4	144	52	16 0	194	71	2 8
45	16	10 0	95	34	16 8	145	53	3 4	195	71	10 0
46	16	17 4	96	35	4 0	146	53	10 8	196	71	17 4
47	17	4 8	97	35	11 4	147	53	18 0	197	72	4 8
48	17	12 0	98	35	18 8	148	54	5 4	198	72	12 0
49	17	19 4	99	36	6 0	149	54	12 8	199	72	19 4
50	18	6 8	100	36	13 4	150	55	0 0	200	73	6 8

250	91 13s 4d	700	256 13s 4d	1200	440 0s 0d	2000	733 6s 8
300	110 0 0	750	275 0 0	1400	513 6 8	2500	916 13 4
400	146 13 4	800	293 6 8	1500	550 0 0	3000	1100 0 0
500	183 6 8	900	330 0 0	1600	586 13 4	4000	1466 13 4
600	220 0s 0d	1000	366 13s 4d	1800	660 0s 0d	5000	1833 6s 8

63⅓% off   (=33⅓% less 5%)

36⅔ Per Cent.

36⅔%

	s.	d.		s.	d.		s.	d.		s.	d.		s.	d.
1d	0s	0¼	4/1	1s	6	8/1	2s	11½	12/1	4s	5¼	16/1	5s	10¾
2d	0	0¾	2	1	6¼	2	3	0	2	4	5½	2	5	11¼
3d	0	1	3	1	6¾	3	3	0¼	3	4	6	3	5	11½
4d	0	1½	4	1	7	4	3	0¾	4	4	6¼	4	5	11¾
5d	0	1¾	5	1	7½	5	3	1	5	4	6¾	5	6	0¼
6d	0	2¼	4/6	1	7¾	8/6	3	1½	12/6	4	7	16/6	6	0½
7d	0	2½	7	1	8¼	7	3	1¾	7	4	7¼	7	6	1
8d	0	3	8	1	8½	8	3	2¼	8	4	7¾	8	6	1¼
9d	0	3¼	9	1	9	9	3	2½	9	4	8	9	6	1¾
10d	0	3¾	10	1	9¼	10	3	2¾	10	4	8½	10	6	2
11d	0	4	11	1	9¾	11	3	3¼	11	4	8¾	11	6	2½
1/-	**0**	**4½**	**5/-**	**1**	**10**	**9/-**	**3**	**3½**	**13/-**	**4**	**9¼**	**17/-**	**6**	**2¾**
1/1	0	4¾	5/1	1	10¼	1	3	4	1	4	9½	1	6	3¼
2	0	5¼	2	1	10¾	2	3	4¼	2	4	10	2	6	3½
3	0	5½	3	1	11	3	3	4¾	3	4	10¼	3	6	4
4	0	5¾	4	1	11½	4	3	5	4	4	10¾	4	6	4¼
5	0	6¼	5	1	11¾	5	3	5½	5	4	11	5	6	4¾
1/6	0	6½	5/6	2	0¼	9/6	3	5¾	13/6	4	11½	17/6	6	5
7	0	7	7	2	0½	7	3	6¼	7	4	11¾	7	6	5¼
8	0	7¼	8	2	1	8	3	6½	8	5	0¼	8	6	5¾
9	0	7¾	9	2	1¼	9	3	7	9	5	0½	9	6	6
10	0	8	10	2	1¾	10	3	7¼	10	5	0¾	10	6	6½
11	0	8½	11	2	2	11	3	7¾	11	5	1¼	11	6	6¾
2/-	**0**	**8¾**	**6/-**	**2**	**2½**	**10/-**	**3**	**8**	**14/-**	**5**	**1½**	**18/-**	**6**	**7¼**
2/1	0	9¼	1	2	2¾	10/1	3	8¼	1	5	2	1	6	7½
2	0	9½	2	2	3¼	2	3	8¾	2	5	2¼	2	6	8
3	0	10	3	2	3½	3	3	9	3	5	2¾	3	6	8¼
4	0	10¼	4	2	3¾	4	3	9½	4	5	3	4	6	8¾
5	0	10¾	5	2	4¼	5	3	9¾	5	5	3½	5	6	9
2/6	0	11	6/6	2	4½	10/6	3	10¼	14/6	5	3¾	18/6	6	9½
7	0	11¼	7	2	5	7	3	10½	7	5	4¼	7	6	9¾
8	0	11¾	8	2	5¼	8	3	11	8	5	4½	8	6	10¼
9	1	0	9	2	5¾	9	3	11¼	9	5	5	9	6	10½
10	1	0½	10	2	6	10	3	11¾	10	5	5¼	10	6	10¾
11	1	0¾	11	2	6½	11	4	0	11	5	5¾	11	6	11¼
3/-	**1**	**1¼**	**7/-**	**2**	**6¾**	**11/-**	**4**	**0½**	**15/-**	**5**	**6**	**19/-**	**6**	**11½**
3/1	1	1½	1	2	7¼	1	4	0¾	15/1	5	6¼	1	7	0
2	1	2	2	2	7½	2	4	1¼	2	5	6¾	2	7	0¼
3	1	2¼	3	2	8	3	4	1½	3	5	7	3	7	0¾
4	1	2¾	4	2	8¼	4	4	1¾	4	5	7½	4	7	1
5	1	3	5	2	8¾	5	4	2¼	5	5	7¾	5	7	1½
3/6	1	3½	7/6	2	9	11/6	4	2½	15/6	5	8¼	19/6	7	1¾
7	1	3¾	7	2	9¼	7	4	3	7	5	8½	7	7	2¼
8	1	4¼	8	2	9¾	8	4	3¼	8	5	9	8	7	2½
9	1	4½	9	2	10	9	4	3¾	9	5	9¼	9	7	3
10	1	4¾	10	2	10½	10	4	4	10	5	9¾	10	7	3¼
11	1	5¼	11	2	10¾	11	4	4½	11	5	10	11	7	3¾
4/-	**1**	**5½**	**8/-**	**2**	**11¼**	**12/-**	**4**	**4¾**	**16/-**	**5**	**10½**	**20/-**	**7**	**4**

												Guineas.			
20/6	7s	6¼	25/6	9s	4¼	31/-	11s	4½	35/6	13s	0¼				
21/-	7	8½	26/-	9	6½	31/6	11	6½	36/-	13	2½	1.	£0	7	8½
22/-	8	0¾	27/-	9	10¾	32/-	11	8¾	37/-	13	6¾	2.	0	15	4¾
22/6	8	3	27/6	10	1	32/6	11	11	37/6	13	9	3.	1	3	1¼
23/-	8	5¼	28/-	10	3¼	33/-	12	1¼	38/-	13	11¼	4.	1	10	9½
24/-	8	9½	29/-	10	7½	34/-	12	5½	39/-	14	3½	5.	1	18	6
25/-	9s	2	**30/-**	11s	0	**35/-**	12s	10	**40/-**	14s	8	6.	£2	6	2½

(=26$\frac{8}{10}$%* on Gross Returns).

£			£			£			£		
£1	£0 7s.	6	£51	19 2s.	6	£101	£37 17s.	6	£151	£56 12s.	6
2	0 15	0	52	19 10	0	102	38 5	0	152	57 0	0
3	1 2	6	53	19 17	6	103	38 12	6	153	57 7	6
4	1 10	0	54	20 5	0	104	39 0	0	154	57 15	0
5	1 17	6	55	20 12	6	105	39 7	6	155	58 2	6
6	2 5	0	56	21 0	0	106	39 15	0	156	58 10	0
7	2 12	6	57	21 7	6	107	40 2	6	157	58 17	6
8	3 0	0	58	21 15	0	108	40 10	0	158	59 5	0
9	3 7	6	59	22 2	6	109	40 17	6	159	59 12	6
10	£3 15s.	0	60	£22 10s.	0	110	£41 5s.	0	160	£60 0s.	0
11	£4 2s.	6	61	22 17s.	6	111	£41 12s.	6	161	£60 7s.	6
12	4 10	0	62	23 5	0	112	42 0	0	162	60 15	0
13	4 17	6	63	23 12	6	113	42 7	6	163	61 2	6
14	5 5	0	64	24 0	0	114	42 15	0	164	61 10	0
15	5 12	6	65	24 7	6	115	43 2	6	165	61 17	6
16	6 0	0	66	24 15	0	116	43 10	0	166	62 5	0
17	6 7	6	67	25 2	6	117	43 17	6	167	62 12	6
18	6 15	0	68	25 10	0	118	44 5	0	168	63 0	0
19	7 2	6	69	25 17	6	119	44 12	6	169	63 7	6
20	£7 10s.	0	70	26 5s.	0	120	£45 0s.	0	170	£63 15s.	0
21	£7 17s.	6	71	26 12s.	6	121	£45 7s.	6	171	£64 2s.	6
22	8 5	0	72	27 0	0	122	45 15	0	172	64 10	0
23	8 12	6	73	27 7	6	123	46 2	6	173	64 17	6
24	9 0	0	74	27 15	0	124	46 10	0	174	65 5	0
25	9 7	6	75	28 2	6	125	46 17	6	175	65 12	6
26	9 15	0	76	28 10	0	126	47 5	0	176	66 0	0
27	10 2	6	77	28 17	6	127	47 12	6	177	66 7	6
28	10 10	0	78	29 5	0	128	48 0	0	178	66 15	0
29	10 17	6	79	29 12	6	129	48 7	6	179	67 2	6
30	11 5s.	0	80	30 0s.	0	130	£48 15s.	0	180	£67 10s.	0
31	11 12s.	6	81	30 7s.	6	131	£49 2s.	6	181	£67 17s.	6
32	12 0	0	82	30 15	0	132	49 10	0	182	68 5	0
33	12 7	6	83	31 2	6	133	49 17	6	183	68 12	6
34	12 15	0	84	31 10	0	134	50 5	0	184	69 0	0
35	13 2	6	85	31 17	6	135	50 12	6	185	69 7	6
36	13 10	0	86	32 5	0	136	51 0	0	186	69 15	0
37	13 17	6	87	32 12	6	137	51 7	6	187	70 2	6
38	14 5	0	88	33 0	0	138	51 15	0	188	70 10	0
39	14 12	6	89	33 7	6	139	52 2	6	189	70 17	6
40	15 0s.	0	90	33 15s.	0	140	£52 10s.	0	190	£71 5s.	0
41	15 7s.	6	91	34 2s.	6	141	£52 17s.	6	191	£71 12s.	6
42	15 15	0	92	34 10	0	142	53 5	0	192	72 0	0
43	16 2	6	93	34 17	6	143	53 12	6	193	72 7	6
44	16 10	0	94	35 5	0	144	54 0	0	194	72 15	0
45	16 17	6	95	35 12	6	145	54 7	6	195	73 2	6
46	17 5	0	96	36 0	0	146	54 15	0	196	73 10	0
47	17 12	6	97	36 7	6	147	55 2	6	197	73 17	6
48	18 0	0	98	36 15	0	148	55 10	0	198	74 5	0
49	18 7	6	99	37 2	6	149	55 17	6	199	74 12	6
50	18 15s.	0	100	37 10s.	0	150	£56 5s.	0	200	£75 0s.	0

250	£93 15s. 0d	700	262 10s. 0	1200	450 0s. 0d	2000	£750 0s. 0
300	112 10 0	750	281 5 0	1400	525 0 0	2500	937 10 0
400	150 0 0	800	300 0 0	1500	562 10 0	3000	1125 0 0
500	187 10 0	900	337 10 0	1600	600 0 0	4000	1500 0 0
600	225 0s. 0d	1000	375 0s. 0d	1800	675 0s. 0d	5000	£1875 0s. 0

62½% off.   (37½%=3-8ths)

37½% **37½ Per Cent.** 37½%

1d	0s. 0½	4/1	1s. 6½	8/1	3s. 0½	12/1	4s. 6½	16/1	6s. 0½
2d	0 0¾	2	1 6¾	2	3 0¾	2	4 6¾	2	6 0¾
3d	0 1¼	3	1 7¼	3	3 1¼	3	4 7¼	3	6 1¼
4d	0 1½	4	1 7½	4	3 1½	4	4 7½	4	6 1½
5d	0 2	5	1 8	5	3 2	5	4 8	5	6 2
6d	0 2¼	4/6	1 8¼	8/6	3 2¼	12/6	4 8¼	16/6	6 2¼
7d	0 2¾	7	1 8¾	7	3 2¾	7	4 8¾	7	6 2¾
8d	0 3	8	1 9	8	3 3	8	4 9	8	6 3
9d	0 3½	9	1 9½	9	3 3½	9	4 9½	9	6 3½
10d	0 3¾	10	1 9¾	10	3 3¾	10	4 9¾	10	6 3¾
11d	0 4¼	11	1 10¼	11	3 4¼	11	4 10¼	11	6 4¼
1/-	0s. 4½	**5/-**	1s.10½	**9/-**	3s. 4½	**13/-**	4s.10½	**17/-**	6s. 4½
1/1	0s. 5	5/1	1s.11	9/1	3s. 5	13/1	4s.11	17/1	6s. 5
2	0 5¼	2	1 11¼	2	3 5¼	2	4 11¼	2	6 5¼
3	0 5¾	3	1 11¾	3	3 5¾	3	4 11¾	3	6 5¾
4	0 6	4	2 0	4	3 6	4	5 0	4	6 6
5	0 6½	5	2 0½	5	3 6½	5	5 0½	5	6 6½
1/6	0 6¾	5/6	2 0¾	9/6	3 6¾	13/6	5 0¾	17/6	6 6¾
7	0 7¼	7	2 1¼	7	3 7¼	7	5 1¼	7	6 7¼
8	0 7½	8	2 1½	8	3 7½	8	5 1½	8	6 7½
9	0 8	9	2 2	9	3 8	9	5 2	9	6 8
10	0 8¼	10	2 2¼	10	3 8¼	10	5 2¼	10	6 8¼
11	0 8¾	11	2 2¾	11	3 8¾	11	5 2¾	11	6 8¾
2/-	0s. 9	**6/-**	2s. 3	**10/-**	3s. 9	**14/-**	5s. 3	**18/-**	6s. 9
2/1	0s. 9½	6/1	2s. 3½	10/1	3s. 9½	14/1	5s. 3½	18/1	6s. 9½
2	0 9¾	2	2 3¾	2	3 9¾	2	5 3¾	2	6 9¾
3	0 10¼	3	2 4¼	3	3 10¼	3	5 4¼	3	6 10¼
4	0 10½	4	2 4½	4	3 10½	4	5 4½	4	6 10½
5	0 11	5	2 5	5	3 11	5	5 5	5	6 11
2/6	0 11¼	6/6	2 5¼	10/6	3 11¼	14/6	5 5¼	18/6	6 11¼
7	0 11¾	7	2 5¾	7	3 11¾	7	5 5¾	7	6 11¾
8	1 0	8	2 6	8	4 0	8	5 6	8	7 0
9	1 0½	9	2 6½	9	4 0½	9	5 6½	9	7 0½
10	1 0¾	10	2 6¾	10	4 0¾	10	5 6¾	10	7 0¾
11	1 1¼	11	2 7¼	11	4 1¼	11	5 7¼	11	7 1¼
3/-	1s. 1½	**7/-**	2s. 7½	**11/-**	4s. 1½	**15/-**	5s. 7½	**19/-**	7s. 1½
3/1	1s. 2	7/1	2s. 8	11/1	4s. 2	15/1	5s. 8	19/1	7s. 2
2	1 2¼	2	2 8¼	2	4 2¼	2	5 8¼	2	7 2¼
3	1 2¾	3	2 8¾	3	4 2¾	3	5 8¾	3	7 2¾
4	1 3	4	2 9	4	4 3	4	5 9	4	7 3
5	1 3½	5	2 9½	5	4 3½	5	5 9½	5	7 3½
3/6	1 3¾	7/6	2 9¾	11/6	4 3¾	15/6	5 9¾	19/6	7 3¾
7	1 4¼	7	2 10¼	7	4 4¼	7	5 10¼	7	7 4¼
8	1 4½	8	2 10½	8	4 4½	8	5 10½	8	7 4½
9	1 5	9	2 11	9	4 5	9	5 11	9	7 5
10	1 5¼	10	2 11¼	10	4 5¼	10	5 11¼	10	7 5¼
11	1 5¾	11	2 11¾	11	4 5¾	11	5 11¾	11	7 5¾
4/-	1s. 6	**8/-**	3s. 0	**12/-**	4s. 6	**16/-**	6s. 0	**20/-**	7s. 6

20/6	7s. 8¼	25/6	9s. 6¾	31/-	11s. 7½	35/6	13s. 3¾	Guineas.	
21/-	7 10½	26/-	9 9	31/6	11 9¾	36/-	13 6	1.	£0 7s.10½
22/-	8 3	27/-	10 1½	32/-	12 0	37/-	13 10½	2.	0 15 9
22/6	8 5¼	27/6	10 3¾	32/6	12 2¼	37/6	14 0¾	3.	1 3 7½
23/-	8 7½	28/-	10 6	33/-	12 4½	38/-	14 3	4.	1 11 6
24/-	9 0	29/-	10 10½	34/-	12 9	39/-	14 7½	5.	1 19 4½
25/-	9s. 4½	**30/-**	11s. 3	**35/-**	13s. 1½	**40/-**	15s. 0	6.	£2 7s. 3

(=27 3/10 %* on Gross Returns).

£	Amount	£	Amount	£	Amount	£	Amount
£1	£0 8s. 0	£51	20 8s. 0	£101	£40 8s. 0	£151	£60 8s. 0
2	0 16 0	52	20 16 0	102	40 16 0	152	60 16 0
3	1 4 0	53	21 4 0	103	41 4 0	153	61 4 0
4	1 12 0	54	21 12 0	104	41 12 0	154	61 12 0
5	2 0 0	55	22 0 0	105	42 0 0	155	62 0 0
6	2 8 0	56	22 8 0	106	42 8 0	156	62 8 0
7	2 16 0	57	22 16 0	107	42 16 0	157	62 16 0
8	3 4 0	58	23 4 0	108	43 4 0	158	63 4 0
9	3 12 0	59	23 12 0	109	43 12 0	159	63 12 0
10	£4 0s. 0	60	24 0s. 0	110	£44 0s. 0	160	£64 0s. 0
11	£4 8s. 0	61	24 8s. 0	111	£44 8s. 0	161	£64 8s. 0
12	4 16 0	62	24 16 0	112	44 16 0	162	64 16 0
13	5 4 0	63	25 4 0	113	45 4 0	163	65 4 0
14	5 12 0	64	25 12 0	114	45 12 0	164	65 12 0
15	6 0 0	65	26 0 0	115	46 0 0	165	66 0 0
16	6 8 0	66	26 8 0	116	46 8 0	166	66 8 0
17	6 16 0	67	26 16 0	117	46 16 0	167	66 16 0
18	7 4 0	68	27 4 0	118	47 4 0	168	67 4 0
19	7 12 0	69	27 12 0	119	47 12 0	169	67 12 0
20	£8 0s. 0	70	28 0s. 0	120	£48 0s. 0	170	£68 0s. 0
21	£8 8s. 0	71	28 8s. 0	121	£48 8s. 0	171	£68 8s. 0
22	8 16 0	72	28 16 0	122	48 16 0	172	68 16 0
23	9 4 0	73	29 4 0	123	49 4 0	173	69 4 0
24	9 12 0	74	29 12 0	124	49 12 0	174	69 12 0
25	10 0 0	75	30 0 0	125	50 0 0	175	70 0 0
26	10 8 0	76	30 8 0	126	50 8 0	176	70 8 0
27	10 16 0	77	30 16 0	127	50 16 0	177	70 16 0
28	11 4 0	78	31 4 0	128	51 4 0	178	71 4 0
29	11 12 0	79	31 12 0	129	51 12 0	179	71 12 0
30	12 0s. 0	80	32 0s. 0	130	£52 0s. 0	180	£72 0s. 0
31	12 8s. 0	81	32 8s. 0	131	£52 8s. 0	181	£72 8s. 0
32	12 16 0	82	32 16 0	132	52 16 0	182	72 16 0
33	13 4 0	83	33 4 0	133	53 4 0	183	73 4 0
34	13 12 0	84	33 12 0	134	53 12 0	184	73 12 0
35	14 0 0	85	34 0 0	135	54 0 0	185	74 0 0
36	14 8 0	86	34 8 0	136	54 8 0	186	74 8 0
37	14 16 0	87	34 16 0	137	54 16 0	187	74 16 0
38	15 4 0	88	35 4 0	138	55 4 0	188	75 4 0
39	15 12 0	89	35 12 0	139	55 12 0	189	75 12 0
40	16 0s. 0	90	36 0s. 0	140	£56 0s. 0	190	£76 0s. 0
41	16 8s. 0	91	36 8s. 0	141	£56 8s. 0	191	£76 8s. 0
42	16 16 0	92	36 16 0	142	56 16 0	192	76 16 0
43	17 4 0	93	37 4 0	143	57 4 0	193	77 4 0
44	17 12 0	94	37 12 0	144	57 12 0	194	77 12 0
45	18 0 0	95	38 0 0	145	58 0 0	195	78 0 0
46	18 8 0	96	38 8 0	146	58 8 0	196	78 8 0
47	18 16 0	97	38 16 0	147	58 16 0	197	78 16 0
48	19 4 0	98	39 4 0	148	59 4 0	198	79 4 0
49	19 12 0	99	39 12 0	149	59 12 0	199	79 12 0
50	20 0s. 0	100	40 0s. 0	150	£60 0s. 0	200	£80 0s. 0

£	Amount	£	Amount	£	Amount	£	Amount
250	100 0s.0d	700	280 0s.0d	1200	480 0s.0d	2000	£800 0s. 0
300	120 0 0	750	300 0 0	1400	560 0 0	2500	1000 0 0
400	160 0 0	800	320 0 0	1500	600 0 0	3000	1200 0 0
500	200 0 0	900	360 0 0	1600	640 0 0	4000	1600 0 0
600	240 0s.0d	1000	400 0s.0d	1800	720 0s.0d	5000	£2000 0s. 0

60% off.   (= 33⅓% less 10%)

40% FORTY PER CENT. 40%

	s.	d.		s.	d.		s.	d.		s.	d.		s.	d.
1d	0s.	0½	4/1	1s.	7½	8/1	3s.	2¾	12/1	4s.	10	16/1	6s.	5¼
2d	0	0¾	2	1	8	2	3	3¼	2	4	10½	2	6	5½
3d	0	1¼	3	1	8½	3	3	3½	3	4	10¾	3	6	6
4d	0	1½	4	1	8¾	4	3	4	4	4	11¼	4	6	6½
5d	0	2	5	1	9¼	5	3	4½	5	4	11½	5	6	6¾
6d	0	2½	4/6	1	9½	8/6	3	4¾	12/6	5	0	16/6	6	7¼
7d	0	2¾	7	1	10	7	3	5¼	7	5	0½	7	6	7½
8d	0	3¼	8	1	10½	8	3	5½	8	5	0¾	8	6	8
9d	0	3½	9	1	10¾	9	3	6	9	5	1¼	9	6	8½
10d	0	4	10	1	11¼	10	3	6½	10	5	1½	10	6	8¾
11d	0	4½	11	1	11½	11	3	6¾	11	5	2	11	6	9¼
1/-	0s.	4¾	**5/-**	2s.	0	**9/-**	3s.	7¼	**13/-**	5s.	2½	**17/-**	6s.	9½
1/1	0s.	5¼	5/1	2s.	0½	9/1	3s.	7½	13/1	5s.	2¾	17/1	6s.	10
2	0	5½	2	2	0¾	2	3	8	2	5	3¼	2	6	10½
3	0	6	3	2	1¼	3	3	8½	3	5	3½	3	6	10¾
4	0	6½	4	2	1½	4	3	8¾	4	5	4	4	6	11¼
5	0	6¾	5	2	2	5	3	9¼	5	5	4½	5	6	11½
1/6	0	7¼	5/6	2	2½	9/6	3	9½	13/6	5	4¾	17/6	7	0
7	0	7½	7	2	2¾	7	3	10	7	5	5¼	7	7	0½
8	0	8	8	2	3¼	8	3	10½	8	5	5½	8	7	0¾
9	0	8½	9	2	3½	9	3	10¾	9	5	6	9	7	1¼
10	0	8¾	10	2	4	10	3	11¼	10	5	6½	10	7	1½
11	0	9¼	11	2	4½	11	3	11½	11	5	6¾	11	7	2
2/-	0s.	9½	**6/-**	2s.	4¾	**10/-**	4s.	0	**14/-**	5s.	7¼	**18/-**	7s.	2½
2/1	0s.	10	6/1	2s.	5¼	10/1	4s.	0½	14/1	5s.	7½	18/1	7s.	2¾
2	0	10½	2	2	5½	2	4	0¾	2	5	8	2	7	3¼
3	0	10¾	3	2	6	3	4	1¼	3	5	8½	3	7	3½
4	0	11¼	4	2	6½	4	4	1½	4	5	8¾	4	7	4
5	0	11½	5	2	6¾	5	4	2	5	5	9¼	5	7	4½
2/6	1	0	6/6	2	7¼	10/6	4	2½	14/6	5	9½	18/6	7	4¾
7	1	0½	7	2	7½	7	4	2¾	7	5	10	7	7	5¼
8	1	0¾	8	2	8	8	4	3¼	8	5	10½	8	7	5½
9	1	1¼	9	2	8½	9	4	3½	9	5	10¾	9	7	6
10	1	1½	10	2	8¾	10	4	4	10	5	11¼	10	7	6½
11	1	2	11	2	9¼	11	4	4½	11	5	11½	11	7	6¾
3/-	1s.	2½	**7/-**	2s.	9½	**11/-**	4s.	4¾	**15/-**	6s.	0	**19/-**	7s.	7¼
3/1	1s.	2¾	7/1	2s.	10	11/1	4s.	5¼	15/1	6s.	0½	19/1	7s.	7½
2	1	3¼	2	2	10½	2	4	5½	2	6	0¾	2	7	8
3	1	3½	3	2	10¾	3	4	6	3	6	1¼	3	7	8½
4	1	4	4	2	11¼	4	4	6½	4	6	1½	4	7	8¾
5	1	4½	5	2	11½	5	4	6¾	5	6	2	5	7	9¼
3/6	1	4¾	7/6	3	0	11/6	4	7¼	15/6	6	2½	19/6	7	9½
7	1	5¼	7	3	0½	7	4	7½	7	6	2¾	7	7	10
8	1	5½	8	3	0¾	8	4	8	8	6	3¼	8	7	10½
9	1	6	9	3	1¼	9	4	8½	9	6	3½	9	7	10¾
10	1	6½	10	3	1½	10	4	8¾	10	6	4	10	7	11¼
11	1	6¾	11	3	2	11	4	9¼	11	6	4½	11	7	11½
4/-	1s.	7¼	**8/-**	3s.	2½	**12/-**	4s.	9½	**16/-**	6s.	4¾	**20/-**	8s.	0

	s.	d.		s.	d.		s.	d.		s.	d.	Guineas.		
20/6	8s.	2½	25/6	10s.	2½	31/-	12s.	4¾	35/6	14s.	2½			
21/-	8	4¾	26/-	10	4¾	31/6	12	7¼	36/-	14	4¾	1.	£0 8s.	4¾
22/-	8	9½	27/-	10	9½	32/-	12	9½	37/-	14	9½	2.	0 16	9½
22/6	9	0	27/6	11	0	32/6	13	0	37/6	15	0	3.	1 5	2½
23/-	9	2½	28/-	11	2½	33/-	13	2½	38/-	15	2½	4.	1 13	7¼
24/-	9	7¼	29/-	11	7¼	34/-	13	7¼	39/-	15	7¼	5.	2 2	0
25/-	10s.	0	**30/-**	12s.	0	**35/-**	14s.	0	**40/-**	16s.	0	6.	£2 10s.	4¾

(=$28\frac{6}{10}$%* on Gross Returns.)

£	s. d.	£	s. d.	£	s. d.	£	s. d.
£1	£0 8s. 6	£51	21 13s. 6	£101	£42 18s. 6	£151	£64 3s. 6
2	0 17 0	52	22 2 0	102	43 7 0	152	64 12 0
3	1 5 6	53	22 10 6	103	43 15 6	153	65 0 6
4	1 14 0	54	22 19 0	104	44 4 0	154	65 9 0
5	2 2 6	55	23 7 6	105	44 12 6	155	65 17 6
6	2 11 0	56	23 16 0	106	45 1 0	156	66 6 0
7	2 19 6	57	24 4 6	107	45 9 6	157	66 14 6
8	3 8 0	58	24 13 0	108	45 18 0	158	67 3 0
9	3 16 6	59	25 1 6	109	46 6 6	159	67 11 6
10	£4 5s. 0	60	25 10s. 0	110	£46 15s. 0	160	£68 0s. 0
11	£4 13s. 6	61	25 18s. 6	111	£47 3s. 6	161	£68 8s. 6
12	5 2 0	62	26 7 0	112	47 12 0	162	68 17 0
13	5 10 6	63	26 15 6	113	48 0 6	163	69 5 6
14	5 19 0	64	27 4 0	114	48 9 0	164	69 14 0
15	6 7 6	65	27 12 6	115	48 17 6	165	70 2 6
16	6 16 0	66	28 1 0	116	49 6 0	166	70 11 0
17	7 4 6	67	28 9 6	117	49 14 6	167	70 19 6
18	7 13 0	68	28 18 0	118	50 3 0	168	71 8 0
19	8 1 6	69	29 6 6	119	50 11 6	169	71 16 6
20	£8 10s. 0	70	29 15s. 0	120	£51 0s. 0	170	£72 5s. 0
21	£8 18s. 6	71	30 3s. 6	121	£51 8s. 6	171	£72 13s. 6
22	9 7 0	72	30 12 0	122	51 17 0	172	73 2 0
23	9 15 6	73	31 0 6	123	52 5 6	173	73 10 6
24	10 4 0	74	31 9 0	124	52 14 0	174	73 19 0
25	10 12 6	75	31 17 6	125	53 2 6	175	74 7 6
26	11 1 0	76	32 6 0	126	53 11 0	176	74 16 0
27	11 9 6	77	32 14 6	127	53 19 6	177	75 4 6
28	11 18 0	78	33 3 0	128	54 8 0	178	75 13 0
29	12 6 6	79	33 11 6	129	54 16 6	179	76 1 6
30	12 15s. 0	80	34 0s. 6	130	£55 5s. 0	180	£76 10s. 0
31	13 3s. 6	81	34 8s. 6	131	£55 13s. 6	181	£76 18s. 6
32	13 12 0	82	34 17 0	132	56 2 0	182	77 7 0
33	14 0 6	83	35 5 6	133	56 10 6	183	77 15 6
34	14 9 0	84	35 14 0	134	56 19 0	184	78 4 0
35	14 17 6	85	36 2 6	135	57 7 6	185	78 12 6
36	15 6 0	86	36 11 0	136	57 16 0	186	79 1 0
37	15 14 6	87	36 19 6	137	58 4 6	187	79 9 6
38	16 3 0	88	37 8 0	138	58 13 0	188	79 18 0
39	16 11 6	89	37 16 6	139	59 1 6	189	80 6 6
40	17 0s. 0	90	38 5s. 0	140	£59 10s. 0	190	£80 15s. 0
41	17 8s. 6	91	38 13s. 6	141	£59 18s. 6	191	£81 3s. 6
42	17 17 0	92	39 2 0	142	60 7 0	192	81 12 0
43	18 5 6	93	39 10 6	143	60 15 6	193	82 0 6
44	18 14 0	94	39 19 0	144	61 4 0	194	82 9 0
45	19 2 6	95	40 7 6	145	61 12 6	195	82 17 6
46	19 11 0	96	40 16 0	146	62 1 0	196	83 6 0
47	19 19 6	97	41 4 6	147	62 9 6	197	83 14 6
48	20 8 0	98	41 13 0	148	62 18 0	198	84 3 0
49	20 16 6	99	42 1 6	149	63 6 6	199	84 11 6
50	21 5s. 0	100	42 10s. 0	150	£63 15s. 0	200	£85 0s. 0

£	s. d.	£	s. d.	£	s. d.	£	s. d.
250	106 5s.0d	700	297 10s.0d	1200	510 0s.0d	2000	£850 0s. 0
300	127 10 0	750	318 15 0	1400	595 0 0	2500	1062 10 0
400	170 0 0	800	340 0 0	1500	637 10 0	3000	1275 0 0
500	212 10 0	900	382 10 0	1600	680 0 0	4000	1700 0 0
600	255 0s.0d	1000	425 0s.0d	1800	765 0s.0d	5000	£2125 0s. 0

57½% off.

42½ Per Cent.

42½%

1d	0s. 0½	4/1	1s. 8¾	8/1	3s. 5¼	12/1	5s. 1¾	16/1	6s.10
2d	0 0¾	2	1 9¼	2	3 5¾	2	5 2	2	6 10½
3d	0 1¼	3	1 9¾	3	3 6	3	5 2½	3	6 11
4d	0 1¾	4	1 10	4	3 6½	4	5 3	4	6 11¼
5d	0 2¼	5	1 10½	5	3 7	5	5 3¼	5	6 11¾
6d	0 2½	4/6	1 11	8/6	3 7¼	12/6	5 3¾	16/6	7 0¼
7d	0 3	7	1 11½	7	3 7¾	7	5 4¼	7	7 0½
8d	0 3½	8	1 11¾	8	3 8¼	8	5 4½	8	7 1
9d	0 3¾	9	2 0¼	9	3 8¾	9	5 5	9	7 1½
10d	0 4¼	10	2 0¾	10	3 9	10	5 5½	10	7 1¾
11d	0 4¾	11	2 1	11	3 9½	11	5 6	11	7 2¼
1/-	0s. 5	**5/-**	2s. 1½	**9/-**	3s.10	**13/-**	5s. 6¼	**17/-**	7s. 2¾
1/1	0s. 5½	5/1	2s. 2	9/1	3s.10¼	13/1	5s. 6¾	17/1	7s. 3¼
2	0 6	2	2 2¼	2	3 10¾	2	5 7¼	2	7 3½
3	0 6½	3	2 2¾	3	3 11¼	3	5 7½	3	7 4
4	0 6¾	4	2 3¼	4	3 11½	4	5 8	4	7 4½
5	0 7¼	5	2 3¾	5	4 0	5	5 8½	5	7 4¾
1/6	0 7¾	5/6	2 4	9/6	4 0½	13/6	5 8¾	17/6	7 5¼
7	0 8	7	2 4½	7	4 1	7	5 9¼	7	7 5¾
8	0 8½	8	2 5	8	4 1¼	8	5 9¾	8	7 6
9	0 9	9	2 5¼	9	4 1¾	9	5 10¼	9	7 6½
10	0 9¼	10	2 5¾	10	4 2¼	10	5 10½	10	7 7
11	0 9¾	11	2 6¼	11	4 2½	11	5 11	11	7 7½
2/-	0s.10¼	**6/-**	2s. 6½	**10/-**	4s. 3	**14/-**	5s.11½	**18/-**	7s. 7¾
2/1	0s.10¾	6/1	2s. 7	10/1	4s. 3½	14/1	5s.11¾	18/1	7s. 8¼
2	0 11	2	2 7½	2	4 3¾	2	6 0¼	2	7 8¾
3	0 11½	3	2 8	3	4 4¼	3	6 0¾	3	7 9
4	1 0	4	2 8¼	4	4 4¾	4	6 1	4	7 9½
5	1 0¼	5	2 8¾	5	4 5¼	5	6 1½	5	7 10
2/6	1 0¾	6/6	2 9¼	10/6	4 5½	14/6	6 2	18/6	7 10¼
7	1 1¼	7	2 9½	7	4 6	7	6 2½	7	7 10¾
8	1 1½	8	2 10	8	4 6½	8	6 2¾	8	7 11¼
9	1 2	9	2 10½	9	4 6¾	9	6 3¼	9	7 11¾
10	1 2½	10	2 10¾	10	4 7¼	10	6 3¾	10	8 0
11	1 3	11	2 11¼	11	4 7¾	11	6 4	11	8 0½
3/-	1s. 3¼	**7/-**	2s.11¾	**11/-**	4s. 8	**15/-**	6s. 4½	**19/-**	8s. 1
3/1	1s. 3¾	7/1	3s. 0¼	11/1	4s. 8½	15/1	6s. 5	19/1	8s. 1¼
2	1 4¼	2	3 0½	2	4 9	2	6 5¼	2	8 1¾
3	1 4½	3	3 1	3	4 9½	3	6 5¾	3	8 2¼
4	1 5	4	3 1½	4	4 9¾	4	6 6¼	4	8 2½
5	1 5½	5	3 1¾	5	4 10¼	5	6 6¾	5	8 3
3/6	1 5¾	7/6	3 2¼	11/6	4 10¾	15/6	6 7	19/6	8 3½
7	1 6¼	7	3 2¾	7	4 11	7	6 7½	7	8 4
8	1 6¾	8	3 3	8	4 11½	8	6 8	8	8 4¼
9	1 7¼	9	3 3½	9	5 0	9	6 8¼	9	8 4¾
10	1 7½	10	3 4	10	5 0¼	10	6 8¾	10	8 5¼
11	1 8	11	3 4½	11	5 0¾	11	6 9¼	11	8 5½
4/-	1s. 8½	**8/-**	3s. 4¾	**12/-**	5s. 1¼	**16/-**	6s. 9½	**20/-**	8s. 6

20/6	8s. 8½	25/6	10s.10	31/-	13s. 2	35/6	15s. 1	Guineas.	
21/-	8 11	26/-	11 0½	31/6	13 4¾	36/-	15 3½	1.	£0 8s.11
22/-	9 4¼	27/-	11 5¾	32/-	13 7¼	37/-	15 8¾	2.	0 17 10¼
22/6	9 6¾	27/6	11 8¼	32/6	13 9¾	37/6	15 11¼	3.	1 6 9¼
23/-	9 9¼	28/-	11 10¾	33/-	14 0¼	38/-	16 1¾	4.	1 15 8½
24/-	10 2½	29/-	12 4	34/-	14 5½	39/-	16 7	5.	2 4 7½
25/-	10s. 7½	**30/-**	12s. 9	**35/-**	14s.10½	**40/-**	17s. 0	6.	£2 13s.6½

(=$29\frac{8}{10}$%* on Gross Returns).

£	s	d	£	s	d	£	s	d	£	s	d
£1	£0 8s	8	£51	22 2s	0	£101	43 15s	4	£151	65 8	8
2	0 17	4	52	22 10	8	102	44 4	0	152	65 17	4
3	1 6	0	53	22 19	4	103	44 12	8	153	66 6	0
4	1 14	8	54	23 8	0	104	45 1	4	154	66 14	8
5	2 3	4	55	23 16	8	105	45 10	0	155	67 3	4
6	2 12	0	56	24 5	4	106	45 18	8	156	67 12	0
7	3 0	8	57	24 14	0	107	46 7	4	157	68 0	8
8	3 9	4	58	25 2	8	108	46 16	0	158	68 9	4
9	3 18	0	59	25 11	4	109	47 4	8	159	68 18	0
10	4 6	8	60	26 0	0	110	47 13	4	160	69 6	8
11	4 15	4	61	26 8	8	111	48 2	0	161	69 15	4
12	5 4	0	62	26 17	4	112	48 10	8	162	70 4	0
13	5 12	8	63	27 6	0	113	48 19	4	163	70 12	8
14	6 1	4	64	27 14	8	114	49 8	0	164	71 1	4
15	6 10	0	65	28 3	4	115	49 16	8	165	71 10	0
16	6 18	8	66	28 12	0	116	50 5	4	166	71 18	8
17	7 7	4	67	29 0	8	117	50 14	0	167	72 7	4
18	7 16	0	68	29 9	4	118	51 2	8	168	72 16	0
19	8 4	8	69	29 18	0	119	51 11	4	169	73 4	8
20	8 13	4	70	30 6	8	120	52 0	0	170	73 13	4
21	9 2	0	71	30 15	4	121	52 8	8	171	74 2	0
22	9 10	8	72	31 4	0	122	52 17	4	172	74 10	8
23	9 19	4	73	31 12	8	123	53 6	0	173	74 19	4
24	10 8	0	74	32 1	4	124	53 14	8	174	75 8	0
25	10 16	8	75	32 10	0	125	54 3	4	175	75 16	8
26	11 5	4	76	32 18	8	126	54 12	0	176	76 5	4
27	11 14	0	77	33 7	4	127	55 0	8	177	76 14	0
28	12 2	8	78	33 16	0	128	55 9	4	178	77 2	8
29	12 11	4	79	34 4	8	129	55 18	0	179	77 11	4
30	13 0	0	80	34 13	4	130	56 6	8	180	78 0	0
31	13 8	8	81	35 2	0	131	56 15	4	181	78 8	8
32	13 17	4	82	35 10	8	132	57 4	0	182	78 17	4
33	14 6	0	83	35 19	4	133	57 12	8	183	79 6	0
34	14 14	8	84	36 8	0	134	58 1	4	184	79 14	8
35	15 3	4	85	36 16	8	135	58 10	0	185	80 3	4
36	15 12	0	86	37 5	4	136	58 18	8	186	80 12	0
37	16 0	8	87	37 14	0	137	59 7	4	187	81 0	8
38	16 9	4	88	38 2	8	138	59 16	0	188	81 9	4
39	16 18	0	89	38 11	4	139	60 4	8	189	81 18	0
40	17 6	8	90	39 0	0	140	60 13	4	190	82 6	8
41	17 15	4	91	39 8	8	141	61 2	0	191	82 15	4
42	18 4	0	92	39 17	4	142	61 10	8	192	83 4	0
43	18 12	8	93	40 6	0	143	61 19	4	193	83 12	8
44	19 1	4	94	40 14	8	144	62 8	0	194	84 1	4
45	19 10	0	95	41 3	4	145	62 16	8	195	84 10	0
46	19 18	8	96	41 12	0	146	63 5	4	196	84 18	8
47	20 7	4	97	42 0	8	147	63 14	0	197	85 7	4
48	20 16	0	98	42 9	4	148	64 2	8	198	85 16	0
49	21 4	8	99	42 18	0	149	64 11	4	199	86 4	8
50	21 13	4	100	43 6	8	150	65 0	0	200	86 13	4

£	s	d	£	s	d	£	s	d	£	s	d
250	108	6s 8	700	303	6s 8	1200	520	0s 0	2000	866	13s 4
300	130	0 0	750	325	0 0	1400	606	13 4	2500	1083	6 8
400	173	6 8	800	346	13 4	1500	650	0 0	3000	1300	0 0
500	216	13 4	900	390	0 0	1600	693	6 8	4000	1733	6 8
600	260	0 0	1000	433	6 8	1800	780	0 0	5000	2166	13 4

56⅔% off.   **(=33⅓% less 15%)**

1d	0s	0½	4/1	1s	9¼	8/1	3s	6	12/1	5s	2¾	16/1	6s	11¾
2d	0	0¾	2	1	9¾	2	3	6½	2	5	3¼	2	7	0
3d	0	1¼	3	1	10	3	3	7	3	5	3¾	3	7	0½
4d	0	1¾	4	1	10½	4	3	7¼	4	5	4¼	4	7	1
5d	0	2¼	5	1	11	5	3	7¾	5	5	4½	5	7	1¼
6d	0	2½	4/6	1	11½	8/6	3	8¼	12/6	5	5	16/6	7	1¾
7d	0	3	7	1	11¾	7	3	8¾	7	5	5½	7	7	2¼
8d	0	3½	8	2	0¼	8	3	9	8	5	5¾	8	7	2¾
9d	0	4	9	2	0¾	9	3	9½	9	5	6¼	9	7	3
10d	0	4¼	10	2	1¼	10	3	10	10	5	6¾	10	7	3½
11d	0	4¾	11	2	1½	11	3	10¼	11	5	7¼	11	7	4
1/-	**0**	**5¼**	**5/-**	**2**	**2**	**9/-**	**3**	**10¾**	**13/-**	**5**	**7½**	**17/-**	**7**	**4½**
1/1	0	5¾	5/1	2	2½	9/1	3	11¼	13/1	5	8	17/1	7	4¾
2	0	6	2	2	2¾	2	3	11¾	2	5	8½	2	7	5¼
3	0	6½	3	2	3¼	3	4	0	3	5	9	3	7	5¾
4	0	7	4	2	3¾	4	4	0½	4	5	9¼	4	7	6¼
5	0	7¼	5	2	4¼	5	4	1	5	5	9¾	5	7	6½
1/6	0	7¾	5/6	2	4½	9/6	4	1½	13/6	5	10¼	17/6	7	7
7	0	8¼	7	2	5	7	4	1¾	7	5	10¾	7	7	7½
8	0	8¾	8	2	5½	8	4	2¼	8	5	11	8	7	7¾
9	0	9	9	2	6	9	4	2¾	9	5	11½	9	7	8¼
10	0	9½	10	2	6¼	10	4	3¼	10	6	0	10	7	8¾
11	0	10	11	2	6¾	11	4	3½	11	6	0¼	11	7	9¼
2/-	**0**	**10½**	**6/-**	**2**	**7¼**	**10/-**	**4**	**4**	**14/-**	**6**	**0¾**	**18/-**	**7**	**9½**
2/1	0	10¾	6/1	2	7¾	10/1	4	4½	14/1	6	1¼	18/1	7	10
2	0	11¼	2	2	8	2	4	4¾	2	6	1¾	2	7	10½
3	0	11¾	3	2	8½	3	4	5¼	3	6	2	3	7	11
4	1	0¼	4	2	9	4	4	5¾	4	6	2½	4	7	11¼
5	1	0½	5	2	9¼	5	4	6¼	5	6	3	5	7	11¾
2/6	1	1	6/6	2	9¾	10/6	4	6½	14/6	6	3½	18/6	8	0¼
7	1	1½	7	2	10¼	7	4	7	7	6	3¾	7	8	0¾
8	1	1¾	8	2	10¾	8	4	7½	8	6	4¼	8	8	1
9	1	2¼	9	2	11	9	4	8	9	6	4¾	9	8	1½
10	1	2¾	10	2	11½	10	4	8¼	10	6	5¼	10	8	2
11	1	3¼	11	3	0	11	4	8¾	11	6	5½	11	8	2¼
3/-	**1**	**3½**	**7/-**	**3**	**0½**	**11/-**	**4**	**9¼**	**15/-**	**6**	**6**	**19/-**	**8**	**2¾**
3/1	1	4	7/1	3	0¾	11/1	4	9¾	15/1	6	6½	19/1	8	3¼
2	1	4½	2	3	1¼	2	4	10	2	6	6¾	2	8	3¾
3	1	5	3	3	1¾	3	4	10½	3	6	7¼	3	8	4
4	1	5¼	4	3	2¼	4	4	11	4	6	7¾	4	8	4½
5	1	5¾	5	3	2½	5	4	11¼	5	6	8¼	5	8	5
3/6	1	6¼	7/6	3	3	11/6	4	11¾	15/6	6	8½	19/6	8	5½
7	1	6¾	7	3	3½	7	5	0¼	7	6	9	7	8	5¾
8	1	7	8	3	3¾	8	5	0¾	8	6	9½	8	8	6¼
9	1	7½	9	3	4¼	9	5	1	9	6	10	9	8	6¾
10	1	8	10	3	4¾	10	5	1½	10	6	10¼	10	8	7¼
11	1	8¼	11	3	5¼	11	5	2	11	6	10¾	11	8	7½
4/-	**1**	**8¾**	**8/-**	**3**	**5½**	**12/-**	**5**	**2½**	**16/-**	**6**	**11¼**	**20/-**	**8**	**8**
20/6	8s	10½	25/6	11s	0½	31/-	13s	5¼	35/6	15s	4½	42/-	18s	2½
21/-	9	1¼	26/-	11	3¼	31/6	13	7¾	36/-	15	7¼	45/-	19	6
22/-	9	6½	27/-	11	8½	32/-	13	10½	37/-	16	0½	50/-	21	8
22/6	9	9	27/6	11	11	32/6	14	1	37/6	16	3	63/-	27	3½
23/-	9	11½	28/-	12	1½	33/-	14	3½	38/-	16	5½	84/-	36	4¾
24/-	10	4¾	29/-	12	6¾	34/-	14	8¾	39/-	16	10¾	105/	45	6
25/-	10	10	**30/-**	13	0	**35/-**	15	2	**40/-**	17	4	126/	54	7¼

(=30$\frac{2}{10}$%* on Gross Returns).

£	£ s d	£	£ s d	£	£ s d	£	£ s d
£1	£0 8s 9	£51	22 6s 3	£101	44 3s 9	£151	66 1s 3
2	0 17 6	52	22 15 0	102	44 12 6	152	66 10 0
3	1 6 3	53	23 3 9	103	45 1 3	153	66 18 9
4	1 15 0	54	23 12 6	104	45 10 0	154	67 7 6
5	2 3 9	55	24 1 3	105	45 18 9	155	67 16 3
6	2 12 6	56	24 10 0	106	46 7 6	156	68 5 0
7	3 1 3	57	24 18 9	107	46 16 3	157	68 13 9
8	3 10 0	58	25 7 6	108	47 5 0	158	69 2 6
9	3 18 9	59	25 16 3	109	47 13 9	159	69 11 3
10	4 7 6	60	26 5 0	110	48 2 6	160	70 0 0
11	4 16 3	61	26 13 9	111	48 11 3	161	70 8 9
12	5 5 0	62	27 2 6	112	49 0 0	162	70 17 6
13	5 13 9	63	27 11 3	113	49 8 9	163	71 6 3
14	6 2 6	64	28 0 0	114	49 17 6	164	71 15 0
15	6 11 3	65	28 8 9	115	50 6 3	165	72 3 9
16	7 0 0	66	28 17 6	116	50 15 0	166	72 12 6
17	7 8 9	67	29 6 3	117	51 3 9	167	73 1 3
18	7 17 6	68	29 15 0	118	51 12 6	168	73 10 0
19	8 6 3	69	30 3 9	119	52 1 3	169	73 18 9
20	8 15 0	70	30 12 6	120	52 10 0	170	74 7 6
21	9 3 9	71	31 1 3	121	52 18 9	171	74 16 3
22	9 12 6	72	31 10 0	122	53 7 6	172	75 5 0
23	10 1 3	73	31 18 9	123	53 16 3	173	75 13 9
24	10 10 0	74	32 7 6	124	54 5 0	174	76 2 6
25	10 18 9	75	32 16 3	125	54 13 9	175	76 11 3
26	11 7 6	76	33 5 0	126	55 2 6	176	77 0 0
27	11 16 3	77	33 13 9	127	55 11 3	177	77 8 9
28	12 5 0	78	34 2 6	128	56 0 0	178	77 17 6
29	12 13 9	79	34 11 3	129	56 8 9	179	78 6 3
30	13 2 6	80	35 0 0	130	56 17 6	180	78 15 0
31	13 11 3	81	35 8 9	131	57 6 3	181	79 3 9
32	14 0 0	82	35 17 6	132	57 15 0	182	79 12 6
33	14 8 9	83	36 6 3	133	58 3 9	183	80 1 3
34	14 17 6	84	36 15 0	134	58 12 6	184	80 10 0
35	15 6 3	85	37 3 9	135	59 1 3	185	80 18 9
36	15 15 0	86	37 12 6	136	59 10 0	186	81 7 6
37	16 3 9	87	38 1 3	137	59 18 9	187	81 16 3
38	16 12 6	88	38 10 0	138	60 7 6	188	82 5 0
39	17 1 3	89	38 18 9	139	60 16 3	189	82 13 9
40	17 10 0	90	39 7 6	140	61 5 0	190	83 2 6
41	17 18 9	91	39 16 3	141	61 13 9	191	83 11 3
42	18 7 6	92	40 5 0	142	62 2 6	192	84 0 0
43	18 16 3	93	40 13 9	143	62 11 3	193	84 8 9
44	19 5 0	94	41 2 6	144	63 0 0	194	84 17 6
45	19 13 9	95	41 11 3	145	63 8 9	195	85 6 3
46	20 2 6	96	42 0 0	146	63 17 6	196	85 15 0
47	20 11 3	97	42 8 9	147	64 6 3	197	86 3 9
48	21 0 0	98	42 17 6	148	64 15 0	198	86 12 6
49	21 8 9	99	43 6 3	149	65 3 9	199	87 1 3
50	21 17 6	100	43 15 0	150	65 12 6	200	87 10 0

£	£ s d	£	£ s d	£	£ s d
250	109 7s 6d	700	306 5s 0d	1200	525 0s 0d
300	131 5 0	750	328 2 6	1400	612 10 0
400	175 0 0	800	350 0 0	1500	656 5 0
500	218 15 0	900	393 15 0	1600	700 0 0
600	262 10s 0d	1000	437 10s 0d	1800	787 10s 0d

£	£ s d
2000	875 0s 0
2500	1093 15 0
3000	1312 10 0
4000	1750 0 0
5000	2187 10s 0

56¼% off.

43¾ Per Cent.

43¾%

1d	0s	0½	4/1	1s	9½	8/1	3s	6½	12/1	5s	3½	16/1	7s	0½
2d	0	1	2	1	10	2	3	7	2	5	4	2	7	1
3d	0	1¼	3	1	10¼	3	3	7¼	3	5	4¼	3	7	1¼
4d	0	1¾	4	1	10¾	4	3	7¾	4	5	4¾	4	7	1¾
5d	0	2¼	5	1	11¼	5	3	8¼	5	5	5¼	5	7	2¼
6d	0	2¾	4/6	1	11¾	8/6	3	8¾	12/6	5	5¾	16/6	7	2¾
7d	0	3	7	2	0	7	3	9	7	5	6	7	7	3
8d	0	3½	8	2	0½	8	3	9½	8	5	6½	8	7	3½
9d	0	4	9	2	1	9	3	10	9	5	7	9	7	4
10d	0	4½	10	2	1½	10	3	10½	10	5	7½	10	7	4½
11d	0	4¾	11	2	1¾	11	3	10¾	11	5	7¾	11	7	4¾
1/-	0	5¼	**5/-**	2	2¼	**9/-**	3	11¼	**13/-**	5	8¼	**17/-**	7	5¼
1/1	0	5¾	5/1	2	2¾	9/1	3	11¾	13/1	5	8¾	17/1	7	5¾
2	0	6¼	2	2	3¼	2	4	0¼	2	5	9¼	2	7	6¼
3	0	6½	3	2	3½	3	4	0½	3	5	9½	3	7	6½
4	0	7	4	2	4	4	4	1	4	5	10	4	7	7
5	0	7½	5	2	4½	5	4	1½	5	5	10½	5	7	7½
1/6	0	8	5/6	2	5	9/6	4	2	13/6	5	11	17/6	7	8
7	0	8¼	7	2	5¼	7	4	2¼	7	5	11¼	7	7	8¼
8	0	8¾	8	2	5¾	8	4	2¾	8	5	11¾	8	7	8¾
9	0	9¼	9	2	6¼	9	4	3¼	9	6	0¼	9	7	9¼
10	0	9¾	10	2	6¾	10	4	3¾	10	6	0¾	10	7	9¾
11	0	10	11	2	7	11	4	4	11	6	1	11	7	10
2/-	0	10½	**6/-**	2	7½	**10/-**	4	4½	**14/-**	6	1½	**18/-**	7	10½
2/1	0	11	6/1	2	8	10/1	4	5	14/1	6	2	18/1	7	11
2	0	11½	2	2	8½	2	4	5½	2	6	2½	2	7	11½
3	0	11¾	3	2	8¾	3	4	5¾	3	6	2¾	3	7	11¾
4	1	0¼	4	2	9¼	4	4	6¼	4	6	3¼	4	8	0¼
5	1	0¾	5	2	9¾	5	4	6¾	5	6	3¾	5	8	0¾
2/6	1	1¼	6/6	2	10¼	10/6	4	7¼	14/6	6	4¼	18/6	8	1¼
7	1	1½	7	2	10½	7	4	7½	7	6	4½	7	8	1½
8	1	2	8	2	11	8	4	8	8	6	5	8	8	2
9	1	2½	9	2	11½	9	4	8½	9	6	5½	9	8	2½
10	1	3	10	3	0	10	4	9	10	6	6	10	8	3
11	1	3¼	11	3	0¼	11	4	9¼	11	6	6¼	11	8	3¼
3/-	1	3¾	**7/-**	3	0¾	**11/-**	4	9¾	**15/-**	6	6¾	**19/-**	8	3¾
3/1	1	4¼	7/1	3	1¼	11/1	4	10¼	15/1	6	7¼	19/1	8	4¼
2	1	4¾	2	3	1¾	2	4	10¾	2	6	7¾	2	8	4¾
3	1	5	3	3	2	3	4	11	3	6	8	3	8	5
4	1	5½	4	3	2½	4	4	11½	4	6	8½	4	8	5½
5	1	6	5	3	3	5	5	0	5	6	9	5	8	6
3/6	1	6½	7/6	3	3½	11/6	5	0½	15/6	6	9½	19/6	8	6½
7	1	6¾	7	3	3¾	7	5	0¾	7	6	9¾	7	8	6¾
8	1	7¼	8	3	4¼	8	5	1¼	8	6	10¼	8	8	7¼
9	1	7¾	9	3	4¾	9	5	1¾	9	6	10¾	9	8	7¾
10	1	8¼	10	3	5¼	10	5	2¼	10	6	11¼	10	8	8¼
11	1	8½	11	3	5½	11	5	2½	11	6	11½	11	8	8½
4/-	1	9	**8/-**	3	6	**12/-**	5	3	**16/-**	7	0	**20/-**	8	9

20/6	8s	11¾	25/6	11s	2	31/-	13s	6¾	35/6	15s	6½	**Guineas.**			
21/-	9	2¼	26/-	11	4½	31/6	13	9½	36/-	15	9	1.	£0	9	2¼
22/-	9	7½	27/-	11	9¾	32/-	14	0	37/-	16	2¼	2.	0	18	4½
22/6	9	10¼	27/6	12	0½	32/6	14	2¾	37/6	16	5	3.	1	7	6¾
23/-	10	0¾	28/-	12	3	33/-	14	5¼	38/-	16	7½	4.	1	16	9
24/-	10	6	29/-	12	8¼	34/-	14	10½	39/-	17	0¾	5.	2	5	11¼
25/-	10	11¼	**30/-**	13	1½	**35/-**	15	3¾	**40/-**	17	6	6.	£2	15	1½

(30 7/16 %* on Gross Returns.)

£1	£0 9s. 0	£51	22 19s. 0	£101	£45 9s. 0	£151	£67 19s. 0
2	0 18 0	52	23 8 0	102	45 18 0	152	68 8 0
3	1 7 0	53	23 17 0	103	46 7 0	153	68 17 0
4	1 16 0	54	24 6 0	104	46 16 0	154	69 6 0
5	2 5 0	55	24 15 0	105	47 5 0	155	69 15 0
6	2 14 0	56	25 4 0	106	47 14 0	156	70 4 0
7	3 3 0	57	25 13 0	107	48 3 0	157	70 13 0
8	3 12 0	58	26 2 0	108	48 12 0	158	71 2 0
9	4 1 0	59	26 11 0	109	49 1 0	159	71 11 0
10	£4 10s. 0	60	27 0s. 0	110	£49 10s. 0	160	£72 0s. 0
11	£4 19s. 0	61	27 9s. 0	111	£49 19s. 0	161	£72 9s. 0
12	5 8 0	62	27 18 0	112	50 8 0	162	72 18 0
13	5 17 0	63	28 7 0	113	50 17 0	163	73 7 0
14	6 6 0	64	28 16 0	114	51 6 0	164	73 16 0
15	6 15 0	65	29 5 0	115	51 15 0	165	74 5 0
16	7 4 0	66	29 14 0	116	52 4 0	166	74 14 0
17	7 13 0	67	30 3 0	117	52 13 0	167	75 3 0
18	8 2 0	68	30 12 0	118	53 2 0	168	75 12 0
19	8 11 0	69	31 1 0	119	53 11 0	169	76 1 0
20	£9 0s. 0	70	31 10s. 0	120	£54 0s. 0	170	£76 10s. 0
21	£9 9s. 0	71	31 19s. 0	121	£54 9s. 0	171	£76 19s. 0
22	9 18 0	72	32 8 0	122	54 18 0	172	77 8 0
23	10 7 0	73	32 17 0	123	55 7 0	173	77 17 0
24	10 16 0	74	33 6 0	124	55 16 0	174	78 6 0
25	11 5 0	75	33 15 0	125	56 5 0	175	78 15 0
26	11 14 0	76	34 4 0	126	56 14 0	176	79 4 0
27	12 3 0	77	34 13 0	127	57 3 0	177	79 13 0
28	12 12 0	78	35 2 0	128	57 12 0	178	80 2 0
29	13 1 0	79	35 11 0	129	58 1 0	179	80 11 0
30	13 10s. 0	80	36 0s. 0	130	£58 10s. 0	180	£81 0s. 0
31	13 19s. 0	81	36 9s. 0	131	£58 19s. 0	181	£81 9s. 0
32	14 8 0	82	36 18 0	132	59 8 0	182	81 18 0
33	14 17 0	83	37 7 0	133	59 17 0	183	82 7 0
34	15 6 0	84	37 16 0	134	60 6 0	184	82 16 0
35	15 15 0	85	38 5 0	135	60 15 0	185	83 5 0
36	16 4 0	86	38 14 0	136	61 4 0	186	83 14 0
37	16 13 0	87	39 3 0	137	61 13 0	187	84 3 0
38	17 2 0	88	39 12 0	138	62 2 0	188	84 12 0
39	17 11 0	89	40 1 0	139	62 11 0	189	85 1 0
40	18 0s. 0	90	40 10s. 0	140	£63 0s. 0	190	£85 10s. 0
41	18 9s. 0	91	40 19s. 0	141	£63 9s. 0	191	£85 19s. 0
42	18 18 0	92	41 8 0	142	63 18 0	192	86 8 0
43	19 7 0	93	41 17 0	143	64 7 0	193	86 17 0
44	19 16 0	94	42 6 0	144	64 16 0	194	87 6 0
45	20 5 0	95	42 15 0	145	65 5 0	195	87 15 0
46	20 14 0	96	43 4 0	146	65 14 0	196	88 4 0
47	21 3 0	97	43 13 0	147	66 3 0	197	88 13 0
48	21 12 0	98	44 2 0	148	66 12 0	198	89 2 0
49	22 1 0	99	44 11 0	149	67 1 0	199	89 11 0
50	22 10s. 0	100	45 0s. 0	150	£67 10s. 0	200	£90 0s. 0
250	112 10s. 0d	700	315 0s. 0d	1200	540 0s. 0d	2000	£900 0s. 0
300	135 0 0	750	337 10 0	1400	630 0 0	2500	1125 0 0
400	180 0 0	800	360 0 0	1500	675 0 0	3000	1350 0 0
500	225 0 0	900	405 0 0	1600	720 0 0	4000	1800 0 0
600	270 0s. 0d	1000	450 0s. 0d	1800	810 0s. 0d	5000	£2250 0s. 0

55% off.

45% FORTY-FIVE PER CENT. 45%

1d	0s. 0½	4/1	1s.10	8/1	3s. 7¾	12/1	5s. 5¼	16/1	7s. 2¾
2d	0 1	2	1 10½	2	3 8	2	5 5¾	2	7 3¼
3d	0 1¼	3	1 11	3	3 8½	3	5 6¼	3	7 3¾
4d	0 1¾	4	1 11½	4	3 9	4	5 6½	4	7 4¼
5d	0 2¼	5	1 11¾	5	3 9½	5	5 7	5	7 4¾
6d	0 2¾	4/6	2 0¼	8/6	3 10	12/6	5 7½	16/6	7 5
7d	0 3¼	7	2 0¾	7	3 10¼	7	5 8	7	7 5½
8d	0 3½	8	2 1¼	8	3 10¾	8	5 8½	8	7 6
9d	0 4	9	2 1¾	9	3 11¼	9	5 8¾	9	7 6½
10d	0 4½	10	2 2	10	3 11¾	10	5 9¼	10	7 7
11d	0 5	11	2 2½	11	4 0¼	11	5 9¾	11	7 7½
1/-	0s. 5½	**5/-**	2s. 3	**9/-**	4s. 0½	**13/-**	5s.10¼	**17/-**	7s. 7¾
1/1	0s. 5¾	5/1	2s. 3½	9/1	4s. 1	13/1	5s.10¾	17/1	7s. 8¼
2	0 6¼	2	2 4	2	4 1½	2	5 11	2	7 8¾
3	0 6¾	3	2 4¼	3	4 2	3	5 11½	3	7 9¼
4	0 7¼	4	2 4¾	4	4 2½	4	6 0	4	7 9½
5	0 7¾	5	2 5¼	5	4 2¾	5	6 0½	5	7 10
1/6	0 8	5/6	2 5¾	9/6	4 3¼	13/6	6 1	17/6	7 10½
7	0 8½	7	2 6¼	7	4 3¾	7	6 1¼	7	7 11
8	0 9	8	2 6½	8	4 4¼	8	6 1¾	8	7 11½
9	0 9½	9	2 7	9	4 4¾	9	6 2¼	9	7 11¾
10	0 10	10	2 7½	10	4 5	10	6 2¾	10	8 0¼
11	0 10¼	11	2 8	11	4 5½	11	6 3¼	11	8 0¾
2/-	0s.10¾	**6/-**	2s. 8½	**10/-**	4s. 6	**14/-**	6s. 3½	**18/-**	8s. 1¼
2/1	0s.11¼	6/1	2s. 8¾	10/1	4s. 6½	14/1	6s. 4	18/1	8s. 1¾
2	0 11¾	2	2 9¼	2	4 7	2	6 4½	2	8 2
3	1 0¼	3	2 9¾	3	4 7¼	3	6 5	3	8 2½
4	1 0½	4	2 10¼	4	4 7¾	4	6 5½	4	8 3
5	1 1	5	2 10¾	5	4 8¼	5	6 5¾	5	8 3½
2/6	1 1½	6/6	2 11	10/6	4 8¾	14/6	6 6¼	18/6	8 4
7	1 2	7	2 11½	7	4 9¼	7	6 6¾	7	8 4¼
8	1 2½	8	3 0	8	4 9½	8	6 7¼	8	8 4¾
9	1 2¾	9	3 0½	9	4 10	9	6 7¾	9	8 5¼
10	1 3¼	10	3 1	10	4 10½	10	6 8	10	8 5¾
11	1 3¾	11	3 1¼	11	4 11	11	6 8½	11	8 6¼
3/-	1s. 4¼	**7/-**	3s. 1¾	**11/-**	4s.11½	**15/-**	6s. 9	**19/-**	8s. 6½
3/1	1s. 4¾	7/1	3s. 2¼	11/1	4s.11¾	15/1	6s. 9½	19/1	8s. 7
2	1 5	2	3 2¾	2	5 0¼	2	6 10	2	8 7½
3	1 5½	3	3 3¼	3	5 0¾	3	6 10¼	3	8 8
4	1 6	4	3 3½	4	5 1¼	4	6 10¾	4	8 8½
5	1 6½	5	3 4	5	5 1¾	5	6 11¼	5	8 8¾
3/6	1 7	7/6	3 4½	11/6	5 2	15/6	6 11¾	19/6	8 9¼
7	1 7¼	7	3 5	7	5 2½	7	7 0¼	7	8 9¾
8	1 7¾	8	3 5½	8	5 3	8	7 0½	8	8 10¼
9	1 8¼	9	3 5¾	9	5 3½	9	7 1	9	8 10¾
10	1 8¾	10	3 6¼	10	5 4	10	7 1½	10	8 11
11	1 9¼	11	3 6¾	11	5 4¼	11	7 2	11	8 11½
4/-	1s. 9½	**8/-**	3s. 7¼	**12/-**	5s. 4¾	**16/-**	7s. 2½	**20/-**	9s. 0

								Guineas.	
20/6	9s. 2¾	25/6	11s. 5¾	31/-	13s.11½	35/6	15s.11¾		
21/-	9 5½	26/-	11 8½	31/6	14 2	36/-	16 2½	1.	£0 9s. 5½
22/-	9 10¾	27/-	12 1¾	32/-	14 4¾	37/-	16 7¾	2.	0 18 10¾
22/6	10 1½	27/6	12 4½	32/6	14 7½	37/6	16 10½	3.	1 8 4¼
23/-	10 4¼	28/-	12 7¼	33/-	14 10¼	38/-	17 1¼	4.	1 17 9½
24/-	10 9½	29/-	13 0½	34/-	15 3½	39/-	17 6½	5.	2 7 3
25/-	11s. 3	**30/-**	13s. 6	**35/-**	15s. 9	**40/-**	18s. 0	6.	£2 16s.8½

(31%* on Gross Returns).

£	£	s	d	£	£	s	d	£	£	s	d	£	£	s	d
£1	£0	9s	4¾	£51	23	19s	4¾	£101	47	9s	4¾	£151	70	19s	4¾
2	0	18	9½	52	24	8	9½	102	47	18	9½	152	71	8	9½
3	1	8	2½	53	24	18	2½	103	48	8	2½	153	71	18	2½
4	1	17	7¼	54	25	7	7¼	104	48	17	7¼	154	72	7	7¼
5	2	7	0	55	25	17	0	105	49	7	0	155	72	17	0
6	2	16	4¾	56	26	6	4¾	106	49	16	4¾	156	73	6	4¾
7	3	5	9½	57	26	15	9½	107	50	5	9½	157	73	15	9½
8	3	15	2½	58	27	5	2½	108	50	15	2½	158	74	5	2½
9	4	4	7¼	59	27	14	7¼	109	51	4	7¼	159	74	14	7¼
10	**4**	**14**	**0**	**60**	**28**	**4**	**0**	**110**	**51**	**14**	**0**	**160**	**75**	**4**	**0**
11	5	3	4¾	61	28	13	4¾	111	52	3	4¾	161	75	13	4¾
12	5	12	9½	62	29	2	9½	112	52	12	9½	162	76	2	9½
13	6	2	2½	63	29	12	2½	113	53	2	2½	163	76	12	2½
14	6	11	7¼	64	30	1	7¼	114	53	11	7¼	164	77	1	7¼
15	7	1	0	65	30	11	0	115	54	1	0	165	77	11	0
16	7	10	4¾	66	31	0	4¾	116	54	10	4¾	166	78	0	4¾
17	7	19	9½	67	31	9	9½	117	54	19	9½	167	78	9	9½
18	8	9	2½	68	31	19	2½	118	55	9	2½	168	78	19	2½
19	8	18	7¼	69	32	8	7¼	119	55	18	7¼	169	79	8	7¼
20	**9**	**8**	**0**	**70**	**32**	**18**	**0**	**120**	**56**	**8**	**0**	**170**	**79**	**18**	**0**
21	9	17	4¾	71	33	7	4¾	121	56	17	4¾	171	80	7	4¾
22	10	6	9½	72	33	16	9½	122	57	6	9½	172	80	16	9½
23	10	16	2½	73	34	6	2½	123	57	16	2½	173	81	6	2½
24	11	5	7¼	74	34	15	7¼	124	58	5	7¼	174	81	15	7¼
25	11	15	0	75	35	5	0	125	58	15	0	175	82	5	0
26	12	4	4¾	76	35	14	4¾	126	59	4	4¾	176	82	14	4¾
27	12	13	9½	77	36	3	9½	127	59	13	9½	177	83	3	9½
28	13	3	2½	78	36	13	2½	128	60	3	2½	178	83	13	2½
29	13	12	7¼	79	37	2	7¼	129	60	12	7¼	179	84	2	7¼
30	**14**	**2**	**0**	**80**	**37**	**12**	**0**	**130**	**61**	**2**	**0**	**180**	**84**	**12**	**0**
31	14	11	4¾	81	38	1	4¾	131	61	11	4¾	181	85	1	4¾
32	15	0	9½	82	38	10	9½	132	62	0	9½	182	85	10	9½
33	15	10	2½	83	39	0	2½	133	62	10	2½	183	86	0	2½
34	15	19	7¼	84	39	9	7¼	134	62	19	7¼	184	86	9	7¼
35	16	9	0	85	39	19	0	135	63	9	0	185	86	19	0
36	16	18	4¾	86	40	8	4¾	136	63	18	4¾	186	87	8	4¾
37	17	7	9½	87	40	17	9½	137	64	7	9½	187	87	17	9½
38	17	17	2½	88	41	7	2½	138	64	17	2½	188	88	7	2½
39	18	6	7¼	89	41	16	7¼	139	65	6	7¼	189	88	16	7¼
40	**18**	**16**	**0**	**90**	**42**	**6**	**0**	**140**	**65**	**16**	**0**	**190**	**89**	**6**	**0**
41	19	5	4¾	91	42	15	4¾	141	66	5	4¾	191	89	15	4½
42	19	14	9½	92	43	4	9½	142	66	14	9½	192	90	4	9½
43	20	4	2½	93	43	14	2½	143	67	4	2½	193	90	14	2½
44	20	13	7¼	94	44	3	7¼	144	67	13	7¼	194	91	3	7¼
45	21	3	0	95	44	13	0	145	68	3	0	195	91	13	0
46	21	12	4¾	96	45	2	4¾	146	68	12	4¾	196	92	2	4¾
47	22	1	9½	97	45	11	9½	147	69	1	9½	197	92	11	9½
48	22	11	2½	98	46	1	2½	148	69	11	2½	198	93	1	2½
49	23	0	7¼	99	46	10	7¼	149	70	0	7¼	199	93	10	7¼
50	**23**	**10**	**0**	**100**	**47**	**0**	**0**	**150**	**70**	**10**	**0**	**200**	**94**	**0**	**0**
250	117	10s	0d	700	329	0s	0d	1200	564	0s	0d	2000	940	0s	0
300	141	0	0	750	352	10	0	1400	658	0	0	2500	1175	0	0
400	188	0	0	800	376	0	0	1500	705	0	0	3000	1410	0	0
500	235	0	0	900	423	0	0	1600	752	0	0	4000	1880	0	0
600	282	0s	0d	1000	470	0s	0d	1800	846	0s	0d	5000	2350	0s	0

53% off

47 Per Cent.

47%

1d	0s 0½	4/1	1s11	8/1	3s 9½	12/1	5s 8¼	16/1	7s 6¾
2d	0 1	2	1 11½	2	3 10	2	5 8½	2	7 7¼
3d	0 1½	3	2 0	3	3 10½	3	5 9	3	7 7¾
4d	0 2	4	2 0½	4	3 11	4	5 9½	4	7 8
5d	0 2¼	5	2 1	5	3 11½	5	5 10	5	7 8½
6d	0 2¾	4/6	2 1½	8/6	4 0	12/6	5 10½	16/6	7 9
7d	0 3¼	7	2 1¾	7	4 0½	7	5 11	7	7 9½
8d	0 3¾	8	2 2¼	8	4 1	8	5 11½	8	7 10
9d	0 4¼	9	2 2¾	9	4 1¼	9	6 0	9	7 10½
10d	0 4¾	10	2 3¼	10	4 1¾	10	6 0½	10	7 11
11d	0 5¼	11	2 3¾	11	4 2¼	11	6 0¾	11	7 11½
1/-	**0 5¾**	**5/-**	**2 4¼**	**9/-**	**4 2¾**	**13/-**	**6 1¼**	**17/-**	**8 0**
1/1	0 6	5/1	2 4¾	1	4 3¼	1	6 1¾	1	8 0¼
2	0 6½	2	2 5¼	2	4 3¾	2	6 2¼	2	8 0¾
3	0 7	3	2 5½	3	4 4¼	3	6 2¾	3	8 1¼
4	0 7½	4	2 6	4	4 4¾	4	6 3¼	4	8 1¾
5	0 8	5	2 6½	5	4 5	5	6 3¾	5	8 2¼
1/6	0 8½	5/6	2 7	9/6	4 5½	13/6	6 4¼	17/6	8 2¾
7	0 9	7	2 7½	7	4 6	7	6 4½	7	8 3¼
8	0 9½	8	2 8	8	4 6½	8	6 5	8	8 3¾
9	0 9¾	9	2 8½	9	4 7	9	6 5½	9	8 4
10	0 10¼	10	2 9	10	4 7½	10	6 6	10	8 4½
11	0 10¾	11	2 9¼	11	4 8	11	6 6½	11	8 5
2/-	**0 11¼**	**6/-**	**2 9¾**	**10/-**	**4 8½**	**14/-**	**6 7**	**18/-**	**8 5½**
2/1	0 11¾	1	2 10¼	10/1	4 8¾	1	6 7½	1	8 6
2	1 0¼	2	2 10¾	2	4 9¼	2	6 8	2	8 6½
3	1 0¾	3	2 11¼	3	4 9¾	3	6 8¼	3	8 7
4	1 1¼	4	2 11¾	4	4 10¼	4	6 8¾	4	8 7½
5	1 1¾	5	3 0¼	5	4 10¾	5	6 9¼	5	8 7¾
2/6	1 2	6/6	3 0¾	10/6	4 11¼	14/6	6 9¾	18/6	8 8¼
7	1 2½	7	3 1¼	7	4 11¾	7	6 10¼	7	8 8¾
8	1 3	8	3 1½	8	5 0¼	8	6 10¾	8	8 9¼
9	1 3½	9	3 2	9	5 0¾	9	6 11¼	9	8 9¾
10	1 4	10	3 2½	10	5 1	10	6 11¾	10	8 10¼
11	1 4½	11	3 3	11	5 1½	11	7 0¼	11	8 10¾
3/-	**1 5**	**7/-**	**3 3½**	**11/-**	**5 2**	**15/-**	**7 0½**	**19/-**	**8 11¼**
3/1	1 5½	1	3 4	1	5 2½	15/1	7 1	1	8 11¾
2	1 5¾	2	3 4½	2	5 3	2	7 1½	2	9 0
3	1 6¼	3	3 5	3	5 3½	3	7 2	3	9 0½
4	1 6¾	4	3 5¼	4	5 4	4	7 2½	4	9 1
5	1 7¼	5	3 5¾	5	5 4½	5	7 3	5	9 1½
3/6	1 7¾	7/6	3 6¼	11/6	5 4¾	15/6	7 3½	19/6	9 2
7	1 8¼	7	3 6¾	7	5 5¼	7	7 4	7	9 2½
8	1 8¾	8	3 7¼	8	5 5¾	8	7 4¼	8	9 3
9	1 9¼	9	3 7¾	9	5 6¼	9	7 4¾	9	9 3½
10	1 9½	10	3 8¼	10	5 6¾	10	7 5¼	10	9 3¾
11	1 10	11	3 8¾	11	5 7¼	11	7 5¾	11	9 4¼
4/-	**1 10½**	**8/-**	**3 9**	**12/-**	**5 7¾**	**16/-**	**7 6½**	**20/-**	**9 4¾**

								Guineas.	
20/6	9s 7½	25/6	11s11¾	31/-	14s 6¾	35/6	16s 8¼		
21/-	9 10½	26/-	12 2¾	31/6	14 9¾	36/-	16 11	1.	£0 9 10½
22/-	10 4	27/-	12 8¼	32/-	15 0½	37/-	17 4¾	2.	0 19 9
22/6	10 7	27/6	12 11	32/6	15 3¼	37/6	17 7½	3.	1 9 7¼
23/-	10 9¾	28/-	13 2	33/-	15 6	38/-	17 10¼	4.	1 19 5¾
24/-	11 3¼	29/-	13 7½	34/-	15 11¾	39/-	18 4	5.	2 9 4¼
25/-	11s 9	**30/-**	14s 1¼	**35/-**	16s 5½	**40/-**	18s 9½	6.	£2 19 2¾

(=32%* on Gross Returns).

£				£				£				£			
£1	£0	9s.	6	£51	24	4s.	6	£101	£47	19s.	6	£151	£71	14s.	6
2	0	19	0	52	24	14	0	102	48	9	0	152	72	4	0
3	1	8	6	53	25	3	6	103	48	18	6	153	72	13	6
4	1	18	0	54	25	13	0	104	49	8	0	154	73	3	0
5	2	7	6	55	26	2	6	105	49	17	6	155	73	12	6
6	2	17	0	56	26	12	0	106	50	7	0	156	74	2	0
7	3	6	6	57	27	1	6	107	50	16	6	157	74	11	6
8	3	16	0	58	27	11	0	108	51	6	0	158	75	1	0
9	4	5	6	59	28	0	6	109	51	15	6	159	75	10	6
10	£4	15s.	0	60	28	10s.	0	110	£52	5s.	0	160	£76	0s.	0
11	£5	4s.	6	61	28	19s.	6	111	£52	14s.	6	161	£76	9s.	6
12	5	14	0	62	29	9	0	112	53	4	0	162	76	19	0
13	6	3	6	63	29	18	6	113	53	13	6	163	77	8	6
14	6	13	0	64	30	8	0	114	54	3	0	164	77	18	0
15	7	2	6	65	30	17	6	115	54	12	6	165	78	7	6
16	7	12	0	66	31	7	0	116	55	2	0	166	78	17	0
17	8	1	6	67	31	16	6	117	55	11	6	167	79	6	6
18	8	11	0	68	32	6	0	118	56	1	0	168	79	16	0
19	9	0	6	69	32	15	6	119	56	10	6	169	80	5	6
20	£9	10s.	0	70	33	5s.	0	120	£57	0s.	0	170	£80	15s.	0
21	£9	19s.	6	71	33	14s.	6	121	£57	9s.	6	171	£81	4s.	6
22	10	9	0	72	34	4	0	122	57	19	0	172	81	14	0
23	10	18	6	73	34	13	6	123	58	8	6	173	82	3	6
24	11	8	0	74	35	3	0	124	58	18	0	174	82	13	0
25	11	17	6	75	35	12	6	125	59	7	6	175	83	2	6
26	12	7	0	76	36	2	0	126	59	17	0	176	83	12	0
27	12	16	6	77	36	11	6	127	60	6	6	177	84	1	6
28	13	6	0	78	37	1	0	128	60	16	0	178	84	11	0
29	13	15	6	79	37	10	6	129	61	5	6	179	85	0	6
30	14	5s.	0	80	38	0s.	0	130	£61	15s.	0	180	£85	10s.	0
31	14	14s.	6	81	38	9s.	6	131	£62	4s.	6	181	£85	19s.	6
32	15	4	0	82	38	19	0	132	62	14	0	182	86	9	0
33	15	13	6	83	39	8	6	133	63	3	6	183	86	18	6
34	16	3	0	84	39	18	0	134	63	13	0	184	87	8	0
35	16	12	6	85	40	7	6	135	64	2	6	185	87	17	6
36	17	2	0	86	40	17	0	136	64	12	0	186	88	7	0
37	17	11	6	87	41	6	6	137	65	1	6	187	88	16	6
38	18	1	0	88	41	16	0	138	65	11	0	188	89	6	0
39	18	10	6	89	42	5	6	139	66	0	6	189	89	15	6
40	19	0s.	0	90	42	15s.	0	140	£66	10s.	0	190	£90	5s.	0
41	19	9s.	6	91	43	4s.	6	141	£66	19s.	6	191	£90	14s.	6
42	19	19	0	92	43	14	0	142	67	9	0	192	91	4	0
43	20	8	6	93	44	3	6	143	67	18	6	193	91	13	6
44	20	18	0	94	44	13	0	144	68	8	0	194	92	3	0
45	21	7	6	95	45	2	6	145	68	17	6	195	92	12	6
46	21	17	0	96	45	12	0	146	69	7	0	196	93	2	0
47	22	6	6	97	46	1	6	147	69	16	6	197	93	11	6
48	22	16	0	98	46	11	0	148	70	6	0	198	94	1	0
49	23	5	6	99	47	0	6	149	70	15	6	199	94	10	6
50	23	15s.	0	100	47	10s.	0	150	£71	5s.	0	200	£95	0s.	0
250	118	15s.	0d	700	332	10s.	0d	1200	570	0s.	0d	2000	£950	0s.	0
300	142	10	0	750	356	5	0	1400	665	0	0	2500	1187	10	0
400	190	0	0	800	380	0	0	1500	712	10	0	3000	1425	0	0
500	237	10	0	900	427	10	0	1600	760	0	0	4000	1900	0	0
600	285	0s.	0d	1000	475	0s.	0d	1800	855	0s.	0d	5000	£2375	0s.	0

52½% off.

1d	0s. 0½	4/1	1s.11¼	8/1	3s.10	12/1	5s. 9	16/1	7s. 7¾
2d	0 1	2	1 11¾	2	3 10½	2	5 9¼	2	7 8¼
3d	0 1½	3	2 0¼	3	3 11	3	5 9¾	3	7 8¾
4d	0 2	4	2 0¾	4	3 11½	4	5 10¼	4	7 9
5d	0 2½	5	2 1¼	5	4 0	5	5 10¾	5	7 9½
6d	0 2¾	4/6	2 1¾	8/6	4 0½	12/6	5 11¼	16/6	7 10
7d	0 3¼	7	2 2¼	7	4 1	7	5 11¾	7	7 10½
8d	0 3¾	8	2 2½	8	4 1½	8	6 0¼	8	7 11
9d	0 4¼	9	2 3	9	4 2	9	6 0¾	9	7 11½
10d	0 4¾	10	2 3½	10	4 2¼	10	6 1¼	10	8 0
11d	0 5¼	11	2 4	11	4 2¾	11	6 1¾	11	8 0½
1/-	0s. 5¾	**5/-**	2s. 4½	**9/-**	4s. 3¼	**13/-**	6s. 2	**17/-**	8s. 1
1/1	0s. 6¼	5/1	2s. 5	9/1	4s. 3¾	13/1	6s. 2½	17/1	8s. 1½
2	0 6¾	2	2 5½	2	4 4¼	2	6 3	2	8 1¾
3	0 7¼	3	2 6	3	4 4¾	3	6 3½	3	8 2¼
4	0 7½	4	2 6½	4	4 5¼	4	6 4	4	8 2¾
5	0 8	5	2 7	5	4 5¾	5	6 4½	5	8 3¼
1/6	0 8½	5/6	2 7¼	9/6	4 6¼	13/6	6 5	17/6	8 3¾
7	0 9	7	2 7¾	7	4 6¾	7	6 5½	7	8 4¼
8	0 9½	8	2 8¼	8	4 7	8	6 6	8	8 4¾
9	0 10	9	2 8¾	9	4 7½	9	6 6½	9	8 5¼
10	0 10½	10	2 9¼	10	4 8	10	6 6¾	10	8 5¾
11	0 11	11	2 9¾	11	4 8½	11	6 7¼	11	8 6¼
2/-	0s.11½	**6/-**	2s.10¼	**10/-**	4s. 9	**14/-**	6s. 7¾	**18/-**	8s. 6½
2/1	1s. 0	6/1	2s.10¾	10/1	4s. 9½	14/1	6s. 8¼	18/1	8s. 7
2	1 0¼	2	2 11¼	2	4 10	2	6 8¾	2	8 7½
3	1 0¾	3	2 11¾	3	4 10½	3	6 9¼	3	8 8
4	1 1¼	4	3 0	4	4 11	4	6 9¾	4	8 8½
5	1 1¾	5	3 0½	5	4 11½	5	6 10¼	5	8 9
2/6	1 2¼	6/6	3 1	10/6	4 11¾	14/6	6 10¾	18/6	8 9½
7	1 2¾	7	3 1½	7	5 0¼	7	6 11¼	7	8 10
8	1 3¼	8	3 2	8	5 0¾	8	6 11½	8	8 10½
9	1 3¾	9	3 2½	9	5 1¼	9	7 0	9	8 11
10	1 4¼	10	3 3	10	5 1¾	10	7 0½	10	8 11¼
11	1 4¾	11	3 3½	11	5 2¼	11	7 1	11	8 11¾
3/-	1s. 5	**7/-**	3s. 4	**11/-**	5s. 2¾	**15/-**	7s. 1½	**19/-**	9s. 0¼
3/1	1s. 5½	7/1	3s. 4½	11/1	5s. 3¼	15/1	7s. 2	19/1	9s. 0¾
2	1 6	2	3 4¾	2	5 3¾	2	7 2½	2	9 1¼
3	1 6½	3	3 5¼	3	5 4¼	3	7 3	3	9 1¾
4	1 7	4	3 5¾	4	5 4½	4	7 3½	4	9 2¼
5	1 7½	5	3 6¼	5	5 5	5	7 4	5	9 2¾
3/6	1 8	7/6	3 6¾	11/6	5 5½	15/6	7 4¼	19/6	9 3¼
7	1 8½	7	3 7¼	7	5 6	7	7 4¾	7	9 3¾
8	1 9	8	3 7¾	8	5 6½	8	7 5¼	8	9 4
9	1 9½	9	3 8¼	9	5 7	9	7 5¾	9	9 4½
10	1 9¾	10	3 8¾	10	5 7½	10	7 6¼	10	9 5
11	1 10¼	11	3 9¼	11	5 8	11	7 6¾	11	9 5½
4/-	1s.10¾	**8/-**	3s. 9½	**12/-**	5s. 8½	**16/-**	7s. 7¼	**20/-**	9s. 6

20/6	9s. 8¾	25/6	12s. 1¼	31/-	14s. 8¾	35/6	16s.10¼	Guineas.	
21/-	9 11¾	26/-	12 4¼	31/6	14 11½	36/-	17 1¼	1.	£0 9s.11¾
22/-	10 5½	27/-	12 10	32/-	15 2½	37/-	17 7	2.	0 19 11½
22/6	10 8¼	27/6	13 0¾	32/6	15 5¼	37/6	17 9¾	3.	1 9 11
23/-	10 11	28/-	13 3½	33/-	15 8	38/-	18 0½	4.	1 19 10¾
24/-	11 4¾	29/-	13 9¼	34/-	16 1¾	39/-	18 6¼	5.	2 9 10½
25/-	11s.10½	**30/-**	14s. 3	**35/-**	16s. 7½	**40/-**	19s. 0	6.	£2 19 10¼

(=32²⁄₁₀%* on Gross Returns).

£	Amount	£	Amount	£	Amount	£	Amount
£1	£0 10s. 0	£51	25 10s. 0	£101	£50 10s. 0	£151	£75 10s. 0
2	1 0 0	52	26 0 0	102	51 0 0	152	76 0 0
3	1 10 0	53	26 10 0	103	51 10 0	153	76 10 0
4	2 0 0	54	27 0 0	104	52 0 0	154	77 0 0
5	2 10 0	55	27 10 0	105	52 10 0	155	77 10 0
6	3 0 0	56	28 0 0	106	53 0 0	156	78 0 0
7	3 10 0	57	28 10 0	107	53 10 0	157	78 10 0
8	4 0 0	58	29 0 0	108	54 0 0	158	79 0 0
9	4 10 0	59	29 10 0	109	54 10 0	159	79 10 0
10	£5 0s. 0	60	30 0s. 0	110	£55 0s. 0	160	£80 0s. 0
11	£5 10s. 0	61	30 10s. 0	111	£55 10s. 0	161	£80 10s. 0
12	6 0 0	62	31 0 0	112	56 0 0	162	81 0 0
13	6 10 0	63	31 10 0	113	56 10 0	163	81 10 0
14	7 0 0	64	32 0 0	114	57 0 0	164	82 0 0
15	7 10 0	65	32 10 0	115	57 10 0	165	82 10 0
16	8 0 0	66	33 0 0	116	58 0 0	166	83 0 0
17	8 10 0	67	33 10 0	117	58 10 0	167	83 10 0
18	9 0 0	68	34 0 0	118	59 0 0	168	84 0 0
19	9 10 0	69	34 10 0	119	59 10 0	169	84 10 0
20	10 0s. 0	70	35 0s. 0	120	£60 0s. 0	170	£85 0s. 0
21	10 10s. 0	71	35 10s. 0	121	£60 10s. 0	171	£85 10s. 0
22	11 0 0	72	36 0 0	122	61 0 0	172	86 0 0
23	11 10 0	73	36 10 0	123	61 10 0	173	86 10 0
24	12 0 0	74	37 0 0	124	62 0 0	174	87 0 0
25	12 10 0	75	37 10 0	125	62 10 0	175	87 10 0
26	13 0 0	76	38 0 0	126	63 0 0	176	88 0 0
27	13 10 0	77	38 10 0	127	63 10 0	177	88 10 0
28	14 0 0	78	39 0 0	128	64 0 0	178	89 0 0
29	14 10 0	79	39 10 0	129	64 10 0	179	89 10 0
30	15 0s. 0	80	40 0s. 0	130	£65 0s. 0	180	£90 0s. 0
31	15 10s. 0	81	40 10s. 0	131	£65 10s. 0	181	£90 10s. 0
32	16 0 0	82	41 0 0	132	66 0 0	182	91 0 0
33	16 10 0	83	41 10 0	133	66 10 0	183	91 10 0
34	17 0 0	84	42 0 0	134	67 0 0	184	92 0 0
35	17 10 0	85	42 10 0	135	67 10 0	185	92 10 0
36	18 0 0	86	43 0 0	136	68 0 0	186	93 0 0
37	18 10 0	87	43 10 0	137	68 10 0	187	93 10 0
38	19 0 0	88	44 0 0	138	69 0 0	188	94 0 0
39	19 10 0	89	44 10 0	139	69 10 0	189	94 10 0
40	20 0s. 0	90	45 0s. 0	140	£70 0s. 0	190	£95 0s. 0
41	20 10s. 0	91	45 10s. 0	141	£70 10s. 0	191	£95 10s. 0
42	21 0 0	92	46 0 0	142	71 0 0	192	96 0 0
43	21 10 0	93	46 10 0	143	71 10 0	193	96 10 0
44	22 0 0	94	47 0 0	144	72 0 0	194	97 0 0
45	22 10 0	95	47 10 0	145	72 10 0	195	97 10 0
46	23 0 0	96	48 0 0	146	73 0 0	196	98 0 0
47	23 10 0	97	48 10 0	147	73 10 0	197	98 10 0
48	24 0 0	98	49 0 0	148	74 0 0	198	99 0 0
49	24 10 0	99	49 10 0	149	74 10 0	199	99 10 0
50	25 0s. 0	100	50 0s. 0	150	£75 0s. 0	200	100 0s. 0
250	125 0s.0d	700	350 0s.d	1200	600 0s.0d	2000	£1000 0s. 0
300	150 0 0	750	375 0 0	1400	700 0 0	2500	1250 0 0
400	200 0 0	800	400 0 0	1500	750 0 0	3000	1500 0 0
500	250 0 0	900	450 0 0	1600	800 0 0	4000	2000 0 0
600	300 0s.0d	1000	500 0s.0d	1800	900 0s.0d	5000	£2500 0s. 0

50% off.   (50%=one-half)

1d	0s. 0½	4/1	2s. 0½	8/1	4s. 0½	12/1	6s. 0½	16/1	8s. 0½
2d	0 1	2	2 1	2	4 1	2	6 1	2	8 1
3d	0 1½	3	2 1½	3	4 1½	3	6 1½	3	8 1½
4d	0 2	4	2 2	4	4 2	4	6 2	4	8 2
5d	0 2½	5	2 2½	5	4 2½	5	6 2½	5	8 2½
6d	0 3	4/6	2 3	8/6	4 3	12/6	6 3	16/6	8 3
7d	0 3½	7	2 3½	7	4 3½	7	6 3½	7	8 3½
8d	0 4	8	2 4	8	4 4	8	6 4	8	8 4
9d	0 4½	9	2 4½	9	4 4½	9	6 4½	9	8 4½
10d	0 5	10	2 5	10	4 5	10	6 5	10	8 5
11d	0 5½	11	2 5½	11	4 5½	11	6 5½	11	8 5½
1/-	**0s. 6**	**5/-**	**2s. 6**	**9/-**	**4s. 6**	**13/-**	**6s. 6**	**17/-**	**8s. 6**
1/1	0s. 6½	5/1	2s. 6½	9/1	4s. 6½	13/1	6s. 6½	17/1	8s. 6½
2	0 7	2	2 7	2	4 7	2	6 7	2	8 7
3	0 7½	3	2 7½	3	4 7½	3	6 7½	3	8 7½
4	0 8	4	2 8	4	4 8	4	6 8	4	8 8
5	0 8½	5	2 8½	5	4 8½	5	6 8½	5	8 8½
1/6	0 9	5/6	2 9	9/6	4 9	13/6	6 9	17/6	8 9
7	0 9½	7	2 9½	7	4 9½	7	6 9½	7	8 9½
8	0 10	8	2 10	8	4 10	8	6 10	8	8 10
9	0 10½	9	2 10½	9	4 10½	9	6 10½	9	8 10½
10	0 11	10	2 11	10	4 11	10	6 11	10	8 11
11	0 11½	11	2 11½	11	4 11½	11	6 11½	11	8 11½
2/-	**1s. 0**	**6/-**	**3s. 0**	**10/-**	**5s. 0**	**14/-**	**7s. 0**	**18/-**	**9s. 0**
2/1	1s. 0½	6/1	3s. 0½	10/1	5s. 0½	14/1	7s. 0½	18/1	9s. 0½
2	1 1	2	3 1	2	5 1	2	7 1	2	9 1
3	1 1½	3	3 1½	3	5 1½	3	7 1½	3	9 1½
4	1 2	4	3 2	4	5 2	4	7 2	4	9 2
5	1 2½	5	3 2½	5	5 2½	5	7 2½	5	9 2½
2/6	1 3	6/6	3 3	10/6	5 3	14/6	7 3	18/6	9 3
7	1 3½	7	3 3½	7	5 3½	7	7 3½	7	9 3½
8	1 4	8	3 4	8	5 4	8	7 4	8	9 4
9	1 4½	9	3 4½	9	5 4½	9	7 4½	9	9 4½
10	1 5	10	3 5	10	5 5	10	7 5	10	9 5
11	1 5½	11	3 5½	11	5 5½	11	7 5½	11	9 5½
3/-	**1s. 6**	**7/-**	**3s. 6**	**11/-**	**5s. 6**	**15/-**	**7s. 6**	**19/-**	**9s. 6**
3/1	1s. 6½	7/1	3s. 6½	11/1	5s. 6½	15/1	7s. 6½	19/1	9s. 6½
2	1 7	2	3 7	2	5 7	2	7 7	2	9 7
3	1 7½	3	3 7½	3	5 7½	3	7 7½	3	9 7½
4	1 8	4	3 8	4	5 8	4	7 8	4	9 8
5	1 8½	5	3 8½	5	5 8½	5	7 8½	5	9 8½
3/6	1 9	7/6	3 9	11/6	5 9	15/6	7 9	19/6	9 9
7	1 9½	7	3 9½	7	5 9½	7	7 9½	7	9 9½
8	1 10	8	3 10	8	5 10	8	7 10	8	9 10
9	1 10½	9	3 10½	9	5 10½	9	7 10½	9	9 10½
10	1 11	10	3 11	10	5 11	10	7 11	10	9 11
11	1 11½	11	3 11½	11	5 11½	11	7 11½	11	9 11½
4/-	**2s. 0**	**8/-**	**4s. 0**	**12/-**	**6s. 0**	**16/-**	**8s. 0**	**20/-**	**10s. 0**

								Guineas.	
20/6	10s. 3	25/6	12s. 9	31/-	15s. 6	35/6	17s. 9		
21/-	10 6	26/-	13 0	31/6	15 9	36/-	18 0	1.	£0 10s. 6
22/-	11 0	27/-	13 6	32/-	16 0	37/-	18 6	2.	1 1 0
22/6	11 3	27/6	13 9	32/6	16 3	37/6	18 9	3.	1 11 6
23/-	11 6	28/-	14 0	33/-	16 6	38/-	19 0	4.	2 2 0
24/-	12 0	29/-	14 6	34/-	17 0	39/-	19 6	5.	2 12 6
25/-	**12s. 6**	**30/-**	**15s. 0**	**35/-**	**17s. 6**	**40/-**	**20s. 0**	**6.**	**£3 3 0**

(33⅓% on Gross Returns).

£1	£0 10s. 6	£51	26 15s. 6	£101	53 0s. 6	£151	£79 5s. 6
2	1 1 0	52	27 6 0	102	53 11 0	152	79 16 0
3	1 11 6	53	27 16 6	103	54 1 6	153	80 6 6
4	2 2 0	54	28 7 0	104	54 12 0	154	80 17 0
5	2 12 6	55	28 17 6	105	55 2 6	155	81 7 6
6	3 3 0	56	29 8 0	106	55 13 0	156	81 18 0
7	3 13 6	57	29 18 6	107	56 3 6	157	82 8 6
8	4 4 0	58	30 9 0	108	56 14 0	158	82 19 0
9	4 14 6	59	30 19 6	109	57 4 6	159	83 9 6
10	5 5s. 0	60	31 10s. 0	110	57 15s. 0	160	84 0s. 0
11	5 15s. 6	61	32 0s. 6	111	58 5s. 6	161	84 10s. 6
12	6 6 0	62	32 11 0	112	58 16 0	162	85 1 0
13	6 16 6	63	33 1 6	113	59 6 6	163	85 11 6
14	7 7 0	64	33 12 0	114	59 17 0	164	86 2 0
15	7 17 6	65	34 2 6	115	60 7 6	165	86 12 6
16	8 8 0	66	34 13 0	116	60 18 0	166	87 3 0
17	8 18 6	67	35 3 6	117	61 8 6	167	87 13 6
18	9 9 0	68	35 14 0	118	61 19 0	168	88 4 0
19	9 19 6	69	36 4 6	119	62 9 6	169	88 14 6
20	10 10s. 0	70	36 15s. 0	120	63 0s. 0	170	89 5s. 0
21	11 0s. 6	71	37 5s. 6	121	63 10s. 6	171	89 15s. 6
22	11 11 0	72	37 16 0	122	64 1 0	172	90 6 0
23	12 1 6	73	38 6 6	123	64 11 6	173	90 16 6
24	12 12 0	74	38 17 0	124	65 2 0	174	91 7 0
25	13 2 6	75	39 7 6	125	65 12 6	175	91 17 6
26	13 13 0	76	39 18 0	126	66 3 0	176	92 8 0
27	14 3 6	77	40 8 6	127	66 13 6	177	92 18 6
28	14 14 0	78	40 19 0	128	67 4 0	178	93 9 0
29	15 4 6	79	41 9 6	129	67 14 6	179	93 19 6
30	15 15s. 0	80	42 0s. 0	130	68 5s. 0	180	94 10s. 0
31	16 5s. 6	81	42 10s. 6	131	68 15s. 6	181	95 0s. 6
32	16 16 0	82	43 1 0	132	69 6 0	182	95 11 0
33	17 6 6	83	43 11 6	133	69 16 6	183	96 1 6
34	17 17 0	84	44 2 0	134	70 7 0	184	96 12 0
35	18 7 6	85	44 12 6	135	70 17 6	185	97 2 6
36	18 18 0	86	45 3 0	136	71 8 0	186	97 13 0
37	19 8 6	87	45 13 6	137	71 18 6	187	98 3 6
38	19 19 0	88	46 4 0	138	72 9 0	188	98 14 0
39	20 9 6	89	46 14 6	139	72 19 6	189	99 4 6
40	21 0s. 0	90	47 5s. 0	140	73 10s. 0	190	99 15s. 0
41	21 10s. 6	91	47 15s. 6	141	74 0s. 6	191	100 5s. 6
42	22 1 0	92	48 6 0	142	74 11 0	192	100 16 0
43	22 11 6	93	48 16 6	143	75 1 6	193	101 6 6
44	23 2 0	94	49 7 0	144	75 12 0	194	101 17 0
45	23 12 6	95	49 17 6	145	76 2 6	195	102 7 6
46	24 3 0	96	50 8 0	146	76 13 0	196	102 18 0
47	24 13 6	97	50 18 6	147	77 3 6	197	103 8 6
48	25 4 0	98	51 9 0	148	77 14 0	198	103 19 0
49	25 14 6	99	51 19 6	149	78 4 6	199	104 9 6
50	26 5s. 0	100	52 10s. 0	150	78 15s. 0	200	105 0s. 0
250	131 5s. 0d	700	367 10s. 0d	1200	630 0s. 0d	2000	£1050 0s. 0
300	157 10 0	750	393 15 0	1400	735 0 0	2500	1312 10 0
400	210 0 0	800	420 0 0	1500	787 10 0	3000	1575 0 0
500	262 10 0	900	472 10 0	1600	840 0 0	4000	2100 0 0
600	315 0s. 0d	1000	525 0s. 0d	1800	945 0s. 0d	5000	£2625 0s. 0

47½% off.

52½% 52½ Per Cent. 52½%

1d	0s. 0½	4/1	2s. 1¾	8/1	4s. 3	12/1	6s. 4¼	16/1	8s. 5¼
2d	0 1	2	2 2¼	2	4 3½	2	6 4¾	2	8 5¾
3d	0 1½	3	2 2¾	3	4 4	3	6 5¼	3	8 6½
4d	0 2	4	2 3¼	4	4 4½	4	6 5¾	4	8 7
5d	0 2¾	5	2 3¾	5	4 5	5	6 6¼	5	8 7½
6d	0 3¼	4/6	2 4¼	8/6	4 5½	12/6	6 6¾	16/6	8 8
7d	0 3¾	7	2 5	7	4 6	7	6 7¼	7	8 8½
8d	0 4¼	8	2 5½	8	4 6½	8	6 7¾	8	8 9
9d	0 4¾	9	2 6	9	4 7¼	9	6 8¼	9	8 9½
10d	0 5¼	10	2 6½	10	4 7¾	10	6 8¾	10	8 10
11d	0 5¾	11	2 7	11	4 8¼	11	6 9½	11	8 10½
1/-	0s. 6¼	**5/-**	2s. 7½	**9/-**	4s. 8¾	**13/-**	6s.10	**17/-**	8s.11
1/1	0s. 6¾	5/1	2s. 8	9/1	4s. 9¼	13[illegible]	[illegible]10½	17/1	8s.11¾
2	0 7¼	2	2 8½	2	4 9¾	[illegible]	6 11	2	9 0¼
3	0 8	3	2 9	3	4 10¼	3	6 11½	3	9 0¾
4	0 8½	4	2 9½	4	4 10¾	4	7 0	4	9 1¼
5	0 9	5	2 10¼	5	4 11¼	5	7 0½	5	9 1¾
1/6	0 9½	5/6	2 10¾	9/6	4 11¾	13/6	7 1	17/6	9 2¼
7	0 10	7	2 11¼	7	5 0½	7	7 1½	7	9 2¾
8	0 10½	8	2 11¾	8	5 1	8	7 2	8	9 3¼
9	0 11	9	3 0¼	9	5 1½	9	7 2¾	9	9 3¾
10	0 11½	10	3 0¾	10	5 2	10	7 3¼	10	9 4¼
11	1 0	11	3 1¼	11	5 2½	11	7 3¾	11	9 5
2/-	1s. 0½	**6/-**	3s. 1¾	**10/-**	5s. 3	**14/-**	7s. 4¼	**18/-**	9s. 5½
2/1	1s. 1¼	6/1	3s. 2¼	10/1	5s. 3½	14/1	7s. 4¾	18/1	9s. 6
2	1 1¾	2	3 2¾	2	5 4	2	7 5¼	2	9 6½
3	1 2¼	3	3 3½	3	5 4½	3	7 5¾	3	9 7
4	1 2¾	4	3 4	4	5 5	4	7 6¼	4	9 7½
5	1 3¼	5	3 4½	5	5 5¾	5	7 6¾	5	9 8
2/6	1 3¾	6/6	3 5	10/6	5 6¼	14/6	7 7¼	18/6	9 8½
7	1 4¼	7	3 5½	7	5 6¾	7	7 8	7	9 9
8	1 4¾	8	3 6	8	5 7¼	8	7 8½	8	9 9½
9	1 5¼	9	3 6½	9	5 7¾	9	7 9	9	9 10¼
10	1 5¾	10	3 7	10	5 8¼	10	7 9½	10	9 10¾
11	1 6½	11	3 7½	11	5 8¾	11	7 10	11	9 11¼
3/-	1s. 7	**7/-**	3s. 8	**11/-**	5s. 9¼	**15/-**	7 10½	**19/-**	9s.11¾
3/1	1s. 7½	7/1	3s. 8¾	11/1	5s. 9¾	15/1	7s.11	19/1	10s. 0¼
2	1 8	2	3 9¼	2	5 10¼	2	7 11½	2	10 0¾
3	1 8½	3	3 9¾	3	5 11	3	8 0	3	10 1¼
4	1 9	4	3 10¼	4	5 11½	4	8 0½	4	10 1¾
5	1 9½	5	3 10¾	5	6 0	5	8 1¼	5	10 2¼
3/6	1 10	7/6	3 11¼	11/6	6 0½	15/6	8 1¾	19/6	10 2¾
7	1 10½	7	3 11¾	7	6 1	7	8 2¼	7	10 3½
8	1 11	8	4 0¼	8	6 1½	8	8 2¾	8	10 4
9	1 11¾	9	4 0¾	9	6 2	9	8 3¼	9	10 4½
10	2 0¼	10	4 1¼	10	6 2½	10	8 3¾	10	10 5
11	2 0¾	11	4 2	11	6 3	11	8 4¼	11	10 5½
4/-	2s. 1¼	**8/-**	4s. 2½	**12/-**	6s. 3½	**16/-**	8s. 4¾	**20/-**	10s. 6

20/6	10s. 9¼	25/6	13s. 4¾	31/-	16s. 3¼	35/6	18s. 7¾	Guineas.	
21/-	11 0¼	26/-	13 7¾	31/6	16 6½	36/-	18 10¾	1.	11s. 0¼
22/-	11 6½	27/-	14 2	32/-	16 9½	37/-	19 5	2.	22 0½
22/6	11 9¾	27/6	14 5¼	32/6	17 0¾	37/6	19 8¼	3.	33 1
23/-	12 1	28/-	14 8½	33/-	17 4	38/-	19 11½	4.	44 1¼
24/-	12 7¼	29/-	15 2¾	34/-	17 10¼	39/-	20 5¾	5.	55 1½
25/-	13 1½	**30/-**	15 9	**35/-**	18 4½	**40/-**	21 0	6.	66s. 1¾

(34 4/10 %* on Gross Returns).

£			£			£			£		
£1	£0 11s.	0	£51	28 1s.	0	£101	£55 11s.	0	£151	£83 1s.	0
2	1 2	0	52	28 12	0	102	56 2	0	152	83 12	0
3	1 13	0	53	29 3	0	103	56·13	0	153	84 3	0
4	2 4	0	54	29 14	0	104	57 4	0	154	84 14	0
5	2 15	0	55	30 5	0	105	57 15	0	155	85 5	0
6	3 6	0	56	30 16	0	106	58 6	0	156	85 16	0
7	3 17	0	57	31 7	0	107	58 17	0	157	86 7	0
8	4 8	0	58	31 18	0	108	59 8	0	158	86 18	0
9	4 19	0	59	32 9	0	109	59 19	0	159	87 9	0
10	£5 10s.	0	60	33 0s.	0	110	£60 10s.	0	160	£88 0s.	0
11	£6 1s.	0	61	33 11s.	0	111	£61 1s.	0	161	£88 11s.	0
12	6 12	0	62	34 2	0	112	61 12	0	162	89 2	0
13	7 3	0	63	34 13	0	113	62 3	0	163	89 13	0
14	7 14	0	64	35 4	0	114	62 14	0	164	90 4	0
15	8 5	0	65	35 15	0	115	63 5	0	165	90 15	0
16	8 16	0	66	36 6	0	116	63 16	0	166	91 6	0
17	9 7	0	67	36 17	0	117	64 7	0	167	91 17	0
18	9 18	0	68	37 8	0	118	64 18	0	168	92 8	0
19	10 9	0	69	37 19	0	119	65 9	0	169	92 19	0
20	11 0s.	0	70	38 10s.	0	120	£66 0s.	0	170	£93 10s.	0
21	11 11s.	0	71	39 1s.	0	121	£66 11s.	0	171	£94 1s.	0
22	12 2	0	72	39 12	0	122	67 2	0	172	94 12	0
23	12 13	0	73	40 3	0	123	67 13	0	173	95 3	0
24	13 4	0	74	40 14	0	124	68 4	0	174	95 14	0
25	13 15	0	75	41 5	0	125	68 15	0	175	96 5	0
26	14 6	0	76	41 16	0	126	69 6	0	176	96 16	0
27	14 17	0	77	42 7	0	127	69 17	0	177	97 7	0
28	15 8	0	78	42 18	0	128	70 8	0	178	97 18	0
29	15 19	0	79	43 9	0	129	70 19	0	179	98 9	0
30	16 10s.	0	80	44 0s.	0	130	£71 10s.	0	180	£99 0s.	0
31	17 1s.	0	81	44 11s.	0	131	£72 1s.	0	181	£99 11s.	0
32	17 12	0	82	45 2	0	132	72 12	0	182	100 2	0
33	18 3	0	83	45 13	0	133	73 3	0	183	100 13	0
34	18 14	0	84	46 4	0	134	73 14	0	184	101 4	0
35	19 5	0	85	46 15	0	135	74 5	0	185	101 15	0
36	19 16	0	86	47 6	0	136	74 16	0	186	102 6	0
37	20 7	0	87	47 17	0	137	75 7	0	187	102 17	0
38	20 18	0	88	48 8	0	138	75 18	0	188	103 8	0
39	21 9	0	89	48 19	0	139	76 9	0	189	103 19	0
40	22 0s.	0	90	49 10s.	0	140	£77 0s.	0	190	104 10s.	0
41	22 11s.	0	91	50 1s.	0	141	£77 11s.	0	191	105 1s.	0
42	23 2	0	92	50 12	0	142	78 2	0	192	105 12	0
43	23 13	0	93	51 3	0	143	78 13	0	193	106 3	0
44	24 4	0	94	51 14	0	144	79 4	0	194	106 14	0
45	24 15	0	95	52 5	0	145	79 15	0	195	107 5	0
46	25 6	0	96	52 16	0	146	80 6	0	196	107 16	0
47	25 17	0	97	53 7	0	147	80 17	0	197	108 7	0
48	26 8	0	98	53 18	0	148	81 8	0	198	108 18	0
49	26 19	0	99	54 9	0	149	81 19	0	199	109 9	0
50	27 10s.	0	100	55 0s.	0	150	£82 10s.	0	200	110 0s.	0

£		£		£		£		
250	137 10s. 0d	700	385 0s. 0d	1200	660 0s. 0d	2000	£1100 0s.	0
300	165 0 0	750	412 10 0	1400	770 0 0	2500	1375 0	0
400	220 0 0	800	440 0 0	1500	825 0 0	3000	1650 0	0
500	275 0 0	900	495 0 0	1600	880 0 0	4000	2200 0	0
600	330 0s. 0	1000	550 0s. 0d	1800	990 0s. 0d	5000	£2750 0s.	0

45% off.

1d	0s.	0½	4/1	2s.	3	8/1	4s.	5¼	12/1	6s.	7¾	16/1	8s.	10¼
2d	0	1	2	2	3½	2	4	6	2	6	8¼	2	8	10¾
3d	0	1¾	3	2	4	3	4	6½	3	6	8¾	3	8	11¼
4d	0	2¼	4	2	4½	4	4	7	4	6	9½	4	8	11¾
5d	0	2¾	5	2	5¼	5	4	7½	5	6	10	5	9	0¼
6d	0	3¼	4/6	2	5¾	8/6	4	8	12/6	6	10½	16/6	9	1
7d	0	3¾	7	2	6¼	7	4	8¾	7	6	11	7	9	1½
8d	0	4½	8	2	6¾	8	4	9¼	8	6	11½	8	9	2
9d	0	5	9	2	7¼	9	4	9¾	9	7	0¼	9	9	2½
10d	0	5½	10	2	8	10	4	10¼	10	7	0¾	10	9	3
11d	0	6	11	2	8½	11	4	10¾	11	7	1¼	11	9	3¾
1/-	0s.	6½	**5/-**	2s.	9	**9/-**	4s.	11½	**13/-**	7s.	1¾	**17/-**	9s.	4¼
1/1	0s.	7¼	5/1	2s.	9½	9/1	5s.	0	13/1	7s.	2¼	17/1	9s.	4¾
2	0	7¾	2	2	10	2	5	0½	2	7	3	2	9	5¼
3	0	8¼	3	2	10¾	3	5	1	3	7	3½	3	9	5¾
4	0	8¾	4	2	11¼	4	5	1½	4	7	4	4	9	6½
5	0	9¼	5	2	11¾	5	5	2¼	5	7	4½	5	9	7
1/6	0	10	5/6	3	0¼	9/6	5	2¾	13/6	7	5	17/6	9	7½
7	0	10½	7	3	0¾	7	5	3¼	7	7	5¾	7	9	8
8	0	11	8	3	1½	8	5	3¾	8	7	6¼	8	9	8½
9	0	11½	9	3	2	9	5	4¼	9	7	6¾	9	9	9¼
10	1	0	10	3	2½	10	5	5	10	7	7¼	10	9	9¾
11	1	0¾	11	3	3	11	5	5½	11	7	7¾	11	9	10¼
2/-	1s.	1¼	**6/-**	3s.	3½	**10/-**	5s.	6	**14/-**	7s.	8½	**18/-**	9s.	10¾
2/1	1s.	1¾	6/1	3s.	4¼	10/1	5s.	6½	14/1	7s.	9	18/1	9s.	11¼
2	1	2¼	2	3	4¾	2	5	7	2	7	9½	2	10	0
3	1	2¾	3	3	5¼	3	5	7¾	3	7	10	3	10	0½
4	1	3½	4	3	5¾	4	5	8¼	4	7	10½	4	10	1
5	1	4	5	3	6¼	5	5	8¾	5	7	11¼	5	10	1½
2/6	1	4½	6/6	3	7	10/6	5	9¼	14/6	7	11¾	18/6	10	2
7	1	5	7	3	7½	7	5	9¾	7	8	0¼	7	10	2¾
8	1	5½	8	3	8	8	5	10½	8	8	0¾	8	10	3¼
9	1	6¼	9	3	8½	9	5	11	9	8	1¼	9	10	3¾
10	1	6¾	10	3	9	10	5	11½	10	8	2	10	10	4¼
11	1	7¼	11	3	9¾	11	6	0	11	8	2½	11	10	4¾
3/-	1s.	7¾	**7/-**	3s.	10¼	**11/-**	6s.	0½	**15/-**	8s.	3	**19/-**	10s.	5½
3/1	1s.	8¼	7/1	3s.	10¾	11/1	6s.	1¼	15/1	8s.	3½	19/1	10s.	6
2	1	9	2	3	11¼	2	6	1¾	2	8	4	2	10	6½
3	1	9½	3	3	11¾	3	6	2¼	3	8	4¾	3	10	7
4	1	10	4	4	0½	4	6	2¾	4	8	5¼	4	10	7½
5	1	10½	5	4	1	5	6	3¼	5	8	5¾	5	10	8¼
3/6	1	11	7/6	4	1½	11/6	6	4	15/6	8	6¼	19/6	10	8¾
7	1	11¾	7	4	2	7	6	4½	7	8	6¾	7	10	9¼
8	2	0¼	8	4	2½	8	6	5	8	8	7½	8	10	9¾
9	2	0¾	9	4	3¼	9	6	5½	9	8	8	9	10	10¼
10	2	1¼	10	4	3¾	10	6	6	10	8	8½	10	10	11
11	2	1¾	11	4	4¼	11	6	6¾	11	8	9	11	10	11½
4/-	2s.	2½	**8/-**	4s.	4¾	**12/-**	6s.	7¼	**16/-**	8s.	9½	**20/-**	11s.	0

												Guineas.			
20/6	11s.	3¼	25/6	14s.	0¼	31/-	17s.	0½	35/6	19s.	6¼	1.	£0	11s.	6½
21/-	11	6½	26/-	14	3½	31/6	17	4	36/-	19	9½	2.	1	3	1¼
22/-	12	1¼	27/-	14	10¼	32/-	17	7¼	37/-	20	4¼	3.	1	14	7¾
22/6	12	4½	27/6	15	1½	32/6	17	10½	37/6	20	7½	4.	2	6	2½
23/-	12	7¾	28/-	15	4¾	33/-	18	1¾	38/-	20	10¾	5.	2	17	9
24/-	13	2½	29/-	15	11½	34/-	18	8½	39/-	21	5½	6.	£3	9	3½
25/-	13s.	9	**30/-**	16s.	6	**35/-**	19s.	3	**40/-**	22s.	0				

(35½%* on Gross Returns).

£1	£0 11s 3	£51	28 13s 9	£101	56 16s 3	£151	84 18s 9
2	1 2 6	52	29 5 0	102	57 7 6	152	85 10 0
3	1 13 9	53	29 16 3	103	57 18 9	153	86 1 3
4	2 5 0	54	30 7 6	104	58 10 0	154	86 12 6
5	2 16 3	55	30 18 9	105	59 1 3	155	87 3 9
6	3 7 6	56	31 10 0	106	59 12 6	156	87 15 0
7	3 18 9	57	32 1 3	107	60 3 9	157	88 6 3
8	4 10 0	58	32 12 6	108	60 15 0	158	88 17 6
9	5 1 3	59	33 3 9	109	61 6 3	159	89 8 9
10	5 12 6	60	33 15 0	110	61 17 6	160	90 0 0
11	6 3 9	61	34 6 3	111	62 8 9	161	90 11 3
12	6 15 0	62	34 17 6	112	63 0 0	162	91 2 6
13	7 6 3	63	35 8 9	113	63 11 3	163	91 13 9
14	7 17 6	64	36 0 0	114	64 2 6	164	92 5 0
15	8 8 9	65	36 11 3	115	64 13 9	165	92 16 3
16	9 0 0	66	37 2 6	116	65 5 0	166	93 7 6
17	9 11 3	67	37 13 9	117	65 16 3	167	93 18 9
18	10 2 6	68	38 5 0	118	66 7 6	168	94 10 0
19	10 13 9	69	38 16 3	119	66 18 9	169	95 1 3
20	11 5 0	70	39 7 6	120	67 10 0	170	95 12 6
21	11 16 3	71	39 18 9	121	68 1 3	171	96 3 9
22	12 7 6	72	40 10 0	122	68 12 6	172	96 15 0
23	12 18 9	73	41 1 3	123	69 3 9	173	97 6 3
24	13 10 0	74	41 12 6	124	69 15 0	174	97 17 6
25	14 1 3	75	42 3 9	125	70 6 3	175	98 8 9
26	14 12 6	76	42 15 0	126	70 17 6	176	99 0 0
27	15 3 9	77	43 6 3	127	71 8 9	177	99 11 3
28	15 15 0	78	43 17 6	128	72 0 0	178	100 2 6
29	16 6 3	79	44 8 9	129	72 11 3	179	100 13 9
30	16 17 6	80	45 0 0	130	73 2 6	180	101 5 0
31	17 8 9	81	45 11 3	131	73 13 9	181	101 16 3
32	18 0 0	82	46 2 6	132	74 5 0	182	102 7 6
33	18 11 3	83	46 13 9	133	74 16 3	183	102 18 9
34	19 2 6	84	47 5 0	134	75 7 6	184	103 10 0
35	19 13 9	85	47 16 3	135	75 18 9	185	104 1 3
36	20 5 0	86	48 7 6	136	76 10 0	186	104 12 6
37	20 16 3	87	48 18 9	137	77 1 3	187	105 3 9
38	21 7 6	88	49 10 0	138	77 12 6	188	105 15 0
39	21 18 9	89	50 1 3	139	78 3 9	189	106 6 3
40	22 10 0	90	50 12 6	140	78 15 0	190	106 17 6
41	23 1 3	91	51 3 9	141	79 6 3	191	107 8 9
42	23 12 6	92	51 15 0	142	79 17 6	192	108 0 0
43	24 3 9	93	52 6 3	143	80 8 9	193	108 11 3
44	24 15 0	94	52 17 6	144	81 0 0	194	109 2 6
45	25 6 3	95	53 8 9	145	81 11 3	195	109 13 9
46	25 17 6	96	54 0 0	146	82 2 6	196	110 5 0
47	26 8 9	97	54 11 3	147	82 13 9	197	110 16 3
48	27 0 0	98	55 2 6	148	83 5 0	198	111 7 6
49	27 11 3	99	55 13 9	149	83 16 3	199	111 18 9
50	28 2 6	100	56 5 0	150	84 7 6	200	112 10 0

250	140 12s 6d	700	393 15s 0d	1200	675 0s 0d	2000	1125 0s 0
300	168 15 0	750	421 17 6	1400	787 10 0	2500	1406 5 0
400	225 0 0	800	450 0 0	1500	843 15 0	3000	1687 10 0
500	281 5 0	900	506 5 0	1600	900 0 0	4000	2250 0 0
600	337 10s 0d	1000	562 10s 0d	1800	1012 10s 0d	5000	2812 10s 0

43¾% off.

56¼ Per Cent.

56¼%

1d	0s	0½	4/1	2s	3½	8/1	4s	6½	12/1	6s	9½	16/1	9s	0½
2d	0	1¼	2	2	4¼	2	4	7¼	2	6	10¼	2	9	1¼
3d	0	1¾	3	2	4¾	3	4	7¾	3	6	10¾	3	9	1¾
4d	0	2¼	4	2	5¼	4	4	8¼	4	6	11¼	4	9	2¼
5d	0	2¾	5	2	5¾	5	4	8¾	5	6	11¾	5	9	2¾
6d	0	3½	4/6	2	6½	8/6	4	9½	12/6	7	0½	16/6	9	3½
7d	0	4	7	2	7	7	4	10	7	7	1	7	9	4
8d	0	4½	8	2	7½	8	4	10½	8	7	1½	8	9	4½
9d	0	5	9	2	8	9	4	11	9	7	2	9	9	5
10d	0	5¾	10	2	8¾	10	4	11¾	10	7	2¾	10	9	5¾
11d	0	6¼	11	2	9¼	11	5	0¼	11	7	3¼	11	9	6¼
1/-	0	6¾	**5/-**	2	9¾	**9/-**	5	0¾	**13/-**	7	3¾	**17/-**	9	6¾
1/1	0	7¼	5/1	2	10¼	9/1	5	1¼	13/1	7	4¼	17/1	9	7¼
2	0	8	2	2	11	2	5	2	2	7	5	2	9	8
3	0	8½	3	2	11½	3	5	2½	3	7	5½	3	9	8½
4	0	9	4	3	0	4	5	3	4	7	6	4	9	9
5	0	9½	5	3	0½	5	5	3½	5	7	6½	5	9	9½
1/6	0	10¼	5/6	3	1¼	9/6	5	4¼	13/6	7	7¼	17/6	9	10¼
7	0	10¾	7	3	1¾	7	5	4¾	7	7	7¾	7	9	10¾
8	0	11¼	8	3	2¼	8	5	5¼	8	7	8¼	8	9	11¼
9	0	11¾	9	3	2¾	9	5	5¾	9	7	8¾	9	9	11¾
10	1	0½	10	3	3½	10	5	6½	10	7	9½	10	10	0½
11	1	1	11	3	4	11	5	7	11	7	10	11	10	1
2/-	1	1½	**6/-**	3	4½	**10/-**	5	7½	**14/-**	7	10½	**18/-**	10	1½
2/1	1	2	6/1	3	5	10/1	5	8	14/1	7	11	18/1	10	2
2	1	2¾	2	3	5¾	2	5	8¾	2	7	11¾	2	10	2¾
3	1	3¼	3	3	6¼	3	5	9¼	3	8	0¼	3	10	3¼
4	1	3¾	4	3	6¾	4	5	9¾	4	8	0¾	4	10	3¾
5	1	4¼	5	3	7¼	5	5	10¼	5	8	1¼	5	10	4¼
2/6	1	5	6/6	3	8	10/6	5	11	14/6	8	2	18/6	10	5
7	1	5½	7	3	8½	7	5	11½	7	8	2½	7	10	5½
8	1	6	8	3	9	8	6	0	8	8	3	8	10	6
9	1	6½	9	3	9½	9	6	0½	9	8	3½	9	10	6½
10	1	7¼	10	3	10¼	10	6	1¼	10	8	4¼	10	10	7¼
11	1	7¾	11	3	10¾	11	6	1¾	11	8	4¾	11	10	7¾
3/-	1	8¼	**7/-**	3	11¼	**11/-**	6	2¼	**15/-**	8	5¼	**19/-**	10	8¼
3/1	1	8¾	7/1	3	11¾	11/1	6	2¾	15/1	8	5¾	19/1	10	8¾
2	1	9½	2	4	0½	2	6	3½	2	8	6½	2	10	9½
3	1	10	3	4	1	3	6	4	3	8	7	3	10	10
4	1	10½	4	4	1½	4	6	4½	4	8	7½	4	10	10½
5	1	11	5	4	2	5	6	5	5	8	8	5	10	11
3/6	1	11¾	7/6	4	2¾	11/6	6	5¾	15/6	8	8¾	19/6	10	11¾
7	2	0¼	7	4	3¼	7	6	6¼	7	8	9¼	7	11	0¼
8	2	0¾	8	4	3¾	8	6	6¾	8	8	9¾	8	11	0¾
9	2	1¼	9	4	4¼	9	6	7¼	9	8	10¼	9	11	1¼
10	2	2	10	4	5	10	6	8	10	8	11	10	11	2
11	2	2½	11	4	5½	11	6	8½	11	8	11½	11	11	2½
4/-	2	3	**8/-**	4	6	**12/-**	6	9	**16/-**	9	0	**20/-**	11	3

20/6	11s	6½	25/6	14s	4¼	31/-	17s	5¼	35/6	19s	11¾	Guineas.		
21/-	11	9¾	26/-	14	7½	31/6	17	8¾	36/-	20	3	1.	£0 11	9¾
22/-	12	4½	27/-	15	2¼	32/-	18	0	37/-	20	9¾	2.	1 3	7½
22/6	12	8	27/6	15	5¾	32/6	18	3½	37/6	21	1¼	3.	1 15	5¼
23/-	12	11¼	28/-	15	9	33/-	18	6¾	38/-	21	4½	4.	2 7	3
24/-	13	6	29/-	16	3¾	34/-	19	1½	39/-	21	11¼	5.	2 19	0¾
25/-	14	0¾	**30/-**	16	10½	**35/-**	19	8¼	**40/-**	22	6	6.	£3 10	10½

(36% on Gross Returns.)

£	£ s. d.	£	£ s. d.	£	£ s. d.	£	£ s. d.
1	0 11s. 6	51	29 6s. 6	101	58 1s. 6	151	86 16s. 6
2	1 3 0	52	29 18 0	102	58 13 0	152	87 8 0
3	1 14 6	53	30 9 6	103	59 4 6	153	87 19 6
4	2 6 0	54	31 1 0	104	59 16 0	154	88 11 0
5	2 17 6	55	31 12 6	105	60 7 6	155	89 2 6
6	3 9 0	56	32 4 0	106	60 19 0	156	89 14 0
7	4 0 6	57	32 15 6	107	61 10 6	157	90 5 6
8	4 12 0	58	33 7 0	108	62 2 0	158	90 17 0
9	5 3 6	59	33 18 6	109	62 13 6	159	91 8 6
10	5 15s. 6	60	34 10s. 0	110	63 5s. 0	160	92 0s. 0
11	6 6s. 6	61	35 1s. 6	111	63 16s. 6	161	92 11s. 6
12	6 18 0	62	35 13 0	112	64 8 0	162	93 3 0
13	7 9 6	63	36 4 6	113	64 19 6	163	93 14 6
14	8 1 0	64	36 16 0	114	65 11 0	164	94 6 0
15	8 12 6	65	37 7 6	115	66 2 6	165	94 17 6
16	9 4 0	66	37 19 0	116	66 14 0	166	95 9 0
17	9 15 6	67	38 10 6	117	67 5 6	167	96 0 6
18	10 7 0	68	39 2 0	118	67 17 0	168	96 12 0
19	10 18 6	69	39 13 6	119	68 8 6	169	97 3 6
20	11 10s. 0	70	40 5s. 0	120	69 0s. 0	170	97 15s. 0
21	12 1s. 6	71	40 16s. 6	121	69 11s. 6	171	98 6s. 6
22	12 13 0	72	41 8 0	122	70 3 0	172	98 18 0
23	13 4 6	73	41 19 6	123	70 14 6	173	99 9 6
24	13 16 0	74	42 11 0	124	71 6 0	174	100 1 0
25	14 7 6	75	43 2 6	125	71 17 6	175	100 12 6
26	14 19 0	76	43 14 0	126	72 9 0	176	101 4 0
27	15 10 6	77	44 5 6	127	73 0 6	177	101 15 6
28	16 2 0	78	44 17 0	128	73 12 0	178	102 7 0
29	16 13 6	79	45 8 6	129	74 3 6	179	102 18 6
30	17 5s. 0	80	46 0s. 0	130	74 15s. 0	180	103 10s. 0
31	17 16s. 6	81	46 11s. 6	131	75 6s. 6	181	104 1s. 6
32	18 8 0	82	47 3 0	132	75 18 0	182	104 13 0
33	18 19 6	83	47 14 6	133	76 9 6	183	105 4 6
34	19 11 0	84	48 6 0	134	77 1 0	184	105 16 0
35	20 2 6	85	48 17 6	135	77 12 6	185	106 7 6
36	20 14 0	86	49 9 0	136	78 4 0	186	106 19 0
37	21 5 6	87	50 0 6	137	78 15 6	187	107 10 6
38	21 17 0	88	50 12 0	138	79 7 0	188	108 2 0
39	22 8 6	89	51 3 6	139	79 18 6	189	108 13 6
40	23 0s. 0	90	51 15s. 0	140	80 10s. 0	190	109 5s. 0
41	23 11s. 6	91	52 6s. 6	141	81 1s. 6	191	109 16s. 6
42	24 3 0	92	52 18 0	142	81 13 0	192	110 8 0
43	24 14 6	93	53 9 6	143	82 4 6	193	110 19 6
44	25 6 0	94	54 1 0	144	82 16 0	194	111 11 0
45	25 17 6	95	54 12 6	145	83 7 6	195	112 2 6
46	26 9 0	96	55 4 0	146	83 19 0	196	112 14 0
47	27 0 6	97	55 15 6	147	84 10 6	197	113 5 6
48	27 12 0	98	56 7 0	148	85 2 0	198	113 17 0
49	28 3 6	99	56 18 6	149	85 13 6	199	114 8 6
50	28 15s. 0	100	57 10s. 0	150	86 5s. 0	200	115 0s. 0

£	£ s. d.	£	£ s. d.	£	£ s. d.	£	£ s. d.
250	143 15s. 0d	700	402 10s. 0d	1200	690 0s.0d	2000	£1150 0s. 0
300	172 10 0	750	431 5 0	1400	805 0 0	2500	1437 10 0
400	230 0 0	800	460 0 0	1500	862 10 0	3000	1725 0 0
500	287 10 0	900	517 10 0	1600	920 0 0	4000	2300 0 0
600	345 0s.0d	1000	575 0s. 0d	1800	1035 0s.0d	5000	£2875 0s. 0

42½% off.

1d	0s. 0½	4/1	2s. 4¼	8/1	4s. 7¾	12/1	6s.11½	16/1	9s. 3
2d	0 1¼	2	2 4¾	2	4 8¼	2	7 0	2	9 3½
3d	0 1¾	3	2 5¼	3	4 9	3	7 0½	3	9 4¼
4d	0 2¼	4	2 6	4	4 9½	4	7 1	4	9 4¾
5d	0 3	5	2 6½	5	4 10	5	7 1¾	5	9 5¼
6d	0 3½	4/6	2 7	8/6	4 10¾	12/6	7 2¼	16/6	9 5¾
7d	0 4	7	2 7¾	7	4 11¼	7	7 2¾	7	9 6½
8d	0 4½	8	2 8¼	8	4 11¾	8	7 3½	8	9 7
9d	0 5¼	9	2 8¾	9	5 0½	9	7 4	9	9 7½
10d	0 5¾	10	2 9¼	10	5 1	10	7 4½	10	9 8¼
11d	0 6¼	11	2 10	11	5 1½	11	7 5¼	11	9 8¾
1/-	0s. 7	5/-	2s.10½	9/-	5s. 2	13/-	7s. 5¾	17/-	9s. 9¼
1/1	0s. 7½	5/1	2s.11	9/1	5s. 2¾	13/1	7s. 6¼	17/1	9s.10
2	0 8	2	2 11¾	2	5 3¼	2	7 6¾	2	9 10½
3	0 8¾	3	3 0¼	3	5 3¾	3	7 7½	3	9 11
4	0 9¼	4	3 0¾	4	5 4½	4	7 8	4	9 11½
5	0 9¾	5	3 1½	5	5 5	5	7 8½	5	10 0¼
1/6	0 10¼	5/6	3 2	9/6	5 5½	13/6	7 9¼	17/6	10 0¾
7	0 11	7	3 2½	7	5 6¼	7	7 9¾	7	10 1¼
8	0 11½	8	3 3	8	5 6¾	8	7 10¼	8	10 2
9	1 0	9	3 3¾	9	5 7¼	9	7 11	9	10 2½
10	1 0¾	10	3 4¼	10	5 7¾	10	7 11½	10	10 3
11	1 1¼	11	3 4¾	11	5 8½	11	8 0	11	10 3¾
2/-	1s. 1¾	6/-	3s. 5½	10/-	5s. 9	14/-	8s. 0½	18/-	10s. 4¼
2/1	1s. 2½	6/1	3s. 6	10/1	5s. 9½	14/1	8s. 1¼	18/1	10s. 4¾
2	1 3	2	3 6½	2	5 10¼	2	8 1¾	2	10 5¼
3	1 3½	3	3 7¼	3	5 10¾	3	8 2¼	3	10 6
4	1 4	4	3 7¾	4	5 11¼	4	8 3	4	10 6½
5	1 4¾	5	3 8¼	5	6 0	5	8 3½	5	10 7
2/6	1 5¼	6/6	3 8¾	10/6	6 0½	14/6	8 4	18/6	10 7¾
7	1 5¾	7	3 9½	7	6 1	7	8 4¾	7	10 8¼
8	1 6½	8	3 10	8	6 1½	8	8 5¼	8	10 8¾
9	1 7	9	3 10½	9	6 2¼	9	8 5¾	9	10 9½
10	1 7½	10	3 11¼	10	6 2¾	10	8 6¼	10	10 10
11	1 8¼	11	3 11¾	11	6 3¼	11	8 7	11	10 10½
3/-	1s. 8¾	7/-	4s. 0¼	11/-	6s. 4	15/-	8 7½	19/-	10s.11
3/1	1s. 9¼	7/1	4s. 1	11/1	6s. 4½	15/1	8s. 8	19/1	10s.11¾
2	1 9¾	2	4 1½	2	6 5	2	8 8¾	2	11 0¼
3	1 10½	3	4 2	3	6 5¾	3	8 9¼	3	11 0¾
4	1 11	4	4 2½	4	6 6¼	4	8 9¾	4	11 1½
5	1 11½	5	4 3¼	5	6 6¾	5	8 10½	5	11 2
3/6	2 0¼	7/6	4 3¾	11/6	6 7¼	15/6	8 11	19/6	11 2½
7	2 0¾	7	4 4¼	7	6 8	7	8 11½	7	11 3¼
8	2 1¼	8	4 5	8	6 8½	8	9 0	8	11 3¾
9	2 2	9	4 5½	9	6 9	9	9 0¾	9	11 4¼
10	2 2½	10	4 6	10	6 9¾	10	9 1¼	10	11 4¾
11	2 3	11	4 6¾	11	6 10¼	11	9 1¾	11	11 5½
4/-	2s. 3½	8/-	4s. 7¼	12/-	6s.10¾	16/-	9s. 2½	20/-	11s. 6

20/6	11s. 9½	25/6	14s. 8d	31/-	17s.10d	35/6	20s. 5d	Guineas.	
21/-	12 1	26/-	14 11½	31/6	18 1¼	36/-	20 8½	1.	12s. 1d
22/-	12 7¾	27/-	15 6¼	32/-	18 4¾	37/-	21 3¼	2.	24 1¾
22/6	12 11¼	27/6	15 9¾	32/6	18 8¼	37/6	21 6¾	3.	36 2¾
23/-	13 2¾	28/-	16 1¼	33/-	18 11¾	38/-	21 10¼	4.	48 3½
24/-	13 9½	29/-	16 8	34/-	19 6½	39/-	22 5	5.	60 4½
25/-	14 4½	30/-	17 3	35/-	20 1½	40/-	23 0	6.	72s. 5½

(36½%* on Gross Returns).

£	value	£	value	£	value	£	value
£1	£0 12s. 0	£51	30 12s. 0	£101	£60 12s. 0	£151	£90 12s. 0
2	1 4 0	52	31 4 0	102	61 4 0	152	91 4 0
3	1 16 0	53	31 16 0	103	61 16 0	153	91 16 0
4	2 8 0	54	32 8 0	104	62 8 0	154	92 8 0
5	3 0 0	55	33 0 0	105	63 0 0	155	93 0 0
6	3 12 0	56	33 12 0	106	63 12 0	156	93 12 0
7	4 4 0	57	34 4 0	107	64 4 0	157	94 4 0
8	4 16 0	58	34 16 0	108	64 16 0	158	94 16 0
9	5 8 0	59	35 8 0	109	65 8 0	159	95 8 0
10	£6 0s. 0	60	£36 0s. 0	110	£66 0s. 0	160	£96 0s. 0
11	£6 12s. 0	61	36 12s. 0	111	£66 12s. 0	161	£96 12s. 0
12	7 4 0	62	37 4 0	112	67 4 0	162	97 4 0
13	7 16 0	63	37 16 0	113	67 16 0	163	97 16 0
14	8 8 0	64	38 8 0	114	68 8 0	164	98 8 0
15	9 0 0	65	39 0 0	115	69 0 0	165	99 0 0
16	9 12 0	66	39 12 0	116	69 12 0	166	99 12 0
17	10 4 0	67	40 4 0	117	70 4 0	167	100 4 0
18	10 16 0	68	40 16 0	118	70 16 0	168	100 16 0
19	11 8 0	69	41 8 0	119	71 8 0	169	101 8 0
20	12 0s. 0	70	42 0s. 0	120	£72 0s. 0	170	102 0s. 0
21	12 12s. 0	71	42 12s. 0	121	£72 12s. 0	171	102 12s. 0
22	13 4 0	72	43 4 0	122	73 4 0	172	103 4 0
23	13 16 0	73	43 16 0	123	73 16 0	173	103 16 0
24	14 8 0	74	44 8 0	124	74 8 0	174	104 8 0
25	15 0 0	75	45 0 0	125	75 0 0	175	105 0 0
26	15 12 0	76	45 12 0	126	75 12 0	176	105 12 0
27	16 4 0	77	46 4 0	127	76 4 0	177	106 4 0
28	16 16 0	78	46 16 0	128	76 16 0	178	106 16 0
29	17 8 0	79	47 8 0	129	77 8 0	179	107 8 0
30	18 0s. 0	80	48 0s. 0	130	£78 0s. 0	180	108 0s. 0
31	18 12s. 0	81	48 12s. 0	131	£78 12s. 0	181	108 12s. 0
32	19 4 0	82	49 4 0	132	79 4 0	182	109 4 0
33	19 16 0	83	49 16 0	133	79 16 0	183	109 16 0
34	20 8 0	84	50 8 0	134	80 8 0	184	110 8 0
35	21 0 0	85	51 0 0	135	81 0 0	185	111 0 0
36	21 12 0	86	51 12 0	136	81 12 0	186	111 12 0
37	22 4 0	87	52 4 0	137	82 4 0	187	112 4 0
38	22 16 0	88	52 16 0	138	82 16 0	188	112 16 0
39	23 8 0	89	53 8 0	139	83 8 0	189	113 8 0
40	24 0s. 0	90	54 0s. 0	140	£84 0s. 0	190	114 0s. 0
41	24 12s. 0	91	54 12s. 0	141	£84 12s. 0	191	114 12s. 0
42	25 4 0	92	55 4 0	142	85 4 0	192	115 4 0
43	25 16 0	93	55 16 0	143	85 16 0	193	115 16 0
44	26 8 0	94	56 8 0	144	86 8 0	194	116 8 0
45	27 0 0	95	57 0 0	145	87 0 0	195	117 0 0
46	27 12 0	96	57 12 0	146	87 12 0	196	117 12 0
47	28 4 0	97	58 4 0	147	88 4 0	197	118 4 0
48	28 16 0	98	58 16 0	148	88 16 0	198	118 16 0
49	29 8 0	99	59 8 0	149	89 8 0	199	119 8 0
50	30 0s. 0	100	60 0s. 0	150	£90 0s. 0	200	120 0s. 0
250	150 0s. 0d	700	420 0s.d	1200	720 0s.d	2000	£1200 0s. 0
300	180 0 0	750	450 0 0	1400	840 0 0	2500	1500 0 0
400	240 0 0	800	480 0 0	1500	900 0 0	3000	1800 0 0
500	300 0 0	900	540 0 0	1600	960 0 0	4000	2400 0 0
600	360 0s. 0d	1000	600 0s.d	1800	1080 0s.d	5000	£3000 0s. 0

40% off.

60% Sixty Per Cent. 60%

1d	0s. 0½	**4/1**	2s. 5½	**8/1**	4s.10¼	**12/1**	7s. 3	**16/1**	9s. 7¾
2d	0 1¼	**2**	2 6	**2**	4 10¾	**2**	7 3½	**2**	9 8½
3d	0 1¾	**3**	2 6½	**3**	4 11½	**3**	7 4¼	**3**	9 9
4d	0 2½	**4**	2 7¼	**4**	5 0	**4**	7 4¾	**4**	9 9½
5d	0 3	**5**	2 7¾	**5**	5 0½	**5**	7 5½	**5**	9 10¼
6d	0 3½	**4/6**	2 8½	**8/6**	5 1¼	**12/6**	7 6	**16/6**	9 10¾
7d	0 4¼	**7**	2 9	**7**	5 1¾	**7**	7 6½	**7**	9 11½
8d	0 4¾	**8**	2 9½	**8**	5 2½	**8**	7 7¼	**8**	10 0
9d	0 5½	**9**	2 10¼	**9**	5 3	**9**	7 7¾	**9**	10 0½
10d	0 6	**10**	2 10¾	**10**	5 3½	**10**	7 8½	**10**	10 1¼
11d	0 6½	**11**	2 11½	**11**	5 4¼	**11**	7 9	**11**	10 1¾
1/-	0s. 7¼	**5/-**	3s. 0	**9/-**	5s. 4¾	**13/-**	7s. 9½	**17/-**	10s. 2½
1/1	0s. 7¾	**5/1**	3s. 0½	**9/1**	5s. 5½	**13/1**	7s.10¼	**17/1**	10s. 3
2	0 8½	**2**	3 1¼	**2**	5 6	**2**	7 10¾	**2**	10 3½
3	0 9	**3**	3 1¾	**3**	5 6½	**3**	7 11½	**3**	10 4¼
4	0 9½	**4**	3 2½	**4**	5 7¼	**4**	8 0	**4**	10 4¾
5	0 10¼	**5**	3 3	**5**	5 7¾	**5**	8 0½	**5**	10 5½
1/6	0 10¾	**5/6**	3 3½	**9/6**	5 8½	**13/6**	8 1¼	**17/6**	10 6
7	0 11½	**7**	3 4¼	**7**	5 9	**7**	8 1¾	**7**	10 6½
8	1 0	**8**	3 4¾	**8**	5 9½	**8**	8 2½	**8**	10 7¼
9	1 0½	**9**	3 5½	**9**	5 10¼	**9**	8 3	**9**	10 7¾
10	1 1¼	**10**	3 6	**10**	5 10¾	**10**	8 3½	**10**	10 8½
11	1 1¾	**11**	3 6½	**11**	5 11½	**11**	8 4¼	**11**	10 9
2/-	1s. 2½	**6/-**	3s. 7¼	**10/-**	6s. 0	**14/-**	8s. 4¾	**18/-**	10s. 9½
2/1	1s. 3	**6/1**	3s. 7¾	**10/1**	6s. 0½	**14/1**	8s. 5½	**18/1**	10s.10¼
2	1 3½	**2**	3 8½	**2**	6 1¼	**2**	8 6	**2**	10 10¾
3	1 4¼	**3**	3 9	**3**	6 1¾	**3**	8 6½	**3**	10 11½
4	1 4¾	**4**	3 9½	**4**	6 2½	**4**	8 7¼	**4**	11 0
5	1 5½	**5**	3 10¼	**5**	6 3	**5**	8 7¾	**5**	11 0½
2/6	1 6	**6/6**	3 10¾	**10/6**	6 3½	**14/6**	8 8½	**18/6**	11 1¼
7	1 6½	**7**	3 11½	**7**	6 4¼	**7**	8 9	**7**	11 1¾
8	1 7¼	**8**	4 0	**8**	6 4¾	**8**	8 9½	**8**	11 2½
9	1 7¾	**9**	4 0½	**9**	6 5½	**9**	8 10¼	**9**	11 3
10	1 8½	**10**	4 1¼	**10**	6 6	**10**	8 10¾	**10**	11 3½
11	1 9	**11**	4 1¾	**11**	6 6½	**11**	8 11½	**11**	11 4¼
3/-	1s. 9½	**7/-**	4s. 2½	**11/-**	6s. 7¼	**15/-**	9s. 0	**19/-**	11s. 4¾
3/1	1s.10¼	**7/1**	4s. 3	**11/1**	6s. 7¾	**15/1**	9s. 0½	**19/1**	11s. 5½
2	1 10¾	**2**	4 3½	**2**	6 8½	**2**	9 1¼	**2**	11 6
3	1 11½	**3**	4 4¼	**3**	6 9	**3**	9 1¾	**3**	11 6½
4	2 0	**4**	4 4¾	**4**	6 9½	**4**	9 2½	**4**	11 7¼
5	2 0½	**5**	4 5½	**5**	6 10¼	**5**	9 3	**5**	11 7¾
3/6	2 1¼	**7/6**	4 6	**11/6**	6 10¾	**15/6**	9 3½	**19/6**	11 8½
7	2 1¾	**7**	4 6½	**7**	6 11½	**7**	9 4¼	**7**	11 9
8	2 2½	**8**	4 7¼	**8**	7 0	**8**	9 4¾	**8**	11 9½
9	2 3	**9**	4 7¾	**9**	7 0½	**9**	9 5½	**9**	11 10¼
10	2 3½	**10**	4 8½	**10**	7 1¼	**10**	9 6	**10**	11 10¾
11	2 4¼	**11**	4 9	**11**	7 1¾	**11**	9 6½	**11**	11 11½
4/-	2s. 4¾	**8/-**	4s. 9½	**12/-**	7s. 2½	**16/-**	9s. 7¼	**20/-**	12s. 0

20/6	12s. 3½	**25/6**	15s. 3½	**31/-**	18s. 7¼	**35/6**	21s. 3½	Guineas.	
21/-	12 7¼	**26/-**	15 7¼	**31/6**	18 10¾	**36/-**	21 7¼	**1.**	£0 12s. 7¼
22/-	13 2½	**27/-**	16 2½	**32/-**	19 2½	**37/-**	22 2½	**2.**	1 5 2½
22/6	13 6	**27/6**	16 6	**32/6**	19 6	**37/6**	22 6	**3.**	1 17 9½
23/-	13 9½	**28/-**	16 9½	**33/-**	19 9½	**38/-**	22 9½	**4.**	2 10 4¾
24/-	14 4¾	**29/-**	17 4¾	**34/-**	20 4¾	**39/-**	23 4¾	**5.**	3 3 0
25/-	15s. 0	**30/-**	18s. 0	**35/-**	21s. 0	**40/-**	24s. 0	**6.**	£3 15 7¼

(37½% on Gross Returns).

£	s.	d.	£	s.	d.	£	s.	d.	£	s.	d.
£1	£0 12s.	6	£51	31 17s.	6	£101	63 2s.	6	£151	£94 7s.	6
2	1 5	0	52	32 10	0	102	63 15	0	152	95 0	0
3	1 17	6	53	33 2	6	103	64 7	6	153	95 12	6
4	2 10	0	54	33 15	0	104	65 0	0	154	96 5	0
5	3 2	6	55	34 7	6	105	65 12	6	155	96 17	6
6	3 15	0	56	35 0	0	106	66 5	0	156	97 10	0
7	4 7	6	57	35 12	6	107	66 17	6	157	98 2	6
8	5 0	0	58	36 5	0	108	67 10	0	158	98 15	0
9	5 12	6	59	36 17	6	109	68 2	6	159	99 7	6
10	6 5s.	0	60	37 10s.	0	110	68 15s.	0	160	100 0s.	0
11	6 17s.	6	61	38 2s.	6	111	69 7s.	6	161	100 12s.	6
12	7 10	0	62	38 15	0	112	70 0	0	162	101 5	0
13	8 2	6	63	39 7	6	113	70 12	6	163	101 17	6
14	8 15	0	64	40 0	0	114	71 5	0	164	102 10	0
15	9 7	6	65	40 12	6	115	71 17	6	165	103 2	6
16	10 0	0	66	41 5	0	116	72 10	0	166	103 15	0
17	10 12	6	67	41 17	6	117	73 2	6	167	104 7	6
18	11 5	0	68	42 10	0	118	73 15	0	168	105 0	0
19	11 17	6	69	43 2	6	119	74 7	6	169	105 12	6
20	12 10s.	0	70	43 15s.	0	120	75 0s.	0	170	106 5s.	0
21	13 2s.	6	71	44 7s.	6	121	75 12s.	6	171	106 17s.	6
22	13 15	0	72	45 0	0	122	76 5	0	172	107 10	0
23	14 7	6	73	45 12	6	123	76 17	6	173	108 2	6
24	15 0	0	74	46 5	0	124	77 10	0	174	108 15	0
25	15 12	6	75	46 17	6	125	78 2	6	175	109 7	6
26	16 5	0	76	47 10	0	126	78 15	0	176	110 0	0
27	16 17	6	77	48 2	6	127	79 7	6	177	110 12	6
28	17 10	0	78	48 15	0	128	80 0	0	178	111 5	0
29	18 2	6	79	49 7	6	129	80 12	6	179	111 17	6
30	18 15s.	0	80	50 0s.	0	130	81 5s.	0	180	112 10s.	0
31	19 7s.	6	81	50 12s.	6	131	81 17s.	6	181	113 2s.	6
32	20 0	0	82	51 5	0	132	82 10	0	182	113 15	0
33	20 12	6	83	51 17	6	133	83 2	6	183	114 7	6
34	21 5	0	84	52 10	0	134	83 15	0	184	115 0	0
35	21 17	6	85	53 2	6	135	84 7	6	185	115 12	6
36	22 10	0	86	53 15	0	136	85 0	0	186	116 5	0
37	23 2	6	87	54 7	6	137	85 12	6	187	116 17	6
38	23 15	0	88	55 0	0	138	86 5	0	188	117 10	0
39	24 7	6	89	55 12	6	139	86 17	6	189	118 2	6
40	25 0s.	0	90	56 5s.	0	140	87 10s.	0	190	118 15s.	0
41	25 12s.	6	91	56 17s.	6	141	88 2s.	6	191	119 7s.	6
42	26 5	0	92	57 10	0	142	88 15	0	192	120 0	0
43	26 17	6	93	58 2	6	143	89 7	6	193	120 12	6
44	27 10	0	94	58 15	0	144	90 0	0	194	121 5	0
45	28 2	6	95	59 7	6	145	90 12	6	195	121 17	6
46	28 15	0	96	60 0	0	146	91 5	0	196	122 10	0
47	29 7	6	97	60 12	6	147	91 17	6	197	123 2	6
48	30 0	0	98	61 5	0	148	92 10	0	198	123 15	0
49	30 12	6	99	61 17	6	149	93 2	6	199	124 7	6
50	31 5s.	0	100	62 10s.	0	150	93 15s.	0	200	125 0s.	0
250	156 5s.	0d	700	437 10s.	0d	1200	750 0s.	0d	2000	£1250 0s.	0
300	187 10	0	750	468 15	0	1400	875 0	0	2500	1562 10	0
400	250 0	0	800	500 0	0	1500	937 10	0	3000	1875 0	0
500	312 10	0	900	562 10	0	1600	1000 0	0	4000	2500 0	0
600	375 0s.	0d	1000	625 0s.	0d	1800	1125 0s.	0d	5000	£3125 0s.	0

37½% off.   (62½% = 5-8ths)

62½ Per Cent.

62½%

1d	0s.	0¾	4/1	2s.	6¾	8/1	5s.	0¾	12/1	7s.	6¾	16/1	10s.	0¾
2d	0	1¼	2	2	7¼	2	5	1¼	2	7	7¼	2	10	1¼
3d	0	2	3	2	8	3	5	2	3	7	8	3	10	2
4d	0	2½	4	2	8½	4	5	2½	4	7	8½	4	10	2½
5d	0	3¼	5	2	9¼	5	5	3¼	5	7	9¼	5	10	3¼
6d	0	3¾	4/6	2	9¾	8/6	5	3¾	12/6	7	9¾	16/6	10	3¾
7d	0	4½	7	2	10½	7	5	4½	7	7	10½	7	10	4½
8d	0	5	8	2	11	8	5	5	8	7	11	8	10	5
9d	0	5¾	9	2	11¾	9	5	5¾	9	7	11¾	9	10	5¾
10d	0	6¼	10	3	0¼	10	5	6¼	10	8	0¼	10	10	6¼
11d	0	7	11	3	1	11	5	7	11	8	1	11	10	7
1/-	0s.	7½	**5/-**	3s.	1½	**9/-**	5s.	7½	**13/-**	8s.	1½	**17/-**	10s.	7½
1/1	0s.	8¼	5/1	3s.	2¼	9/1	5s.	8¼	13/1	8s.	2¼	17/1	10s.	8¼
2	0	8¾	2	3	2¾	2	5	8¾	2	8	2¾	2	10	8¾
3	0	9½	3	3	3½	3	5	9½	3	8	3½	3	10	9½
4	0	10	4	3	4	4	5	10	4	8	4	4	10	10
5	0	10¾	5	3	4¾	5	5	10¾	5	8	4¾	5	10	10¾
1/6	0	11¼	5/6	3	5¼	9/6	5	11¼	13/6	8	5¼	17/6	10	11¼
7	1	0	7	3	6	7	6	0	7	8	6	7	11	0
8	1	0½	8	3	6½	8	6	0½	8	8	6½	8	11	0½
9	1	1¼	9	3	7¼	9	6	1¼	9	8	7¼	9	11	1¼
10	1	1¾	10	3	7¾	10	6	1¾	10	8	7¾	10	11	1¾
11	1	2½	11	3	8½	11	6	2½	11	8	8½	11	11	2½
2/-	1s.	3	**6/-**	3s.	9	**10/-**	6s.	3	**14/-**	8s.	9	**18/-**	11s.	3
2/1	1s.	3¾	6/1	3s.	9¾	10/1	6s.	3¾	14/1	8s.	9¾	18/1	11s.	3¾
2	1	4¼	2	3	10¼	2	6	4¼	2	8	10¼	2	11	4¼
3	1	5	3	3	11	3	6	5	3	8	11	3	11	5
4	1	5½	4	3	11½	4	6	5½	4	8	11½	4	11	5½
5	1	6¼	5	4	0¼	5	6	6¼	5	9	0¼	5	11	6¼
2/6	1	6¾	6/6	4	0¾	10/6	6	6¾	14/6	9	0¾	18/6	11	6¾
7	1	7½	7	4	1½	7	6	7½	7	9	1½	7	11	7½
8	1	8	8	4	2	8	6	8	8	9	2	8	11	8
9	1	8¾	9	4	2¾	9	6	8¾	9	9	2¾	9	11	8¾
10	1	9¼	10	4	3¼	10	6	9¼	10	9	3¼	10	11	9¼
11	1	10	11	4	4	11	6	10	11	9	4	11	11	10
3/-	1s.	10½	**7/-**	4s.	4½	**11/-**	6s.	10½	**15/-**	9	4½	**19/-**	11s.	10½
3/1	1s.	11¼	7/1	4s.	5¼	11/1	6s.	11¼	15/1	9s.	5¼	19/1	11s.	11¼
2	1	11¾	2	4	5¾	2	6	11¾	2	9	5¾	2	11	11¾
3	2	0½	3	4	6½	3	7	0½	3	9	6½	3	12	0½
4	2	1	4	4	7	4	7	1	4	9	7	4	12	1
5	2	1¾	5	4	7¾	5	7	1¾	5	9	7¾	5	12	1¾
3/6	2	2¼	7/6	4	8¼	11/6	7	2¼	15/6	9	8¼	19/6	12	2¼
7	2	3	7	4	9	7	7	3	7	9	9	7	12	3
8	2	3½	8	4	9½	8	7	3½	8	9	9½	8	12	3½
9	2	4¼	9	4	10¼	9	7	4¼	9	9	10¼	9	12	4¼
10	2	4¾	10	4	10¾	10	7	4¾	10	9	10¾	10	12	4¾
11	2	5½	11	4	11½	11	7	5½	11	9	11½	11	12	5½
4/-	2s.	6	**8/-**	5s.	0	**12/-**	7s	6	**16/-**	10s.	0	**20/-**	12s.	6

20/6	12s.	9¾	25/6	15s.	11¼	31/-	19s.	4½	35/6	22s.	2¼	Guineas.		
21/-	13	1½	26/-	16	3	31/6	19	8¼	36/-	22	6	1.	13s.	1½
22/-	13	9	27/-	16	10½	32/-	20	0	37/-	23	1½	2.	26	3
22/6	14	0¾	27/6	17	2¼	32/6	20	3¾	37/6	23	5¼	3.	39	4½
23/-	14	4½	28/-	17	6	33/-	20	7½	38/-	23	9	4.	52	6
24/-	15	0	29/-	18	1½	34/-	21	3	39/-	24	4½	5.	65	7½
25/-	15	7½	**30/-**	18	9	**35/-**	21	10½	**40/-**	25	0	6.	78s.	9

(38½%* on Gross Returns).

No.	£ s. d.	No.	£ s. d.	No.	£ s. d.	No.	£ s. d.
£1	£0 13s. 0	£51	33 3s. 0	£101	£65 13s. 0	£151	£98 3s. 0
2	1 6 0	52	33 16 0	102	66 6 0	152	98 16 0
3	1 19 0	53	34 9 0	103	66 19 0	153	99 9 0
4	2 12 0	54	35 2 0	104	67 12 0	154	100 2 0
5	3 5 0	55	35 15 0	105	68 5 0	155	100 15 0
6	3 18 0	56	36 8 0	106	68 18 0	156	101 8 0
7	4 11 0	57	37 1 0	107	69 11 0	157	102 1 0
8	5 4 0	58	37 14 0	108	70 4 0	158	102 14 0
9	5 17 0	59	38 7 0	109	70 17 0	159	103 7 0
10	£6 10s. 0	60	39 0s. 0	110	£71 10s. 0	160	104 0s. 0
11	£7 3s. 0	61	39 13s. 0	111	£72 3s. 0	161	104 13s. 0
12	7 16 0	62	40 6 0	112	72 16 0	162	105 6 0
13	8 9 0	63	40 19 0	113	73 9 0	163	105 19 0
14	9 2 0	64	41 12 0	114	74 2 0	164	106 12 0
15	9 15 0	65	42 5 0	115	74 15 0	165	107 5 0
16	10 8 0	66	42 18 0	116	75 8 0	166	107 18 0
17	11 1 0	67	43 11 0	117	76 1 0	167	108 11 0
18	11 14 0	68	44 4 0	118	76 14 0	168	109 4 0
19	12 7 0	69	44 17 0	119	77 7 0	169	109 17 0
20	13 0s. 0	70	45 10s. 0	120	£78 0s. 0	170	£110 10s. 0
21	13 13s. 0	71	46 3s. 0	121	£78 13s. 0	171	111 3s. 0
22	14 6 0	72	46 16 0	122	79 6 0	172	111 16 0
23	14 19 0	73	47 9 0	123	79 19 0	173	112 9 0
24	15 12 0	74	48 2 0	124	80 12 0	174	113 2 0
25	16 5 0	75	48 15 0	125	81 5 0	175	113 15 0
26	16 18 0	76	49 8 0	126	81 18 0	176	114 8 0
27	17 11 0	77	50 1 0	127	82 11 0	177	115 1 0
28	18 4 0	78	50 14 0	128	83 4 0	178	115 14 0
29	18 17 0	79	51 7 0	129	83 17 0	179	116 7 0
30	19 10s. 0	80	52 0s. 0	130	£84 10s. 0	180	117 0s. 0
31	20 3s. 0	81	52 13s. 0	131	£85 3s. 0	181	117 13s. 0
32	20 16 0	82	53 6 0	132	85 16 0	182	118 6 0
33	21 9 0	83	53 19 0	133	86 9 0	183	118 19 0
34	22 2 0	84	54 12 0	134	87 2 0	184	119 12 0
35	22 15 0	85	55 5 0	135	87 15 0	185	120 5 0
36	23 8 0	86	55 18 0	136	88 8 0	186	120 18 0
37	24 1 0	87	56 11 0	137	89 1 0	187	121 11 0
38	24 14 0	88	57 4 0	138	89 14 0	188	122 4 0
39	25 7 0	89	57 17 0	139	90 7 0	189	122 17 0
40	26 0s. 0	90	58 10s. 0	140	£91 0s. 0	190	£123 10s. 0
41	26 13s. 0	91	59 3s. 0	141	£91 13s. 0	191	124 3s. 0
42	27 6 0	92	59 16 0	142	92 6 0	192	124 16 0
43	27 19 0	93	60 9 0	143	92 19 0	193	125 9 0
44	28 12 0	94	61 2 0	144	93 12 0	194	126 2 0
45	29 5 0	95	61 15 0	145	94 5 0	195	126 15 0
46	29 18 0	96	62 8 0	146	94 18 0	196	127 8 0
47	30 11 0	97	63 1 0	147	95 11 0	197	128 1 0
48	31 4 0	98	63 14 0	148	96 4 0	198	128 14 0
49	31 17 0	99	64 7 0	149	96 17 0	199	129 7 0
50	32 10s. 0	100	65 0s. 0	150	£97 10s. 0	200	130 0s. 0

No.	£ s. d.	No.	£ s. d.	No.	£ s. d.	No.	£ s. d.
250	162 10s. 0d	700	455 0s.0d	1200	780 0s.0d	2000	£1300 0s. 0
300	195 0 0	750	487 10 0	1400	910 0 0	2500	1625 0 0
400	260 0 0	800	520 0 0	1500	975 0 0	3000	1950 0 0
500	325 0 0	900	585 0 0	1600	1040 0 0	4000	2600 0 0
600	390 0s.0d	1000	650 0s.0d	1800	1170 0s.0d	5000	£3250 0s. 0

35% off.

65% SIXTY-FIVE PER CENT. 65%

1d	0s. 0¾	4/1	2s. 7¾	8/1	5s. 3	12/1	7s. 10¼	16/1	10s. 5½
2d	0 1¼	2	2 8½	2	5 3¾	2	7 11	2	10 6
3d	0 2	3	2 9¼	3	5 4¼	3	7 11½	3	10 6¾
4d	0 2½	4	2 9¾	4	5 5	4	8 0¼	4	10 7½
5d	0 3¼	5	2 10½	5	5 5¾	5	8 0¾	5	10 8
6d	0 4	4/6	2 11	8/6	5 6¼	12/6	8 1½	16/6	10 8¾
7d	0 4½	7	2 11¾	7	5 7	7	8 2¼	7	10 9¼
8d	0 5¼	8	3 0½	8	5 7½	8	8 2¾	8	10 10
9d	0 5¾	9	3 1	9	5 8¼	9	8 3½	9	10 10¾
10d	0 6½	10	3 1¾	10	5 9	10	8 4	10	10 11¼
11d	0 7¼	11	3 2¼	11	5 9½	11	8 4¾	11	11 0
1/-	0s. 7¾	**5/-**	3s. 3	**9/-**	5s. 10¼	**13/-**	8s. 5½	**17/-**	11s. 0½
1/1	0s. 8½	5/1	3s. 3¾	9/1	5s. 10¾	13/1	8s. 6	17/1	11s. 1¼
2	0 9	2	3 4¼	2	5 11½	2	8 6¾	2	11 2
3	0 9¾	3	3 5	3	6 0¼	3	8 7¼	3	11 2½
4	0 10½	4	3 5½	4	6 0¾	4	8 8	4	11 3¼
5	0 11	5	3 6¼	5	6 1½	5	8 8¾	5	11 3¾
1/6	0 11¾	5/6	3 7	9/6	6 2	13/6	8 9¼	17/6	11 4½
7	1 0¼	7	3 7½	7	6 2¾	7	8 10	7	11 5¼
8	1 1	8	3 8¼	8	6 3½	8	8 10½	8	11 5¾
9	1 1¾	9	3 8¾	9	6 4	9	8 11¼	9	11 6½
10	1 2¼	10	3 9½	10	6 4¾	10	9 0	10	11 7
11	1 3	11	3 10¼	11	6 5¼	11	9 0½	11	11 7¾
2/-	1s. 3½	**6/-**	3s. 10¾	**10/-**	6s. 6	**14/-**	9s. 1¼	**18/-**	11s. 8½
2/1	1s. 4¼	6/1	3s. 11½	10/1	6s. 6¾	14/1	9s. 1¾	18/1	11s. 9
2	1 5	2	4 0	2	6 7¼	2	9 2½	2	11 9¾
3	1 5½	3	4 0¾	3	6 8	3	9 3¼	3	11 10¼
4	1 6¼	4	4 1½	4	6 8½	4	9 3¾	4	11 11
5	1 6¾	5	4 2	5	6 9¼	5	9 4½	5	11 11¾
2/6	1 7½	6/6	4 2¾	10/6	6 10	14/6	9 5	18/6	12 0¼
7	1 8¼	7	4 3¼	7	6 10½	7	9 5¾	7	12 1
8	1 8¾	8	4 4	8	6 11¼	8	9 6½	8	12 1½
9	1 9½	9	4 4¾	9	6 11¾	9	9 7	9	12 2¼
10	1 10	10	4 5¼	10	7 0½	10	9 7¾	10	12 3
11	1 10¾	11	4 6	11	7 1¼	11	9 8¼	11	12 3½
3/-	1s. 11½	**7/-**	4s. 6½	**11/-**	7s. 1¾	**15/-**	9s. 9	**19/-**	12s. 4¼
3/1	2s. 0	7/1	4s. 7¼	11/1	7s. 2½	15/1	9s. 9¾	19/1	12s. 4¾
2	2 0¾	2	4 8	2	7 3	2	9 10¼	2	12 5½
3	2 1¼	3	4 8½	3	7 3¾	3	9 11	3	12 6¼
4	2 2	4	4 9¼	4	7 4½	4	9 11½	4	12 6¾
5	2 2¾	5	4 9¾	5	7 5	5	10 0¼	5	12 7½
3/6	2 3¼	7/6	4 10½	11/6	7 5¾	15/6	10 1	19/6	12 8
7	2 4	7	4 11¼	7	7 6¼	7	10 1½	7	12 8¾
8	2 4½	8	4 11¾	8	7 7	8	10 2¼	8	12 9½
9	2 5¼	9	5 0½	9	7 7¾	9	10 2¾	9	12 10
10	2 6	10	5 1	10	7 8¼	10	10 3½	10	12 10¾
11	2 6½	11	5 1¾	11	7 9	11	10 4¼	11	12 11¼
4/-	2s. 7¼	**8/-**	5s. 2½	**12/-**	7s. 9½	**16/-**	10s. 4¾	**20/-**	13s. 0

20/6	13s. 4	25/6	16s. 7	31/-	20s. 1¾	35/6	23s. 1	**Guineas.**	
21/-	13 7¾	26/-	16 10¾	31/6	20 5¾	36/-	23 4¾	1.	£0 13s. 7¾
22/-	14 3½	27/-	17 6½	32/-	20 9½	37/-	24 0½	2.	1 7 3½
22/6	14 7½	27/6	17 10½	32/6	21 1½	37/6	24 4½	3.	2 0 11½
23/-	14 11½	28/-	18 2½	33/-	21 5½	38/-	24 8½	4.	2 14 7¼
24/-	15 7¼	29/-	18 10¼	34/-	22 1¼	39/-	25 4¼	5.	3 8 3
25/-	16s. 3	**30/-**	19s. 6	**35/-**	22s. 9	**40/-**	26s. 0	6.	£4 1 10¾

(=39$\frac{4}{10}$%* on Gross Returns).

£		£		£		£	
£1	£0 13s. 4	£51	34 0s.	£101	£67 6s. 8	£151	100 13s. 4
2	1 6 8	52	34 13 4	102	68 0 0	152	101 6 8
3	2 0 0	53	35 6 8	103	68 13 4	153	102 0 0
4	2 13 4	54	36 0 0	104	69 6 8	154	102 13 4
5	3 6 8	55	36 13 4	105	70 0 0	155	103 6 8
6	4 0 0	56	37 6 8	106	70 13 4	156	104 0 0
7	4 13 4	57	38 0 0	107	71 6 8	157	104 13 4
8	5 6 8	58	38 13 4	108	72 0 0	158	105 6 8
9	6 0 0	59	39 6 8	109	72 13 4	159	106 0 0
10	£6 13s. 4	60	40 0s.	110	£73 6s. 8	160	106 13s. 4
11	£7 6s. 8	61	40 13s.	111	£74 0s. 0	161	107 6s. 8
12	8 0 0	62	41 6 8	112	74 13 4	162	108 0 0
13	8 13 4	63	42 0 0	113	75 6 8	163	108 13 4
14	9 6 8	64	42 13 4	114	76 0 0	164	109 6 8
15	10 0 0	65	43 6 8	115	76 13 4	165	110 0 0
16	10 13 4	66	44 0 0	116	77 6 8	166	110 13 4
17	11 6 8	67	44 13 4	117	78 0 0	167	111 6 8
18	12 0 0	68	45 6 8	118	78 13 4	168	112 0 0
19	12 13 4	69	46 0 0	119	79 6 8	169	112 13 4
20	13 6s. 8	70	46 13s. 4	120	£80 0s. 0	170	113 6s. 8
21	14 0s. 0	71	47 6s. 8	121	£80 13s. 4	171	114 0s. 0
22	14 13 4	72	48 0 0	122	81 6 8	172	114 13 4
23	15 6 8	73	48 13 4	123	82 0 0	173	115 6 8
24	16 0 0	74	49 6 8	124	82 13 4	174	116 0 0
25	16 13 4	75	50 0 0	125	83 6 8	175	116 13 4
26	17 6 8	76	50 13 4	126	84 0 0	176	117 6 8
27	18 0 0	77	51 6 8	127	84 13 4	177	118 0 0
28	18 13 4	78	52 0 0	128	85 6 8	178	118 13 4
29	19 6 8	79	52 13 4	129	86 0 0	179	119 6 8
30	20 0s. 0	80	53 6s. 8	130	£86 13s. 4	180	120 0s. 0
31	20 13s. 4	81	54 0s. 0	131	£87 6s. 8	181	120 13s. 4
32	21 6 8	82	54 13 4	132	88 0 0	182	121 6 8
33	22 0 0	83	55 6 8	133	88 13 4	183	122 0 0
34	22 13 4	84	56 0 0	134	89 6 8	184	122 13 4
35	23 6 8	85	56 13 4	135	90 0 0	185	123 6 8
36	24 0 0	86	57 6 8	136	90 13 4	186	124 0 0
37	24 13 4	87	58 0 0	137	91 6 8	187	124 13 4
38	25 6 8	88	58 13 4	138	92 0 0	188	125 6 8
39	26 0 0	89	59 6 8	139	92 13 4	189	126 0 0
40	26 13s. 4	90	60 0s. 0	140	£93 6s. 8	190	126 13s. 4
41	27 6s. 8	91	60 13s. 4	141	£94 0s. 0	191	127 6s. 8
42	28 0 0	92	61 6 8	142	94 13 4	192	128 0 0
43	28 13 4	93	62 0 0	143	95 6 8	193	128 13 4
44	29 6 8	94	62 13 4	144	96 0 0	194	129 6 8
45	30 0 0	95	63 6 8	145	96 13 4	195	130 0 0
46	30 13 4	96	64 0 0	146	97 6 8	196	130 13 4
47	31 6 8	97	64 13 4	147	98 0 0	197	131 6 8
48	32 0 0	98	65 6 8	148	98 13 4	198	132 0 0
49	32 13 4	99	66 0 0	149	99 6 8	199	132 13 4
50	33 6s. 8	100	66 13s. 4	150	100 0s. 0	200	133 6s. 8
250	166 13s. 4d	700	466 13s.4d	1200	800 0s.0d	2000	£1333 6s. 8
300	200 0 0	750	500 0 0	1400	933 6 8	2500	1666 13 4
400	266 13 4	800	533 6 8	1500	1000 0 0	3000	2000 0 0
500	333 6 8	900	600 0 0	1600	1066 13 4	4000	2666 13 4
600	400 0s.0d	1000	666 13s.4d	1800	1200 0s.0d	5000	£3333 6s. 8

33⅓ off. (66⅔%=2-3rds)

66⅔%

66⅔ Per Cent.

66⅔%

1d	0s.	0¾	4/1	2s.	8¾	8/1	5s.	4¾	12/1	8s.	0¾	16/1	10s.	8¾
2d	0	1¼	2	2	9¼	2	5	5¼	2	8	1¼	2	10	9¼
3d	0	2	3	2	10	3	5	6	3	8	2	3	10	10
4d	0	2¾	4	2	10¾	4	5	6¾	4	8	2¾	4	10	10¾
5d	0	3¼	5	2	11¼	5	5	7¼	5	8	3¼	5	10	11¼
6d	0	4	4/6	3	0	8/6	5	8	12/6	8	4	16/6	11	0
7d	0	4¾	7	3	0¾	7	5	8¾	7	8	4¾	7	11	0¾
8d	0	5¼	8	3	1¼	8	5	9¼	8	8	5¼	8	11	1¼
9d	0	6	9	3	2	9	5	10	9	8	6	9	11	2
10d	0	6¾	10	3	2¾	10	5	10¾	10	8	6¾	10	11	2¾
11d	0	7¼	11	3	3¼	11	5	11¼	11	8	7¼	11	11	3¼
1/-	0s.	8	**5/-**	3s.	4	**9/-**	6s.	0	**13/-**	8s.	8	**17/-**	11s.	4
1/1	0s.	8¾	5/1	3s.	4¾	9/1	6s.	0¾	13/1	8s.	8¾	17/1	11s.	4¾
2	0	9¼	2	3	5¼	2	6	1¼	2	8	9¼	2	11	5¼
3	0	10	3	3	6	3	6	2	3	8	10	3	11	6
4	0	10¾	4	3	6¾	4	6	2¾	4	8	10¾	4	11	6¾
5	0	11¼	5	3	7¼	5	6	3¼	5	8	11¼	5	11	7¼
1/6	1	0	5/6	3	8	9/6	6	4	13/6	9	0	17/6	11	8
7	1	0¾	7	3	8¾	7	6	4¾	7	9	0¾	7	11	8¾
8	1	1¼	8	3	9¼	8	6	5¼	8	9	1¼	8	11	9¼
9	1	2	9	3	10	9	6	6	9	9	2	9	11	10
10	1	2¾	10	3	10¾	10	6	6¾	10	9	2¾	10	11	10¾
11	1	3¼	11	3	11¼	11	6	7¼	11	9	3¼	11	11	11¼
2/-	1s.	4	**6/-**	4s.	0	**10/-**	6s.	8	**14/-**	9s.	4	**18/-**	12s.	0
2/1	1s.	4¾	6/1	4s.	0¾	10/1	6s.	8¾	14/1	9s.	4¾	18/1	12s.	0¾
2	1	5¼	2	4	1¼	2	6	9¼	2	9	5¼	2	12	1¼
3	1	6	3	4	2	3	6	10	3	9	6	3	12	2
4	1	6¾	4	4	2¾	4	6	10¾	4	9	6¾	4	12	2¾
5	1	7¼	5	4	3¼	5	6	11¼	5	9	7¼	5	12	3¼
2/6	1	8	6/6	4	4	10/6	7	0	14/6	9	8	18/6	12	4
7	1	8¾	7	4	4¾	7	7	0¾	7	9	8¾	7	12	4¾
8	1	9¼	8	4	5¼	8	7	1¼	8	9	9¼	8	12	5¼
9	1	10	9	4	6	9	7	2	9	9	10	9	12	6
10	1	10¾	10	4	6¾	10	7	2¾	10	9	10¾	10	12	6¾
11	1	11¼	11	4	7¼	11	7	3¼	11	9	11¼	11	12	7¼
3/-	2s.	0	**7/-**	4s.	8	**11/-**	7s.	4	**15/-**	10s.	0	**19/-**	12s.	8
3/1	2s.	0¾	7/1	4s.	8¾	11/1	7s.	4¾	15/1	10s.	0¾	19/1	12s.	8¾
2	2	1¼	2	4	9¼	2	7	5¼	2	10	1¼	2	12	9¼
3	2	2	3	4	10	3	7	6	3	10	2	3	12	10
4	2	2¾	4	4	10¾	4	7	6¾	4	10	2¾	4	12	10¾
5	2	3¼	5	4	11¼	5	7	7¼	5	10	3¼	5	12	11¼
3/6	2	4	7/6	5	0	11/6	7	8	15/6	10	4	19/6	13	0
7	2	4¾	7	5	0¾	7	7	8¾	7	10	4¾	7	13	0¾
8	2	5¼	8	5	1¼	8	7	9¼	8	10	5¼	8	13	1¼
9	2	6	9	5	2	9	7	10	9	10	6	9	13	2
10	2	6¾	10	5	2¾	10	7	10¾	10	10	6¾	10	13	2¾
11	2	7¼	11	5	3¼	11	7	11¼	11	10	7¼	11	13	3¼
4/-	2s.	8	**8/-**	5s.	4	**12/-**	8s.	0	**16/-**	10s.	8	**20/-**	13s.	4

												Guineas.			
20/6	13s.	8	25/6	17s.	0	31/-	20s.	8	35/6	23s.	8	1.	£0	14s.	0
21/-	14	0	26/-	17	4	31/6	21	0	36/-	24	0	2.	1	8	0
22/-	14	8	27/-	18	0	32/-	21	4	37/-	24	8	3.	2	2	0
22/6	15	0	27/6	18	4	32/6	21	8	37/6	25	0	4.	2	16	0
23/-	15	4	28/-	18	8	33/-	22	0	38/-	25	4	5.	3	10	0
24/-	16	0	29/-	19	4	34/-	22	8	39/-	26	0	6.	£4	4	0
25/-	16s.	8	**30/-**	20s.	0	**35/-**	23s.	4	**40/-**	26s.	8				

(40% on Gross Returns)

£1	£0 13s. 6	£51	34 8s. 6	£101	£68 3s. 6	£151	101.18 6
2	1 7 0	52	35 2 0	102	68 17 0	152	102 12 0
3	2 0 6	53	35 15 6	103	69 10 6	153	103 5 6
4	2 14 0	54	36 9 0	104	70 4 0	154	103 19 0
5	3 7 6	55	37 2 6	105	70 17 6	155	104 12 6
6	4 1 0	56	37 16 0	106	71 11 0	156	105 6 0
7	4 14 6	57	38 9 6	107	72 4 6	157	105 19 6
8	5 8 0	58	39 3 0	108	72 18 0	158	106 13 0
9	6 1 6	59	39 16 6	109	73 11 6	159	107 6 6
10	6 15s. 0	60	40 10s. 0	110	74 5s. 0	160	108 0s. 0
11	7 8s. 6	61	41 3s. 6	111	74 18s. 6	161	108 13s. 6
12	8 2 0	62	41 17 0	112	75 12 0	162	109 7 0
13	8 15 6	63	42 10 6	113	76 5 6	163	110 0 6
14	9 9 0	64	43 4 0	114	76 19 0	164	110 14 0
15	10 2 6	65	43 17 6	115	77 12 6	165	111 7 6
16	10 16 0	66	44 11 0	116	78 6 0	166	112 1 0
17	11 9 6	67	45 4 6	117	78 19 6	167	112 14 6
18	12 3 0	68	45 18 0	118	79 13 0	168	113 8 0
19	12 16 6	69	46 11 6	119	80 6 6	169	114 1 6
20	13 10s. 0	70	47 5s. 0	120	81 0s. 0	170	114 15s. 0
21	14 3s. 6	71	47 18s. 6	121	81 13s. 6	171	115 8s. 6
22	14 17 0	72	48 12 0	122	82 7 0	172	116 2 0
23	15 10 6	73	49 5 6	123	83 0 6	173	116 15 6
24	16 4 0	74	49 19 0	124	83 14 0	174	117 9 0
25	16 17 6	75	50 12 6	125	84 7 6	175	118 2 6
26	17 11 0	76	51 6 0	126	85 1 0	176	118 16 0
27	18 4 6	77	51 19 6	127	85 14 6	177	119 9 6
28	18 18 0	78	52 13 0	128	86 8 0	178	120 3 0
29	19 11 6	79	53 6 6	129	87 1 6	179	120 16 6
30	20 5s. 0	80	54 0s. 0	130	87 15s. 0	180	121 10s. 0
31	20 18s. 6	81	54 13s. 6	131	88 8s. 6	181	122 3s. 6
32	21 12 0	82	55 7 0	132	89 2 0	182	122 17 0
33	22 5 6	83	56 0 6	133	89 15 6	183	123 10 6
34	22 19 0	84	56 14 0	134	90 9 0	184	124 4 0
35	23 12 6	85	57 7 6	135	91 2 6	185	124 17 6
36	24 6 0	86	58 1 0	136	91 16 0	186	125 11 0
37	24 19 6	87	58 14 6	137	92 9 6	187	126 4 6
38	25 13 0	88	59 8 0	138	93 3 0	188	126 18 0
39	26 6 6	89	60 1 6	139	93 16 6	189	127 11 6
40	27 0s. 0	90	60 15s. 0	140	94 10s. 0	190	128 5s. 0
41	27 13s. 6	91	61 8s. 6	141	95 3s. 6	191	128 18s. 6
42	28 7 0	92	62 2 0	142	95 17 0	192	129 12 0
43	29 0 6	93	62 15 6	143	96 10 6	193	130 5 6
44	29 14 0	94	63 9 0	144	97 4 0	194	130 19 0
45	30 7 6	95	64 2 6	145	97 17 6	195	131 12 6
46	31 1 0	96	64 16 0	146	98 11 0	196	132 6 0
47	31 14 6	97	65 9 6	147	99 4 6	197	132 19 6
48	32 8 0	98	66 3 0	148	99 18 0	198	133 13 0
49	33 1 6	99	66 16 6	149	100 11 6	199	134 6 6
50	33 15s. 0	100	67 10s. 0	150	101 5s. 0	200	135 0s. 0
250	168 15s. 0d	700	472 10s. 0d	1200	810 0s. 0d	2000	£1350 0s. 0
300	202 10 0	750	506 5 0	1400	945 0 0	2500	1687 10 0
400	270 0 0	800	540 0 0	1500	1012 10 0	3000	2025 0 0
500	337 10 0	900	607 10 0	1600	1080 0 0	4000	2700 0 0
600	405 0s. 0d	1000	675 0s. 0d	1800	1215 0s. 0d	5000	£3375 0s. 0

32½% off.

67½% 67½ Per Cent. 67½%

1d	0s. 0¾	4/1	2s. 9	8/1	5s. 5½	12/1	8s. 2	16/1	10s.10¼
2d	0 1¼	2	2 9¾	2	5 6¼	2	8 2½	2	10 11
3d	0 2	3	2 10½	3	5 6¾	3	8 3¼	3	10 11¾
4d	0 2¾	4	2 11	4	5 7½	4	8 4	4	11 0¼
5d	0 3½	5	2 11¾	5	5 8¼	5	8 4½	5	11 1
6d	0 4	4/6	3 0½	8/6	5 8¾	12/6	8 5¼	16/6	11 1¾
7d	0 4¾	7	3 1¼	7	5 9½	7	8 6	7	11 2¼
8d	0 5½	8	3 1¾	8	5 10¼	8	8 6½	8	11 3
9d	0 6	9	3 2½	9	5 11	9	8 7¼	9	11 3¾
10d	0 6¾	10	3 3¼	10	5 11½	10	8 8	10	11 4¼
11d	0 7½	11	3 3¾	11	6 0¼	11	8 8¾	11	11 5
1/-	0s. 8	**5/-**	3s. 4½	**9/-**	6s. 1	**13/-**	8s. 9¼	**17/-**	11s. 5¾
1/1	0s. 8¾	5/1	3s. 5¼	9/1	6s. 1½	13/1	8s.10	17/1	11s. 6½
2	0 9½	2	3 5¾	2	6 2¼	2	8 10¾	2	11 7
3	0 10¼	3	3 6½	3	6 3	3	8 11¼	3	11 7¾
4	0 10¾	4	3 7¼	4	6 3½	4	9 0	4	11 8½
5	0 11½	5	3 8	5	6 4¼	5	9 0¾	5	11 9
1/6	1 0¼	5/6	3 8½	9/6	6 5	13/6	9 1¼	17/6	11 9¾
7	1 0¾	7	3 9¼	7	6 5¾	7	9 2	7	11 10½
8	1 1½	8	3 10	8	6 6¼	8	9 2¾	8	11 11
9	1 2¼	9	3 10½	9	6 7	9	9 3½	9	11 11¾
10	1 2¾	10	3 11¼	10	6 7¾	10	9 4	10	12 0½
11	1 3½	11	4 0	11	6 8¼	11	9 4¾	11	12 1¼
2/-	1s. 4¼	**6/-**	4s. 0½	**10/-**	6s. 9	**14/-**	9s. 5½	**18/-**	12s. 1¾
2/1	1s. 5	6/1	4s. 1¼	10/1	6s. 9¾	14/1	9s. 6	18/1	12s. 2½
2	1 5½	2	4 2	2	6 10¼	2	9 6¾	2	12 3¼
3	1 6¼	3	4 2¾	3	6 11	3	9 7½	3	12 3¾
4	1 7	4	4 3¼	4	6 11¾	4	9 8	4	12 4½
5	1 7½	5	4 4	5	7 0½	5	9 8¾	5	12 5¼
2/6	1 8¼	6/6	4 4¾	10/6	7 1	14/6	9 9½	18/6	12 5¾
7	1 9	7	4 5¼	7	7 1¾	7	9 10¼	7	12 6½
8	1 9½	8	4 6	8	7 2½	8	9 10¾	8	12 7¼
9	1 10¼	9	4 6¾	9	7 3	9	9 11½	9	12 8
10	1 11	10	4 7¼	10	7 3¾	10	10 0¼	10	12 8½
11	1 11¾	11	4 8	11	7 4½	11	10 0¾	11	12 9¼
3/-	2s. 0¼	**7/-**	4s. 8¾	**11/-**	7s. 5	**15/-**	10s. 1½	**19/-**	12s.10
3/1	2s. 1	7/1	4s. 9½	11/1	7s. 5¾	15/1	10s. 2¼	19/1	12s.10½
2	2 1¾	2	4 10	2	7 6½	2	10 2¾	2	12 11¼
3	2 2¼	3	4 10¾	3	7 7¼	3	10 3½	3	13 0
4	2 3	4	4 11½	4	7 7¾	4	10 4¼	4	13 0½
5	2 3¾	5	5 0	5	7 8½	5	10 5	5	13 1¼
3/6	2 4¼	7/6	5 0¾	11/6	7 9¼	15/6	10 5½	19/6	13 2
7	2 5	7	5 1½	7	7 9¾	7	10 6¼	7	13 2¾
8	2 5¾	8	5 2	8	7 10½	8	10 7	8	13 3¼
9	2 6½	9	5 2¾	9	7 11¼	9	10 7½	9	13 4
10	2 7	10	5 3½	10	7 11¾	10	10 8¼	10	13 4¾
11	2 7¾	11	5 4¼	11	8 0½	11	10 9	11	13 5½
4/-	2s. 8½	**8/-**	5s. 4¾	**12/-**	8s 1¼	**16/-**	10s. 9½	**20/-**	13s 6

20/6	13s.10d	25/6	17s. 2½	31/-	20s.11d	35/6	23s.11½	Guineas.	
21/-	14 2	26/-	17 6½	31/6	21 3¼	36/-	24 3½	1.	14s. 2d
22/-	14 10¼	27/-	18 2¾	32/-	21 7¼	37/-	24 11¾	2.	28 4¼
22/6	15 2¼	27/6	18 6¾	32/6	21 11¼	37/6	25 3¾	3.	42 6¼
23/-	15 6¼	28/-	18 10¾	33/-	22 3¼	38/-	25 7¾	4.	56 8½
24/-	16 2½	29/-	19 7	34/-	22 11½	39/-	26 4	5.	70 10½
25/-	16 10½	**30/-**	20 3	**35/-**	23 7½	**40/-**	27 0	6.	85s. 0½

($40\frac{3}{10}$%* on Gross Returns).

£	£ s d	£	£ s d	£	£ s d	£	£ s d
1	£0 13s 9	51	35 1 3	101	£69 8 9	151	103 16 3
2	1 7 6	52	35 15 0	102	70 2 6	152	104 10 0
3	2 1 3	53	36 8 9	103	70 16 3	153	105 3 9
4	2 15 0	54	37 2 6	104	71 10 0	154	105 17 6
5	3 8 9	55	37 16 3	105	72 3 9	155	106 11 3
6	4 2 6	56	38 10 0	106	72 17 6	156	107 5 0
7	4 16 3	57	39 3 9	107	73 11 3	157	107 18 9
8	5 10 0	58	39 17 6	108	74 5 0	158	108 12 6
9	6 3 9	59	40 11 3	109	74 18 9	159	109 6 3
10	6 17 6	60	41 5 0	110	75 12 6	160	110 0 0
11	7 11 3	61	41 18 9	111	76 6 3	161	110 13 9
12	8 5 0	62	42 12 6	112	77 0 0	162	111 7 6
13	8 18 9	63	43 6 3	113	77 13 9	163	112 1 3
14	9 12 6	64	44 0 0	114	78 7 6	164	112 15 0
15	10 6 3	65	44 13 9	115	79 1 3	165	113 8 9
16	11 0 0	66	45 7 6	116	79 15 0	166	114 2 6
17	11 13 9	67	46 1 3	117	80 8 9	167	114 16 3
18	12 7 6	68	46 15 0	118	81 2 6	168	115 10 0
19	13 1 3	69	47 8 9	119	81 16 3	169	116 3 9
20	13 15 0	70	48 2 6	120	82 10 0	170	116 17 6
21	14 8 9	71	48 16 3	121	83 3 9	171	117 11 3
22	15 2 6	72	49 10 0	122	83 17 6	172	118 5 0
23	15 16 3	73	50 3 9	123	84 11 3	173	118 18 9
24	16 10 0	74	50 17 6	124	85 5 0	174	119 12 6
25	17 3 9	75	51 11 3	125	85 18 9	175	120 6 3
26	17 17 6	76	52 5 0	126	86 12 6	176	121 0 0
27	18 11 3	77	52 18 9	127	87 6 3	177	121 13 9
28	19 5 0	78	53 12 6	128	88 0 0	178	122 7 6
29	19 18 9	79	54 6 3	129	88 13 9	179	123 1 3
30	20 12 6	80	55 0 0	130	89 7 6	180	123 15 0
31	21 6 3	81	55 13 9	131	90 1 3	181	124 8 9
32	22 0 0	82	56 7 6	132	90 15 0	182	125 2 6
33	22 13 9	83	57 1 3	133	91 8 9	183	125 16 3
34	23 7 6	84	57 15 0	134	92 2 6	184	126 10 0
35	24 1 3	85	58 8 9	135	92 16 3	185	127 3 9
36	24 15 0	86	59 2 6	136	93 10 0	186	127 17 6
37	25 8 9	87	59 16 3	137	94 3 9	187	128 11 3
38	26 2 6	88	60 10 0	138	94 17 6	188	129 5 0
39	26 16 3	89	61 3 9	139	95 11 3	189	129 18 9
40	27 10 0	90	61 17 6	140	96 5 0	190	130 12 6
41	28 3 9	91	62 11 3	141	96 18 9	191	131 6 3
42	28 17 6	92	63 5 0	142	97 12 6	192	132 0 0
43	29 11 3	93	63 18 9	143	98 6 3	193	132 13 9
44	30 5 0	94	64 12 6	144	99 0 0	194	133 7 6
45	30 18 9	95	65 6 3	145	99 13 9	195	134 1 3
46	31 12 6	96	66 0 0	146	100 7 6	196	134 15 0
47	32 6 3	97	66 13 9	147	101 1 3	197	135 8 9
48	33 0 0	98	67 7 6	148	101 15 0	198	136 2 6
49	33 13 9	99	68 1 3	149	102 8 9	199	136 16 3
50	34 7 6	100	68 15 0	150	103 2 6	200	137 10 0

250	171 17s 6d	700	481 5s 0d	1200	825 0s 0d	2000	1375 0s 0d
300	206 5 0	750	515 12 6	1400	962 10 0	2500	1718 15 0
400	275 0 0	800	550 0 0	1500	1031 5 0	3000	2062 10 0
500	343 15 0	900	618 15 0	1600	1100 0 0	4000	2750 0 0
600	412 10s 0d	1000	687 10s 0d	1800	1237 10s 0d	5000	3437 10s 0d

31¼% off.

68¾% 68¾ PER CENT. 68¾%

1d	0s	0¾	4/1	2s	9¾	8/1	5s	6¾	12/1	8s	3¾	16/1	11s	0¾
2d	0	1½	2	2	10½	2	5	7½	2	8	4½	2	11	1½
3d	0	2	3	2	11	3	5	8	3	8	5	3	11	2
4d	0	2¾	4	2	11¾	4	5	8¾	4	8	5¾	4	11	2¾
5d	0	3½	5	3	0½	5	5	9½	5	8	6½	5	11	3½
6d	0	4¼	4/6	3	1¼	8/6	5	10¼	12/6	8	7¼	16/6	11	4¼
7d	0	4¾	7	3	1¾	7	5	10¾	7	8	7¾	7	11	4¾
8d	0	5½	8	3	2½	8	5	11½	8	8	8½	8	11	5½
9d	0	6¼	9	3	3¼	9	6	0¼	9	8	9¼	9	11	6¼
10d	0	7	10	3	4	10	6	1	10	8	10	10	11	7
11d	0	7½	11	3	4½	11	6	1½	11	8	10½	11	11	7½
1/-	**0**	**8¼**	**5/-**	**3**	**5¼**	**9/-**	**6**	**2¼**	**13/-**	**8**	**11¼**	**17/-**	**11**	**8¼**
1/1	0	9	5/1	3	6	9/1	6	3	13/1	9	0	17/1	11	9
2	0	9¾	2	3	6¾	2	6	3¾	2	9	0¾	2	11	9¾
3	0	10¼	3	3	7¼	3	6	4¼	3	9	1¼	3	11	10¼
4	0	11	4	3	8	4	6	5	4	9	2	4	11	11
5	0	11¾	5	3	8¾	5	6	5¾	5	9	2¾	5	11	11¾
1/6	1	0½	5/6	3	9½	9/6	6	6½	13/6	9	3½	17/6	12	0½
7	1	1	7	3	10	7	6	7	7	9	4	7	12	1
8	1	1¾	8	3	10¾	8	6	7¾	8	9	4¾	8	12	1¾
9	1	2½	9	3	11½	9	6	8½	9	9	5½	9	12	2½
10	1	3¼	10	4	0¼	10	6	9¼	10	9	6¼	10	12	3¼
11	1	3¾	11	4	0¾	11	6	9¾	11	9	6¾	11	12	3¾
2/-	**1**	**4½**	**6/-**	**4**	**1½**	**10/-**	**6**	**10½**	**14/-**	**9**	**7½**	**18/-**	**12**	**4½**
2/1	1	5¼	6/1	4	2¼	10/1	6	11¼	14/1	9	8¼	18/1	12	5¼
2	1	6	2	4	3	2	7	0	2	9	9	2	12	6
3	1	6½	3	4	3½	3	7	0½	3	9	9½	3	12	6½
4	1	7¼	4	4	4¼	4	7	1¼	4	9	10¼	4	12	7¼
5	1	8	5	4	5	5	7	2	5	9	11	5	12	8
2/6	1	8¾	6/6	4	5¾	10/6	7	2¾	14/6	9	11¾	18/6	12	8¾
7	1	9¼	7	4	6¼	7	7	3¼	7	10	0¼	7	12	9¼
8	1	10	8	4	7	8	7	4	8	10	1	8	12	10
9	1	10¾	9	4	7¾	9	7	4¾	9	10	1¾	9	12	10¾
10	1	11½	10	4	8½	10	7	5½	10	10	2½	10	12	11½
11	2	0	11	4	9	11	7	6	11	10	3	11	13	0
3/-	**2**	**0¾**	**7/-**	**4**	**9¾**	**11/-**	**7**	**6¾**	**15/-**	**10**	**3¾**	**19/-**	**13**	**0¾**
3/1	2	1½	7/1	4	10½	11/1	7	7½	15/1	10	4½	19/1	13	1½
2	2	2¼	2	4	11¼	2	7	8¼	2	10	5¼	2	13	2¼
3	2	2¾	3	4	11¾	3	7	8¾	3	10	5¾	3	13	2¾
4	2	3½	4	5	0½	4	7	9½	4	10	6½	4	13	3½
5	2	4¼	5	5	1¼	5	7	10¼	5	10	7¼	5	13	4¼
3/6	2	5	7/6	5	2	11/6	7	11	15/6	10	8	19/6	13	5
7	2	5½	7	5	2½	7	7	11½	7	10	8½	7	13	5½
8	2	6¼	8	5	3¼	8	8	0¼	8	10	9¼	8	13	6¼
9	2	7	9	5	4	9	8	1	9	10	10	9	13	7
10	2	7¾	10	5	4¾	10	8	1¾	10	10	10¾	10	13	7¾
11	2	8¼	11	5	5¼	11	8	2¼	11	10	11¼	11	13	8¼
4/-	**2**	**9**	**8/-**	**5**	**6**	**12/-**	**8**	**3**	**16/-**	**11**	**0**	**20/-**	**13**	**9**

												Guineas.			
20/6	14s	1¼	25/6	17s	6½	31/-	21s	3¾	35/6	24s	5				
21/-	14	5¼	26/-	17	10½	31/6	21	8	36/-	24	9	1.	£0	14	5¼
22/-	15	1½	27/-	18	6¾	32/-	22	0	37/-	25	5¼	2.	1	8	10½
22/6	15	5¾	27/6	18	11	32/6	22	4¼	37/6	25	9½	3.	2	3	3¾
23/-	15	9¾	28/-	19	3	33/-	22	8¼	38/-	26	1½	4.	2	17	9
24/-	16	6	29/-	19	11¼	34/-	23	4½	39/-	26	9¾	5.	3	12	2¼
25/-	17	2¼	30/-	20	7½	35/-	24	0¾	40/-	27	6	6.	£4	6	7½

(40¾%* on Gross Returns).

£	£ s. d.	£	£ s. d.	£	£ s. d.	£	£ s. d.
£1	£0 14s. 0	£51	35 14s. 0	£101	£70 14s. 0	£151	105 14s. 0
2	1 8 0	52	36 8 0	102	71 8 0	152	106 8 0
3	2 2 0	53	37 2 0	103	72 2 0	153	107 2 0
4	2 16 0	54	37 16 0	104	72 16 0	154	107 16 0
5	3 10 0	55	38 10 0	105	73 10 0	155	108 10 0
6	4 4 0	56	39 4 0	106	74 4 0	156	109 4 0
7	4 18 0	57	39 18 0	107	74 18 0	157	109 18 0
8	5 12 0	58	40 12 0	108	75 12 0	158	110 12 0
9	6 6 0	59	41 6 0	109	76 6 0	159	111 6 0
10	£7 0s. 0	60	42 0s. 0	110	£77 0s. 0	160	112 0s. 0
11	£7 14s. 0	61	42 14s. 0	111	£77 14s. 0	161	112 14s. 0
12	8 8 0	62	43 8 0	112	78 8 0	162	113 8 0
13	9 2 0	63	44 2 0	113	79 2 0	163	114 2 0
14	9 16 0	64	44 16 0	114	79 16 0	164	114 16 0
15	10 10 0	65	45 10 0	115	80 10 0	165	115 10 0
16	11 4 0	66	46 4 0	116	81 4 0	166	116 4 0
17	11 18 0	67	46 18 0	117	81 18 0	167	116 18 0
18	12 12 0	68	47 12 0	118	82 12 0	168	117 12 0
19	13 6 0	69	48 6 0	119	83 6 0	169	118 6 0
20	14 0s. 0	70	49 0s. 0	120	£84 0s. 0	170	119 0s. 0
21	14 14s. 0	71	49 14s. 0	121	£84 14s. 0	171	119 14s. 0
22	15 8 0	72	50 8 0	122	85 8 0	172	120 8 0
23	16 2 0	73	51 2 0	123	86 2 0	173	121 2 0
24	16 16 0	74	51 16 0	124	86 16 0	174	121 16 0
25	17 10 0	75	52 10 0	125	87 10 0	175	122 10 0
26	18 4 0	76	53 4 0	126	88 4 0	176	123 4 0
27	18 18 0	77	53 18 0	127	88 18 0	177	123 18 0
28	19 12 0	78	54 12 0	128	89 12 0	178	124 12 0
29	20 6 0	79	55 6 0	129	90 6 0	179	125 6 0
30	21 0s. 0	80	56 0s. 0	130	£91 0s. 0	180	126 0s. 0
31	21 14s. 0	81	56 14s. 0	131	£91 14s. 0	181	126 14s. 0
32	22 8 0	82	57 8 0	132	92 8 0	182	127 8 0
33	23 2 0	83	58 2 0	133	93 2 0	183	128 2 0
34	23 16 0	84	58 16 0	134	93 16 0	184	128 16 0
35	24 10 0	85	59 10 0	135	94 10 0	185	129 10 0
36	25 4 0	86	60 4 0	136	95 4 0	186	130 4 0
37	25 18 0	87	60 18 0	137	95 18 0	187	130 18 0
38	26 12 0	88	61 12 0	138	96 12 0	188	131 12 0
39	27 6 0	89	62 6 0	139	97 6 0	189	132 6 0
40	28 0s. 0	90	63 0s. 0	140	£98 0s. 0	190	133 0s. 0
41	28 14s. 0	91	63 14s. 0	141	£98 14s. 0	191	133 14s. 0
42	29 8 0	92	64 8 0	142	99 8 0	192	134 8 0
43	30 2 0	93	65 2 0	143	100 2 0	193	135 2 0
44	30 16 0	94	65 16 0	144	100 16 0	194	135 16 0
45	31 10 0	95	66 10 0	145	101 10 0	195	136 10 0
46	32 4 0	96	67 4 0	146	102 4 0	196	137 4 0
47	32 18 0	97	67 18 0	147	102 18 0	197	137 18 0
48	33 12 0	98	68 12 0	148	103 12 0	198	138 12 0
49	34 6 0	99	69 6 0	149	104 6 0	199	139 6 0
50	35 0s. 0	100	70 0s. 0	150	105 0s 0	200	140 0s. 0
250	175 0s.0d	700	490 0s.0d	1200	840 0s.0d	2000	£1400 0s. 0
300	210 0 0	750	525 0 0	1400	980 0 0	2500	1750 0 0
400	280 0 0	800	560 0 0	1500	1050 0 0	3000	2100 0 0
500	350 0 0	900	630 0 0	1600	1120 0 0	4000	2800 0 0
600	420 0s.0d	1000	700 0s.0d	1800	1260 0s.0d	5000	£3500 0s. 0

30% off.

1d	0s. 0¾	4/1	2s.10¼	8/1	5s. 8	12/1	8s. 5½	16/1	11s. 3
2d	0 1½	2	2 11	2	5 8½	2	8 6¼	2	11 3¾
3d	0 2	3	2 11¾	3	5 9¼	3	8 7	3	11 4½
4d	0 2¾	4	3 0½	4	5 10	4	8 7½	4	11 5¼
5d	0 3½	5	3 1	5	5 10¾	5	8 8¼	5	11 6
6d	0 4¼	4/6	3 1¾	8/6	5 11½	12/6	8 9	16/6	11 6½
7d	0 5	7	3 2½	7	6 0	7	8 9¾	7	11 7¼
8d	0 5½	8	3 3¼	8	6 0¾	8	8 10½	8	11 8
9d	0 6¼	9	3 4	9	6 1½	9	8 11	9	11 8¾
10d	0 7	10	3 4½	10	6 2¼	10	8 11¾	10	11 9½
11d	0 7¾	11	3 5¼	11	6 3	11	9 0½	11	11 10
1/-	0s. 8½	**5/-**	3s. 6	**9/-**	6s. 3½	**13/-**	9s. 1¼	**17/-**	11s.10¾
1/1	0s. 9	5/1	3s. 6¾	9/1	6s. 4¼	13/1	9s. 2	17/1	11s.11½
2	0 9¾	2	3 7½	2	6 5	2	9 2½	2	12 0¼
3	0 10½	3	3 8	3	6 5¾	3	9 3¼	3	12 1
4	0 11¼	4	3 8¾	4	6 6½	4	9 4	4	12 1½
5	1 0	5	3 9½	5	6 7	5	9 4¾	5	12 2¼
1/6	1 0½	5/6	3 10¼	9/6	6 7¾	13/6	9 5½	17/6	12 3
7	1 1¼	7	3 11	7	6 8½	7	9 6	7	12 3¾
8	1 2	8	3 11½	8	6 9¼	8	9 6¾	8	12 4½
9	1 2¾	9	4 0¼	9	6 10	9	9 7½	9	12 5
10	1 3½	10	4 1	10	6 10½	10	9 8¼	10	12 5¾
11	1 4	11	4 1¾	11	6 11¼	11	9 9	11	12 6½
2/-	1s. 4¾	**6/-**	4s. 2½	**10/-**	7s. 0	**14/-**	9s. 9½	**18/-**	12s. 7¼
2/1	1s. 5½	6/1	4s. 3	10/1	7s. 0¾	14/1	9s.10¼	18/1	12s. 8
2	1 6¼	2	4 3¾	2	7 1½	2	9 11	2	12 8½
3	1 7	3	4 4½	3	7 2	3	9 11¾	3	12 9¼
4	1 7½	4	4 5¼	4	7 2¾	4	10 0½	4	12 10
5	1 8¼	5	4 6	5	7 3½	5	10 1	5	12 10¾
2/6	1 9	6/6	4 6½	10/6	7 4¼	14/6	10 1¾	18/6	12 11½
7	1 9¾	7	4 7¼	7	7 5	7	10 2½	7	13 0
8	1 10½	8	4 8	8	7 5½	8	10 3¼	8	13 0¾
9	1 11	9	4 8¾	9	7 6¼	9	10 4	9	13 1½
10	1 11¾	10	4 9½	10	7 7	10	10 4½	10	13 2¼
11	2 0½	11	4 10	11	7 7¾	11	10 5¼	11	13 3
3/-	2s. 1¼	**7/-**	4s.10¾	**11/-**	7s. 8½	**15/-**	10s. 6	**19/-**	13s. 3½
3/1	2s. 2	7/1	4s.11½	11/1	7s. 9	15/1	10s. 6¾	19/1	13s. 4¼
2	2 2½	2	5 0¼	2	7 9¾	2	10 7½	2	13 5
3	2 3¼	3	5 1	3	7 10½	3	10 8	3	13 5¾
4	2 4	4	5 1½	4	7 11¼	4	10 8¾	4	13 6½
5	2 4¾	5	5 2¼	5	8 0	5	10 9½	5	13 7
3/6	2 5½	7/6	5 3	11/6	8 0½	15/6	10 10¼	19/6	13 7¾
7	2 6	7	5 3¾	7	8 1¼	7	10 11	7	13 8½
8	2 6¾	8	5 4½	8	8 2	8	10 11½	8	13 9¼
9	2 7½	9	5 5	9	8 2¾	9	11 0¼	9	13 10
10	2 8¼	10	5 5¾	10	8 3½	10	11 1	10	13 10½
11	2 9	11	5 6½	11	8 4	11	11 1¾	11	13 11¼
4/-	2s. 9½	**8/-**	5s. 7¼	**12/-**	8s. 4¾	**16/-**	11s. 2½	**20/-**	14s. 0

								Guineas.	
20/6	14s. 4¼	25/6	17s.10¼	31/-	21s. 8½	35/6	24s.10¼		
21/-	14 8½	26/-	18 2½	31/6	22 0½	36/-	25 2½	1.	£0 14s. 8½
22/-	15 4¾	27/-	18 10¾	32/-	22 4¾	37/-	25 10¾	2.	1 9 4¾
22/6	15 9	27/6	19 3	32/6	22 9	37/6	26 3	3.	2 4 1¼
23/-	16 1¼	28/-	19 7¼	33/-	23 1¼	38/-	26 7¼	4.	2 18 9½
24/-	16 9½	29/-	20 3½	34/-	23 9½	39/-	27 3½	5.	3 13 6
25/-	17s. 6	**30/-**	21s. 0	**35/-**	24s. 6	**40/-**	28s. 0	6.	£4 8 2½

(=41$\frac{2}{10}$%* on Gross Returns.)

£		£		£		£	
£1	£0 14s. 6	£51	36 19s. 6	£101	£73 4s. 6	£151	109 9s. 6
2	1 9 0	52	37 14 0	102	73 19 0	152	110 4 0
3	2 3 6	53	38 8 6	103	74 13 6	153	110 18 6
4	2 18 0	54	39 3 0	104	75 8 0	154	111 13 0
5	3 12 6	55	39 17 6	105	76 2 6	155	112 7 6
6	4 7 0	56	40 12 0	106	76 17 0	156	113 2 0
7	5 1 6	57	41 6 6	107	77 11 6	157	113 16 6
8	5 16 0	58	42 1 0	108	78 6 0	158	114 11 0
9	6 10 6	59	42 15 6	109	79 0 6	159	115 5 6
10	7 5s. 0	60	43 10s. 0	110	79 15s. 0	160	116 0s. 0
11	7 19s. 6	61	44 4s. 6	111	80 9s. 6	161	116 14s. 6
12	8 14 0	62	44 19 0	112	81 4 0	162	117 9 0
13	9 8 6	63	45 13 6	113	81 18 6	163	118 3 6
14	10 3 0	64	46 8 0	114	82 13 0	164	118 18 0
15	10 17 6	65	47 2 6	115	83 7 6	165	119 12 6
16	11 12 0	66	47 17 0	116	84 2 0	166	120 7 0
17	12 6 6	67	48 11 6	117	84 16 6	167	121 1 6
18	13 1 0	68	49 6 0	118	85 11 0	168	121 16 0
19	13 15 6	69	50 0 6	119	86 5 6	169	122 10 6
20	14 10s. 0	70	50 15s. 0	120	87 0s. 0	170	123 5s. 0
21	15 4s. 6	71	51 9s. 6	121	87 14s. 6	171	123 19s. 6
22	15 19 0	72	52 4 0	122	88 9 0	172	124 14 0
23	16 13 6	73	52 18 6	123	89 3 6	173	125 8 6
24	17 8 0	74	53 13 0	124	89 18 0	174	126 3 0
25	18 2 6	75	54 7 6	125	90 12 6	175	126 17 6
26	18 17 0	76	55 2 0	126	91 7 0	176	127 12 0
27	19 11 6	77	55 16 6	127	92 1 6	177	128 6 6
28	20 6 0	78	56 11 0	128	92 16 0	178	129 1 0
29	21 0 6	79	57 5 6	129	93 10 6	179	129 15 6
30	21 15s. 0	80	58 0s. 0	130	94 5s. 0	180	130 10s. 0
31	22 9s. 6	81	58 14s. 6	131	94 19s. 6	181	131 4s. 6
32	23 4 0	82	59 9 0	132	95 14 0	182	131 19 0
33	23 18 6	83	60 3 6	133	96 8 6	183	132 13 6
34	24 13 0	84	60 18 0	134	97 3 0	184	133 8 0
35	25 7 6	85	61 12 6	135	97 17 6	185	134 2 6
36	26 2 0	86	62 7 0	136	98 12 0	186	134 17 0
37	26 16 6	87	63 1 6	137	99 6 6	187	135 11 6
38	27 11 0	88	63 16 0	138	100 1 0	188	136 6 0
39	28 5 6	89	64 10 6	139	100 15 6	189	137 0 6
40	29 0s. 0	90	65 5s. 0	140	101 10s. 0	190	137 15s. 0
41	29 14s. 6	91	65 19s. 6	141	102 4s. 6	191	138 9s. 6
42	30 9 0	92	66 14 0	142	102 19 0	192	139 4 0
43	31 3 6	93	67 8 6	143	103 13 6	193	139 18 6
44	31 18 0	94	68 3 0	144	104 8 0	194	140 13 0
45	32 12 6	95	68 17 6	145	105 2 6	195	141 7 6
46	33 7 0	96	69 12 0	146	105 17 0	196	142 2 0
47	34 1 6	97	70 6 6	147	106 11 6	197	142 16 6
48	34 16 0	98	71 1 0	148	107 6 0	198	143 11 0
49	35 10 6	99	71 15 6	149	108 0 6	199	144 5 6
50	36 5s. 0	100	72 10s. 0	150	108 15s. 0	200	145 0s. 0
250	181 5s.0d	700	507 10s.0d	1200	870 0s.0d	2000	£1450 0s. 0
300	217 10 0	750	543 15 0	1400	1015 0 0	2500	1812 10 0
400	290 0 0	800	580 0 0	1500	1087 10 0	3000	2175 0 0
500	362 10 0	900	652 10 0	1600	1160 0 0	4000	2900 0 0
600	435 0s.0d	1000	725 0s. 0d	1800	1305 0s.0d	5000	£3625 0s. 0

27½% off.

72½ Per Cent.

72½%

1d	0s. 0¾	4/1	2s.11½	8/1	5s.10¼	12/1	8s. 9¼	16/1	11s. 8
2d	0 1½	2	3 0¼	2	5 11	2	8 9¾	2	11 8¾
3d	0 2¼	3	3 1	3	5 11¾	3	8 10½	3	11 9½
4d	0 3	4	3 1¾	4	6 0½	4	8 11¼	4	11 10
5d	0 3¾	5	3 2½	5	6 1¼	5	9 0	5	11 10¾
6d	0 4½	4/6	3 3¼	8/6	6 2	12/6	9 0¾	16/6	11 11½
7d	0 5	7	3 4	7	6 2¾	7	9 1½	7	12 0¼
8d	0 5¾	8	3 4½	8	6 3½	8	9 2¼	8	12 1
9d	0 6½	9	3 5¼	9	6 4¼	9	9 3	9	12 1¾
10d	0 7¼	10	3 6	10	6 4¾	10	9 3¾	10	12 2½
11d	0 8	11	3 6¾	11	6 5½	11	9 4½	11	12 3¼
1/-	0s. 8¾	**5/-**	3s. 7½	**9/-**	6s. 6¼	**13/-**	9s. 5	**17/-**	12s. 4
1/1	0s. 9½	5/1	3s. 8¼	9/1	6s. 7	13/1	9s. 5¾	17/1	12s. 4¾
2	0 10¼	2	3 9	2	6 7¾	2	9 6½	2	12 5¼
3	0 11	3	3 9¾	3	6 8½	3	9 7¼	3	12 6
4	0 11½	4	3 10½	4	6 9¼	4	9 8	4	12 6¾
5	1 0¼	5	3 11¼	5	6 10	5	9 8¾	5	12 7½
1/6	1 1	5/6	3 11¾	9/6	6 10¾	13/6	9 9½	17/6	12 8¼
7	1 1¾	7	4 0½	7	6 11½	7	9 10¼	7	12 9
8	1 2½	8	4 1¼	8	7 0	8	9 11	8	12 9¾
9	1 3¼	9	4 2	9	7 0¾	9	9 11¾	9	12 10½
10	1 4	10	4 2¾	10	7 1½	10	10 0¼	10	12 11¼
11	1 4¾	11	4 3½	11	7 2¼	11	10 1	11	13 0
2/-	1s. 5½	**6/-**	4s. 4¼	**10/-**	7s. 3	**14/-**	10s. 1¾	**18/-**	13s. 0½
2/1	1s. 6¼	6/1	4s. 5	10/1	7s. 3¾	14/1	10s. 2½	18/1	13s. 1¼
2	1 6¾	2	4 5¾	2	7 4½	2	10 3¼	2	13 2
3	1 7½	3	4 6½	3	7 5¼	3	10 4	3	13 2¾
4	1 8¼	4	4 7	4	7 6	4	10 4¾	4	13 3½
5	1 9	5	4 7¾	5	7 6¾	5	10 5½	5	13 4¼
2/6	1 9¾	6/6	4 8½	10/6	7 7¼	14/6	10 6¼	18/6	13 5
7	1 10½	7	4 9¼	7	7 8	7	10 7	7	13 5¾
8	1 11¼	8	4 10	8	7 8¾	8	10 7½	8	13 6½
9	2 0	9	4 10¾	9	7 9½	9	10 8¼	9	13 7¼
10	2 0¾	10	4 11½	10	7 10¼	10	10 9	10	13 7¾
11	2 1½	11	5 0¼	11	7 11	11	10 9¾	11	13 8½
3/-	2s. 2	**7/-**	5s. 1	**11/-**	7s.11¾	**15/-**	10s.10½	**19/-**	13s. 9¼
3/1	2s. 2¾	7/1	5s. 1¾	11/1	8s. 0½	15/1	10s.11¼	19/1	13s.10
2	2 3½	2	5 2¼	2	8 1¼	2	11 0	2	13 10¾
3	2 4¼	3	5 3	3	8 2	3	11 0¾	3	13 11½
4	2 5	4	5 3¾	4	8 2½	4	11 1½	4	14 0¼
5	2 5¾	5	5 4½	5	8 3¼	5	11 2¼	5	14 1
3/6	2 6½	7/6	5 5¼	11/6	8 4	15/6	11 2¾	19/6	14 1¾
7	2 7¼	7	5 6	7	8 4¾	7	11 3½	7	14 2½
8	2 8	8	5 6¾	8	8 5½	8	11 4¼	8	14 3
9	2 8¾	9	5 7½	9	8 6¼	9	11 5	9	14 3¾
10	2 9¼	10	5 8¼	10	8 7	10	11 5¾	10	14 4½
11	2 10	11	5 9	11	8 7¾	11	11 6½	11	14 5¼
4/-	2s.10¾	**8/-**	5s. 9½	**12/-**	8s. 8½	**16/-**	11s. 7¼	**20/-**	14s. 6

20/6	14s.10¼	25/6	18s. 5¾	31/-	22s. 5¾	35/6	25s. 8¾	Guineas.	
21/-	15 2¾	26/-	18 10¼	31/6	22 10	36/-	26 1¼	1.	15s. 2¾
22/-	15 11½	27/-	19 7	32/-	23 2½	37/-	26 10	2.	30 5½
22/6	16 3¾	27/6	19 11¼	32/6	23 6¾	37/6	27 2¼	3.	45 8
23/-	16 8	28/-	20 3½	33/-	23 11	38/-	27 6½	4.	60 10¾
24/-	17 4¾	29/-	21 0¼	34/-	24 7¾	39/-	28 3¼	5.	76 1½
25/-	18 1½	**30/-**	21 9	**35/-**	25 4½	**40/-**	29 0	6.	91s. 4¼

(42%* on Gross Returns).

£1	£0 15s. 0	£51	38 5s. 0	£101	£75 15s. 0	£151	113 5s. 0
2	1 10 0	52	39 0 0	102	76 10 0	152	114 0 0
3	2 5 0	53	39 15 0	103	77 5 0	153	114 15 0
4	3 0 0	54	40 10 0	104	78 0 0	154	115 10 0
5	3 15 0	55	41 5 0	105	78 15 0	155	116 5 0
6	4 10 0	56	42 0 0	106	79 10 0	156	117 0 0
7	5 5 0	57	42 15 0	107	80 5 0	157	117 15 0
8	6 0 0	58	43 10 0	108	81 0 0	158	118 10 0
9	6 15 0	59	44 5 0	109	81 15 0	159	119 5 0
10	£7 10s. 0	60	45 0s. 0	110	£82 10s. 0	160	120 0s. 0
11	£8 5s. 0	61	45 15s. 0	111	£83 5s. 0	161	120 15s. 0
12	9 0 0	62	46 10 0	112	84 0 0	162	121 10 0
13	9 15 0	63	47 5 0	113	84 15 0	163	122 5 0
14	10 10 0	64	48 0 0	114	85 10 0	164	123 0 0
15	11 5 0	65	48 15 0	115	86 5 0	165	123 15 0
16	12 0 0	66	49 10 0	116	87 0 0	166	124 10 0
17	12 15 0	67	50 5 0	117	87 15 0	167	125 5 0
18	13 10 0	68	51 0 0	118	88 10 0	168	126 0 0
19	14 5 0	69	51 15 0	119	89 5 0	169	126 15 0
20	15 0s. 0	70	52 10s. 0	120	£90 0s. 0	170	127 10s. 0
21	15 15s. 0	71	53 5s. 0	121	£90 15s. 0	171	128 5s. 0
22	16 10 0	72	54 0 0	122	91 10 0	172	129 0 0
23	17 5 0	73	54 15 0	123	92 5 0	173	129 15 0
24	18 0 0	74	55 10 0	124	93 0 0	174	130 10 0
25	18 15 0	75	56 5 0	125	93 15 0	175	131 5 0
26	19 10 0	76	57 0 0	126	94 10 0	176	132 0 0
27	20 5 0	77	57 15 0	127	95 5 0	177	132 15 0
28	21 0 0	78	58 10 0	128	96 0 0	178	133 10 0
29	21 15 0	79	59 5 0	129	96 15 0	179	134 5 0
30	22 10s. 0	80	60 0s. 0	130	£97 10s. 0	180	135 0s. 0
31	23 5s. 0	81	60 15s. 0	131	£98 5s. 0	181	135 15s. 0
32	24 0 0	82	61 10 0	132	99 0 0	182	136 10 0
33	24 15 0	83	62 5 0	133	99 15 0	183	137 5 0
34	25 10 0	84	63 0 0	134	100 10 0	184	138 0 0
35	26 5 0	85	63 15 0	135	101 5 0	185	138 15 0
36	27 0 0	86	64 10 0	136	102 0 0	186	139 10 0
37	27 15 0	87	65 5 0	137	102 15 0	187	140 5 0
38	28 10 0	88	66 0 0	138	103 10 0	188	141 0 0
39	29 5 0	89	66 15 0	139	104 5 0	189	141 15 0
40	30 0s. 0	90	67 10s. 0	140	105 0s. 0	190	142 10s. 0
41	30 15s. 0	91	68 5s. 0	141	105 15s. 0	191	143 5s. 0
42	31 10 0	92	69 0 0	142	106 10 0	192	144 0 0
43	32 5 0	93	69 15 0	143	107 5 0	193	144 15 0
44	33 0 0	94	70 10 0	144	108 0 0	194	145 10 0
45	33 15 0	95	71 5 0	145	108 15 0	195	146 5 0
46	34 10 0	96	72 0 0	146	109 10 0	196	147 0 0
47	35 5 0	97	72 15 0	147	110 5 0	197	147 15 0
48	36 0 0	98	73 10 0	148	111 0 0	198	148 10 0
49	36 15 0	99	74 5 0	149	111 15 0	199	149 5 0
50	37 10s. 0	100	75 0s. 0	150	112 10s. 0	200	150 0s. 0

250	187 10s.0d	700	525 0s.0d	1200	900 0s.0d	2000	£1500 0s. 0
300	225 0 0	750	562 10 0	1400	1050 0 0	2500	1875 0 0
400	300 0 0	800	600 0 0	1500	1125 0 0	3000	2250 0 0
500	375 0 0	900	675 0 0			4000	3000 0 0
600	450 0s.0d	1000	750 0s.0d	1800	1350 0s.0d	5000	£3750 0s. 0

25% off.   (75%=3-4ths)

1d	0s.	0¾	4/1	3s.	0¾	8/1	6s.	0¾	12/1	9s.	0¾	16/1	12s.	0¾
2d	0	1½	2	3	1½	2	6	1½	2	9	1½	2	12	1½
3d	0	2¼	3	3	2¼	3	6	2¼	3	9	2¼	3	12	2¼
4d	0	3	4	3	3	4	6	3	4	9	3	4	12	3
5d	0	3¾	5	3	3¾	5	6	3¾	5	9	3¾	5	12	3¾
6d	0	4½	4/6	3	4½	8/6	6	4½	12/6	9	4½	16/6	12	4½
7d	0	5¼	7	3	5¼	7	6	5¼	7	9	5¼	7	12	5¼
8d	0	6	8	3	6	8	6	6	8	9	6	8	12	6
9d	0	6¾	9	3	6¾	9	6	6¾	9	9	6¾	9	12	6¾
10d	0	7½	10	3	7½	10	6	7½	10	9	7½	10	12	7½
11d	0	8¼	11	3	8¼	11	6	8¼	11	9	8¼	11	12	8¼
1/-	0s.	9	**5/-**	3s.	9	**9/-**	6s.	9	**13/-**	9s.	9	**17/-**	12s.	9
1/1	0s.	9¾	5/1	3s.	9¾	9/1	6s.	9¾	13/1	9s.	9¾	17/1	12s.	9¾
2	0	10½	2	3	10½	2	6	10½	2	9	10½	2	12	10½
3	0	11¼	3	3	11¼	3	6	11¼	3	9	11¼	3	12	11¼
4	1	0	4	4	0	4	7	0	4	10	0	4	13	0
5	1	0¾	5	4	0¾	5	7	0¾	5	10	0¾	5	13	0¾
1/6	1	1½	5/6	4	1½	9/6	7	1½	13/6	10	1½	17/6	13	1½
7	1	2¼	7	4	2¼	7	7	2¼	7	10	2¼	7	13	2¼
8	1	3	8	4	3	8	7	3	8	10	3	8	13	3
9	1	3¾	9	4	3¾	9	7	3¾	9	10	3¾	9	13	3¾
10	1	4½	10	4	4½	10	7	4½	10	10	4½	10	13	4½
11	1	5¼	11	4	5¼	11	7	5¼	11	10	5¼	11	13	5¼
2/-	1s.	6	**6/-**	4s.	6	**10/-**	7s.	6	**14/-**	10s.	6	**18/-**	13s.	6
2/1	1s.	6¾	6/1	4s.	6¾	10/1	7s.	6¾	14/1	10s.	6¾	18/1	13s.	6¾
2	1	7½	2	4	7½	2	7	7½	2	10	7½	2	13	7½
3	1	8¼	3	4	8¼	3	7	8¼	3	10	8¼	3	13	8¼
4	1	9	4	4	9	4	7	9	4	10	9	4	13	9
5	1	9¾	5	4	9¾	5	7	9¾	5	10	9¾	5	13	9¾
2/6	1	10½	6/6	4	10½	10/6	7	10½	14/6	10	10½	18/6	13	10½
7	1	11¼	7	4	11¼	7	7	11¼	7	10	11¼	7	13	11¼
8	2	0	8	5	0	8	8	0	8	11	0	8	14	0
9	2	0¾	9	5	0¾	9	8	0¾	9	11	0¾	9	14	0¾
10	2	1½	10	5	1½	10	8	1½	10	11	1½	10	14	1½
11	2	2¼	11	5	2¼	11	8	2¼	11	11	2¼	11	14	2¼
3/-	2s.	3	**7/-**	5s.	3	**11/-**	8s.	3	**15/-**	11s.	3	**19/-**	14s.	3
3/1	2s.	3¾	7/1	5s.	3¾	11/1	8s.	3¾	15/1	11s.	3¾	19/1	14s.	3¾
2	2	4½	2	5	4½	2	8	4½	2	11	4½	2	14	4½
3	2	5¼	3	5	5¼	3	8	5¼	3	11	5¼	3	14	5¼
4	2	6	4	5	6	4	8	6	4	11	6	4	14	6
5	2	6¾	5	5	6¾	5	8	6¾	5	11	6¾	5	14	6¾
3/6	2	7½	7/6	5	7½	11/6	8	7½	15/6	11	7½	19/6	14	7½
7	2	8¼	7	5	8¼	7	8	8¼	7	11	8¼	7	14	8¼
8	2	9	8	5	9	8	8	9	8	11	9	8	14	9
9	2	9¾	9	5	9¾	9	8	9¾	9	11	9¾	9	14	9¾
10	2	10½	10	5	10½	10	8	10½	10	11	10½	10	14	10½
11	2	11¼	11	5	11¼	11	8	11¼	11	11	11¼	11	14	11¼
4/-	3s.	0	**8/-**	6s.	0	**12/-**	9s.	0	**16/-**	12s.	0	**20/-**	15s.	0

20/6	15s.	4½	25/6	19s.	1½	31/-	23s.	3	35/6	26s.	7½	Guineas.			
21/-	15	9	26/-	19	6	31/6	23	7½	36/-	27	0	1.	£0	15s.	9
22/-	16	6	27/-	20	3	32/-	24	0	37/-	27	9	2.	1	11	6
22/6	16	10½	27/6	20	7½	32/6	24	4½	37/6	28	1½	3.	2	7	3
23/-	17	3	28/-	21	0	33/-	24	9	38/-	28	6	4.	3	3	0
24/-	18	0	29/-	21	9	34/-	25	6	39/-	29	3	5.	3	18	9
25/-	18s.	9	**30/-**	22s.	6	**35/-**	26s.	3	**40/-**	30s.	0	6.	£4	14	6

(42$\frac{9}{10}$%* on Gross Returns).

£	£ s. d.	£	£ s. d.	£	£ s. d.	£	£ s. d.
£1	£0 15s. 6	£51	39 10s. 6	£101	£78 5s. 6	£151	117 0s. 6
2	1 11 0	52	40 6 0	102	79 1 0	152	117 16 0
3	2 6 6	53	41 1 6	103	79 16 6	153	118 11 6
4	3 2 0	54	41 17 0	104	80 12 0	154	119 7 0
5	3 17 6	55	42 12 6	105	81 7 6	155	120 2 6
6	4 13 0	56	43 8 0	106	82 3 0	156	120 18 0
7	5 8 6	57	44 3 6	107	82 18 6	157	121 13 6
8	6 4 0	58	44 19 0	108	83 14 0	158	122 9 0
9	6 19 6	59	45 14 6	109	84 9 6	159	123 4 6
10	7 15s. 0	60	46 10s. 0	110	85 5s. 0	160	124 0s. 0
11	8 10s. 6	61	47 5s. 6	111	86 0s. 6	161	124 15s. 6
12	9 6 0	62	48 1 0	112	86 16 0	162	125 11 0
13	10 1 6	63	48 16 6	113	87 11 6	163	126 6 6
14	10 17 0	64	49 12 0	114	88 7 0	164	127 2 0
15	11 12 6	65	50 7 6	115	89 2 6	165	127 17 6
16	12 8 0	66	51 3 0	116	89 18 0	166	128 13 0
17	13 3 6	67	51 18 6	117	90 13 6	167	129 8 6
18	13 19 0	68	52 14 0	118	91 9 0	168	130 4 0
19	14 14 6	69	53 9 6	119	92 4 6	169	130 19 6
20	15 10s. 0	70	54 5s. 0	120	93 0s. 0	170	131 15s. 0
21	16 5s. 6	71	55 0s. 6	121	93 15s. 6	171	132 10s. 6
22	17 1 0	72	55 16 0	122	94 11 0	172	133 6 0
23	17 16 6	73	56 11 6	123	95 6 6	173	134 1 6
24	18 12 0	74	57 7 0	124	96 2 0	174	134 17 0
25	19 7 6	75	58 2 6	125	96 17 6	175	135 12 6
26	20 3 0	76	58 18 0	126	97 13 0	176	136 8 0
27	20 18 6	77	59 13 6	127	98 8 6	177	137 3 6
28	21 14 0	78	60 9 0	128	99 4 0	178	137 19 0
29	22 9 6	79	61 4 6	129	99 19 6	179	138·14 6
30	23 5s. 0	80	62 0s. 0	130	100 15s. 0	180	139 10s. 0
31	24 0s. 6	81	62 15s. 6	131	101 10s. 6	181	140 5s. 6
32	24 16 0	82	63 11 0	132	102 6 0	182	141 1 0
33	25 11 6	83	64 6 6	133	103 1 6	183	141 16 6
34	26 7 0	84	65 2 0	134	103 17 0	184	142 12 0
35	27 2 6	85	65 17 6	135	104 12 6	185	143 7 6
36	27 18 0	86	66 13 0	136	105 8 0	186	144 3 0
37	28 13 6	87	67 8 6	137	106 3 6	187	144 18 6
38	29 9 0	88	68 4 0	138	106 19 0	188	145 14 0
39	30 4 6	89	68 19 6	139	107 14 6	189	146 9 6
40	31 0s. 0	90	69 15s. 0	140	108 10s. 0	190	147 5s. 0
41	31 15s. 6	91	70 10s. 6	141	109 5s. 6	191	148 0s. 6
42	32 11 0	92	71 6 0	142	110 1 0	192	148 16 0
43	33 6 6	93	72 1 6	143	110 16 6	193	149 11 6
44	34 2 0	94	72 17 0	144	111 12 0	194	150 7 0
45	34 17 6	95	73 12 6	145	112 7 6	195	151 2 6
46	35 13 0	96	74 8 0	146	113 3 0	196	151 18 0
47	36 8 6	97	75 3 6	147	113 18 6	197	152 13 6
48	37 4 0	98	75 19 0	148	114 14 0	198	153 9 0
49	37 19 6	99	76 14 6	149	115 9 6	199	154 4 6
50	38 15s. 0	100	77 10s. 0	150	116 5s. 0	200	155 0s. 0
250	193 15s. 0d	700	542 10s. 0	1200	930 0s. 0d	2000	£1550 0s. 6
300	232 10 0	750	581 5 0	1400	1085 0 0	2500	1937 10 0
400	310 0 0	800	620 0 0	1500	1162 10 0	3000	2325 0 0
500	387 10 0	900	697 10 0	1600	1240 0 0	4000	3100 0 0
600	465 0s. 0d	1000	775 0s. 0d	1800	1395 0s. 0d	5000	£3875 0s. 0

22½% off.

1d	0s.	0¾	4/1	3s.	2	8/1	6s.	3¼	12/1	9s.	4½	16/1	12s.	5½
2d	0	1½	2	3	2¾	2	6	4	2	9	5¼	2	12	6¼
3d	0	2¼	3	3	3½	3	6	4¾	3	9	6	3	12	7¼
4d	0	3	4	3	4¼	4	6	5½	4	9	6¾	4	12	8
5d	0	4	5	3	5	5	6	6¼	5	9	7½	5	12	8¾
6d	0	4¾	4/6	3	5¾	8/6	6	7	12/6	9	8¼	16/6	12	9½
7d	0	5½	7	3	6¾	7	6	7¾	7	9	9	7	12	10¼
8d	0	6¼	8	3	7½	8	6	8½	8	9	9¾	8	12	11
9d	0	7	9	3	8¼	9	6	9½	9	9	10½	9	12	11¾
10d	0	7¾	10	3	9	10	6	10¼	10	9	11¼	10	13	0½
11d	0	8½	11	3	9¾	11	6	11	11	10	0¼	11	13	1¼
1/-	0s.	9¼	**5/-**	3s.	10½	**9/-**	6s.	11¾	**13/-**	10s.	1	**17/-**	13s.	2
1/1	0s.	10	5/1	3s.	11¼	9/1	7s.	0½	13/1	10s.	1¾	17/1	13s.	3
2	0	10¾	2	4	0	2	7	1¼	2	10	2½	2	13	3¾
3	0	11¾	3	4	0¾	3	7	2	3	10	3¼	3	13	4½
4	1	0½	4	4	1½	4	7	2¾	4	10	4	4	13	5¼
5	1	1¼	5	4	2½	5	7	3¼	5	10	4¾	5	13	6
1/6	1	2	5/6	4	3¼	9/6	7	4¼	13/6	10	5½	17/6	13	6¾
7	1	2¾	7	4	4	7	7	5¼	7	10	6¼	7	13	7½
8	1	3½	8	4	4¾	8	7	6	8	10	7	8	13	8¼
9	1	4¼	9	4	5½	9	7	6¾	9	10	8	9	13	9
10	1	5	10	4	6¼	10	7	7½	10	10	8¾	10	13	9¾
11	1	5¾	11	4	7	11	7	8¼	11	10	9½	11	13	10¾
2/-	1s.	6½	**6/-**	4s.	7¾	**10/-**	7s.	9	**14/-**	10s.	10¼	**18/-**	13s.	11½
2/1	1s.	7½	6/1	4s.	8½	10/1	7s.	9¾	14/1	10s.	11	18/1	14s.	0¼
2	1	8¼	2	4	9¼	2	7	10½	2	10	11¾	2	14	1
3	1	9	3	4	10¼	3	7	11¼	3	11	0½	3	14	1¾
4	1	9¾	4	4	11	4	8	0	4	11	1¼	4	14	2½
5	1	10½	5	4	11¾	5	8	1	5	11	2	5	14	3¼
2/6	1	11¼	6/6	5	0½	10/6	8	1¾	14/6	11	2¾	18/6	14	4
7	2	0	7	5	1¼	7	8	2½	7	11	3¾	7	14	4¾
8	2	0¾	8	5	2	8	8	3¼	8	11	4½	8	14	5½
9	2	1½	9	5	2¾	9	8	4	9	11	5¼	9	14	6½
10	2	2¼	10	5	3½	10	8	4¾	10	11	6	10	14	7¼
11	2	3¼	11	5	4¼	11	8	5½	11	11	6¾	11	14	8
3/-	2s.	4	**7/-**	5s.	5	**11/-**	8s.	6¼	**15/-**	11s.	7½	**19/-**	14s.	8¾
3/1	2s.	4¾	7/1	5s.	6	11/1	8s.	7	15/1	11s.	8¼	19/1	14s.	9½
2	2	5½	2	5	6¾	2	8	7¾	2	11	9	2	14	10¼
3	2	6¼	3	5	7½	3	8	8¾	3	11	9¾	3	14	11
4	2	7	4	5	8¼	4	8	9½	4	11	10½	4	14	11¾
5	2	7¾	5	5	9	5	8	10¼	5	11	11½	5	15	0½
3/6	2	8½	7/6	5	9¾	11/6	8	11	15/6	12	0¼	19/6	15	1¼
7	2	9¼	7	5	10½	7	8	11¾	7	12	1	7	15	2¼
8	2	10	8	5	11¼	8	9	0½	8	12	1¾	8	15	3
9	2	11	9	6	0	9	9	1¼	9	12	2½	9	15	3¾
10	2	11¾	10	6	0¾	10	9	2	10	12	3¼	10	15	4½
11	3	0½	11	6	1¾	11	9	2¾	11	12	4	11	15	5¼
4/-	3s.	1¼	**8/-**	6s.	2½	**12/-**	9s.	3½	**16/-**	12s.	4¾	**20/-**	15s.	6

								Guineas.	
20/6	15s. 10¾	25/6	19s. 9¼	31/-	24s. 0¼	35/6	27s. 6¼		
21/-	16 3¼	26/-	20 1¾	31/6	24 5	36/-	27 10¾	1.	16s. 3¼
22/-	17 0½	27/-	20 11	32/-	24 9½	37/-	28 8	2.	32 6½
22/6	17 5¼	27/6	21 3¾	32/6	25 2¼	37/6	29 0¾	3.	48 10
23/-	17 10	28/-	21 8½	33/-	25 7	38/-	29 5½	4.	65 1¼
24/-	18 7¼	29/-	22 5¾	34/-	26 4¼	39/-	30 2¾	5.	81 4½
25/-	19 4½	**30/-**	23 3	**35/-**	27 1½	**40/-**	31 0	6.	97s. 7¾

($43\frac{7}{10}$%* on Gross Returns).

80%　　EIGHTY PER CENT.　　80%

No.	£ s. d.	No.	£ s. d.	No.	£ s. d.	No.	£ s. d.
£1	£0 16s. 0	£51	40 16s. 0	£101	£80 16s. 0	£151	120 16s. 0
2	1 12 0	52	41 12 0	102	81 12 0	152	121 12 0
3	2 8 0	53	42 8 0	103	82 8 0	153	122 8 0
4	3 4 0	54	43 4 0	104	83 4 0	154	123 4 0
5	4 0 0	55	44 0 0	105	84 0 0	155	124 0 0
6	4 16 0	56	44 16 0	106	84 16 0	156	124 16 0
7	5 12 0	57	45 12 0	107	85 12 0	157	125 12 0
8	6 8 0	58	46 8 0	108	86 8 0	158	126 8 0
9	7 4 0	59	47 4 0	109	87 4 0	159	127 4 0
10	£8 0s. 0	60	48 0s. 0	110	£88 0s. 0	160	128 0s. 0
11	£8 16s. 0	61	48 16s. 0	111	£88 16s. 0	161	128 16s. 0
12	9 12 0	62	49 12 0	112	89 12 0	162	129 12 0
13	10 8 0	63	50 8 0	113	90 8 0	163	130 8 0
14	11 4 0	64	51 4 0	114	91 4 0	164	131 4 0
15	12 0 0	65	52 0 0	115	92 0 0	165	132 0 0
16	12 16 0	66	52 16 0	116	92 16 0	166	132 16 0
17	13 12 0	67	53 12 0	117	93 12 0	167	133 12 0
18	14 8 0	68	54 8 0	118	94 8 0	168	134 8 0
19	15 4 0	69	55 4 0	119	95 4 0	169	135 4 0
20	16 0s. 0	70	56 0s. 0	120	£96 0s. 0	170	136 0s. 0
21	16 16s. 0	71	56 16s. 0	121	£96 16s. 0	171	136 16s. 0
22	17 12 0	72	57 12 0	122	97 12 0	172	137 12 0
23	18 8 0	73	58 8 0	123	98 8 0	173	138 8 0
24	19 4 0	74	59 4 0	124	99 4 0	174	139 4 0
25	20 0 0	75	60 0 0	125	100 0 0	175	140 0 0
26	20 16 0	76	60 16 0	126	100 16 0	176	140 16 0
27	21 12 0	77	61 12 0	127	101 12 0	177	141 12 0
28	22 8 0	78	62 8 0	128	102 8 0	178	142 8 0
29	23 4 0	79	63 4 0	129	103 4 0	179	143 4 0
30	24 0s. 0	80	64 0s. 0	130	104 0s. 0	180	144 0s. 0
31	24 16s. 0	81	64 16s. 0	131	104 16s. 0	181	144 16s. 0
32	25 12 0	82	65 12 0	132	105 12 0	182	145 12 0
33	26 8 0	83	66 8 0	133	106 8 0	183	146 8 0
34	27 4 0	84	67 4 0	134	107 4 0	184	147 4 0
35	28 0 0	85	68 0 0	135	108 0 0	185	148 0 0
36	28 16 0	86	68 16 0	136	108 16 0	186	148 16 0
37	29 12 0	87	69 12 0	137	109 12 0	187	149 12 0
38	30 8 0	88	70 8 0	138	110 8 0	188	150 8 0
39	31 4 0	89	71 4 0	139	111 4 0	189	151 4 0
40	32 0s. 0	90	72 0s. 0	140	112 0s. 0	190	152 0s. 0
41	32 16s. 0	91	72 16s. 0	141	112 16s. 0	191	152 16s. 0
42	33 12 0	92	73 12 0	142	113 12 0	192	153 12 0
43	34 8 0	93	74 8 0	143	114 8 0	193	154 8 0
44	35 4 0	94	75 4 0	144	115 4 0	194	155 4 0
45	36 0 0	95	76 0 0	145	116 0 0	195	156 0 0
46	36 16 0	96	76 16 0	146	116 16 0	196	156 16 0
47	37 12 0	97	77 12 0	147	117 12 0	197	157 12 0
48	38 8 0	98	78 8 0	148	118 8 0	198	158 8 0
49	39 4 0	99	79 4 0	149	119 4 0	199	159 4 0
50	40 0s. 0	100	80 0s. 0	150	120 0s 0	200	160 0s. 0

No.	£ s. d.	No.	£ s. d.	No.	£ s. d.	No.	£ s. d.
250	200 0s.0d	700	560 0s.0d	1200	960 0s.0d	2000	£1600 0s. 0
300	240 0 0	750	600 0 0	1400	1120 0 0	2500	2000 0 0
400	320 0 0	800	640 0 0	1500	1200 0 0	3000	2400 0 0
500	400 0 0	900	720 0 0	1600	1280 0 0	4000	3200 0 0
600	480 0s.0d	1000	800 0s.0d	1800	1440 0s.0d	5000	£4000 0s. 0

20% off.

80% EIGHTY PER CENT. 80%

1d	0s. 0¾	4/1	3s. 3¼	8/1	6s. 5½	12/1	9s. 8	16/1	12s.10½
2d	0 1½	2	3 4	2	6 6½	2	9 8¾	2	12 11¼
3d	0 2½	3	3 4¾	3	6 7¼	3	9 9½	3	13 0
4d	0 3¼	4	3 5½	4	6 8	4	9 10½	4	13 0¾
5d	0 4	5	3 6½	5	6 8¾	5	9 11¼	5	13 1½
6d	0 4¾	4/6	3 7¼	8/6	6 9½	12/6	10 0	16/6	13 2½
7d	0 5½	7	3 8	7	6 10½	7	10 0¾	7	13 3¼
8d	0 6½	8	3 8¾	8	6 11¼	8	10 1½	8	13 4
9d	0 7¼	9	3 9½	9	7 0	9	10 2½	9	13 4¾
10d	0 8	10	3 10½	10	7 0¾	10	10 3¼	10	13 5½
11d	0 8¾	11	3 11¼	11	7 1½	11	10 4	11	13 6½
1/-	0s. 9½	**5/-**	4s. 0	**9/-**	7s. 2½	**13/-**	10s. 4¾	**17/-**	13s. 7¼
1/1	0s.10½	5/1	4s. 0¾	9/1	7s. 3¼	13/1	10s. 5½	17/1	13s. 8
2	0 11¼	2	4 1½	2	7 4	2	10 6½	2	13 8¾
3	1 0	3	4 2½	3	7 4¾	3	10 7¼	3	13 9½
4	1 0¾	4	4 3¼	4	7 5½	4	10 8	4	13 10½
5	1 1½	5	4 4	5	7 6½	5	10 8¾	5	13 11¼
1/6	1 2½	5/6	4 4¾	9/6	7 7¼	13/6	10 9½	17/6	14 0
7	1 3¼	7	4 5½	7	7 8	7	10 10½	7	14 0¾
8	1 4	8	4 6½	8	7 8¾	8	10 11¼	8	14 1½
9	1 4¾	9	4 7¼	9	7 9½	9	11 0	9	14 2½
10	1 5½	10	4 8	10	7 10½	10	11 0¾	10	14 3¼
11	1 6½	11	4 8¾	11	7 11¼	11	11 1½	11	14 4
2/-	1s. 7¼	**6/-**	4s. 9½	**10/-**	8s. 0	**14/-**	11s. 2½	**18/-**	14s. 4¾
2/1	1s. 8	6/1	4s.10½	10/1	8s. 0¾	14/1	11s. 3¼	18/1	14s. 5½
2	1 8¾	2	4 11¼	2	8 1½	2	11 4	2	14 6½
3	1 9½	3	5 0	3	8 2½	3	11 4¾	3	14 7¼
4	1 10½	4	5 0¾	4	8 3¼	4	11 5½	4	14 8
5	1 11¼	5	5 1½	5	8 4	5	11 6½	5	14 8¾
2/6	2 0	6/6	5 2½	10/6	8 4¾	14/6	11 7¼	18/6	14 9½
7	2 0¾	7	5 3¼	7	8 5½	7	11 8	7	14 10½
8	2 1½	8	5 4	8	8 6½	8	11 8¾	8	14 11¼
9	2 2½	9	5 4¾	9	8 7¼	9	11 9½	9	15 0
10	2 3¼	10	5 5½	10	8 8	10	11 10½	10	15 0¾
11	2 4	11	5 6½	11	8 8¾	11	11 11¼	11	15 1½
3/-	2s. 4¾	**7/-**	5s. 7¼	**11/-**	8s. 9½	**15/-**	12s. 0	**19/-**	15s. 2½
3/1	2s. 5½	7/1	5s. 8	11/1	8s.10½	15/1	12s. 0¾	19/1	15s. 3¼
2	2 6½	2	5 8¾	2	8 11¼	2	12 1½	2	15 4
3	2 7¼	3	5 9½	3	9 0	3	12 2½	3	15 4¾
4	2 8	4	5 10½	4	9 0¾	4	12 3¼	4	15 5½
5	2 8¾	5	5 11¼	5	9 1½	5	12 4	5	15 6½
3/6	2 9½	7/6	6 0	11/6	9 2½	15/6	12 4¾	19/6	15 7¼
7	2 10½	7	6 0¾	7	9 3¼	7	12 5½	7	15 8
8	2 11¼	8	6 1½	8	9 4	8	12 6½	8	15 8¾
9	3 0	9	6 2½	9	9 4¾	9	12 7¼	9	15 9½
10	3 0¾	10	6 3¼	10	9 5½	10	12 8	10	15 10½
11	3 1½	11	6 4	11	9 6½	11	12 8¾	11	15 11¼
4/-	3s. 2½	**8/-**	6s. 4¾	**12/-**	9s. 7¼	**16/-**	12s. 9½	**20/-**	16s. 0

20/6	16s. 4¾	25/6	20s. 4¾	31/-	24s. 9½	35/6	28s. 4¾	**Guineas.**	
21/-	16 9½	26/-	20 9½	31/6	25 2½	36/-	28 9½	1.	£0 16s. 9½
22/-	17 7¼	27/-	21 7¼	32/-	25 7¼	37/-	29 7¼	2.	1 13 7¼
22/6	18 0	27/6	22 0	32/6	26 0	37/6	30 0	3.	2 10 4¾
23/-	18 4¾	28/-	22 4¾	33/-	26 4¾	38/-	30 4¾	4.	3 7 2½
24/-	19 2½	29/-	23 2½	34/-	27 2½	39/-	31 2½	5.	4 4 0
25/-	20s. 0	**30/-**	24s. 0	**35/-**	28s. 0	**40/-**	32s. 0	6.	£5 0 9½

(44 4/10%* on Gross Returns).

£	£ s d	£	£ s d	£	£ s d	£	£ s d
£1	£0 16s 3	£51	41 8 9	£101	£82 1 3	£151	122 13 9
2	1 12 6	52	42 5 0	102	82 17 6	152	123 10 0
3	2 8 9	53	43 1 3	103	83 13 9	153	124 6 3
4	3 5 0	54	43 17 6	104	84 10 0	154	125 2 6
5	4 1 3	55	44 13 9	105	85 6 3	155	125 18 9
6	4 17 6	56	45 10 0	106	86 2 6	156	126 15 0
7	5 13 9	57	46 6 3	107	86 18 9	157	127 11 3
8	6 10 0	58	47 2 6	108	87 15 0	158	128 7 6
9	7 6 3	59	47 18 9	109	88 11 3	159	129 3 9
10	8 2 6	60	48 15 0	110	89 7 6	160	130 0 0
11	8 18 9	61	49 11 3	111	90 3 9	161	130 16 3
12	9 15 0	62	50 7 6	112	91 0 0	162	131 12 6
13	10 11 3	63	51 3 9	113	91 16 3	163	132 8 9
14	11 7 6	64	52 0 0	114	92 12 6	164	133 5 0
15	12 3 9	65	52 16 3	115	93 8 9	165	134 1 3
16	13 0 0	66	53 12 6	116	94 5 0	166	134 17 6
17	13 16 3	67	54 8 9	117	95 1 3	167	135 13 9
18	14 12 6	68	55 5 0	118	95 17 6	168	136 10 0
19	15 8 9	69	56 1 3	119	96 13 9	169	137 6 3
20	16 5 0	70	56 17 6	120	97 10 0	170	138 2 6
21	17 1 3	71	57 13 9	121	98 6 3	171	138 18 9
22	17 17 6	72	58 10 0	122	99 2 6	172	139 15 0
23	18 13 9	73	59 6 3	123	99 18 9	173	140 11 3
24	19 10 0	74	60 2 6	124	100 15 0	174	141 7 6
25	20 6 3	75	60 18 9	125	101 11 3	175	142 3 9
26	21 2 6	76	61 15 0	126	102 7 6	176	143 0 0
27	21 18 9	77	62 11 3	127	103 3 9	177	143 16 3
28	22 15 0	78	63 7 6	128	104 0 0	178	144 12 6
29	23 11 3	79	64 3 9	129	104 16 3	179	145 8 9
30	24 7 6	80	65 0 0	130	105 12 6	180	146 5 0
31	25 3 9	81	65 16 3	131	106 8 9	181	147 1 3
32	26 0 0	82	66 12 6	132	107 5 0	182	147 17 6
33	26 16 3	83	67 8 9	133	108 1 3	183	148 13 9
34	27 12 6	84	68 5 0	134	108 17 6	184	149 10 0
35	28 8 9	85	69 1 3	135	109 13 9	185	150 6 3
36	29 5 0	86	69 17 6	136	110 10 0	186	151 2 6
37	30 1 3	87	70 13 9	137	111 6 3	187	151 18 9
38	30 17 6	88	71 10 0	138	112 2 6	188	152 15 0
39	31 13 9	89	72 6 3	139	112 18 9	189	153 11 3
40	32 10 0	90	73 2 6	140	113 15 0	190	154 7 6
41	33 6 3	91	73 18 9	141	114 11 3	191	155 3 9
42	34 2 6	92	74 15 0	142	115 7 6	192	156 0 0
43	34 18 9	93	75 11 3	143	116 3 9	193	156 16 3
44	35 15 0	94	76 7 6	144	117 0 0	194	157 12 6
45	36 11 3	95	77 3 9	145	117 16 3	195	158 8 9
46	37 7 6	96	78 0 0	146	118 12 6	196	159 5 0
47	38 3 9	97	78 16 3	147	119 8 9	197	160 1 3
48	39 0 0	98	79 12 6	148	120 5 0	198	160 17 6
49	39 16 3	99	80 8 9	149	121 1 3	199	161 13 9
50	40 12 6	100	81 5 0	150	121 17 6	200	162 10 0

£	£ s d	£	£ s d	£	£ s d
250	203 2s 6d	700	568 15s 0d	1200	975 0s 0d
300	243 15 0	750	609 7 6	1400	1137 10 0
400	325 0 0	800	650 0 0	1500	1218 15 0
500	406 5 0	900	731 5 0	1600	1300 0 0
600	487 10s 0d	1000	812 10s 0d	1800	1462 10s 0d

£	£ s d
2000	1625 0s 0d
2500	2031 5 0
3000	2437 10 0
4000	3250 0 0
5000	4062 10s 0d

18¾% off.

81¼ Per Cent.

81¼%

1d	0s	0¾	4/1	3s	3¾	8/1	6s	6¾	12/1	9s	9¾	16/1	13s	0¾
2d	0	1¾	2	3	4¾	2	6	7¾	2	9	10¾	2	13	1¾
3d	0	2½	3	3	5½	3	6	8½	3	9	11½	3	13	2½
4d	0	3¼	4	3	6¼	4	6	9¼	4	10	0¼	4	13	3¼
5d	0	4	5	3	7	5	6	10	5	10	1	5	13	4
6d	0	5	4/6	3	8	8/6	6	11	12/6	10	2	16/6	13	5
7d	0	5¾	7	3	8¾	7	6	11¾	7	10	2¾	7	13	5¾
8d	0	6½	8	3	9½	8	7	0½	8	10	3½	8	13	6½
9d	0	7¼	9	3	10¼	9	7	1¼	9	10	4¼	9	13	7¼
10d	0	8¼	10	3	11¼	10	7	2¼	10	10	5¼	10	13	8¼
11d	0	9	11	4	0	11	7	3	11	10	6	11	13	9
1/-	**0**	**9¾**	**5/-**	**4**	**0¾**	**9/-**	**7**	**3¾**	**13/-**	**10**	**6¾**	**17/-**	**13**	**9¾**
1/1	0	10½	5/1	4	1½	9/1	7	4½	13/1	10	7½	17/1	13	10½
2	0	11½	2	4	2½	2	7	5½	2	10	8½	2	13	11½
3	1	0¼	3	4	3¼	3	7	6¼	3	10	9¼	3	14	0¼
4	1	1	4	4	4	4	7	7	4	10	10	4	14	1
5	1	1¾	5	4	4¾	5	7	7¾	5	10	10¾	5	14	1¾
1/6	1	2¾	5/6	4	5¾	9/6	7	8¾	13/6	10	11¾	17/6	14	2¾
7	1	3½	7	4	6½	7	7	9½	7	11	0½	7	14	3½
8	1	4¼	8	4	7¼	8	7	10¼	8	11	1¼	8	14	4¼
9	1	5	9	4	8	9	7	11	9	11	2	9	14	5
10	1	6	10	4	9	10	8	0	10	11	3	10	14	6
11	1	6¾	11	4	9¾	11	8	0¾	11	11	3¾	11	14	6¾
2/-	**1**	**7½**	**6/-**	**4**	**10½**	**10/-**	**8**	**1½**	**14/-**	**11**	**4½**	**18/-**	**14**	**7½**
2/1	1	8¼	6/1	4	11¼	10/1	8	2¼	14/1	11	5¼	18/1	14	8¼
2	1	9¼	2	5	0¼	2	8	3¼	2	11	6¼	2	14	9¼
3	1	10	3	5	1	3	8	4	3	11	7	3	14	10
4	1	10¾	4	5	1¾	4	8	4¾	4	11	7¾	4	14	10¾
5	1	11½	5	5	2½	5	8	5½	5	11	8½	5	14	11½
2/6	2	0½	6/6	5	3½	10/6	8	6½	14/6	11	9½	18/6	15	0½
7	2	1¼	7	5	4¼	7	8	7¼	7	11	10¼	7	15	1¼
8	2	2	8	5	5	8	8	8	8	11	11	8	15	2
9	2	2¾	9	5	5¾	9	8	8¾	9	11	11¾	9	15	2¾
10	2	3¾	10	5	6¾	10	8	9¾	10	12	0¾	10	15	3¾
11	2	4½	11	5	7½	11	8	10½	11	12	1½	11	15	4½
3/-	**2**	**5¼**	**7/-**	**5**	**8¼**	**11/-**	**8**	**11¼**	**15/-**	**12**	**2¼**	**19/-**	**15**	**5¼**
3/1	2	6	7/1	5	9	11/1	9	0	15/1	12	3	19/1	15	6
2	2	7	2	5	10	2	9	1	2	12	4	2	15	7
3	2	7¾	3	5	10¾	3	9	1¾	3	12	4¾	3	15	7¾
4	2	8½	4	5	11½	4	9	2½	4	12	5½	4	15	8½
5	2	9¼	5	6	0¼	5	9	3¼	5	12	6¼	5	15	9¼
3/6	2	10¼	7/6	6	1¼	11/6	9	4¼	15/6	12	7¼	19/6	15	10¼
7	2	11	7	6	2	7	9	5	7	12	8	7	15	11
8	2	11¾	8	6	2¾	8	9	5¾	8	12	8¾	8	15	11¾
9	3	0½	9	6	3½	9	9	6½	9	12	9½	9	16	0½
10	3	1½	10	6	4½	10	9	7½	10	12	10½	10	16	1½
11	3	2¼	11	6	5¼	11	9	8¼	11	12	11¼	11	16	2¼
4/-	**3**	**3**	**8/-**	**6**	**6**	**12/-**	**9**	**9**	**16/-**	**13**	**0**	**20/-**	**16**	**3**

20/6	16s	8	25/6	20s	8¾	31/-	25s	2¼	35/6	28s	10¼	Guineas.			
21/-	17	0¾	26/-	21	1½	31/6	25	7¼	36/-	29	3	1.	£0	17	0¾
22/-	17	10½	27/-	21	11¼	32/-	26	0	37/-	30	0¾	2.	1	14	1½
22/6	18	3½	27/6	22	4¼	32/6	26	5	37/6	30	5¾	3.	2	11	2¼
23/-	18	8¼	28/-	22	9	33/-	26	9¾	38/-	30	10½	4.	3	8	3
24/-	19	6	29/-	23	6¾	34/-	27	7½	39/-	31	8¼	5.	4	5	3¾
25/-	20	3¾	**30/-**	24	4½	**35/-**	28	5¼	**40/-**	32	6	6.	£5	2	4½

(44 13/16%* on Gross Returns).

£1	£0 16s. 6	£51	42 1s. 6	£101	£83 6s. 6	£151	124 11s. 6
2	1 13 0	52	42 18 0	102	84 3 0	152	125 8 0
3	2 9 6	53	43 14 6	103	84 19 6	153	126 4 6
4	3 6 0	54	44 11 0	104	85 16 0	154	127 1 0
5	4 2 6	55	45 7 6	105	86 12 6	155	127 17 6
6	4 19 0	56	46 4 0	106	87 9 0	156	128 14 0
7	5 15 6	57	47 0 6	107	88 5 6	157	129 10 6
8	6 12 0	58	47 17 0	108	89 2 0	158	130 7 0
9	7 8 6	59	48 13 6	109	89 18 6	159	131 3 6
10	8 5s. 0	60	49 10s. 0	110	90 15s. 0	160	132 0s. 0
11	9 1s. 6	61	50 6s. 6	111	91 11s 6	161	132 16s. 6
12	9 18 0	62	51 3 0	112	92 8 0	162	133 13 0
13	10 14 6	63	51 19 6	113	93 4 6	163	134 9 6
14	11 11 0	64	52 16 0	114	94 1 0	164	135 6 0
15	12 7 6	65	53 12 6	115	94 17 6	165	136 2 6
16	13 4 0	66	54 9 0	116	95 14 0	166	136 19 0
17	14 0 6	67	55 5 6	117	96 10 6	167	137 15 6
18	14 17 0	68	56 2 0	118	97 7 0	168	138 12 0
19	15 13 6	69	56 18 6	119	98 3 6	169	139 8 6
20	16 10s. 0	70	57 15s. 0	120	99 0s. 0	170	140 5s. 0
21	17 6s. 6	71	58 11s. 6	121	99 16s. 6	171	141 1s. 6
22	18 3 0	72	59 8 0	122	100 13 0	172	141 18 0
23	18 19 6	73	60 4 6	123	101 9 6	173	142 14 6
24	19 16 0	74	61 1 0	124	102 6 0	174	143 11 0
25	20 12 6	75	61 17 6	125	103 2 6	175	144 7 6
26	21 9 0	76	62 14 0	126	103 19 0	176	145 4 0
27	22 5 6	77	63 10 6	127	104 15 6	177	146 0 6
28	23 2 0	78	64 7 0	128	105 12 0	178	146 17 0
29	23 18 6	79	65 3 6	129	106 8 6	179	147 13 6
30	24 15s. 0	80	66 0s. 0	130	107 5s. 0	180	148 10s. 0
31	25 11s. 6	81	66 16s. 6	131	108 1s. 6	181	149 6s. 6
32	26 8 0	82	67 13 0	132	108 18 0	182	150 3 0
33	27 4 6	83	68 9 6	133	109 14 6	183	150 19 6
34	28 1 0	84	69 6 0	134	110 11 0	184	151 16 0
35	28 17 6	85	70 2 6	135	111 7 6	185	152 12 6
36	29 14 0	86	70 19 0	136	112 4 0	186	153 9 0
37	30 10 6	87	71 15 6	137	113 0 6	187	154 5 6
38	31 7 0	88	72 12 0	138	113 17 0	188	155 2 0
39	32 3 6	89	73 8 6	139	114 13 6	189	155 18 6
40	33 0s. 0	90	74 4s. 0	140	115 10s. 0	190	156 15s. 0
41	33 16s. 6	91	75 1s. 6	141	116 6s. 6	191	157 11s. 6
42	34 13 0	92	75 18 0	142	117 3 0	192	158 8 0
43	35 9 6	93	76 14 6	143	117 19 6	193	159 4 6
44	36 6 0	94	77 11 0	144	118 16 0	194	160 1 0
45	37 2 6	95	78 7 6	145	119 12 6	195	160 17 6
46	37 19 0	96	79 4 0	146	120 9 0	196	161 14 0
47	38 15 6	97	80 0 6	147	121 5 6	197	162 10 6
48	39 12 0	98	80 17 0	148	122 2 0	198	163 7 0
49	40 8 6	99	81 13 6	149	122 18 6	199	164 3 6
50	41 5s. 0	100	82 10s. 0	150	123 15s. 0	200	165 0s. 0
250	206 5s. 0d	700	577 10s. 0d	1200	990 0s. 0	2000	£1650 0s. 0
300	247 10 0	750	618 15 0	1400	1155 0 0	2500	2062 10 0
400	330 0 0	800	660 0 0	1500	1237 10 0	3000	2475 0 0
500	412 10 0	900	742 10 0	1600	1320 0 0	4000	3300 0 0
600	495 0s. 0d	1000	825 0s. 0d	1800	1485 0s. 0d	5000	£4125 0s. 0

17½% off.

1d	0s. 0¾	4/1	3s. 4½	8/1	6s. 8	12/1	9s.11¾	16/1	13s. 3¼
2d	0 1¾	2	3 5¼	2	6 8¾	2	10 0½	2	13 4
3d	0 2½	3	3 6	3	6 9¾	3	10 1¼	3	13 5
4d	0 3¼	4	3 7	4	6 10½	4	10 2	4	13 5¾
5d	0 4¼	5	3 7¾	5	6 11½	5	10 3	5	13 6½
6d	0 5	4/6	3 8½	8/6	7 0¼	12/6	10 3¾	16/6	13 7¼
7d	0 5¾	7	3 9½	7	7 1	7	10 4½	7	13 8¼
8d	0 6½	8	3 10¼	8	7 1¾	8	10 5½	8	13 9
9d	0 7½	9	3 11	9	7 2¾	9	10 6¼	9	13 9¾
10d	0 8¼	10	3 11¾	10	7 3½	10	10 7	10	13 10¾
11d	0 9	11	4 0¾	11	7 4¼	11	10 8	11	13 11½
1/-	0s. 10	**5/-**	4s. 1½	**9/-**	7s. 5	**13/-**	10s. 8¾	**17/-**	14s. 0¼
1/1	0s.10¾	5/1	4s. 2¼	9/1	7s. 6	13/1	10s. 9½	17/1	14s. 1¼
2	0 11½	2	4 3¼	2	7 6¾	2	10 10¼	2	14 2
3	1 0½	3	4 4	3	7 7½	3	10 11¼	3	14 2¾
4	1 1¼	4	4 4¾	4	7 8½	4	11 0	4	14 3½
5	1 2	5	4 5¾	5	7 9¼	5	11 0¾	5	14 4½
1/6	1 2¾	5/6	4 6½	9/6	7 10	13/6	11 1¾	17/6	14 5¼
7	1 3¾	7	4 7¼	7	7 11	7	11 2½	7	14 6
8	1 4½	8	4 8	8	7 11¾	8	11 3¼	8	14 7
9	1 5¼	9	4 9	9	8 0½	9	11 4¼	9	14 7¾
10	1 6¼	10	4 9¾	10	8 1¼	10	11 5	10	14 8½
11	1 7	11	4 10½	11	8 2¼	11	11 5¾	11	14 9½
2/-	1s. 7¾	**6/-**	4s.11½	**10/-**	8s. 3	**14/-**	11s. 6½	**18/-**	14s.10¼
2/1	1s. 8¾	6/1	5s. 0¼	10/1	8s. 3¾	14/1	11s. 7½	18/1	14s.11
2	1 9½	2	5 1	2	8 4¾	2	11 8¼	2	14 11¾
3	1 10¼	3	5 2	3	8 5½	3	11 9	3	15 0¾
4	1 11	4	5 2¾	4	8 6¼	4	11 10	4	15 1½
5	2 0	5	5 3½	5	8 7¼	5	11 10¾	5	15 2¼
2/6	2 0¾	6/6	5 4¼	10/6	8 8	14/6	11 11½	18/6	15 3¼
7	2 1½	7	5 5¼	7	8 8¾	7	12 0½	7	15 4
8	2 2½	8	5 6	8	8 9½	8	12 1¼	8	15 4¾
9	2 3¼	9	5 6¾	9	8 10½	9	12 2	9	15 5¾
10	2 4	10	5 7¾	10	8 11¼	10	12 2¾	10	15 6½
11	2 5	11	5 8½	11	9 0	11	12 3¾	11	15 7¼
3/-	2s. 5¾	**7/-**	5s. 9¼	**11/-**	9s. 1	**15/-**	12s. 4½	**19/-**	15s. 8
3/1	2s. 6½	7/1	5s.10¼	11/1	9s. 1¾	15/1	12s. 5¼	19/1	15s. 9
2	2 7¼	2	5 11	2	9 2½	2	12 6¼	2	15 9¾
3	2 8¼	3	5 11¾	3	9 3½	3	12 7	3	15 10½
4	2 9	4	6 0½	4	9 4¼	4	12 7¾	4	15 11½
5	2 9¾	5	6 1½	5	9 5	5	12 8¾	5	16 0¼
3/6	2 10¾	7/6	6 2¼	11/6	9 5¾	15/6	12 9½	19/6	16 1
7	2 11½	7	6 3	7	9 6¾	7	12 10¼	7	16 2
8	3 0¼	8	6 4	8	9 7½	8	12 11	8	16 2¾
9	3 1¼	9	6 4¾	9	9 8¼	9	13 0	9	16 3½
10	3 2	10	6 5½	10	9 9¼	10	13 0¾	10	16 4¼
11	3 2¾	11	6 6½	11	9 10	11	13 1½	11	16 5¼
4/-	3s. 3½	**8/-**	6s. 7¼	**12/-**	9s.10¾	**16/-**	13s. 2½	**20/-**	16s. 6

								Guineas.	
20/6	16s.11d	25/6	21s. 0½	31/-	25s. 7d	35/6	29s. 3½		
21/-	17 4	26/-	21 5½	31/6	25 11¾	36/-	29 8½	1.	17s. 4d
22/-	18 1¾	27/-	22 3¼	32/-	26 4¾	37/-	30 6¼	2.	34 7¾
22/6	18 6¾	27/6	22 8¼	32/6	26 9¾	37/6	30 11¼	3.	51 11¾
23/-	18 11¾	28/-	23 1¼	33/-	27 2¾	38/-	31 4¼	4.	69 3½
24/-	19 9½	29/-	23 11	34/-	28 0½	39/-	32 2	5.	86 7½
25/-	20s. 7½	**30/-**	24s. 9d	**35/-**	28s.10½	**40/-**	33s. 0d	6.	103s.11¼

(45 2/10 %* on Gross Returns).

£	£	s	d	£	£	s	d	£	£	s	d	£	£	s	d
1	0	16	8	51	42	10s	0	101	84	3s	4	151	125	16s	8
2	1	13	4	52	43	6	8	102	85	0	0	152	126	13	4
3	2	10	0	53	44	3	4	103	85	16	8	153	127	10	0
4	3	6	8	54	45	0	0	104	86	13	4	154	128	6	8
5	4	3	4	55	45	16	8	105	87	10	0	155	129	3	4
6	5	0	0	56	46	13	4	106	88	6	8	156	130	0	0
7	5	16	8	57	47	10	0	107	89	3	4	157	130	16	8
8	6	13	4	58	48	6	8	108	90	0	0	158	131	13	4
9	7	10	0	59	49	3	4	109	90	16	8	159	132	10	0
10	8	6	8	60	50	0	0	110	91	13	4	160	133	6	8
11	9	3	4	61	50	16	8	111	92	10	0	161	134	3	4
12	10	0	0	62	51	13	4	112	93	6	8	162	135	0	0
13	10	16	8	63	52	10	0	113	94	3	4	163	135	16	8
14	11	13	4	64	53	6	8	114	95	0	0	164	136	13	4
15	12	10	0	65	54	3	4	115	95	16	8	165	137	10	0
16	13	6	8	66	55	0	0	116	96	13	4	166	138	6	8
17	14	3	4	67	55	16	8	117	97	10	0	167	139	3	4
18	15	0	0	68	56	13	4	118	98	6	8	168	140	0	0
19	15	16	8	69	57	10	0	119	99	3	4	169	140	16	8
20	16	13	4	70	58	6	8	120	100	0	0	170	141	13	4
21	17	10	0	71	59	3	4	121	100	16	8	171	142	10	0
22	18	6	8	72	60	0	0	122	101	13	4	172	143	6	8
23	19	3	4	73	60	16	8	123	102	10	0	173	144	3	4
24	20	0	0	74	61	13	4	124	103	6	8	174	145	0	0
25	20	16	8	75	62	10	0	125	104	3	4	175	145	16	8
26	21	13	4	76	63	6	8	126	105	0	0	176	146	13	4
27	22	10	0	77	64	3	4	127	105	16	8	177	147	10	0
28	23	6	8	78	65	0	0	128	106	13	4	178	148	6	8
29	24	3	4	79	65	16	8	129	107	10	0	179	149	3	4
30	25	0	0	80	66	13	4	130	108	6	8	180	150	0	0
31	25	16	8	81	67	10	0	131	109	3	4	181	150	16	8
32	26	13	4	82	68	6	8	132	110	0	0	182	151	13	4
33	27	10	0	83	69	3	4	133	110	16	8	183	152	10	0
34	28	6	8	84	70	0	0	134	111	13	4	184	153	6	8
35	29	3	4	85	70	16	8	135	112	10	0	185	154	3	4
36	30	0	0	86	71	13	4	136	113	6	8	186	155	0	0
37	30	16	8	87	72	10	0	137	114	3	4	187	155	16	8
38	31	13	4	88	73	6	8	138	115	0	0	188	156	13	4
39	32	10	0	89	74	3	4	139	115	16	8	189	157	10	0
40	33	6	8	90	75	0	0	140	116	13	4	190	158	6	8
41	34	3	4	91	75	16	8	141	117	10	0	191	159	3	4
42	35	0	0	92	76	13	4	142	118	6	8	192	160	0	0
43	35	16	8	93	77	10	0	143	119	3	4	193	160	16	8
44	36	13	4	94	78	6	8	144	120	0	0	194	161	13	4
45	37	10	0	95	79	3	4	145	120	16	8	195	162	10	0
46	38	6	8	96	80	0	0	146	121	13	4	196	163	6	8
47	39	3	4	97	80	16	8	147	122	10	0	197	164	3	4
48	40	0	0	98	81	13	4	148	123	6	8	198	165	0	0
49	40	16	8	99	82	10	0	149	124	3	4	199	165	16	8
50	41	13	4	100	83	6	8	150	125	0	0	200	166	13	4

£	£	s	d	£	£	s	d	£	£	s	d	£	£	s	d
250	208	6s	8d	700	583	6s	8d	1200	1000	0s	0d	2000	1666	13s	4d
300	250	0	0	750	625	0	0	1400	1166	13	4	2500	2083	6	8
400	333	6	8	800	666	13	4	1500	1250	0	0	3000	2500	0	0
500	416	13	4	900	750	0	0	1600	1333	6	8	4000	3333	6	8
600	500	0s	0d	1000	833	6	8	1800	1500	0s	0d	5000	4166	13s	4d

16⅔% off.　　　　(83⅓%=5-6ths)

83⅓% **83⅓ Per Cent.** 83⅓%

1d	0s	0¾	4/1	3s	4¾	8/1	6s	8¾	12/1	10s	0¾	16/1	13s	4¾
2d	0	1¾	2	3	5¾	2	6	9¾	2	10	1¾	2	13	5¾
3d	0	2½	3	3	6½	3	6	10½	3	10	2½	3	13	6½
4d	0	3¼	4	3	7¼	4	6	11¼	4	10	3¼	4	13	7¼
5d	0	4¼	5	3	8¼	5	7	0¼	5	10	4¼	5	13	8¼
6d	0	5	4/6	3	9	8/6	7	1	12/6	10	5	16/6	13	9
7d	0	5¾	7	3	9¾	7	7	1¾	7	10	5¾	7	13	9¾
8d	0	6¾	8	3	10¾	8	7	2¾	8	10	6¾	8	13	10¾
9d	0	7½	9	3	11½	9	7	3½	9	10	7½	9	13	11½
10d	0	8¼	10	4	0¼	10	7	4¼	10	10	8¼	10	14	0¼
11d	0	9¼	11	4	1¼	11	7	5¼	11	10	9¼	11	14	1¼
1/-	0	10	**5/-**	4	2	**9/-**	7	6	**13/-**	10	10	**17/-**	14	2
1/1	0	10¾	5/1	4	2¾	9/1	7	6¾	13/1	10	10¾	17/1	14	2¾
2	0	11¾	2	4	3¾	2	7	7¾	2	10	11¾	2	14	3¾
3	1	0½	3	4	4½	3	7	8½	3	11	0½	3	14	4½
4	1	1¼	4	4	5¼	4	7	9¼	4	11	1¼	4	14	5¼
5	1	2¼	5	4	6¼	5	7	10¼	5	11	2¼	5	14	6¼
1/6	1	3	5/6	4	7	9/6	7	11	13/6	11	3	17/6	14	7
7	1	3¾	7	4	7¾	7	7	11¾	7	11	3¾	7	14	7¾
8	1	4¾	8	4	8¾	8	8	0¾	8	11	4¾	8	14	8¾
9	1	5½	9	4	9½	9	8	1½	9	11	5½	9	14	9½
10	1	6¼	10	4	10¼	10	8	2¼	10	11	6¼	10	14	10¼
11	1	7¼	11	4	11¼	11	8	3¼	11	11	7¼	11	14	11¼
2/-	1	8	**6/-**	5	0	**10/-**	8	4	**14/-**	11	8	**18/-**	15	0
2/1	1	8¾	6/1	5	0¾	10/1	8	4¾	14/1	11	8¾	18/1	15	0¾
2	1	9¾	2	5	1¾	2	8	5¾	2	11	9¾	2	15	1¾
3	1	10½	3	5	2½	3	8	6½	3	11	10½	3	15	2½
4	1	11¼	4	5	3¼	4	8	7¼	4	11	11¼	4	15	3¼
5	2	0¼	5	5	4¼	5	8	8¼	5	12	0¼	5	15	4¼
2/6	2	1	6/6	5	5	10/6	8	9	14/6	12	1	18/6	15	5
7	2	1¾	7	5	5¾	7	8	9¾	7	12	1¾	7	15	5¾
8	2	2¾	8	5	6¾	8	8	10¾	8	12	2¾	8	15	6¾
9	2	3½	9	5	7½	9	8	11½	9	12	3½	9	15	7½
10	2	4¼	10	5	8¼	10	9	0¼	10	12	4¼	10	15	8¼
11	2	5¼	11	5	9¼	11	9	1¼	11	12	5¼	11	15	9¼
3/-	2	6	**7/-**	5	10	**11/-**	9	2	**15/-**	12	6	**19/-**	15	10
3/1	2	6¾	7/1	5	10¾	11/1	9	2¾	15/1	12	6¾	19/1	15	10¾
2	2	7¾	2	5	11¾	2	9	3¾	2	12	7¾	2	15	11¾
3	2	8½	3	6	0½	3	9	4½	3	12	8½	3	16	0½
4	2	9¼	4	6	1¼	4	9	5¼	4	12	9¼	4	16	1¼
5	2	10¼	5	6	2¼	5	9	6¼	5	12	10¼	5	16	2¼
3/6	2	11	7/6	6	3	11/6	9	7	15/6	12	11	19/6	16	3
7	2	11¾	7	6	3¾	7	9	7¾	7	12	11¾	7	16	3¾
8	3	0¾	8	6	4¾	8	9	8¾	8	13	0¾	8	16	4¾
9	3	1½	9	6	5½	9	9	9½	9	13	1½	9	16	5½
10	3	2¼	10	6	6¼	10	9	10¼	10	13	2¼	10	16	6¼
11	3	3¼	11	6	7¼	11	9	11¼	11	13	3¼	11	16	7¼
4/-	3	4	**8/-**	6	8	**12/-**	10	0	**16/-**	13	4	**20/-**	16	8

20/6	17s	1d	25/6	21s	3d	31/-	25s	10d	35/6	29s	7d	Guineas.			
21/-	17	6	26/-	21	8	31/6	26	3	36/-	30	0	1.	£0	17s	6
22/-	18	4	27/-	22	6	32/-	26	8	37/-	30	10	2.	1	15	0
22/6	18	9	27/6	22	11	32/6	27	1	37/6	31	3	3.	2	12	6
23/-	19	2	28/-	23	4	33/-	27	6	38/-	31	8	4.	3	10	0
24/-	20	0	29/-	24	2	34/-	28	4	39/-	32	6	5.	4	7	6
25/-	20	10	**30/-**	25	0	**35/-**	29	2	**40/-**	33	4	6.	£5	5	0

(45½%* on Gross Returns).

£			£			£			£		
£1	£0 17s.	0	£51	43 7s.	0	£101	£85 17s.	0	£151	128 7s.	0
2	1 14	0	52	44 4	0	102	86 14	0	152	129 4	0
3	2 11	0	53	45 1	0	103	87 11	0	153	130 1	0
4	3 8	0	54	45 18	0	104	88 8	0	154	130 18	0
5	4 5	0	55	46 15	0	105	89 5	0	155	131 15	0
6	5 2	0	56	47 12	0	106	90 2	0	156	132 12	0
7	5 19	0	57	48 9	0	107	90 19	0	157	133 9	0
8	6 16	0	58	49 6	0	108	91 16	0	158	134 6	0
9	7 13	0	59	50 3	0	109	92 13	0	159	135 3	0
10	£8 10s.	0	60	£51 0s.	0	110	£93 10s.	0	160	136 0s.	0
11	£9 7s.	0	61	51 17s.	0	111	£94 7s.	0	161	136 17s.	0
12	10 4	0	62	52 14	0	112	95 4	0	162	137 14	0
13	11 1	0	63	53 11	0	113	96 1	0	163	138 11	0
14	11 18	0	64	54 8	0	114	96 18	0	164	139 8	0
15	12 15	0	65	55 5	0	115	97 15	0	165	140 5	0
16	13 12	0	66	56 2	0	116	98 12	0	166	141 2	0
17	14 9	0	67	56 19	0	117	99 9	0	167	141 19	0
18	15 6	0	68	57 16	0	118	100 6	0	168	142 16	0
19	16 3	0	69	58 13	0	119	101 3	0	169	143 13	0
20	17 0s.	0	70	59 10s.	0	120	102 0s.	0	170	144 10s.	0
21	17 17s.	0	71	60 7s.	0	121	102 17s.	0	171	145 7s.	0
22	18 14	0	72	61 4	0	122	103 14	0	172	146 4	0.
23	19 11	0	73	62 1	0	123	104 11	0	173	147 1	0
24	20 8	0	74	62 18	0	124	105 8	0	174	147 18	0
25	21 5	0	75	63 15	0	125	106 5	0	175	148 15	0
26	22 2	0	76	64 12	0	126	107 2	0	176	149 12	0
27	22 19	0	77	65 9	0	127	107 19	0	177	150 9	0
28	23 16	0	78	66 6	0	128	108 16	0	178	151 6	0
29	24 13	0	79	67 3	0	129	109 13	0	179	152 3	0
30	25 10s.	0	80	68 0s.	0	130	110 10s.	0	180	153 0s.	0
31	26 7s.	0	81	68 17s.	0	131	111 7s.	0	181	153 17s.	0
32	27 4	0	82	69 14	0	132	112 4	0	182	154 14	0
33	28 1	0	83	70 11	0	133	113 1	0	183	155 11	0
34	28 18	0	84	71 8	0	134	113 18	0	184	156 8	0
35	29 15	0	85	72 5	0	135	114 15	0	185	157 5	0
36	30 12	0	86	73 2	0	136	115 12	0	186	158 2	0
37	31 9	0	87	73 19	0	137	116 9	0	187	158 19	0
38	32 6	0	88	74 16	0	138	117 6	0	188	159 16	0
39	33 3	0	89	75 13	0	139	118 3	0	189	160 13	0
40	34 0s.	0	90	76 10s.	0	140	119 0s.	0	190	161 10s.	0
41	34 17s.	0	91	77 7s.	0	141	119 17s.	0	191	162 7s.	0
42	35 14	0	92	78 4	0	142	120 14	0	192	163 4	0
43	36 11	0	93	79 1	0	143	121 11	0	193	164 1	0
44	37 8	0	94	79 18	0	144	122 8	0	194	164 18	0
45	38 5	0	95	80 15	0	145	123 5	0	195	165 15	0
46	39 2	0	96	81 12	0	146	124 2	0	196	166 12	0
47	39 19	0	97	82 9	0	147	124 19	0	197	167 9	0
48	40 16	0	98	83 6	0	148	125 16	0	198	168 6	0
49	41 13	0	99	84 3	0	149	126 13	0	199	169 3	0
50	42 10s.	0	100	85 0s.	0	150	127 10s	0	200	170 0s.	0
250	212 10s. 0		700	595 0s.0d		1200	1020 0s.0d		2000	£1700 0s. 0	
300	255 0 0		750	637 10 0		1400	1190 0 0		2500	2125 0 0	
400	340 0 0		800	680 0 0		1500	1275 0 0		3000	2550 0 0	
500	425 0 0		900	765 0 0		1600	1360 0 0		4000	3400 0 0	
600	510 0s.0d		1000	850 0s.0d		1800	1530 0s.0d		5000	£4250 0s. 0	

15% off.

85% Eighty-five Per Cent. 85%

1d	0s. 0¾	4/1	3s. 5¾	8/1	6s.10½	12/1	10s. 3¼	16/1	13s. 8
2d	0 1¾	2	3 6½	2	6 11¼	2	10 4	2	13 9
3d	0 2½	3	3 7¼	3	7 0¼	3	10 5	3	13 9¾
4d	0 3½	4	3 8¼	4	7 1	4	10 5¾	4	13 10½
5d	0 4¼	5	3 9	5	7 1¾	5	10 6¾	5	13 11½
6d	0 5	4/6	3 10	8/6	7 2¾	12/6	10 7½	16/6	14 0¼
7d	0 6	7	3 10¾	7	7 3½	7	10 8¼	7	14 1¼
8d	0 6¾	8	3 11½	8	7 4½	8	10 9¼	8	14 2
9d	0 7¾	9	4 0½	9	7 5¼	9	10 10	9	14 2¾
10d	0 8½	10	4 1¼	10	7 6	10	10 11	10	14 3¾
11d	0 9¼	11	4 2¼	11	7 7	11	10 11¾	11	14 4½
1/-	0s.10¼	**5/-**	4s. 3	**9/-**	7s. 7¾	**13/-**	11s. 0½	**17/-**	14s. 5½
1/1	0s.11	5/1	4s. 3¾	9/1	7s. 8¾	13/1	11s. 1½	17/1	14s. 6¼
2	1 0	2	4 4¾	2	7 9½	2	11 2¼	2	14 7
3	1 0¾	3	4 5½	3	7 10¼	3	11 3¼	3	14 8
4	1 1½	4	4 6½	4	7 11¼	4	11 4	4	14 8¾
5	1 2½	5	4 7¼	5	8 0	5	11 4¾	5	14 9¾
1/6	1 3¼	5/6	4 8	9/6	8 1	13/6	11 5¾	17/6	14 10½
7	1 4¼	7	4 9	7	8 1¾	7	11 6½	7	14 11¼
8	1 5	8	4 9¾	8	8 2½	8	11 7½	8	15 0¼
9	1 5¾	9	4 10¾	9	8 3½	9	11 8¼	9	15 1
10	1 6¾	10	4 11½	10	8 4¼	10	11 9	10	15 2
11	1 7½	11	5 0¼	11	8 5¼	11	11 10	11	15 2¾
2/-	1s. 8½	**6/-**	5s. 1¼	**10/-**	8s. 6	**14/-**	11s.10¾	**18/-**	15s. 3½
2/1	1s. 9¼	6/1	5s. 2	10/1	8s. 6¾	14/1	11s.11¾	18/1	15s. 4½
2	1 10	2	5 3	2	8 7¾	2	12 0½	2	15 5¼
3	1 11	3	5 3¾	3	8 8½	3	12 1¼	3	15 6¼
4	1 11¾	4	5 4½	4	8 9½	4	12 2¼	4	15 7
5	2 0¾	5	5 5½	5	8 10¼	5	12 3	5	15 7¾
2/6	2 1½	6/6	5 6¼	10/6	8 11	14/6	12 4	18/6	15 8¾
7	2 2¼	7	5 7¼	7	9 0	7	12 4¾	7	15 9½
8	2 3¼	8	5 8	8	9 0¾	8	12 5½	8	15 10½
9	2 4	9	5 8¾	9	9 1¾	9	12 6½	9	15 11¼
10	2 5	10	5 9¾	10	9 2½	10	12 7¼	10	16 0
11	2 5¾	11	5 10½	11	9 3¼	11	12 8¼	11	16 1
3/-	2s. 6½	**7/-**	5s.11½	**11/-**	9s. 4¼	**15/-**	12s. 9	**19/-**	16s. 1¾
3/1	2s. 7½	7/1	6s. 0¼	11/1	9s. 5	15/1	12s. 9¾	19/1	16s. 2¾
2	2 8¼	2	6 1	2	9 6	2	12 10¾	2	16 3½
3	2 9¼	3	6 2	3	9 6¾	3	12 11½	3	16 4¼
4	2 10	4	6 2¾	4	9 7½	4	13 0½	4	16 5¼
5	2 10¾	5	6 3¾	5	9 8½	5	13 1¼	5	16 6
3/6	2 11¾	7/6	6 4½	11/6	9 9¼	15/6	13 2	19/6	16 7
7	3 0½	7	6 5¼	7	9 10¼	7	13 3	7	16 7¾
8	3 1½	8	6 6¼	8	9 11	8	13 3¾	8	16 8½
9	3 2¼	9	6 7	9	9 11¾	9	13 4¾	9	16 9½
10	3 3	10	6 8	10	10 0¾	10	13 5½	10	16 10¼
11	3 4	11	6 8¾	11	10 1½	11	13 6¼	11	16 11¼
4/-	3s. 4¾	**8/-**	6s. 9½	**12/-**	10s. 2½	**16/-**	13s. 7¼	**20/-**	17s. 0

								Guineas.	
20/6	17s. 5	25/6	21s. 8	31/-	26s. 4¼	35/6	30s. 2		
21/-	17 10¼	26/-	22 1¼	31/6	26 9¼	36/-	30 7¼	1.	£0 17 10¼
22/-	18 8½	27/-	22 11½	32/-	27 2½	37/-	31 5½	2.	1 15 8½
22/6	19 1½	27/6	23 4½	32/6	27 7½	37/6	31 10½	3.	2 13 6½
23/-	19 6½	28/-	23 9½	33/-	28 0½	38/-	32 3½	4.	3 11 4¾
24/-	20 4¾	29/-	24 7¾	34/-	28 10¾	39/-	33 1¾	5.	4 9 3
25/-	21s. 3	**30/-**	25s. 6	**35/-**	29s. 9	**40/-**	34s. 0	6.	£5 7 1¼

(45 9/10%* on Gross Returns).

£	£ s. d.	£	£ s. d.	£	£ s. d.	£	£ s. d.
£1	£0 17s. 6	£51	44 12s. 6	£101	£88 7s. 6	£151	132 2s. 6
2	1 15 0	52	45 10 0	102	89 5 0	152	133 0 0
3	2 12 6	53	46 7 6	103	90 2 6	153	133 17 6
4	3 10 0	54	47 5 0	104	91 0 0	154	134 15 0
5	4 7 6	55	48 2 6	105	91 17 6	155	135 12 6
6	5 5 0	56	49 0 0	106	92 15 0	156	136 10 0
7	6 2 6	57	49 17 6	107	93 12 6	157	137 7 6
8	7 0 0	58	50 15 0	108	94 10 0	158	138 5 0
9	7 17 6	59	51 12 6	109	95 7 6	159	139 2 6
10	8 15s. 0	60	52 10s. 0	110	96 5s. 0	160	140 0s. 0
11	9 12s. 6	61	53 7s. 6	111	97 2s. 6	161	140 17s. 6
12	10 10 0	62	54 5 0	112	98 0 0	162	141 15 0
13	11 7 6	63	55 2 6	113	98 17 6	163	142 12 6
14	12 5 0	64	56 0 0	114	99 15 0	164	143 10 0
15	13 2 6	65	56 17 6	115	100 12 6	165	144 7 6
16	14 0 0	66	57 15 0	116	101 10 0	166	145 5 0
17	14 17 6	67	58 12 6	117	102 7 6	167	146 2 6
18	15 15 0	68	59 10 0	118	103 5 0	168	147 0 0
19	16 12 6	69	60 7 6	119	104 2 6	169	147 17 6
20	17 10s. 0	70	61 5s. 0	120	105 0s. 0	170	148 15s. 0
21	18 7s. 6	71	62 2s. 6	121	105 17s. 6	171	149 12s. 6
22	19 5 0	72	63 0 0	122	106 15 0	172	150 10 0
23	20 2 6	73	63 17 6	123	107 12 6	173	151 7 6
24	21 0 0	74	64 15 0	124	108 10 0	174	152 5 0
25	21 17 6	75	65 12 6	125	109 7 6	175	153 2 6
26	22 15 0	76	66 10 0	126	110 5 0	176	154 0 0
27	23 12 6	77	67 7 6	127	111 2 6	177	154 17 6
28	24 10 0	78	68 5 0	128	112 0 0	178	155 15 0
29	25 7 6	79	69 2 6	129	112 17 6	179	156 12 6
30	26 5s. 0	80	70 0s. 0	130	113 15s. 0	180	157 10s. 0
31	27 2s. 6	81	70 17s. 6	131	114 12s. 6	181	158 7s. 6
32	28 0 0	82	71 15 0	132	115 10 0	182	159 5 0
33	28 17 6	83	72 12 6	133	116 7 6	183	160 2 6
34	29 15 0	84	73 10 0	134	117 5 0	184	161 0 0
35	30 12 6	85	74 7 6	135	118 2 6	185	161 17 6
36	31 10 0	86	75 5 6	136	119 0 0	186	162 15 0
37	32 7 6	87	76 2 6	137	119 17 6	187	163 12 6
38	33 5 0	88	77 0 0	138	120 15 0	188	164 10 0
39	34 2 6	89	77 17 6	139	121 12 6	189	165 7 6
40	35 0s. 0	90	78 15s. 0	140	122 10s. 0	190	166 5s. 0
41	35 17s. 6	91	79 12s. 6	141	123 7s. 6	191	167 2s. 6
42	36 15 0	92	80 10 0	142	124 5 0	192	168 0 0
43	37 12 6	93	81 7 6	143	125 2 6	193	168 17 6
44	38 10 0	94	82 5 0	144	126 0 0	194	169 15 0
45	39 7 6	95	83 2 6	145	126 17 6	195	170 12 6
46	40 5 0	96	84 0 0	146	127 15 0	196	171 10 0
47	41 2 6	97	84 17 6	147	128 12 6	197	172 7 6
48	42 0 0	98	85 15 0	148	129 10 0	198	173 5 0
49	42 17 6	99	86 12 6	149	130 7 6	199	174 2 6
50	43 15s. 0	100	87 10s. 0	150	131 5s. 0	200	175 0s. 0
250	218 15s. 0d	700	612 10s. 0	1200	1050 0s. 0	2000	£1750 0s. 0
300	262 10 0	750	656 5 0	1400	1225 0 0	2500	2187 10 0
400	350 0 0	800	700 0 0	1500	1312 10 0	3000	2625 0 0
500	437 10 0	900	787 10 0	1600	1400 0 0	4000	3500 0 0
600	525 0s. 0d	1000	875 0s. 0d	1800	1575 0s. 0d	5000	£4375 0s. 0

87½ Per Cent.

1d	0s. 1	4/1	3s. 7	8/1	7s. 1	12/1	10s. 7	16/1	14s. 1
2d	0 1¾	2	3 7¾	2	7 1¾	2	10 7¾	2	14 1¾
3d	0 2¾	3	3 8¾	3	7 2¾	3	10 8¾	3	14 2¾
4d	0 3½	4	3 9½	4	7 3½	4	10 9½	4	14 3½
5d	0 4½	5	3 10½	5	7 4½	5	10 10½	5	14 4½
6d	0 5¼	4/6	3 11¼	8/6	7 5¼	12/6	10 11¼	16/6	14 5¼
7d	0 6¼	7	4 0¼	7	7 6¼	7	11 0¼	7	14 6¼
8d	0 7	8	4 1	8	7 7	8	11 1	8	14 7
9d	0 8	9	4 2	9	7 8	9	11 2	9	14 8
10d	0 8¾	10	4 2¾	10	7 8¾	10	11 2¾	10	14 8¾
11d	0 9¾	11	4 3¾	11	7 9¾	11	11 3¾	11	14 9¾
1/-	0s.10½	**5/-**	4s. 4½	**9/-**	7s.10½	**13/-**	11s. 4½	**17/-**	14s.10½
1/1	0s.11½	5/1	4s. 5½	9/1	7s.11½	13/1	11s. 5½	17/1	14s.11½
2	1 0¼	2	4 6¼	2	8 0¼	2	11 6¼	2	15 0¼
3	1 1¼	3	4 7¼	3	8 1¼	3	11 7¼	3	15 1¼
4	1 2	4	4 8	4	8 2	4	11 8	4	15 2
5	1 3	5	4 9	5	8 3	5	11 9	5	15 3
1/6	1 3¾	5/6	4 9¾	9/6	8 3¾	13/6	11 9¾	17/6	15 3¾
7	1 4¾	7	4 10¾	7	8 4¾	7	11 10¾	7	15 4¾
8	1 5½	8	4 11½	8	8 5½	8	11 11½	8	15 5½
9	1 6½	9	5 0½	9	8 6½	9	12 0½	9	15 6½
10	1 7¼	10	5 1¼	10	8 7¼	10	12 1¼	10	15 7¼
11	1 8¼	11	5 2¼	11	8 8¼	11	12 2¼	11	15 8¼
2/-	1s. 9	**6/-**	5s. 3	**10/-**	8s. 9	**14/-**	12s. 3	**18/-**	15s. 9
2/1	1s.10	6/1	5s. 4	10/1	8s.10	14/1	12s. 4	18/1	15s.10
2	1 10¾	2	5 4¾	2	8 10¾	2	12 4¾	2	15 10¾
3	1 11¾	3	5 5¾	3	8 11¾	3	12 5¾	3	15 11¾
4	2 0½	4	5 6½	4	9 0½	4	12 6½	4	16 0½
5	2 1½	5	5 7½	5	9 1½	5	12 7½	5	16 1½
2/6	2 2¼	6/6	5 8¼	10/6	9 2¼	14/6	12 8¼	18/6	16 2¼
7	2 3¼	7	5 9¼	7	9 3¼	7	12 9¼	7	16 3¼
8	2 4	8	5 10	8	9 4	8	12 10	8	16 4
9	2 5	9	5 11	9	9 5	9	12 11	9	16 5
10	2 5¾	10	5 11¾	10	9 5¾	10	12 11¾	10	16 5¾
11	2 6¾	11	6 0¾	11	9 6¾	11	13 0¾	11	16 6¾
3/-	2s. 7½	**7/-**	6s. 1½	**1/-**	9s. 7½	**15/-**	13s. 1½	**19/-**	16s. 7½
3/1	2s. 8½	7/1	6s. 2½	11/1	9s. 8½	15/1	13s. 2½	19/1	16s. 8½
2	2 9¼	2	6 3¼	2	9 9¼	2	13 3¼	2	16 9¼
3	2 10¼	3	6 4¼	3	9 10¼	3	13 4¼	3	16 10¼
4	2 11	4	6 5	4	9 11	4	13 5	4	16 11
5	3 0	5	6 6	5	10 0	5	13 6	5	17 0
3/6	3 0¾	7/6	6 6¾	11/6	10 0¾	15/6	13 6¾	19/6	17 0¾
7	3 1¾	7	6 7¾	7	10 1¾	7	13 7¾	7	17 1¾
8	3 2½	8	6 8½	8	10 2½	8	13 8½	8	17 2½
9	3 3½	9	6 9½	9	10 3½	9	13 9½	9	17 3½
10	3 4¼	10	6 10¼	10	10 4¼	10	13 10¼	10	17 4¼
11	3 5¼	11	6 11¼	11	10 5¼	11	13 11¼	11	17 5¼
4/-	3s. 6	**8/-**	7s. 0	**12/-**	10s. 6	**16/-**	14s. 0	**20/-**	17s. 6
20/6	17s.11¼	25/6	22s. 3¾	31/-	27s. 1½	35/6	31s. 0¾	Guineas.	
21/-	18 4½	26/-	22 9	31/6	27 6¾	36/-	31 6	1.	18s. 4½
22/-	19 3	27/-	23 7½	32/-	28 0	37/-	32 4½	2.	36 9
22/6	19 8¼	27/6	24 0¾	32/6	28 5¼	37/6	32 9¾	3.	55 1½
23/-	20 1½	28/-	24 6	33/-	28 10½	38/-	33 3	4.	73 6
24/-	21 0	29/-	25 4½	34/-	29 9	39/-	34 1½	5.	91 10½
25/-	21s.10½	**30/-**	26s. 3d	**35/-**	30s. 7½	**40/-**	35s. 0d	6.	110s. 3d

(46$\frac{7}{10}$%* on Gross Returns).

£1	£0 18s. 0	£51	45 18s. 0	£101	£90 18s. 0	£151	135 18s. 0
2	1 16 0	52	46 16 0	102	91 16 0	152	136 16 0
3	2 14 0	53	47 14 0	103	92 14 0	153	137 14 0
4	3 12 0	54	48 12 0	104	93 12 0	154	138 12 0
5	4 10 0	55	49 10 0	105	94 10 0	155	139 10 0
6	5 8 0	56	50 8 0	106	95 8 0	156	140 8 0
7	6 6 0	57	51 6 0	107	96 6 0	157	141 6 0
8	7 4 0	58	52 4 0	108	97 4 0	158	142 4 0
9	8 2 0	59	53 2 0	109	98 2 0	159	143 2 0
10	£9 0s. 0	60	54 0s. 0	110	£99 0s. 0	160	144 0s. 0
11	£9 18s. 0	61	54 18s. 0	111	£99 18s. 0	161	144 18s. 0
12	10 16 0	62	55 16 0	112	100 16 0	162	145 16 0
13	11 14 0	63	56 14 0	113	101 14 0	163	146 14 0
14	12 12 0	64	57 12 0	114	102 12 0	164	147 12 0
15	13 10 0	65	58 10 0	115	103 10 0	165	148 10 0
16	14 8 0	66	59 8 0	116	104 8 0	166	149 8 0
17	15 6 0	67	60 6 0	117	105 6 0	167	150 6 0
18	16 4 0	68	61 4 0	118	106 4 0	168	151 4 0
19	17 2 0	69	62 2 0	119	107 2 0	169	152 2 0
20	18 0s. 0	70	63 0s. 0	120	108 0s. 0	170	153 0s. 0
21	18 18s. 0	71	63 18s. 0	121	108 18s. 0	171	153 18s. 0
22	19 16 0	72	64 16 0	122	109 16 0	172	154 16 0
23	20 14 0	73	65 14 0	123	110 14 0	173	155 14 0
24	21 12 0	74	66 12 0	124	111 12 0	174	156 12 0
25	22 10 0	75	67 10 0	125	112 10 0	175	157 10 0
26	23 8 0	76	68 8 0	126	113 8 0	176	158 8 0
27	24 6 0	77	69 6 0	127	114 6 0	177	159 6 0
28	25 4 0	78	70 4 0	128	115 4 0	178	160 4 0
29	26 2 0	79	71 2 0	129	116 2 0	179	161 2 0
30	27 0s. 0	80	72 0s. 0	130	117 0s. 0	180	162 0s. 0
31	27 18s. 0	81	72 18s. 0	131	117 18s. 0	181	162 18s. 0
32	28 16 0	82	73 16 0	132	118 16 0	182	163 16 0
33	29 14 0	83	74 14 0	133	119 14 0	183	164 14 0
34	30 12 0	84	75 12 0	134	120 12 0	184	165 12 0
35	31 10 0	85	76 10 0	135	121 10 0	185	166 10 0
36	32 8 0	86	77 8 0	136	122 8 0	186	167 8 0
37	33 6 0	87	78 6 0	137	123 6 0	187	168 6 0
38	34 4 0	88	79 4 0	138	124 4 0	188	169 4 0
39	35 2 0	89	80 2 0	139	125 2 0	189	170 2 0
40	36 0s. 0	90	81 0s. 0	140	126 0s. 0	190	171 0s. 0
41	36 18s. 0	91	81 18s. 0	141	126 18s. 0	191	171 18s. 0
42	37 16 0	92	82 16 0	142	127 16 0	192	172 16 0
43	38 14 0	93	83 14 0	143	128 14 0	193	173 14 0
44	39 12 0	94	84 12 0	144	129 12 0	194	174 12 0
45	40 10 0	95	85 10 0	145	130 10 0	195	175 10 0
46	41 8 0	96	86 8 0	146	131 8 0	196	176 8 0
47	42 6 0	97	87 6 0	147	132 6 0	197	177 6 0
48	43 4 0	98	88 4 0	148	133 4 0	198	178 4 0
49	44 2 0	99	89 2 0	149	134 2 0	199	179 2 0
50	45 0s. 0	100	90 0s. 0	150	135 0s. 0	200	180 0s. 0
250	225 0s. 0d	700	630 0s. 0d	1200	1080 0s. 0d	2000	£1800 0s. 0
300	270 0 0	750	675 0 0	1400	1260 0 0	2500	2250 0 0
400	360 0 0	800	720 0 0	1500	1350 0 0	3000	2700 0 0
500	450 0 0	900	810 0 0	1600	1440 0 0	4000	3600 0 0
600	540 0s. 0d	1000	900 0s. 0d	1800	1620 0s. 0d	5000	£4500 0s. 0

10% off.

1d	0s.	1	**4/1**	3s.	8	**8/1**	7s.	3¼	**12/1**	10s.	10½	**16/1**	14s.	5¾
2d	0	1¾	**2**	3	9	**2**	7	4¼	**2**	10	11½	**2**	14	6½
3d	0	2¾	**3**	3	10	**3**	7	5	**3**	11	0¼	**3**	14	7½
4d	0	3½	**4**	3	10¾	**4**	7	6	**4**	11	1¼	**4**	14	8½
5d	0	4½	**5**	3	11¾	**5**	7	7	**5**	11	2	**5**	14	9¼
6d	0	5½	**4/6**	4	0½	**8/6**	7	7¾	**12/6**	11	3	**16/6**	14	10¼
7d	0	6¼	**7**	4	1½	**7**	7	8¾	**7**	11	4	**7**	14	11
8d	0	7¼	**8**	4	2½	**8**	7	9½	**8**	11	4¾	**8**	15	0
9d	0	8	**9**	4	3¼	**9**	7	10½	**9**	11	5¾	**9**	15	1
10d	0	9	**10**	4	4¼	**10**	7	11½	**10**	11	6½	**10**	15	1¾
11d	0	10	**11**	4	5	**11**	8	0¼	**11**	11	7½	**11**	15	2¾
1/-	0s.	10¾	**5/-**	4s.	6	**9/-**	8s.	1¼	**13/-**	11s.	8½	**17/-**	15s.	3½
1/1	0s.	11¾	**5/1**	4s.	7	**9/1**	8s.	2	**13/1**	11s.	9¼	**17/1**	15s.	4½
2	1	0½	**2**	4	7¾	**2**	8	3	**2**	11	10¼	**2**	15	5½
3	1	1½	**3**	4	8¾	**3**	8	4	**3**	11	11	**3**	15	6¼
4	1	2½	**4**	4	9½	**4**	8	4¾	**4**	12	0	**4**	15	7¼
5	1	3¼	**5**	4	10½	**5**	8	5¾	**5**	12	1	**5**	15	8
1/6	1	4¼	**5/6**	4	11½	**9/6**	8	6½	**13/6**	12	1¾	**17/6**	15	9
7	1	5	**7**	5	0¼	**7**	8	7½	**7**	12	2¾	**7**	15	10
8	1	6	**8**	5	1¼	**8**	8	8½	**8**	12	3½	**8**	15	10¾
9	1	7	**9**	5	2	**9**	8	9¼	**9**	12	4½	**9**	15	11¾
10	1	7¾	**10**	5	3	**10**	8	10¼	**10**	12	5½	**10**	16	0½
11	1	8¾	**11**	5	4	**11**	8	11	**11**	12	6¼	**11**	16	1½
2/-	1s.	9½	**6/-**	5s.	4¾	**10/-**	9s.	0	**14/-**	12s.	7¼	**18/-**	16s.	2½
2/1	1s.	10½	**6/1**	5s.	5¾	**10/1**	9s.	1	**14/1**	12s.	8	**18/1**	16s.	3¼
2	1	11½	**2**	5	6½	**2**	9	1¾	**2**	12	9	**2**	16	4¼
3	2	0¼	**3**	5	7½	**3**	9	2¾	**3**	12	10	**3**	16	5
4	2	1¼	**4**	5	8½	**4**	9	3½	**4**	12	10¾	**4**	16	6
5	2	2	**5**	5	9¼	**5**	9	4½	**5**	12	11¾	**5**	16	7
2/6	2	3	**6/6**	5	10¼	**10/6**	9	5½	**14/6**	13	0½	**18/6**	16	7¾
7	2	4	**7**	5	11	**7**	9	6¼	**7**	13	1½	**7**	16	8¾
8	2	4¾	**8**	6	0	**8**	9	7¼	**8**	13	2½	**8**	16	9½
9	2	5¾	**9**	6	1	**9**	9	8	**9**	13	3¼	**9**	16	10½
10	2	6½	**10**	6	1¾	**10**	9	9	**10**	13	4¼	**10**	16	11½
11	2	7½	**11**	6	2¾	**11**	9	10	**11**	13	5	**11**	17	0¼
3/-	2s.	8½	**7/-**	6s.	3½	**11/-**	9s.	10¾	**15/-**	13s.	6	**19/-**	17s.	1¼
3/1	2s.	9¼	**7/1**	6s.	4½	**11/1**	9s.	11¾	**15/1**	13s.	7	**19/1**	17s.	2
2	2	10¼	**2**	6	5½	**2**	10	0½	**2**	13	7¾	**2**	17	3
3	2	11	**3**	6	6¼	**3**	10	1½	**3**	13	8¾	**3**	17	4
4	3	0	**4**	6	7¼	**4**	10	2½	**4**	13	9½	**4**	17	4¾
5	3	1	**5**	6	8	**5**	10	3¼	**5**	13	10½	**5**	17	5¾
3/6	3	1¾	**7/6**	6	9	**11/6**	10	4¼	**15/6**	13	11½	**19/6**	17	6½
7	3	2¾	**7**	6	10	**7**	10	5	**7**	14	0¼	**7**	17	7½
8	3	3½	**8**	6	10¾	**8**	10	6	**8**	14	1¼	**8**	17	8¼
9	3	4½	**9**	6	11¾	**9**	10	7	**9**	14	2	**9**	17	9¼
10	3	5½	**10**	7	0½	**10**	10	7¾	**10**	14	3	**10**	17	10¼
11	3	6¼	**11**	7	1½	**11**	10	8¾	**11**	14	4	**11**	17	11
4/-	3s.	7¼	**8/-**	7s.	2½	**12/-**	10s.	9½	**16/-**	14s.	4¾	**20/-**	18s.	0

20/6	18s. 5½	**25/6**	22s. 11½	**31/-**	27s. 10¾	**35/6**	31s. 11½	Guineas.			
21/-	18 10¾	**26/-**	23 4¼	**31/6**	28 4¼	**36/-**	32 4¾	**1.**	£0	18	10¾
22/-	19 9½	**27/-**	24 3½	**32/-**	28 9½	**37/-**	33 3½	**2.**	1	17	9½
22/6	20 3	**27/6**	24 9	**32/6**	29 3	**37/6**	33 9	**3.**	2	16	8½
23/-	20 8½	**28/-**	25 2½	**33/-**	29 8½	**38/-**	34 2½	**4.**	3	15	7¼
24/-	21 7¼	**29/-**	26 1¼	**34/-**	30 7¼	**39/-**	35 1¼	**5.**	4	14	6
25/-	22s. 6	**30/-**	27s. 0	**35/-**	31s. 6	**40/-**	36s. 0	**6.**	£5	13	4¾

(47$\frac{4}{10}$%* on Gross Returns).

£	£ s. d.	£	£ s. d.	£	£ s. d.	£	£ s. d.
1	£0 18s. 3	51	46 10s. 9	101	£92 3s. 3	151	137 15s. 9
2	1 16 6	52	47 9 0	102	93 1 6	152	138 14 0
3	2 14 9	53	48 7 3	103	93 19 9	153	139 12 3
4	3 13 0	54	49 5 6	104	94 18 0	154	140 10 6
5	4 11 3	55	50 3 9	105	95 16 3	155	141 8 9
6	5 9 6	56	51 2 0	106	96 14 6	156	142 7 0
7	6 7 9	57	52 0 3	107	97 12 9	157	143 5 3
8	7 6 0	58	52 18 6	108	98 11 0	158	144 3 6
9	8 4 3	59	53 16 9	109	99 9 3	159	145 1 9
10	9 2s. 6	60	54 15s. 0	110	100 7s. 6	160	146 0s. 0
11	10 0s. 9	61	55 13s. 3	111	101 5s. 9	161	146 18s. 3
12	10 19 0	62	56 11 6	112	102 4 0	162	147 16 6
13	11 17 3	63	57 9 9	113	103 2 3	163	148 14 9
14	12 15 6	64	58 8 0	114	104 0 6	164	149 13 0
15	13 13 9	65	59 6 3	115	104 18 9	165	150 11 3
16	14 12 0	66	60 4 6	116	105 17 0	166	151 9 6
17	15 10 3	67	61 2 9	117	106 15 3	167	152 7 9
18	16 8 6	68	62 1 0	118	107 13 6	168	153 6 0
19	17 6 9	69	62 19 3	119	108 11 9	169	154 4 3
20	18 5s. 0	70	63 17s. 6	120	109 10s. 0	170	155 2s. 6
21	19 3s. 3	71	64 15s. 9	121	110 8s. 3	171	156 0s. 9
22	20 1 6	72	65 14 0	122	111 6 6	172	156 19 0
23	20 19 9	73	66 12 3	123	112 4 9	173	157 17 3
24	21 18 0	74	67 10 6	124	113 3 0	174	158 15 6
25	22 16 3	75	68 8 9	125	114 1 3	175	159 13 9
26	23 14 6	76	69 7 0	126	114 19 6	176	160 12 0
27	24 12 9	77	70 5 3	127	115 17 9	177	161 10 3
28	25 11 0	78	71 3 6	128	116 16 0	178	162 8 6
29	26 9 3	79	72 1 9	129	117 14 3	179	163 6 9
30	27 7s. 6	80	73 0s. 0	130	118 12s. 6	180	164 5s. 0
31	28 5s. 9	81	73 18s. 3	131	119 10s. 9	181	165 3s. 3
32	29 4 0	82	74 16 6	132	120 9 0	182	166 1 6
33	30 2 3	83	75 14 9	133	121 7 3	183	166 19 9
34	31 0 6	84	76 13 0	134	122 5 6	184	167 18 0
35	31 18 9	85	77 11 3	135	123 3 9	185	168 16 3
36	32 17 0	86	78 9 6	136	124 2 0	186	169 14 6
37	33 15 3	87	79 7 9	137	125 0 3	187	170 12 9
38	34 13 6	88	80 6 0	138	125 18 6	188	171 11 0
39	35 11 9	89	81 4 3	139	126 16 9	189	172 9 3
40	36 10s. 0	90	82 2s. 6	140	127 15s. 0	190	173 7s. 6
41	37 8s. 3	91	83 0s. 9	141	128 13s. 3	191	174 5s 9
42	38 6 6	92	83 19 0	142	129 11 6	192	175 4 0
43	39 4 9	93	84·17 3	143	130 9 9	193	176 2 3
44	40 3 0	94	85 15 6	144	131 8 0	194	177 0 6
45	41 1 3	95	86 13 9	145	132 6 3	195	177 18 9
46	41 19 6	96	87 12 0	146	133 4 6	196	178 17 0
47	42 17 9	97	88 10 3	147	134 2 9	197	179 15 3
48	43 16 0	98	89 8 6	148	135 1 0	198	180 13 6
49	44 14 3	99	90 6 9	149	135 19 3	199	181 11 9
50	45 12s. 6	100	91 5s. 0	150	136 17s. 6	200	182 10s. 0

£	£ s. d.	£	£ s. d.	£	£ s. d.	£	£ s. d.
250	228 2s. 6d	700	638 15s. 0d	1200	1095 0s. 0d	2000	£1825 0s. 0
300	273 15 0	750	684 7 6	1400	1277 10 0	2500	2281 5 0
400	365 0 0	800	730 0 0	1500	1368 15 0	3000	2737 10 0
500	456 5 0	900	821 5 0	1600	1460 0 0	4000	3650 0 0
600	547 10s. 0	1000	912 10s. 0d	1800	1642 10s. 0d	5000	£4562 10s. 0

8¾% off.

1d	0s. 1	4/1	3s. 8¾	8/1	7s. 4½	12/1	11s. 0¼	16/1	14s. 8
2d	0 1¾	2	3 9¾	2	7 5½	2	11 1¼	2	14 9
3d	0 2¾	3	3 10½	3	7 6¼	3	11 2¼	3	14 10
4d	0 3¾	4	3 11½	4	7 7¼	4	11 3	4	14 10¾
5d	0 4½	5	4 0¼	5	7 8¼	5	11 4	5	14 11¾
6d	0 5½	4/6	4 1¼	8/6	7 9	12/6	11 5	16/6	15 0¾
7d	0 6½	7	4 2¼	7	7 10	7	11 5¾	7	15 1½
8d	0 7¼	8	4 3	8	7 11	8	11 6¾	8	15 2½
9d	0 8¼	9	4 4	9	7 11¾	9	11 7½	9	15 3½
10d	0 9¼	10	4 5	10	8 0¾	10	11 8½	10	15 4¼
11d	0 10	11	4 5¾	11	8 1¾	11	11 9½	11	15 5¼
1/-	0s.11	5/-	4s. 6¾	9/-	8s. 2½	13/-	11s.10¼	17/-	15s. 6¼
1/1	0s.11¾	5/1	4s. 7¾	9/1	8s. 3½	13/1	11s.11¼	17/1	15s. 7
2	1 0¾	2	4 8½	2	8 4½	2	12 0¼	2	15 8
3	1 1¾	3	4 9½	3	8 5¼	3	12 1	3	15 9
4	1 2½	4	4 10½	4	8 6¼	4	12 2	4	15 9¾
5	1 3½	5	4 11¼	5	8 7	5	12 3	5	15 10¾
1/6	1 4½	5/6	5 0¼	9/6	8 8	13/6	12 3¾	17/6	15 11¾
7	1 5¼	7	5 1¼	7	8 9	7	12 4¾	7	16 0½
8	1 6¼	8	5 2	8	8 9¾	8	12 5¾	8	16 1½
9	1 7¼	9	5 3	9	8 10¾	9	12 6½	9	16 2¼
10	1 8	10	5 4	10	8 11¾	10	12 7½	10	16 3¼
11	1 9	11	5 4¾	11	9 0½	11	12 8½	11	16 4¼
2/-	1s.10	6/-	5s. 5¾	10/-	9s. 1½	14/-	12s. 9¼	18/-	16s. 5
2/1	1s.10¾	6/1	5s 6½	10/1	9s. 2½	14/1	12s.10¼	18/1	16 6
2	1 11¾	2	5 7½	2	9 3¼	2	12 11¼	2	16 7
3	2 0¾	3	5 8½	3	9 4¼	3	13 0	3	16 7¾
4	2 1½	4	5 9¼	4	9 5¼	4	13 1	4	16 8¾
5	2 2½	5	5 10¼	5	9 6	5	13 1¾	5	16 9¾
2/6	2 3½	6/6	5 11¼	10/6	9 7	14/6	13 2¾	18/6	16 10½
7	2 4¼	7	6 0	7	9 8	7	13 3¾	7	16 11½
8	2 5¼	8	6 1	8	9 8¾	8	13 4½	8	17 0½
9	2 6	9	6 2	9	9 9¾	9	13 5½	9	17 1¼
10	2 7	10	6 2¾	10	9 10¾	10	13 6½	10	17 2¼
11	2 8	11	6 3¾	11	9 11½	11	13 7¼	11	17 3¼
3/-	2s. 8¾	7/-	6s. 4¾	11/-	10s. 0½	15/-	13s 8¼	19/-	17s. 4
3/1	2s. 9¾	7/1	6s. 5½	11/1	10s. 1¼	15/1	13s. 9¼	19/1	17s. 5
2	2 10¾	2	6 6½	2	10 2¼	2	13 10	2	17 6
3	2 11½	3	6 7½	3	10 3¼	3	13 11	3	17 6¾
4	3 0½	4	6 8¼	4	10 4	4	14 0	4	17 7¾
5	3 1½	5	6 9¼	5	10 5	5	14 0¾	5	17 8½
3/6	3 2¼	7/6	6 10¼	11/6	10 6	15/6	14 1¾	19/6	17 9½
7	3 3¼	7	6 11	7	10 6¾	7	14 2¾	7	17 10½
8	3 4¼	8	7 0	8	10 7¾	8	14 3½	8	17 11¼
9	3 5	9	7 0¾	9	10 8¾	9	14 4½	9	18 0¼
10	3 6	10	7 1¾	10	10 9½	10	14 5½	10	18 1¼
11	3 7	11	7 2¾	11	10 10½	11	14 6¼	11	18 2
4/-	3s. 7¾	8/-	7s. 3½	12/-	10s.11½	16/-	14s. 7¼	20/-	18s. 3

20/6	18s. 8½	25/6	23s. 3¼	31/-	28s. 3½	35/6	32s. 4¾	Guineas.	
21/-	19 2	26/-	23 8¾	31/6	28 9	36/-	32 10¼	1.	19s. 2
22/-	20 1	27/-	24 7¾	32/-	29 2½	37/-	33 9¼	2.	38 4
22/6	20 6½	27/6	25 1¼	32/6	29 8	37/6	34 2¾	3.	57 5¾
23/-	20 11¾	28/-	25 6½	33/-	30 1¼	38/-	34 8	4.	76 7¾
24/-	21 10¾	29/-	26 5½	34/-	31 0¼	39/-	35 7	5.	95 9¾
25/-	22s. 9¾	30/-	27s. 4½	35/-	31s.11¼	40/-	36s. 6	6.	114s.11¾

($47\frac{7}{10}$%* on Gross Returns).

£		s.	d.	£		s.	d.	£		s.	d.	£		s.	d.
£1	£0	18s.	6	£51	47	3s.	6	£101	£93	8s.	6	£151	139	13s.	6
2	1	17	0	52	48	2	0	102	94	7	0	152	140	12	0
3	2	15	6	53	49	0	6	103	95	5	6	153	141	10	6
4	3	14	0	54	49	19	0	104	96	4	0	154	142	9	0
5	4	12	6	55	50	17	6	105	97	2	6	155	143	7	6
6	5	11	0	56	51	16	0	106	98	1	0	156	144	6	0
7	6	9	6	57	52	14	6	107	98	19	6	157	145	4	6
8	7	8	0	58	53	13	0	108	99	18	0	158	146	3	0
9	8	6	6	59	54	11	6	109	100	16	6	159	147	1	6
10	9	5s.	0	60	55	10s.	0	110	101	15s.	0	160	148	0s.	0
11	10	3s.	6	61	56	8s.	6	111	102	13s.	6	161	148	18s.	6
12	11	2	0	62	57	7	0	112	103	12	0	162	149	17	0
13	12	0	6	63	58	5	6	113	104	10	6	163	150	15	6
14	12	19	0	64	59	4	0	114	105	9	0	164	151	14	0
15	13	17	6	65	60	2	6	115	106	7	6	165	152	12	6
16	14	16	0	66	61	1	0	116	107	6	0	166	153	11	0
17	15	14	6	67	61	19	6	117	108	4	6	167	154	9	6
18	16	13	0	68	62	18	0	118	109	3	0	168	155	8	0
19	17	11	6	69	63	16	6	119	110	1	6	169	156	6	6
20	18	10s.	0	70	64	15s.	0	120	111	0s.	0	170	157	5s.	0
21	19	8s.	6	71	65	13s.	6	121	111	18s.	6	171	158	3s.	6
22	20	7	0	72	66	12	0	122	112	17	0	172	159	2	0
23	21	5	6	73	67	10	6	123	113	15	6	173	160	0	6
24	22	4	0	74	68	9	0	124	114	14	0	174	160	19	0
25	23	2	6	75	69	7	6	125	115	12	6	175	161	17	6
26	24	1	0	76	70	6	0	126	116	11	0	176	162	16	0
27	24	19	6	77	71	4	6	127	117	9	6	177	163	14	6
28	25	18	0	78	72	3	0	128	118	8	0	178	164	13	0
29	26	16	6	79	73	1	6	129	119	6	6	179	165	11	6
30	27	15s.	0	80	74	0s.	0	130	120	5s.	0	180	166	10s.	0
31	28	13s.	6	81	74	18s.	6	131	121	3s.	6	181	167	8s.	6
32	29	12	0	82	75	17	0	132	122	2	0	182	168	7	0
33	30	10	6	83	76	15	6	133	123	0	6	183	169	5	6
34	31	9	0	84	77	14	0	134	123	19	0	184	170	4	0
35	32	7	6	85	78	12	6	135	124	17	6	185	171	2	6
36	33	6	0	86	79	11	0	136	125	16	0	186	172	1	0
37	34	4	6	87	80	9	6	137	126	14	6	187	172	19	6
38	35	3	0	88	81	8	0	138	127	13	0	188	173	18	0
39	36	1	6	89	82	6	6	139	128	11	6	189	174	16	6
40	37	0s.	0	90	83	5s.	0	140	129	10s.	0	190	175	15s.	0
41	37	18s.	6	91	84	3s.	6	141	130	8s.	6	191	176	13s.	6
42	38	17	0	92	85	2	0	142	131	7	0	192	177	12	0
43	39	15	6	93	86	0	6	143	132	5	6	193	178	10	6
44	40	14	0	94	86	19	0	144	133	4	0	194	179	9	0
45	41	12	6	95	87	17	6	145	134	2	6	195	180	7	6
46	42	11	0	96	88	16	0	146	135	1	0	196	181	6	0
47	43	9	6	97	89	14	6	147	135	19	6	197	182	4	6
48	44	8	0	98	90	13	0	148	136	18	0	198	183	3	0
49	45	6	6	99	91	11	6	149	137	16	6	199	184	1	6
50	46	5s.	0	100	92	10s.	0	150	138	15s.	0	200	185	0s.	0

£		s.	d.	£		s.	d.	£		s.	d.	£		s.	d.
250	231	5s.	0d	700	647	10s.	0d	1200	1110	0s.	0d	2000	£1850	0s.	0
300	277	10	0	750	693	15	0	1400	1295	0	0	2500	2312	10	0
400	370	0	0	800	740	0	0	1500	1387	10	0	3000	2775	0	0
500	462	10	0	900	832	10	0	1600	1480	0	0	4000	3700	0	0
600	555	0s.	0d	1000	925	0s.	0d	1800	1665	0s.	0d	5000	£4625	0s.	0

7½% off.

92½ Per Cent.

1d	0s. 1	4/1	3s. 9¼	8/1	7s. 5¾	12/1	11s. 2¼	16/1	14s.10½
2d	0 1¾	2	3 10¼	2	7 6¾	2	11 3	2	14 11½
3d	0 2¾	3	3 11¼	3	7 7½	3	11 4	3	15 0½
4d	0 3¾	4	4 0	4	7 8½	4	11 5	4	15 1¼
5d	0 4¾	5	4 1	5	7 9½	5	11 5¾	5	15 2¼
6d	0 5½	4/6	4 2	8/6	7 10¼	12/6	11 6¾	16/6	15 3¼
7d	0 6½	7	4 3	7	7 11¼	7	11 7¾	7	15 4
8d	0 7½	8	4 3¾	8	8 0¼	8	11 8½	8	15 5
9d	0 8¼	9	4 4¾	9	8 1¼	9	11 9½	9	15 6
10d	0 9¼	10	4 5¾	10	8 2	10	11 10½	10	15 6¾
11d	0 10¼	11	4 6½	11	8 3	11	11 11½	11	15 7¾
1/-	0s.11	**5/-**	4s. 7½	**9/-**	8s. 4	**13/-**	12s. 0¼	**17/-**	15s. 8¾
1/1	1s. 0	5/1	4s. 8½	9/1	8s. 4¾	13/1	12s. 1¼	17/1	15s. 9¾
2	1 1	2	4 9¼	2	8 5¾	2	12 2¼	2	15 10½
3	1 2	3	4 10¼	3	8 6¾	3	12 3	3	15 11½
4	1 2¾	4	4 11¼	4	8 7½	4	12 4	4	16 0½
5	1 3¾	5	5 0¼	5	8 8½	5	12 5	5	16 1¼
1/6	1 4¾	5/6	5 1	9/6	8 9½	13/6	12 5¾	17/6	16 2¼
7	1 5½	7	5 2	7	8 10½	7	12 6¾	7	16 3¼
8	1 6½	8	5 3	8	8 11¼	8	12 7¾	8	16 4
9	1 7½	9	5 3¾	9	9 0¼	9	12 8¾	9	16 5
10	1 8¼	10	5 4¾	10	9 1¼	10	12 9½	10	16 6
11	1 9¼	11	5 5¾	11	9 2	11	12 10½	11	16 7
2/-	1s.10¼	**6/-**	5s. 6½	**10/-**	9s. 3	**14/-**	12s.11½	**18/-**	16s. 7¾
2/1	1s.11¼	6/1	5s. 7½	10/1	9s. 4	14/1	13s. 0¼	18/1	16s. 8¾
2	2 0	2	5 8½	2	9 4¾	2	13 1¼	2	16 9¾
3	2 1	3	5 9½	3	9 5¾	3	13 2¼	3	16 10½
4	2 2	4	5 10¼	4	9 6¾	4	13 3	4	16 11½
5	2 2¾	5	5 11¼	5	9 7¾	5	13 4	5	17 0½
2/6	2 3¾	6/6	6 0¼	10/6	9 8½	14/6	13 5	18/6	17 1¼
7	2 4¾	7	6 1	7	9 9½	7	13 6	7	17 2¼
8	2 5½	8	6 2	8	9 10½	8	13 6¾	8	17 3¼
9	2 6½	9	6 3	9	9 11¼	9	13 7¾	9	17 4¼
10	2 7½	10	6 3¾	10	10 0¼	10	13 8¾	10	17 5
11	2 8½	11	6 4¾	11	10 1¼	11	13 9½	11	17 6
3/-	2s. 9¼	**7/-**	6s. 5¾	**11/-**	10s. 2	**15/-**	13s.10½	**19/-**	17s. 7
3/1	2s.10¼	7/1	6s. 6¾	11/1	10s. 3	15/1	13s.11½	19/1	17s. 7¾
2	2 11¼	2	6 7½	2	10 4	2	14 0¼	2	17 8¾
3	3 0	3	6 8½	3	10 5	3	14 1¼	3	17 9¾
4	3 1	4	6 9½	4	10 5¾	4	14 2¼	4	17 10½
5	3 2	5	6 10¼	5	10 6¾	5	14 3¼	5	17 11½
3/6	3 2¾	7/6	6 11¼	11/6	10 7¾	15/6	14 4	19/6	18 0½
7	3 3¾	7	7 0¼	7	10 8½	7	14 5	7	18 1½
8	3 4¾	8	7 1	8	10 9½	8	14 6	8	18 2½
9	3 5¾	9	7 2	9	10 10½	9	14 6¾	9	18 3¼
10	3 6½	10	7 3	10	10 11¼	10	14 7¾	10	18 4¼
11	3 7½	11	7 4	11	11 0¼	11	14 8¾	11	18 5
4/-	3s. 8½	**8/-**	7s. 4¾	**12/-**	11s. 1¼	**16/-**	14s. 9½	**20/-**	18s. 6

20/6	18s.11½	25/6	23s. 7d	31/-	28s. 8d	35/6	32s.10d	Guineas.	
21/-	19 5	26/-	24 0½	31/6	29 1¾	36/-	33 3½	1.	19s. 5d
22/-	20 4¼	27/-	24 11¾	32/-	29 7¼	37/-	34 2¾	2.	38 10¼
22/6	20 9¾	27/6	25 5¼	32/6	30 0¾	37/6	34 8¼	3.	58 3¼
23/-	21 3¼	28/-	25 10¾	33/-	30 6¼	38/-	35 1¾	4.	77 8½
24/-	22 2½	29/-	26 10	34/-	31 5½	39/-	36 1	5.	97 1½
25/-	23s. 1½	**30/-**	27s. 9d	**35/-**	32s. 4½	**40/-**	37s. 0d	6.	116s. 6½

(48$\frac{1}{10}$%* on Gross Returns).

£	£ s. d.	£	£ s. d.	£	£ s. d.	£	£ s. d.
£1	£0 18s. 9	£51	47 16s. 3	£101	£94 13s. 9	£151	141 11s. 3
2	1 17 6	52	48 15 0	102	95 12 6	152	142 10 0
3	2 16 3	53	49 13 9	103	96 11 3	153	143 8 9
4	3 15 0	54	50 12 6	104	97 10 0	154	144 7 6
5	4 13 9	55	51 11 3	105	98 8 9	155	145 6 3
6	5 12 6	56	52 10 0	106	99 7 6	156	146 5 0
7	6 11 3	57	53 8 9	107	100 6 3	157	147 3 9
8	7 10 0	58	54 7 6	108	101 5 0	158	148 2 6
9	8 8 9	59	55 6 3	109	102 3 9	159	149 1 3
10	9 7s. 6	60	56 5s. 0	110	103 2s. 6	160	150 0s. 0
11	10 6s. 3	61	57 3s. 9	111	104 1s. 3	161	150 18s. 9
12	11 5 0	62	58 2 6	112	105 0 0	162	151 17 6
13	12 3 9	63	59 1 3	113	105 18 9	163	152 16 3
14	13 2 6	64	60 0 0	114	106 17 6	164	153 15 0
15	14 1 3	65	60 18 9	115	107 16 3	165	154 13 9
16	15 0 0	66	61 17 6	116	108 15 0	166	155 12 6
17	15 18 9	67	62 16 3	117	109 13 9	167	156 11 3
18	16 17 6	68	63 15 0	118	110 12 6	168	157 10 0
19	17 16 3	69	64 13 9	119	111 11 3	169	158 8 9
20	18 15s. 0	70	65 12s. 6	120	112 10s. 0	170	159 7s. 6
21	19 13s. 9	71	66 11s. 3	121	113 8s. 9	171	160 6s 3
22	20 12 6	72	67 10 0	122	114 7 6	172	161 5 0
23	21 11 3	73	68 8 9	123	115 6 3	173	162 3 9
24	22 10 0	74	69 7 6	124	116 5 0	174	163 2 6
25	23 8, 9	75	70 6 3	125	117 3 9	175	164 1 3
26	24 7 6	76	71 5 0	126	118 2 6	176	165 0 0
27	25 6 3	77	72 3 9	127	119 1 3	177	165 18 9
28	26 5 0	78	73 2 6	128	120 0 0	178	166 17 6
29	27 3 9	79	74 1 3	129	120 18 9	179	167 16 3
30	28 2s. 6	80	75 0s. 0	130	121 17s. 6	180	168 15s. 0
31	29 1s. 3	81	75 18s. 9	131	122 16s. 3	181	169 13s 9
32	30 0 0	82	76 17 6	132	123 15 0	182	170 12 6
33	30 18 9	83	77 16 3	133	124 13 9	183	171 11 3
34	31 17 6	84	78 15 0	134	125 12 6	184	172 10 0
35	32 16 3	85	79 13 9	135	126 11 3	185	173 8 9
36	33 15 0	86	80 12 6	136	127 10 0	186	174 7 6
37	34 13 9	87	81 11 3	137	128 8 9	187	175 6 3
38	35 12 6	88	82 10 0	138	129 7 6	188	176 5 0
39	36 11 3	89	83 8 9	139	130 6 3	189	177 3 9
40	37 10s. 0	90	84 7s. 6	140	131 5s. 0	190	178 2s. 6
41	38 8s. 9	91	85 6s. 3	141	132 3s. 9	191	179 1s 3
42	39 7 6	92	86 5 0	142	133 2 6	192	180 0 0
43	40 6 3	93	87 3 9	143	134 1 3	193	180 18 9
44	41 5 0	94	88 2 6	144	135 0 0	194	181 17 6
45	42 3 9	95	89 1 3	145	135 18 9	195	182 16 3
46	43 2 6	96	90 0 0	146	136 17 6	196	183 15 0
47	44 1 3	97	90 18 9	147	137 16 3	197	184 13 9
48	45 0 0	98	91 17 6	148	138 15 0	198	185 12 6
49	45 18 9	99	92 16 3	149	139 13 9	199	186 11 3
50	46 17s. 6	100	93 15s. 0	150	140 12s. 6	200	187 10s. 0

£	£ s. d.	£	£ s. d.	£	£ s. d.	£	£ s. d.
250	234 7s. 6d	700	656 5s. 0d	1200	1125 0s. 0d	2000	£1875 0s. 0
300	281 5 0	750	703 2 6	1400	1312 10 0	2500	2343 15 0
400	375 0 0	800	750 0 0	1500	1406 5 0	3000	2812 10 0
500	468 15 0	900	843 15 0	1600	1500 0 0	4000	3750 0 0
600	562 10s. 0d	1000	937 10s. 0d	1800	1687 10s. 0d	5000	£4687 10s. 0

6¼% off.

1d	0s. 1	4/1	3s.10	8/1	7s. 7	12/1	11s. 4	16/1	15 1
2d	0 2	2	3 11	2	7 8	2	11 5	2	15 2
3d	0 2¾	3	3 11¾	3	7 8¾	3	11 5¾	3	15 2¾
4d	0 3¾	4	4 0¾	4	7 9¾	4	11 6¾	4	15 3¾
5d	0 4¾	5	4 1¾	5	7 10¾	5	11 7¾	5	15 4¾
6d	0 5¾	4/6	4 2¾	8/6	7 11¾	12/6	11 8¾	16/6	15s. 5¾
7d	0 6½	7	4 3½	7	8 0½	7	11 9½	7	15 6½
8d	0 7½	8	4 4½	8	8 1½	8	11 10½	8	15 7½
9d	0 8½	9	4 5½	9	8 2½	9	11 11½	9	15 8½
10d	0 9½	10	4 6½	10	8 3½	10	12 0½	10	15 9½
11d	0 10¼	11	4 7¼	11	8 4¼	11	12 1¼	11	15 10¼
1/-	0s.11¼	**5/-**	4s. 8¼	**9/-**	8s. 5¼	**13/-**	12s. 2¼	**17/-**	15s.11¼
1/1	1s. 0¼	5/1	4s. 9¼	9/1	8s. 6¼	13/1	12s. 3¼	17/1	16 0¼
2	1 1¼	2	4 10¼	2	8 7¼	2	12 4¼	2	16 1¼
3	1 2	3	4 11	3	8 8	3	12 5	3	16 2
4	1 3	4	5 0	4	8 9	4	12 6	4	16 3
5	1 4	5	5 1	5	8 10	5	12 7	5	16 4
1/6	1 5	5/6	5 2	9/6	8 11	13/6	12 8	17/6	16 5
7	1 5¾	7	5 2¾	7	8s.11¾	7	12 8¾	7	16 5¾
8	1 6¾	8	5 3¾	8	9 0¾	8	12 9¾	8	16 6¾
9	1 7¾	9	5 4¾	9	9 1¾	9	12 10¾	9	16 7¾
10	1 8¾	10	5 5¾	10	9 2¾	10	12 11¾	10	16 8¾
11	1 9½	11	5 6½	11	9 3½	11	13 0½	11	16 9½
2/-	1s.10½	**6/-**	5s. 7½	**10/-**	9s. 4½	**14/-**	13s. 1½	**18/-**	16s.10½
2/1	1s.11½	6/1	5s 8½	10/1	9s. 5½	14/1	13 2½	18/1	16s.11½
2	2 0½	2	5 9½	2	9 6½	2	13 3½	2	17 0½
3	2 1¼	3	5 10¼	3	9 7¼	3	13 4¼	3	17 1¼
4	2 2¼	4	5 11¼	4	9 8¼	4	13 5¼	4	17 2¼
5	2 3¼	5	6 0¼	5	9 9¼	5	13s. 6¼	5	17 3¼
2/6	2 4¼	6/6	6 1¼	10/6	9 10¼	14/6	13 7¼	18/6	17 4¼
7	2 5	7	6 2	7	9 11	7	13 8	7	17 5
8	2 6	8	6 3	8	10 0	8	13 9	8	17 6
9	2 7	9	6 4	9	10 1	9	13 10	9	17 7
10	2 8	10	6 5	10	10 2	10	13 11	10	17 8
11	2 8¾	11	6 5¾	11	10 2¾	11	13 11¾	11	17 8¾
3/-	2s. 9¾	**7/-**	6s. 6¾	**11/-**	10s. 3¾	**15/-**	14s 0¾	**19/-**	17s. 9¾
3/1	2s.10¾	7/1	6s. 7¾	11/1	10s. 4¾	15/1	14s. 1¾	19/1	17s.10¾
2	2 11¾	2	6 8¾	2	10 5¾	2	14 2¾	2	17 11¾
3	3 0½	3	6 9½	3	10 6½	3	14 3½	3	18 0½
4	3 1½	4	6 10½	4	10 7½	4	14 4½	4	18 1½
5	3 2½	5	6 11½	5	10 8½	5	14 5½	5	18 2½
3/6	3 3½	7/6	7 0½	11/6	10 9½	15/6	14 6½	19/6	18 3½
7	3 4¼	7	7 1¼	7	10 10¼	7	14 7¼	7	18 4¼
8	3 5¼	8	7 2¼	8	10 11¼	8	14 8¼	8	18 5¼
9	3 6¼	9	7 3¼	9	11 0¼	9	14 9¼	9	18 6¼
10	3 7¼	10	7 4¼	10	11 1¼	10	14 10¼	10	18 7¼
11	3 8	11	7 5	11	11 2	11	14 11	11	18 8
4/-	3s. 9	**8/-**	7s. 6	**12/-**	11s. 3	**16/-**	15s. 0	**20/-**	18 9

								Guineas.	
20/6	19s. 2¾	25/6	23s.11	31/-	29s. 0¾	35/6	33s. 3½		
21/-	19 8¼	26/-	24 4½	31/6	29 6½	36/-	33 9	1.	19s. 8¼
22/-	20 7½	27/-	25 3¾	32/-	30 0	37/-	34 8¼	2.	39 4½
22/6	21 1¼	27/6	25 9½	32/6	30 5¾	37/6	35 2	3.	59 0¾
23/-	21 6¾	28/-	26 3	33/-	30 11¼	38/-	35 7½	4.	78 9
24/-	22 6	29/-	27 2¼	34/-	31 10½	39/-	36 6¾	5.	98 5¼
25/-	23s. 5¼	**30/-**	28s. 1½	**35/-**	32s. 9¾	**40/-**	37s. 6	6.	118s. 1½

($48\frac{4}{10}$%* on Gross Returns).

£1	£0 19s. 0	£51	48 9s. 0	£101	£95 19s. 0	£151	143 9s. 0
2	1 18 0	52	49 8 0	102	96 18 0	152	144 8 0
3	2 17 0	53	50 7 0	103	97 17 0	153	145 7 0
4	3 16 0	54	51 6 0	104	98 16 0	154	146 6 0
5	4 15 0	55	52 5 0	105	99 15 0	155	147 5 0
6	5 14 0	56	53 4 0	106	100 14 0	156	148 4 0
7	6 13 0	57	54 3 0	107	101 13 0	157	149 3 0
8	7 12 0	58	55 2 0	108	102 12 0	158	150 2 0
9	8 11 0	59	56 1 0	109	103 11 0	159	151 1 0
10	£9 10s. 0	60	57 0s. 0	110	104 10s. 0	160	152 0s. 0
11	10 9s. 0	61	57 19s. 0	111	105 9s. 0	161	152 19s. 0
12	11 8 0	62	58 18 0	112	106 8 0	162	153 18 0
13	12 7 0	63	59 17 0	113	107 7 0	163	154 17 0
14	13 6 0	64	60 16 0	114	108 6 0	164	155 16 0
15	14 5 0	65	61 15 0	115	109 5 0	165	156 15 0
16	15 4 0	66	62 14 0	116	110 4 0	166	157 14 0
17	16 3 0	67	63 13 0	117	111 3 0	167	158 13 0
18	17 2 0	68	64 12 0	118	112 2 0	168	159 12 0
19	18 1 0	69	65 11 0	119	113 1 0	169	160 11 0
20	19 0s. 0	70	66 10s. 0	120	114 0s. 0	170	161 10s. 0
21	19 19s. 0	71	67 9s. 0	121	114 19s. 0	171	162 9s. 0
22	20 18 0	72	68 8 0	122	115 18 0	172	163 8 0
23	21 17 0	73	69 7 0	123	116 17 0	173	164 7 0
24	22 16 0	74	70 6 0	124	117 16 0	174	165 6 0
25	23 15 0	75	71 5 0	125	118 15 0	175	166 5 0
26	24 14 0	76	72 4 0	126	119 14 0	176	167 4 0
27	25 13 0	77	73 3 0	127	120 13 0	177	168 3 0
28	26 12 0	78	74 2 0	128	121 12 0	178	169 2 0
29	27 11 0	79	75 1 0	129	122 11 0	179	170 1 0
30	28 10s. 0	80	76 0s. 0	130	123 10s. 0	180	171 0s. 0
31	29 9s. 0	81	76 19s. 0	131	124 9s. 0	181	171 19s. 0
32	30 8 0	82	77 18 0	132	125 8 0	182	172 18 0
33	31 7 0	83	78 17 0	133	126 7 0	183	173 17 0
34	32 6 0	84	79 16 0	134	127 6 0	184	174 16 0
35	33 5 0	85	80 15 0	135	128 5 0	185	175 15 0
36	34 4 0	86	81 14 0	136	129 4 0	186	176 14 0
37	35 3 0	87	82 13 0	137	130 3 0	187	177 13 0
38	36 2 0	88	83 12 0	138	131 2 0	188	178 12 0
39	37 1 0	89	84 11 0	139	132 1 0	189	179 11 0
40	38 0s. 0	90	85 10s. 0	140	133 0s. 0	190	180 10s. 0
41	38 19s. 0	91	86 9s. 0	141	133 19s. 0	191	181 9s. 0
42	39 18 0	92	87 8 0	142	134 18 0	192	182 8 0
43	40 17 0	93	88 7 0	143	135 17 0	193	183 7 0
44	41 16 0	94	89 6 0	144	136 16 0	194	184 6 0
45	42 15 0	95	90 5 0	145	137 15 0	195	185 5 0
46	43 14 0	96	91 4 0	146	138 14 0	196	186 4 0
47	44 13 0	97	92 3 0	147	139 13 0	197	187 3 0
48	45 12 0	98	93 2 0	148	140 12 0	198	188 2 0
49	46 11 0	99	94 1 0	149	141 11 0	199	189 1 0
50	47 10s. 0	100	95 0s. 0	150	142 10s. 0	200	190 0s. 0
250	237 10s. 0d	700	665 0s.0d	1200	1140 0s.0d	2000	£1900 0s. 0
300	285 0 0	750	712 10 0	1400	1330 0 0	2500	2375 0 0
400	380 0 0	800	760 0 0	1500	1425 0 0	3000	2850 0 0
500	475 0 0	900	855 0 0	1600	1520 0 0	4000	3800 0 0
600	570 0s.0d	1000	950 0s.0d	1800	1710 9s.0d	5000	£4750 0s. 0

5% off.

95% NINETY-FIVE PER CENT. 95%

1d	0s. 1	4/1	3s.10½	8/1	7s. 8¼	12/1	11s. 5¾	16/1	15s. 3¼
2d	0 2	2	3 11½	2	7 9	2	11 6¾	2	15 4¼
3d	0 2¾	3	4 0½	3	7 10	3	11 7¾	3	15 5¼
4d	0 3¾	4	4 1½	4	7 11	4	11 8½	4	15 6¼
5d	0 4¾	5	4 2¼	5	8 0	5	11 9½	5	15 7¼
6d	0 5¾	4/6	4 3¼	8/6	8 1	12/6	11 10½	16/6	15 8
7d	0 6¾	7	4 4¼	7	8 1¾	7	11 11½	7	15 9
8d	0 7½	8	4 5¼	8	8 2¾	8	12 0½	8	15 10
9d	0 8½	9	4 6¼	9	8 3¾	9	12 1¼	9	15 11
10d	0 9½	10	4 7	10	8 4¾	10	12 2¼	10	16 0
11d	0 10½	11	4 8	11	8 5¾	11	12 3¼	11	16 0¾
1/-	0s.11½	**5/-**	4s. 9	**9/-**	8s. 6½	**13/-**	12s. 4¼	**17/-**	16s. 1¾
1/1	1s. 0¼	5/1	4s.10	9/1	8s. 7½	13/1	12s. 5¼	17/1	16s. 2¾
2	1 1¼	2	4 11	2	8 8½	2	12 6	2	16 3¾
3	1 2¼	3	4 11¾	3	8 9½	3	12 7	3	16 4¾
4	1 3¼	4	5 0¾	4	8 10½	4	12 8	4	16 5½
5	1 4¼	5	5 1¾	5	8 11¼	5	12 9	5	16 6½
1/6	1 5	5/6	5 2¾	9/6	9 0¼	13/6	12 10	17/6	16 7½
7	1 6	7	5 3¾	7	9 1¼	7	12 10¾	7	16 8½
8	1 7	8	5 4½	8	9 2¼	8	12 11¾	8	16 9½
9	1 8	9	5 5½	9	9 3¼	9	13 0¾	9	16 10¼
10	1 9	10	5 6½	10	9 4	10	13 1¾	10	16 11¼
11	1 9¾	11	5 7½	11	9 5	11	13 2¾	11	17 0¼
2/-	1s.10¾	**6/-**	5s. 8½	**10/-**	9s. 6	**14/-**	13s. 3½	**18/-**	17s. 1¼
2/1	1s.11¾	6/1	5s. 9¼	10/1	9s. 7	14/1	13s. 4½	18/1	17s. 2¼
2	2 0¾	2	5 10¼	2	9 8	2	13 5½	2	17 3
3	2 1¾	3	5 11¼	3	9 8¾	3	13 6½	3	17 4
4	2 2½	4	6 0¼	4	9 9¾	4	13 7½	4	17 5
5	2 3½	5	6 1¼	5	9 10¾	5	13 8¼	5	17 6
2/6	2 4½	6/6	6 2	10/6	9 11¾	14/6	13 9¼	18/6	17 7
7	2 5½	7	6 3	7	10 0¾	7	13 10¼	7	17 7¾
8	2 6½	8	6 4	8	10 1½	8	13 11¼	8	17 8¾
9	2 7¼	9	6 5	9	10 2½	9	14 0¼	9	17 9¾
10	2 8¼	10	6 6	10	10 3½	10	14 1	10	17 10¾
11	2 9¼	11	6 6¾	11	10 4½	11	14 2	11	17 11¾
3/-	2s.10¼	**7/-**	6s. 7¾	**11/-**	10s. 5½	**15/-**	14s. 3	**19/-**	18s. 0½
3/1	2s.11¼	7/1	6s. 8¾	11/1	10s. 6¼	15/1	14s. 4	19/1	18s. 1½
2	3 0	2	6 9¾	2	10 7¼	2	14 5	2	18 2½
3	3 1	3	6 10¾	3	10 8¼	3	14 5¾	3	18 3½
4	3 2	4	6 11½	4	10 9¼	4	14 6¾	4	18 4½
5	3 3	5	7 0½	5	10 10¼	5	14 7¾	5	18 5¼
3/6	3 4	7/6	7 1½	11/6	10 11	15/6	14 8¾	19/6	18 6¼
7	3 4¾	7	7 2½	7	11 0	7	14 9¾	7	18 7¼
8	3 5¾	8	7 3½	8	11 1	8	14 10½	8	18 8¼
9	3 6¾	9	7 4¼	9	11 2	9	14 11½	9	18 9¼
10	3 7¾	10	7 5¼	10	11 3	10	15 0½	10	18 10
11	3 8¾	11	7 6¼	11	11 3¾	11	15 1½	11	18 11
4/-	3s. 9½	**8/-**	7s. 7¼	**12/-**	11s. 4¾	**16/-**	15s. 2½	**20/-**	19s. 0

								Guineas.	
20/6	19s. 5¾	25/6	24s. 2¾	31/-	29s. 5½	35/6	33s. 8¾	1.	£0 19 11½
21/-	19 11½	26/-	24 8½	31/6	29 11	36/-	34 2½	2.	1 19 10¾
22/-	20 10¾	27/-	25 7¾	32/-	30 4¾	37/-	35 1¾	3.	2 19 10¼
22/6	21 4½	27/6	26 1½	32/6	30 10½	37/6	35 7½	4.	3 19 9½
23/-	21 10¼	28/-	26 7¼	33/-	31 4¼	38/-	36 1¼	5.	4 19 9
24/-	22 9½	29/-	27 6½	34/-	32 3½	39/-	37 0½	6.	£5 19 8½
25/-	23s. 9	**30/-**	28s. 6	**35/-**	33s. 3	**40/-**	38s. 0		

(48$\frac{7}{10}$%* on Gross Returns).

£	£ s. d.	£	£ s. d.	£	£ s. d.	£	£ s. d.
£1	£0 19s. 3	£51	49 1s. 9	£101	£97 4s. 3	£151	145 6s. 9
2	1 18 6	52	50 1 0	102	98 3 6	152	146 6 0
3	2 17 9	53	51 0 3	103	99 2 9	153	147 5 3
4	3 17 0	54	51 19 6	104	100 2 0	154	148 4 6
5	4 16 3	55	52 18 9	105	101 1 3	155	149 3 9
6	5 15 6	56	53 18 0	106	102 0 6	156	150 3 0
7	6 14 9	57	54 17 3	107	102 19 9	157	151 2 3
8	7 14 0	58	55 16 6	108	103 19 0	158	152 1 6
9	8 13 3	59	56 15 9	109	104 18 3	159	153 0 9
10	9 12s. 6	60	57 15s. 0	110	105 17s. 6	160	154 0s. 0
11	10 11s. 9	61	58 14s. 3	111	106 16s. 9	161	154 19s. 3
12	11 11 0	62	59 13 6	112	107 16 0	162	155 18 6
13	12 10 3	63	60 12 9	113	108 15 3	163	156 17 9
14	13 9 6	64	61 12 0	114	109 14 6	164	157 17 0
15	14 8 9	65	62 11 3	115	110 13 9	165	158 16 3
16	15 8 0	66	63 10 6	116	111 13 0	166	159 15 6
17	16 7 3	67	64 9 9	117	112 12 3	167	160 14 9
18	17 6 6	68	65 9 0	118	113 11 6	168	161 14 0
19	18 5 9	69	66 8 3	119	114 10 9	169	162 13 3
20	19 5s. 0	70	67 7s. 6	120	115 10s. 0	170	163 12s. 6
21	20 4s. 3	71	68 6s. 9	121	116 9s. 3	171	164 11s. 9
22	21 3 6	72	69 6 0	122	117 8 6	172	165 11 0
23	22 2 9	73	70 5 3	123	118 7 9	173	166 10 3
24	23 2 0	74	71 4 6	124	119 7 0	174	167 9 6
25	24 1 3	75	72 3 9	125	120 6 3	175	168 8 9
26	25 0 6	76	73 3 0	126	121 5 6	176	169 8 0
27	25 19 9	77	74 2 3	127	122 4 9	177	170 7 3
28	26 19 0	78	75 1 6	128	123 4 0	178	171 6 6
29	27 18 3	79	76 0 9	129	124 3 3	179	172 5 9
30	28 17s. 6	80	77 0s. 0	130	125 2s. 6	180	173 5s. 0
31	29 16s. 9	81	77 19s. 3	131	126 1s. 9	181	174 4s. 3
32	30 16 0	82	78 18 6	132	127 1 0	182	175 3 6
33	31 15 3	83	79 17 9	133	128 0 3	183	176 2 9
34	32 14 6	84	80 17 0	134	128 19 6	184	177 2 0
35	33 13 9	85	81 16 3	135	129 18 9	185	178 1 3
36	34 13 0	86	82 15 6	136	130 18 0	186	179 0 6
37	35 12 3	87	83 14 9	137	131 17 3	187	179 19 9
38	36 11 6	88	84 14 0	138	132 16 6	188	180 19 0
39	37 10 9	89	85 13 3	139	133 15 9	189	181 18 3
40	38 10s. 0	90	86 12s. 6	140	134 15s. 0	190	182 17s. 6
41	39 9s. 3	91	87 11s. 9	141	135 14s. 3	191	183 16s. 9
42	40 8 6	92	88 11 0	142	136 13 6	192	184 16 0
43	41 7 9	93	89 10 3	143	137 12 9	193	185 15 3
44	42 7 0	94	90 9 6	144	138 12 0	194	186 14 6
45	43 6 3	95	91 8 9	145	139 11 3	195	187 13 9
46	44 5 6	96	92 8 0	146	140 10 6	196	188 13 0
47	45 4 9	97	93 7 3	147	141 9 9	197	189 12 3
48	46 4 0	98	94 6 6	148	142 9 0	198	190 11 6
49	47 3 3	99	95 5 9	149	143 8 3	199	191 10 9
50	48 2s. 6	100	96 5s. 0	150	144 7s. 6	200	192 10s. 0
250	240 12s. 6d	700	673 15s. 0d	1200	1155 0s. 0d	2000	£1925 0s. 0
300	288 15 0	750	721 17 6	1300	1251 5 0	2500	2406 5 0
400	385 0 0	800	770 0 0	1400	1347 10 0	3000	2887 10 0
500	481 5 0	900	866 5 0	1500	1443 15 0	4000	3850 0 0
600	577 10s. 0d	1000	962 10s. 0d	1800	1732 10s. 0d	5000	£4812 10s. 0

¼% off

1d	0s. 1	4/1	3s.11¼	8/1	7s. 9¼	12/1	11s. 7½	16/1	15s. 5¾
2d	0 2	2	4 0¼	2	7 10¼	2	11 8½	2	15 6¾
3d	0 3	3	4 1	3	7 11¼	3	11 9½	3	15 7¾
4d	0 3¾	4	4 2	4	8 0¼	4	11 10½	4	15 8¾
5d	0 4¾	5	4 3	5	8 1¼	5	11 11½	5	15 9½
6d	0 5¾	4/6	4 4	8/6	8 2¼	12/6	12 0½	16/6	15 10½
7d	0 6¾	7	4 5	7	8 3¼	7	12 1¼	7	15 11½
8d	0 7¾	8	4 6	8	8 4	8	12 2¼	8	16 0½
9d	0 8¾	9	4 6¾	9	8 5	9	12 3¼	9	16 1½
10d	0 9¾	10	4 7¾	10	8 6	10	12 4¼	10	16 2½
11d	0 10½	11	4 8¾	11	8 7	11	12 5¼	11	16 3½
1/-	0s.11½	**5/-**	4s. 9¾	**9/-**	8s. 8	**13/-**	12s. 6¼	**17/-**	16s. 4¼
1/1	1s. 0½	5/1	4s.10¾	9/1	8s. 9	13/1	12s. 7	17/1	16 5¼
2	1 1½	2	4 11¾	2	8 10	2	12 8	2	16 6¼
3	1 2½	3	5 0¾	3	8 10¾	3	12 9	3	16 7¼
4	1 3½	4	5 1½	4	8s.11¾	4	12 10	4	16 8¼
5	1 4¼	5	5 2½	5	9 0¾	5	12 11	5	16 9¼
1/6	1 5¼	5/6	5 3½	9/6	9 1¾	13/6	13 0	17/6	16 10¼
7	1 6¼	7	5 4½	7	9 2¾	7	13 1	7	16 11
8	1 7¼	8	5 5½	8	9 3¾	8	13 1¾	8	17 0
9	1 8¼	9	5 6½	9	9 4½	9	13 2¾	9	17 1
10	1 9¼	10	5 7½	10	9 5½	10	13 3¾	10	17 2
11	1 10¼	11	5 8¼	11	9 6½	11	13 4¾	11	17 3
2/-	1s.11	**6/-**	5s. 9¼	**10/-**	9s. 7½	**14/-**	13s. 5¾	**18/-**	17s. 4
2/1	2s. 0	6/1	5s 10¼	10/1	9s. 8½	14/1	13s. 6¾	18/1	17s. 4¾
2	2 1	2	5 11¼	2	9 9½	2	13 7¾	2	17 5¾
3	2 2	3	6 0¼	3	9 10½	3	13 8½	3	17 6¾
4	2 3	4	6 1¼	4	9 11¼	4	13 9½	4	17 7¾
5	2 4	5	6 2	5	10 0¼	5	13 10½	5	17 8¾
2/6	2 5	6/6	6 3	10/6	10 1¼	14/6	13 11½	18/6	17 9¾
7	2 5¾	7	6 4	7	10 2¼	7	14 0½	7	17 10¾
8	2 6¾	8	6 5	8	10 3¼	8	14 1½	8	17 11½
9	2 7¾	9	6 6	9	10 4¼	9	14 2¼	9	18 0½
10	2 8¾	10	6 7	10	10 5¼	10	14 3¼	10	18 1½
11	2 9¾	11	6 8	11	10 6	11	14 4¼	11	18 2½
3/-	2s.10¾	**7/-**	6s. 8¾	**11/-**	10s. 7	**15/-**	14s 5¼	**19/-**	18s. 3½
3/1	2s.11½	7/1	6s. 9¾	11/1	10s. 8	15/1	14s. 6¼	19/1	18s. 4½
2	3 0½	2	6 10¾	2	10 9	2	14 7¼	2	18 5½
3	3 1½	3	6 11¾	3	10 10	3	14 8¼	3	18 6¼
4	3 2½	4	7 0¾	4	10 11	4	14 9	4	18 7¼
5	3 3½	5	7 1¾	5	10 11¾	5	14 10	5	18 8¼
3/6	3 4½	7/6	7 2¾	11/6	11 0¾	15/6	14 11	19/6	18 9¼
7	3 5½	7	7 3½	7	11 1¾	7	15 0	7	18 10¼
8	3 6¼	8	7 4½	8	11 2¾	8	15 1	8	18 11¼
9	3 7¼	9	7 5½	9	11 3¾	9	15 2	9	19 0
10	3 8¼	10	7 6½	10	11 4¾	10	15 3	10	19 1
11	3 9¼	11	7 7½	11	11 5¾	11	15 3¾	11	19 2
4/-	3s.10¼	**8/-**	7s. 8½	**12/-**	11s. 6½	**16/-**	15s. 4¾	**20/-**	19 3

20/6	19s. 8¾	25/6	24s. 6½	31/-	29s.10	35/6	34s. 2	Guineas.	
21/-	20 2½	26/-	25 0¼	31/6	30 3¾	36/-	34 7¾	1.	20s. 2½
22/-	21 2	27/-	25 11¾	32/-	30 9½	37/-	35 7¼	2.	40 5
22/6	21 8	27/6	26 5¾	32/6	31 3½	37/6	36 1¼	3.	60 7¾
23/-	22 1¾	28/-	26 11½	33/-	31 9¼	38/-	36 7	4.	80 10¼
24/-	23 1¼	29/-	27 11	34/-	32 8¾	39/-	37 6½	5.	101 0¾
25/-	24s. 0¾	**30/-**	28s.10½	**35/-**	33s. 8¼	**40/-**	38s. 6	6.	121s. 3¼

(4[illegible]%* on Gross Returns).

£		£		£		£	
£1	£0 19s. 6	£51	49 14s. 6	£101	£98 9s. 6	£151	£147 4s. 6
2	1 19 0	52	50 14 0	102	99 9 0	152	148 4 0
3	2 18 6	53	51 13 6	103	100 8 6	153	149 3 6
4	3 18 0	54	52 13 0	104	101 8 0	154	150 3 0
5	4 17 6	55	53 12 6	105	102 7 6	155	151 2 6
6	5 17 0	56	54 12 0	106	103 7 0	156	152 2 0
7	6 16 6	57	55 11 6	107	104 6 6	157	153 1 6
8	7 16 0	58	56 11 0	108	105 6 0	158	154 1 0
9	8 15 6	59	57 10 6	109	106 5 6	159	155 0 6
10	9 15s. 0	60	58 10s. 0	110	107 5s. 0	160	156 0s. 0
11	10 14s. 6	61	59 9s. 6	111	108 4s. 6	161	156 19s. 6
12	11 14 0	62	60 9 0	112	109 4 0	162	157 19 0
13	12 13 6	63	61 8 6	113	110 3 6	163	158 18 6
14	13 13 0	64	62 8 0	114	111 3 0	164	159 18 0
15	14 12 6	65	63 7 6	115	112 2 6	165	160 17 6
16	15 12 0	66	64 7 0	116	113 2 0	166	161 17 0
17	16 11 6	67	65 6 6	117	114 1 6	167	162 16 6
18	17 11 0	68	66 6 0	118	115 1 0	168	163 16 0
19	18 10 6	69	67 5 6	119	116 0 6	169	164 15 6
20	19 10s. 0	70	68 5s. 0	120	117 0s. 0	170	165 15s. 0
21	20 9s. 6	71	69 4s. 6	121	117 19s. 6	171	166 14s. 6
22	21 9 0	72	70 4 0	122	118 19 0	172	167 14 0
23	22 8 6	73	71 3 6	123	119 18 6	173	168 13 6
24	23 8 0	74	72 3 0	124	120 18 0	174	169 13 0
25	24 7 6	75	73 2 6	125	121 17 6	175	170 12 6
26	25 7 0	76	74 2 0	126	122 17 0	176	171 12 0
27	26 6 6	77	75 1 6	127	123 16 6	177	172 11 6
28	27 6 0	78	76 1 0	128	124 16 0	178	173 11 0
29	28 5 6	79	77 0 6	129	125 15 6	179	174 10 6
30	29 5s. 0	80	78 0s. 0	130	126 15s. 0	180	175 10s. 0
31	30 4s. 6	81	78 19s. 6	131	127 14s. 6	181	176 9s. 6
32	31 4 0	82	79 19 0	132	128 14 0	182	177 9 0
33	32 3 6	83	80 18 6	133	129 13 6	183	178 8 6
34	33 3 0	84	81 18 0	134	130 13 0	184	179 8 0
35	34 2 6	85	82 17 6	135	131 12 6	185	180 7 6
36	35 2 0	86	83 17 0	136	132 12 0	186	181 7 0
37	36 1 6	87	84 16 6	137	133 11 6	187	182 6 6
38	37 1 0	88	85 16 0	138	134 11 0	188	183 6 0
39	38 0 6	89	86 15 6	139	135 10 6	189	184 5 6
40	39 0s. 0	90	87 15s. 0	140	136 10s. 0	190	185 5s. 0
41	39 19s. 6	91	88 14s. 6	141	137 9s. 6	191	186 4s. 6
42	40 19 0	92	89 14 0	142	138 9 0	192	187 4 0
43	41 18 6	93	90 13 6	143	139 8 6	193	188 3 6
44	42 18 0	94	91 13 0	144	140 8 0	194	189 3 0
45	43 17 6	95	92 12 6	145	141 7 6	195	190 2 6
46	44 17 0	96	93 12 0	146	142 7 0	196	191 2 0
47	45 16 6	97	94 11 6	147	143 6 6	197	192 1 6
48	46 16 0	98	95 11 0	148	144 6 0	198	193 1 0
49	47 15 6	99	96 10 6	149	145 5 6	199	194 0 6
50	48 15s. 0	100	97 10s. 0	150	146 5s. 0	200	195 0s. 0
250	243 15s. 0d	700	682 10s. 0d	1200	1170 0s. 0d	2000	£1950 0s. 0
300	292 10 0	750	731 5 0	1400	1365 0 0	2500	2437 10 0
400	390 0 0	800	780 0 0	1500	1462 10 0	3000	2925 0 0
500	487 10 0	900	877 10 0	1600	1560 0 0	4000	3900 0 0
600	585 0s. 0d	1000	975 0s. 0d	1800	1755 0s. 0d	5000	£4875 0s. 0

2½% off.

97½ Per Cent.

97½%

1d	0s. 1	4/1	3s.11¾	8/1	7s.10½	12/1	11s. 9½	16/1	15s. 8¼
2d	0 2	2	4 0¾	2	7 11½	2	11 10¼	2	15 9¼
3d	0 3	3	4 1¾	3	8 0½	3	11 11¼	3	15 10¼
4d	0 4	4	4 2¾	4	8 1½	4	12 0¼	4	15 11
5d	0 5	5	4 3¾	5	8 2½	5	12 1¼	5	16 0
6d	0 5¾	4/6	4 4¾	8/6	8 3½	12/6	12 2¼	16/6	16 1
7d	0 6¾	7	4 5¾	7	8 4½	7	12 3¼	7	16 2
8d	0 7¾	8	4 6½	8	8 5½	8	12 4¼	8	16 3
9d	0 8¾	9	4 7½	9	8 6½	9	12 5¼	9	16 4
10d	0 9¾	10	4 8½	10	8 7¼	10	12 6¼	10	16 5
11d	0 10¾	11	4 9½	11	8 8¼	11	12 7¼	11	16 6
1/-	0s.11¾	5/-	4s.10½	9/-	8s. 9¼	13/-	12s. 8	17/-	16s. 7
1/1	1s. 0¾	5/1	4s.11½	9/1	8s.10¼	13/1	12s. 9	17/1	16s. 8
2	1 1¾	2	5 0½	2	8 11¼	2	12 10	2	16 8¾
3	1 2¾	3	5 1½	3	9 0¼	3	12 11	3	16 9¾
4	1 3½	4	5 2½	4	9 1¼	4	13 0	4	16 10¾
5	1 4½	5	5 3½	5	9 2¼	5	13 1	5	16 11¾
1/6	1 5½	5/6	5 4¼	9/6	9 3¼	13/6	13 2	17/6	17 0¾
7	1 6½	7	5 5¼	7	9 4¼	7	13 3	7	17 1¾
8	1 7½	8	5 6¼	8	9 5	8	13 4	8	17 2¾
9	1 8½	9	5 7¼	9	9 6	9	13 5	9	17 3¾
10	1 9½	10	5 8¼	10	9 7	10	13 5¾	10	17 4¾
11	1 10½	11	5 9¼	11	9 8	11	13 6¾	11	17 5¾
2/-	1s.11½	6/-	5s.10¼	10/-	9s. 9	14/-	13s. 7¾	18/-	17s. 6½
2/1	2s. 0½	6/1	5s.11¼	10/1	9s.10	14/1	13s. 8¾	18/1	17s. 7½
2	2 1¼	2	6 0¼	2	9 11	2	13 9¾	2	17 8½
3	2 2¼	3	6 1¼	3	10 0	3	13 10¾	3	17 9½
4	2 3¼	4	6 2	4	10 1	4	13 11¾	4	17 10½
5	2 4¼	5	6 3	5	10 2	5	14 0¾	5	17 11½
2/6	2 5¼	6/6	6 4	10/6	10 2¾	14/6	14 1¾	18/6	18 0½
7	2 6¼	7	6 5	7	10 3¾	7	14 2¾	7	18 1½
8	2 7¼	8	6 6	8	10 4¾	8	14 3½	8	18 2½
9	2 8¼	9	6 7	9	10 5¾	9	14 4½	9	18 3½
10	2 9¼	10	6 8	10	10 6¾	10	14 5½	10	18 4¼
11	2 10¼	11	6 9	11	10 7¾	11	14 6½	11	18 5¼
3/-	2s.11	7/-	6s.10	11/-	10s. 8¾	15/-	14s. 7½	19/-	18s. 6¼
3/1	3s. 0	7/1	6s.11	11/1	10s. 9¾	15/1	14s. 8½	19/1	18s. 7¼
2	3 1	2	6 11¾	2	10 10¾	2	14 9½	2	18 8¼
3	3 2	3	7 0¾	3	10 11¾	3	14 10½	3	18 9¼
4	3 3	4	7 1¾	4	11 0½	4	14 11½	4	18 10¼
5	3 4	5	7 2¾	5	11 1½	5	15 0½	5	18 11¼
3/6	3 5	7/6	7 3¾	11/6	11 2½	15/6	15 1¼	19/6	19 0¼
7	3 6	7	7 4¾	7	11 3½	7	15 2¼	7	19 1¼
8	3 7	8	7 5¾	8	11 4½	8	15 3¼	8	19 2
9	3 8	9	7 6¾	9	11 5½	9	15 4¼	9	19 3
10	3 8¾	10	7 7¾	10	11 6½	10	15 5¼	10	19 4
11	3 9¾	11	7 8¾	11	11 7½	11	15 6¼	11	19 5
4/-	3s.10¾	8/-	7s. 9½	12/-	11s. 8½	16/-	15s. 7¼	20/-	19s. 6

20/6	19s.11¾	25/6	24s.10¼	31/-	30s. 2¾	35/6	34s. 7¼	Guineas.	
21/-	20 5¾	26/-	25 4¼	31/6	30 8½	36/-	35 1¼	1.	20s. 5¾
22/-	21 5½	27/-	26 4	32/-	31 2½	37/-	36 1	2.	40 11½
22/6	21 11¼	27/6	26 9¾	32/6	31 8¼	37/6	36 6¾	3.	61 5
23/-	22 5	28/-	27 3½	33/-	32 2	38/-	37 0½	4.	81 10¾
24/-	23 4¾	29/-	28 3¼	34/-	33 1¾	39/-	38 0¼	5.	102 4½
25/-	24s. 4½	30/-	29s. 3d	35/-	34s. 1½	40/-	39s. 0	6.	122s.10¼

($49\frac{1}{16}$%* on Gross Returns).

£	£ s. d.	£	£ s. d.	£	£ s. d.	£	£ s. d.
£1	£0 19s. 9	£51	50 7s. 3	£101	£99 14s. 9	£151	149 2s. 3
2	1 19 6	52	51 7 0	102	100 14 6	152	150 2 0
3	2 19 3	53	52 6 9	103	101 14 3	153	151 1 9
4	3 19 0	54	53 6 6	104	102 14 0	154	152 1 6
5	4 18 9	55	54 6 3	105	103 13 9	155	153 1 3
6	5 18 6	56	55 6 0	106	104 13 6	156	154 1 0
7	6 18 3	57	56 5 9	107	105 13 3	157	155 0 9
8	7 18 0	58	57 5 6	108	106 13 0	158	156 0 6
9	8 17 9	59	58 5 3	109	107 12 9	159	157 0 3
10	9 17s. 6	60	59 5s. 0	110	108 12s. 6	160	158 0s. 0
11	10 17s. 3	61	60 4s. 9	111	109 12s. 3	161	158 19s. 9
12	11 17 0	62	61 4 6	112	110 12 0	162	159 19 6
13	12 16 9	63	62 4 3	113	111 11 9	163	160 19 3
14	13 16 6	64	63 4 0	114	112 11 6	164	161 19 0
15	14 16 3	65	64 3 9	115	113 11 3	165	162 18 9
16	15 16 0	66	65 3 6	116	114 11 0	166	163 18 6
17	16 15 9	67	66 3 3	117	115 10 9	167	164 18 3
18	17 15 6	68	67 3 0	118	116 10 6	168	165 18 0
19	18 15 3	69	68 2 9	119	117 10 3	169	166 17 9
20	19 15s. 0	70	69 2s. 6	120	118 10s. 0	170	167 17s. 6
21	20 14s. 9	71	70 2s. 3	121	119 9s. 9	171	168 17s. 3
22	21 14 6	72	71 2 0	122	120 9 6	172	169 17 0
23	22 14 3	73	72 1 9	123	121 9 3	173	170 16 9
24	23 14 0	74	73 1 6	124	122 9 0	174	171 16 6
25	24 13 9	75	74 1 3	125	123 8 9	175	172 16 3
26	25 13 6	76	75 1 0	126	124 8 6	176	173 16 0
27	26 13 3	77	76 0 9	127	125 8 3	177	174 15 9
28	27 13 0	78	77 0 6	128	126 8 0	178	175 15 6
29	28 12 9	79	78 0 3	129	127 7 9	179	176 15 3
30	29 12s. 6	80	79 0s. 0	130	128 7s. 6	180	177 15s. 0
31	30 12s. 3	81	79 19s. 9	131	129 7s. 3	181	178 14s. 9
32	31 12 0	82	80 19 6	132	130 7 0	182	179 14 6
33	32 11 9	83	81 19 3	133	131 6 9	183	180 14 3
34	33 11 6	84	82 19 0	134	132 6 6	184	181 14 0
35	34 11 3	85	83 18 9	135	133 6 3	185	182 13 9
36	35 11 0	86	84 18 6	136	134 6 0	186	183 13 6
37	36 10 9	87	85 18 3	137	135 5 9	187	184 13 3
38	37 10 6	88	86 18 0	138	136 5 6	188	185 13 0
39	38 10 3	89	87 17 9	139	137 5 3	189	186 12 9
40	39 10s. 0	90	88 17s. 6	140	138 5s. 0	190	187 12s. 6
41	40 9s. 9	91	89 17s. 3	141	139 4s. 9	191	188 12s. 3
42	41 9 6	92	90 17 0	142	140 4 6	192	189 12 0
43	42 9 3	93	91 16 9	143	141 4 3	193	190 11 9
44	43 9 0	94	92 16 6	144	142 4 0	194	191 11 6
45	44 8 9	95	93 16 3	145	143 3 9	195	192 11 3
46	45 8 6	96	94 16 0	146	144 3 6	196	193 11 0
47	46 8 3	97	95 15 9	147	145 3 3	197	194 10 9
48	47 8 0	98	96 15 6	148	146 3 0	198	195 10 6
49	48 7 9	99	97 15 3	149	147 2 9	199	196 10 3
50	49 7s. 6	100	98 15s. 0	150	148 2s. 6	200	197 10s. 0

£	£ s. d.	£	£ s. d.	£	£ s. d.	£	£ s. d.
250	246 17s. 6d	700	691 5s. 0d	1200	1185 0s. 0d	2000	£1975 0s. 0
300	296 5 0	750	740 12 6	1400	1382 10 0	2500	2468 15 0
400	395 0 0	800	790 0 0	1500	1481 5 0	3000	2962 10 0
500	493 15 0	900	888 15 0	1600	1580 0 0	4000	3950 0 0
600	592 10s. 0d	1000	987 10s. 0d	1800	1777 10s. 0d	5000	£4937 10s. 0

1¼% off.

1d	0s.	1	4/1	4s.	0½	8/1	7s.	11¾	12/1	11s.	11¼	16/1	15s.	10½
2d	0	2	2	4	1½	2	8	0¾	2	12	0¼	2	15	11½
3d	0	3	3	4	2¼	3	8	1¾	3	12	1¼	3	16	0½
4d	0	4	4	4	3¼	4	8	2¾	4	12	2¼	4	16	1½
5d	0	5	5	4	4¼	5	8	3¾	5	12	3¼	5	16	2½
6d	0	6	4/6	4	5¼	8/6	8	4¾	12/6	12	4¼	16/6	16	3½
7d	0	7	7	4	6¼	7	8	5¾	7	12	5	7	16	4½
8d	0	8	8	4	7¼	8	8	6¾	8	12	6	8	16	5½
9d	0	9	9	4	8¼	9	8	7¾	9	12	7	9	16	6½
10d	0	10	10	4	9¼	10	8	8¾	10	12	8	10	16	7½
11d	0	10¾	11	4	10¼	11	8	9¾	11	12	9	11	16	8½
1/-	0s.	11¾	**5/-**	4s.	11¼	**9/-**	8s.	10¾	**13/-**	12s.	10	**17/-**	16s.	9½
1/1	1s.	0¾	5/1	5s.	0¼	9/1	8s.	11¾	13/1	12s.	11	17/1	16	10½
2	1	1¾	2	5	1¼	2	9	0¾	2	13	0	2	16	11½
3	1	2¾	3	5	2¼	3	9	1½	3	13	1	3	17	0½
4	1	3¾	4	5	3¼	4	9	2½	4	13	2	4	17	1½
5	1	4¾	5	5	4¼	5	9	3½	5	13	3	5	17	2½
1/6	1	5¾	5/6	5	5¼	9/6	9	4½	13/6	13	4	17/6	17	3½
7	1	6¾	7	5	6¼	7	9	5½	7	13	5	7	17	4¼
8	1	7¾	8	5	7¼	8	9	6½	8	13	6	8	17	5¼
9	1	8¾	9	5	8¼	9	9	7½	9	13	7	9	17	6¼
10	1	9¾	10	5	9¼	10	9	8½	10	13	8	10	17	7¼
11	1	10¾	11	5	10	11	9	9½	11	13	9	11	17	8¼
2/-	1s.	11¾	**6/-**	5s.	11	**10/-**	9s.	10½	**14/-**	13s.	10	**18/-**	17s.	9¼
2/1	2s.	0¾	6/1	6s.	0	10/1	9s.	11½	14/1	13s.	11	18/1	17s.	10¼
2	2	1¾	2	6	1	2	10	0½	2	14	0	2	17	11¼
3	2	2¾	3	6	2	3	10	1½	3	14	0¾	3	18	0¼
4	2	3¾	4	6	3	4	10	2½	4	14	1¾	4	18	1¼
5	2	4¾	5	6	4	5	10	3½	5	14	2¾	5	18	2¼
2/6	2	5¾	6/6	6	5	10/6	10	4½	14/6	14	3¾	18/6	18	3¼
7	2	6½	7	6	6	7	10	5½	7	14	4¾	7	18	4¼
8	2	7½	8	6	7	8	10	6½	8	14	5¾	8	18	5¼
9	2	8½	9	6	8	9	10	7½	9	14	6¾	9	18	6¼
10	2	9½	10	6	9	10	10	8½	10	14	7¾	10	18	7¼
11	2	10½	11	6	10	11	10	9¼	11	14	8¾	11	18	8¼
3/-	2s.	11½	**7/-**	6s.	11	**11/-**	10s.	10¼	**15/-**	14s.	9¾	**19/-**	18s.	9¼
3/1	3s.	0½	7/1	7s.	0	11/1	10s.	11¼	15/1	14s.	10¾	19/1	18s.	10¼
2	3	1½	2	7	1	2	11	0¼	2	14	11¾	2	18	11¼
3	3	2½	3	7	2	3	11	1¼	3	15	0¾	3	19	0
4	3	3½	4	7	3	4	11	2¼	4	15	1¾	4	19	1
5	3	4½	5	7	4	5	11	3¼	5	15	2¾	5	19	2
3/6	3	5½	7/6	7	5	11/6	11	4¼	15/6	15	3¾	19/6	19	3
7	3	6½	7	7	5¾	7	11	5¼	7	15	4¾	7	19	4
8	3	7½	8	7	6¾	8	11	6¼	8	15	5¾	8	19	5
9	3	8½	9	7	7¾	9	11	7¼	9	15	6¾	9	19	6
10	3	9½	10	7	8¾	10	11	8¼	10	15	7¾	10	19	7
11	3	10½	11	7	9¾	11	11	9¼	11	15	8½	11	19	8
4/-	3s.	11½	**8/-**	7s.	10¾	**12/-**	11s.	10¼	**16/-**	15s.	9½	**20/-**	19s.	9

20/6	20s.	3	25/6	25s.	2¼	31/-	30s.	7¼	35/6	35s.	0¾	Guineas.		
21/-	20	8¾	26/-	25	8	31/6	31	1¼	36/-	35	6½	1.	20s.	8¾
22/-	21	8¾	27/-	26	8	32/-	31	7¼	37/-	36	6½	2.	41	5¾
22/6	22	2¾	27/6	27	2	32/6	32	1¼	37/6	37	0½	3.	62	2½
23/-	22	8½	28/-	27	7¾	33/-	32	7	38/-	37	6¼	4.	82	11½
24/-	23	8½	29/-	28	7¾	34/-	33	7	39/-	38	6¼	5.	103	8¼
25/-	24s.	8¼	**30/-**	29s.	7½	**35/-**	34s.	6¾	**40/-**	39s.	6	6.	124s.	5

($49\frac{7}{10}$%* on Gross Returns).

PROFIT AND DISCOUNT

At various Rates per cent.

(For multiples of £1, see page 301.)

THE first of the three columns for each rate °/. gives the amount of discount on the sum; the second the amount *plus* the discount; and the third the nett amount after deducting the discount. A half-farthing has been reckoned as a farthing (after ¼d.).

The exact discount at any rate per cent., on any amount, may be found from the column headed 1 °/., which gives the discount in pence and decimal parts of 1d. Find from the table the discount on the amount at 1 °/.; then multiply by the given rate per cent. The answer gives the exact discount.

Example.—Find discount on £180·1·5½ at 3½ °/.. From the tables the discount at 1 °/. on the sum is found to be £1, 16s. 0·175d. Multiplying by 3½ gives the answer £6, 6s. 0·6125d.

⅛ = ·125; ¼ = ·25; ⅜ = ·375; ½ = ·5; ⅝ = ·625; ¾ = ·75; ⅞ = ·875.

In-voice.	1% Disct.	2½%			3%			4%		
		Disct.	ON	OFF	Disct.	ON	OFF	Disct.	ON	OFF
1d.	·01d.									
1¼d.	·0125									
1½d.	·015									
1¾d.	·0175									
2d.	·02d.									
2¼d.	·0225									
2½d.	·025									
2¾d.	·0275									
3D.	·03d.									
3¼d.	·0325									
3½d.	·035									
3¾d.	·0375									
4d.	·04d.									
4¼d.	·0425									
4½d.	·045									
4¾d.	·0475									
5d.	·05d.	⅛d.	...	...	⅛d.	...	...	⅛d.	...	...
5¼d.	·0525	,,	...	...	,,	...	...	,,	...	...
5½d.	·055	,,	...	...	,,	...	...	,,	...	...
5¾d.	·0575	,,	...	...	,,	...	...	,,	...	...
6D.	·06d.	,,	...	...	,,	...	...	,,	...	...
6¼d.	·0625	,,	...	...	,,	...	...	¼d.	6½d.	6d.
6½d.	·065	,,	...	...	,,	...	...	,,	6¾d.	6¼d.
6¾d.	·0675	,,	...	...	,,	...	...	,,	7d.	6½d.
7d.	·07d.	,,	...	...	,,	...	...	,,	7¼d.	6¾d.
7¼d.	·0725	,,	...	...	,,	...	...	,,	7½d.	7d.
7½d.	·075	,,	...	...	,,	...	...	,,	7¾d.	7¼d.
7¾d.	·0775	,,	...	...	,,	...	...	,,	8d.	7½d.
8d.	·08d.	,,	...	...	,,	...	...	,,	8¼d.	7¾d.
8¼d.	·0825	,,	...	...	,,	...	...	,,	8½d.	8d.
8½d.	·085	,,	...	...	¼d.	8¾d.	8¼d.	,,	8¾d.	8¼d.
8¾d.	·0875	,,	...	...	,,	9d.	8½d.	,,	9d.	8½d.
9D.	·09d.	,,	...	...	,,	9¼d.	8¾d.	,,	9¼d.	8¾d.
9¼d.	·0925	,,	...	...	,,	9½d.	9d.	,,	9½d.	9d.
9½d.	·095	,,	...	...	,,	9¾d.	9¼d.	½d.	10d.	9d.
9¾d.	·0975	,,	...	...	,,	10d.	9½d.	,,	10¼d.	9¼d.
10d.	·1d.	¼d.	10¼d.	9¾d.	,,	10¼d.	9¾d.	,,	10½d.	9½d.
10¼d.	·1025	,,	10½d.	10d.	,,	10½d.	10d.	,,	10¾d.	9¾d.
10½d.	·105	,,	10¾d.	10¼d.	,,	10¾d.	10¼d.	,,	11d.	10d.
10¾d.	·1075	,,	11d.	10½d.	,,	11d.	10½d.	,,	11¼d.	10¼d.
11d.	·11d.	,,	11¼d.	10¾d.	,,	11¼d.	10¾d.	,,	11½d.	10½d.
11¼d.	·1125	,,	11½d.	11d.	,,	11½d.	11d.	,,	11¾d.	10¾d.
11½d.	·115	,,	11¾d.	11¼d.	,,	11¾d.	11¼d.	,,	1/-	11d.
11¾d.	·1175	,,	1/-	11½d.	,,	1/-	11½d.	,,	1/0¼	11¼d.
1/-	·12d.	,,	1/0¼	11¾d.	,,	1/0¼	11¾d.	,,	1/0½	11½d.
1/0½	·125	,,	1/0¾	1/0¼	½d.	1/1	1/-	,,	1/1	1/-
1/1	·13d.	,,	1/1¼	1/0¾	,,	1/1½	1/0½	,,	1/1½	1/0½
1/1½	·135	,,	1/1¾	1/1¼	,,	1/2	1/1	,,	1/2	1/1
1/2	·14d.	,,	1/2¼	1/1¾	,,	1/2½	1/1½	,,	1/2½	1/1½
1/2½	·145	,,	1/2¾	1/2¼	,,	1/3	1/2	,,	1/3	1/2
1/3	·15d.	½d.	1/3½	1/2½	,,	1/3½	1/2½	,,	1/3½	1/2½
1/3½	·155	,,	1/4	1/3	,,	1/4	1/3	,,	1/4	1/3
1/4	·16d.	,,	1/4½	1/3½	,,	1/4½	1/3½	¾d.	1/4¾	1/3¼
1/4½	·165	,,	1/5	1/4	,,	1/5	1/4	,,	1/5¼	1/3¾
1/5	·17d.	,,	1/5½	1/4½	,,	1/5½	1/4½	,,	1/5¾	1/4¼
1/5½	·175	,,	1/6	1/5	,,	1/6	1/5	,,	1/6¼	1/4¾
1/6	·18d.	,,	1/6½	1/5½	,,	1/6½	1/5½	,,	1/6¾	1/5¼

	4½%	5%			7½%			10%		
INV.	Disct.	Disct.	**ON**	**OFF**	Disct.	**ON**	**OFF**	Disct.	**ON**	**OFF**
1d.	..	..	..	..	..	..	..	..	..	..
1¼d.	..	..	..	..	..	..	..	⅛d.	..	..
1½d.	..	..	..	..	..	..	..	,,	..	..
1¾d.	..	..	..	..	⅛d.	..	..	,,	..	..
2d.	..	..	..	..	,,	..	..	,,	..	..
2¼d.	...	...	...	...	,,	...	...	,,	...	...
2½d.	...	⅛d.	...	...	,,	...	...	¼d.	2¾d.	2¼d.
2¾d.	...	,,	...	...	,,	...	...	,,	3d.	2½d.
3D.	⅛d.	,,	...	...	,,	...	...	,,	3¼d.	2¾d.
3¼d.	,,	,,	...	...	,,	...	...	,,	3½d.	3d.
3½d.	,,	,,	...	...	¼d.	3¾d.	3¼d.	,,	3¾d.	3¼d.
3¾d.	,,	,,	...	...	,,	4d.	3½d.	½d.	4¼d.	3¼d.
4d.	,,	,,	...	...	,,	4¼d.	3¾d.	,,	4½d.	3½d.
4¼d.	,,	,,	...	...	,,	4½d.	4d.	,,	4¾d.	3¾d.
4½d.	,,	,,	...	...	,,	4¾d.	4¼d.	,,	5d.	4d.
4¾d.	,,	,,	...	...	,,	5d.	4½d.	,,	5¼d.	4¼d.
5d.	,,	¼d.	5¼d.	4¾d.	½d.	5½d.	4½d.	,,	5½d.	4½d
5¼d.	,,	,,	5½d.	5d.	,,	5¾d.	4¾d.	,,	5¾d.	4¾d.
5½d.	,,	,,	5¾d.	5¼d.	,,	6d.	5d.	,,	6d.	5d.
5¾d.	¼d.	,,	6d.	5½d.	,,	6¼d.	5¼d.	,,	6¼d.	5¼d.
6D.	,,	,,	6¼d.	5¾d.	,,	6½d.	5½d.	,,	6½d.	5½d.
6¼d.	,,	,,	6½d.	6d.	,,	6¾d.	5¾d.	¾d.	7d.	5½d.
6½d.	,,	,,	6¾d.	6¼d.	,,	7d.	6d.	,,	7¼d.	5¾d.
6¾d.	,,	,,	7d.	6½d.	,,	7¼d.	6¼d.	,,	7½d.	6d.
7d.	,,	,,	7¼d.	6¾d.	,,	7½d.	6½d.	,,	7¾d.	6¼d.
7¼d.	,,	,,	7½d.	7d.	,,	7¾d.	6¾d.	,,	8d.	6½d.
7½d.	,,	½d.	8d.	7d.	,,	8d.	7d.	,,	8¼d.	6¾d.
7¾d.	,,	,,	8¼d.	7¼d.	,,	8¼d.	7¼d.	,,	8½d.	7d.
8d.	,,	,,	8½d.	7½d.	,,	8½d.	7½d.	,,	8¾d.	7¼d.
8¼d.	,,	,,	8¾d.	7¾d.	,,	8¾d.	7¾d.	,,	9d.	7½d.
8½d.	½d.	,,	9d.	8d.	¾d.	9¼d.	7¾d.	,,	9¼d.	7¾d.
8¾d.	,,	,,	9¼d.	8¼d.	,,	9½d.	8d.	1d.	9¾d.	7¾d.
9D.	,,	,,	9½d.	8½d.	,,	9¾d.	8¼d.	,,	10d.	8d.
9¼d.	,,	,,	9¾d.	8¾d.	,,	10d.	8½d.	,,	10¼d.	8¼d.
9½d.	,,	,,	10d.	9d.	,,	10¼d.	8¾d.	,,	10½d.	8½d.
9¾d.	,,	,,	10¼d.	9¼d.	,,	10½d.	9d.	,,	10¾d.	8¾d.
10d.	,,	,,	10½d.	9½d.	,,	10¾d.	9¼d.	,,	11d.	9d.
10¼d.	,,	,,	10¾d.	9¾d.	,,	11d.	9½d.	,,	11¼d.	9¼d.
10½d.	,,	,,	11d.	10d.	,,	11¼d.	9¾d.	,,	11½d.	9½d.
10¾d.	,,	,,	11¼d.	10¼d.	,,	11½d.	10d.	,,	11¾d.	9¾d.
11d.	,,	,,	11½d.	10½d.	,,	11¾d.	10¼d.	,,	1/-	10d.
11¼d.	,,	,,	11¾d.	10¾d.	,,	1/-	10½d.	1¼d.	1/0½	10d.
11½d.	,,	,,	1/-	11d.	,,	1/0¼	10¾d.	,,	1/0¾	10¼d.
11¾d.	,,	,,	1/0¼	11¼d.	1d.	1/0¾	10¾d.	,,	1/1	10½d.
1/-	,,	,,	1/0½	11½d.	,,	1/1	11d.	,,	1/1¼	10¾d.
1/0½	,,	¾d.	1/1¼	11¾d.	,,	1/1½	11½d.	,,	1/1¾	11¼d.
1/1	,,	,,	1/1¾	1/0¼	,,	1/2	1/-	,,	1/2¼	11¾d.
1/1½	,,	,,	1/2¼	1/0¾	,,	1/2½	1/0½	,,	1/2¾	1/0¼
1/2	¾d.	,,	1/2¾	1/1¼	,,	1/3	1/1	1½d.	1/3½	1/0½
1/2½	,,	,,	1/3¼	1/1¾	,,	1/3½	1/1½	,,	1/4	1/1
1/3	,,	,,	1/3¾	1/2¼	1¼d.	1/4¼	1/1¾	,,	1/4½	1/1½
1/3½	,,	,,	1/4¼	1/2¾	,,	1/4¾	1/2¼	,,	1/5	1/2
1/4	,,	,,	1/4¾	1/3¼	,,	1/5¼	1/2¾	,,	1/5½	1/2½
1/4½	,,	,,	1/5¼	1/3¾	,,	1/5¾	1/3¼	1¾d.	1/6¼	1/2¾
1/5	,,	,,	1/5¾	1/4¼	,,	1/6¼	1/3¾	,,	1/6¾	1/3¼
1/5½	,,	1d.	1/6½	1/4½	,,	1/6¾	1/4¼	,,	1/7¼	1/3¾
1/6	,,	,,	1/7	1/5	,,	1/7¼	1/4¾	,,	1/7¾	1/4¼

	1%	2½%			3%			4%		
INV.	Disct.	Disct.	**ON**	**OFF**	Disct.	**ON**	**OFF**	Disct.	**ON**	**OFF**
1/6½	·185	½d.	1/7	1/6	½d.	1/7	1/6	¾d.	1/7¼	1/5¾
1/7	·19d.	,,	1/7½	1/6½	,,	1/7½	1/6½	,,	1/7¾	1/6¼
1/7½	·195	,,	1/8	1/7	,,	1/8	1/7	,,	1/8¼	1/6¾
1/8	·20d.	,,	1/8½	1/7½	,,	1/8½	1/7½	,,	1/8¾	1/7¼
1/8½	·205	,,	1/9	1/8	,,	1/9	1/8	,,	1/9¼	1/7¾
1/9	.21d.	,,	**1/9½**	**1/8½**	¾d.	**1/9¾**	**1/8¼**	,,	**1/9¾**	**1/8¼**
1/9½	.215	,,	1/10	1/9	,,	1/10¼	1/8¾	,,	1/10¼	1/8¾
1/10	.22d.	,,	1/10½	1/9½	,,	1/10¾	1/9¼	1d.	1/11	1/9
1/10½	.225	,,	1/11	1/10	,,	1/11¼	1/9¾	,,	1/11½	1/9½
1/11	.23d.	,,	1/11½	1/10½	,,	1/11¾	1/10¼	,,	2/-	1/10
1/11½	.235	,,	2/-	1/11	,,	2/0¼	1/10¾	,,	2/0½	1/10½
2/-	.24d.	,,	**2/0½**	**1/11½**	,,	**2/0¾**	**1/11¼**	,,	**2/1**	**1/11**
2/0½	.245	,,	2/1	2/-	,,	2/1¼	1/11¾	,,	2/1½	1/11½
2/1	.25d.	¾d.	2/1¾	2/0¼	,,	2/1¾	2/0¼	,,	2/2	2/-
2/1½	.255	,,	2/2¼	2/0¾	,,	2/2¼	2/0¾	,,	2/2½	2/0½
2/2	.26d.	,,	2/2¾	2/1¼	,,	2/2¾	2/1¼	,,	2/3	2/1
2/3	.27d.	,,	2/3¾	2/2¼	,,	2/3¾	2/2¼	,,	2/4	2/2
2/4	.28d.	,,	2/4¾	2/3¼	,,	2/4¾	2/3¼	,,	2/5	2/3
2/5	.29d.	,,	2/5¾	2/4¼	,,	2/5¾	2/4¼	1¼d.	2/6¼	2/3¾
2/6	.30d.	,,	**2/6¾**	**2/5¼**	1d.	**2/7**	**2/5**	,,	**2/7¼**	**2/4¾**
2/7	.31d.	,,	2/7¾	2/6¼	,,	2/8	2/6	,,	2/8¼	2/5¾
2/8	·32d.	,,	2/8¾	2/7¼	,,	2/9	2/7	,,	2/9¼	2/6¾
2/9	·33d.	,,	2/9¾	2/8¼	,,	2/10	2/8	,,	2/10¼	2/7¾
2/10	·34d.	,,	2/10¾	2/9¼	,,	2/11	2/9	,,	2/11¼	2/8¾
2/11	·35d.	1d.	3/-	2/10	,,	3/-	2/10	1½d.	3/0½	2/9½
3/-	·36d.	,,	**3/1**	**2/11**	,,	**3/1**	**2/11**	,,	**3/1½**	**2/10½**
3/1	·37d.	,,	3/2	3/-	,,	3/2	3/-	,,	3/2½	2/11½
3/2	·38d.	,,	3/3	3/1	1¼d.	3/3¼	3/0¾	,,	3/3½	3/0½
3/3	·39d.	,,	3/4	3/2	,,	3/4¼	3/1¾	,,	3/4½	3/1½
3/4	·40d.	,,	3/5	3/3	,,	3/5¼	3/2¾	,,	3/5½	3/2½
3/5	·41d.	,,	3/6	3/4	,,	3/6¼	3/3¾	1¾d.	3/6¾	3/3¼
3/6	·42d.	,,	**3/7**	**3/5**	,,	**3/7¼**	**3/4¾**	,,	**3/7¾**	**3/4¼**
3/7	·43d.	,,	3/8	3/6	,,	3/8¼	3/5¾	,,	3/8¾	3/5¼
3/8	·44d.	,,	3/9	3/7	,,	3/9¼	3/6¾	,,	3/9¾	3/6¼
3/9	·45d.	1¼d.	3/10¼	3/7¾	,,	3/10¼	3/7¾	,,	3/10¾	3/7¼
3/10	·46d.	,,	3/11¼	3/8¾	1½d.	3/11½	3/8½	,,	3/11¾	3/8¼
3/11	·47d.	,,	4/0¼	3/9¾	,,	4/0½	3/9½	2d.	4/1	3/9
4/-	·48d.	,,	**4/1¼**	**3/10¾**	,,	**4/1½**	**3/10½**	,,	**4/2**	**3/10**
4/1	·49d.	,,	4/2¼	3/11¾	,,	4/2½	3/11½	,,	4/3	3/11
4/2	·50d.	,,	4/3¼	4/0¾	,,	4/3½	4/0½	,,	4/4	4/-
4/3	·51d.	,,	4/4¼	4/1¾	,,	4/4½	4/1½	,,	4/5	4/1
4/4	·52d.	,,	4/5¼	4/2¾	,,	4/5½	4/2½	,,	4/6	4/2
4/5	·53d.	,,	4/6¼	4/3¾	,,	4/6½	4/3½	,,	4/7	4/3
4/6	·54d.	,,	**4/7¼**	**4/4¾**	,,	**4/7½**	**4/4½**	2¼d.	**4/8¼**	**4/3¾**
4/7	·55d.	1½d.	4/8½	4/5½	1¾d.	4/8¾	4/5¼	,,	4/9¼	4/4¾
4/8	·56d.	,,	4/9½	4/6½	,,	4/9¾	4/6¼	,,	4/10¼	4/5¾
4/9	·57d.	,,	4/10½	4/7½	,,	4/10¾	4/7¼	,,	4/11¼	4/6¾
4/10	·58d.	,,	4/11½	4/8½	,,	4/11¾	4/8¼	,,	5/0¼	4/7¾
4/11	·59d.	,,	5/0½	4/9½	,,	5/0¾	4/9¼	,,	5/1¼	4/8¾
5/-	·60d.	,,	**5/1½**	**4/10½**	,,	**5/1¾**	**4/10¼**	2½d.	**5/2½**	**4/9½**
5/1	·61d.	,,	5/2½	4/11½	,,	5/2¾	4/11¼	,,	5/3½	4/10½
5/2	·62d.	,,	5/3½	5/0½	,,	5/3¾	5/0¼	,,	5/4½	4/11½
5/3	·63d.	,,	5/4½	5/1½	2d.	5/5	5/1	,,	5/5½	5/0½
5/4	·64d.	,,	5/5½	5/2½	,,	5/6	5/2	,,	5/6½	5/1½
5/5	·65d.	1¾d.	5/6¾	5/3¼	,,	5/7	5/3	,,	5/7½	5/2½
5/6	·66d.	,,	**5/7¾**	**5/4¼**	,,	**5/8**	**5/4**	2¾d.	**5/8¾**	**5/3¼**

INV.	4½% Disct.	5% Disct.	5% ON	5% OFF	7½% Disct.	7½% ON	7½% OFF	10% Disct.	10% ON	10% OFF
1/6½	¾d.	1d.	1/7½	1/5½	1½d.	1/8	1/5	1¾d.	1/8¼	1/4¾
1/7	,,	,,	1/8	1/6	,,	1/8½	1/5½	2d.	1/9	1/5
1/7½	1d.	,,	1/8½	1/6½	,,	1/9	1/6	,,	1/9½	1/5½
1/8	,,	,,	1/9	1/7	,,	1/9½	1/6½	,,	1/10	1/6
1/8½	,,	,,	1/9½	1/7½	,,	1/10	1/7	,,	1/10½	1/6½
1/9	,,	,,	**1/10**	**1/8**	,,	**1/10½**	**1/7½**	,,	**1/11**	**1/7**
1/9½	,,	,,	1/10½	1/8½	,,	1/11	1/8	2¼d.	1/11¾	1/7¼
1/10	,,	,,	1/11	1/9	1¾d.	1/11¾	1/8¼	,,	2/0¼	1/7¾
1/10½	,,	1¼d.	1/11¾	1/9¼	,,	2/0¼	1/8¾	,,	2/0¾	1/8¼
1/11	,,	,,	2/0¼	1/9¾	,,	2/0¾	1/9¼	,,	2/1¼	1/8¾
1/11½	,,	,,	2/0¾	1/10¼	,,	2/1¼	1/9¾	,,	2/1¾	1/9¼
2/-	,,	,,	**2/1¼**	**1/10¾**	,,	**2/1¾**	**1/10¼**	2½d.	**2/2½**	**1/9½**
2/0½	,,	,,	2/1¾	1/11¼	,,	2/2¼	1/10¾	,,	2/3	1/10
2/1	1¼d.	,,	2/2¼	1/11¾	2d.	2/3	1/11	,,	2/3½	1/10½
2/1½	,,	,,	2/2¾	2/0¼	,,	2/3½	1/11½	,,	2/4	1/11
2/2	,,	,,	2/3¼	2/0¾	,,	2/4	2/-	,,	2/4½	1/11½
2/3	,,	,,	2/4¼	2/1¾	,,	2/5	2/1	2¾d.	2/5¾	2/0¼
2/4	,,	1½d.	2/5½	2/2½	,,	2/6	2/2	,,	2/6¾	2/1¼
2/5	,,	,,	2/6½	2/3½	2¼d.	2/7¼	2/2¾	3d.	2/8	2/2
2/6	,,	,,	**2/7½**	**2/4½**	,,	**2/8¼**	**2/3¾**	,,	**2/9**	**2/3**
2/7	1½d.	,,	2/8½	2/5½	,,	2/9¼	2/4¾	,,	2/10	2/4
2/8	,,	,,	2/9½	2/6½	2½d.	2/10½	2/5½	3¼d.	2/11¼	2/4¾
2/9	,,	1¾d.	2/10¾	2/7¼	,,	2/11½	2/6½	,,	3/0¼	2/5¾
2/10	,,	,,	2/11¾	2/8¼	,,	3/0½	2/7½	3½d.	3/1½	2/6½
2/11	,,	,,	3/0¾	2/9¼	2¾d.	3/1¾	2/8¼	,,	3/2½	2/7½
3/-	,,	,,	**3/1¾**	**2/10¼**	,,	**3/2¾**	**2/9¼**	,,	**3/3½**	**2/8½**
3/1	1¾d.	,,	3/2¾	2/11¼	,,	3/3¾	2/10¼	3¾d.	3/4¾	2/9¼
3/2	,,	2d.	3/4	3/-	,,	3/4¾	2/11¼	,,	3/5¾	2/10¼
3/3	,,	,,	3/5	3/1	3d.	3/6	3/-	4d.	3/7	2/11
3/4	,,	,,	3/6	3/2	,,	3/7	3/1	,,	3/8	3/-
3/5	,,	,,	3/7	3/3	,,	3/8	3/2	,,	3/9	3/1
3/6	2d.	,,	**3/8**	**3/4**	3¼d.	**3/9¼**	**3/2¾**	4¼d.	**3/10¼**	**3/1¾**
3/7	,,	2¼d.	3/9¼	3/4¾	,,	3/10¼	3/3¾	,,	3/11¼	3/2¾
3/8	,,	,,	3/10¼	3/5¾	,,	3/11¼	3/4¾	4½d.	4/0½	3/3½
3/9	,,	,,	3/11¼	3/6¾	3½d.	4/0½	3/5½	,,	4/1½	3/4½
3/10	,,	,,	4/0¼	3/7¾	,,	4/1½	3/6½	,,	4/2½	3/5½
3/11	,,	,,	4/1¼	3/8¾	,,	4/2½	3/7½	4¾d.	4/3¾	3/6¼
4/-	2¼d.	2½d.	**4/2½**	**3/9½**	,,	**4/3½**	**3/8½**	,,	**4/4¾**	**3/7¼**
4/1	,,	,,	4/3½	3/10½	3¾d.	4/4¾	3/9¼	5d.	4/6	3/8
4/2	,,	,,	4/4½	3/11½	,,	4/5¾	3/10¼	,,	4/7	3/9
4/3	,,	,,	4/5½	4/0½	,,	4/6¾	3/11¼	,,	4/8	3/10
4/4	,,	,,	4/6½	4/1½	4d.	4/8	4/-	5¼d.	4/9¼	3/10¾
4/5	2½d.	2¾d.	4/7¾	4/2¼	,,	4/9	4/1	,,	4/10¼	3/11¾
4/6	,,	,,	**4/8¾**	**4/3¼**	,,	**4/10**	**4/2**	5½d.	**4/11½**	**4/0½**
4/7	,,	,,	4/9¾	4/4¼	4¼d.	4/11¼	4/2¾	,,	5/0½	4/1½
4/8	,,	,,	4/10¾	4/5¼	,,	5/0¼	4/3¾	,,	5/1½	4/2½
4/9	,,	,,	4/11¾	4/6¼	,,	5/1¼	4/4¾	5¾d.	5/2¾	4/3¼
4/10	,,	3d.	5/1	4/7	,,	5/2¼	4/5¾	,,	5/3¾	4/4¼
4/11	2¾d.	,,	5/2	4/8	4½d.	5/3½	4/6½	6d.	5/5	4/5
5/-	,,	,,	**5/3**	**4/9**	,,	**5/4½**	**4/7½**	,,	**5/6**	**4/6**
5/1	,,	,,	5/4	4/10	,,	5/5½	4/8½	,,	5/7	4/7
5/2	,,	,,	5/5	4/11	4¾d.	5/6¾	4/9¼	6¼d.	5/8¼	4/7¾
5/3	,,	3¼d.	5/6¼	4/11¾	,,	5/7¾	4/10¼	,,	5/9¼	4/8¾
5/4	3d.	,,	5/7¼	5/0¾	,,	5/8¾	4/11¼	6½d.	5/10½	4/9½
5/5	,,	,,	5/8¼	5/1¾	5d.	5/10	5/-	,,	5/11½	4/10½
5/6	,,	,,	**5/9¼**	**5/2¾**	,,	**5/11**	**5/1**	,,	**6/0½**	**4/11½**

	1%	2½%			3%			4%		
INV.	Dec.	Disct.	ON	OFF	Disct.	ON	OFF	Disct.	ON	OFF
5/7	·67d.	1¾d.	5/8¾	5/5¼	2d.	5/9	5/5	2¾d.	5/9¾	5/4¼
5/8	·68d.	,,	5/9¾	5/6¼	,,	5/10	5/6	,,	5/10¾	5/5¼
5/9	·69d.	,,	5/10¾	5/7¼	,,	5/11	5/7	,,	5/11¾	5/6¼
5/10	·70d.	,,	5/11¾	5/8¼	,,	6/-	5/8	,,	6/0¾	5/7¼
5/11	·71d.	,,	6/0¾	5/9¼	2¼d.	6/1¼	5/8¾	,,	6/1¾	5/8¼
6/-	·72d.	,,	6/1¾	5/10¼	,,	6/2¼	5/9¾	3d.	6/3	5/9
6/1	·73d.	,,	6/2¾	5/11¼	,,	6/3¼	5/10¾	,,	6/4	5/10
6/2	·74d.	,,	6/3¾	6/0¼	,,	6/4¼	5/11¾	,,	6/5	5/11
6/3	·75d.	2d.	6/5	6/1	,,	6/5¼	6/0¾	,,	6/6	6/-
6/4	·76d.	,,	6/6	6/2	,,	6/6¼	6/1¾	,,	6/7	6/1
6/5	·77d.	,,	6/7	6/3	,,	6/7¼	6/2¾	,,	6/8	6/2
6/6	·78d.	,,	6/8	6/4	,,	6/8¼	6/3¾	,,	6/9	6/3
6/7	·79d.	,,	6/9	6/5	,,	6/9¼	6/4¾	3¼d.	6/10¼	6/3¾
6/8	·80d.	,,	6/10	6/6	2½d.	6/10½	6/5½	,,	6/11¼	6/4¾
6/9	·81d.	,,	6/11	6/7	,,	6/11½	6/6½	,,	7/0¼	6/5¾
6/10	·82d.	,,	7/-	6/8	,,	7/0½	6/7½	,,	7/1¼	6/6¾
6/11	·83d.	,,	7/1	6/9	,,	7/1½	6/8½	,,	7/2¼	6/7¾
7/-	·84d.	,,	7/2	6/10	,,	7/2½	6/9½	,,	7/3¼	6/8¾
7/1	·85d.	2¼d.	7/3¼	6/10¾	,,	7/3½	6/10½	3½d.	7/4½	6/9½
7/2	·86d.	,,	7/4¼	6/11¾	,,	7/4½	6/11½	,,	7/5½	6/10½
7/3	·87d.	,,	7/5¼	7/0¾	,,	7/5½	7/0½	,,	7/6½	6/11½
7/4	·88d.	,,	7/6¼	7/1¾	2¾d.	7/6¾	7/1¼	,,	7/7½	7/0½
7/5	·89d.	,,	7/7¼	7/2¾	,,	7/7¾	7/2¼	,,	7/8½	7/1½
7/6	·90d.	,,	7/8¼	7/3¾	,,	7/8¾	7/3¼	,,	7/9½	7/2½
7/7	·91d.	,,	7/9¼	7/4¾	,,	7/9¾	7/4¼	3¾d.	7/10¾	7/3¼
7/8	·92d.	,,	7/10¼	7/5¾	,,	7/10¾	7/5¼	,,	7/11¾	7/4¼
7/9	·93d.	,,	7/11¼	7/6¾	,,	7/11¾	7/6¼	,,	8/0¾	7/5¼
7/10	·94d.	,,	8/0¼	7/7¾	,,	8/0¾	7/7¼	,,	8/1¾	7/6¼
7/11	·95d.	2½d.	8/1½	7/8½	,,	8/1¾	7/8¼	,,	8/2¾	7/7¼
8/-	·96d.	,,	8/2½	7/9½	3d.	8/3	7/9	,,	8/3¾	7/8¼
8/1	·97d.	,,	8/3½	7/10½	,,	8/4	7/10	4d.	8/5	7/9
8/2	·98d.	,,	8/4½	7/11½	,,	8/5	7/11	,,	8/6	7/10
8/3	·99d.	,,	8/5½	8/0½	,,	8/6	8/-	,,	8/7	7/11
8/4	1d.	,,	8/6½	8/1½	,,	8/7	8/1	,,	8/8	8/-
8/5	1·01d.	,,	8/7½	8/2½	,,	8/8	8/2	,,	8/9	8/1
8/6	1·02d.	,,	8/8½	8/3½	,,	8/9	8/3	,,	8/10	8/2
8/7	1·03d.	,,	8/9½	8/4½	,,	8/10	8/4	,,	8/11	8/3
8/8	1·04d.	,,	8/10½	8/5½	,,	8/11	8/5	4¼d.	9/0¼	8/3¾
8/9	1·05d.	2¾d.	8/11¾	8/6¼	3¼d.	9/0¼	8/5¾	,,	9/1¼	8/4¾
8/10	1·06d.	,,	9/0¾	8/7¼	,,	9/1¼	8/6¾	,,	9/2¼	8/5¾
8/11	1·07d.	,,	9/1¾	8/8¼	,,	9/2¼	8/7¾	,,	9/3¼	8/6¾
9/-	1·08d.	,,	9/2¾	8/9¼	,,	9/3¼	8/8¾	,,	9/4¼	8/7¾
9/1	1·09d.	,,	9/3¾	8/10¼	,,	9/4¼	8/9¾	,,	9/5¼	8/8¾
9/2	1·1d.	,,	9/4¾	8/11¼	,,	9/5¼	8/10¾	4½d.	9/6½	8/9½
9/3	1·11d.	,,	9/5¾	9/0¼	,,	9/6¼	8/11¾	,,	9/7½	8/10½
9/4	1·12d.	,,	9/6¾	9/1¼	,,	9/7¼	9/0¾	,,	9/8½	8/11½
9/5	1·13d.	,,	9/7¾	9/2¼	3½d.	9/8½	9/1½	,,	9/9½	9/0½
9/6	1·14d.	,,	9/8¾	9/3¼	,,	9/9½	9/2½	,,	9/10½	9/1½
9/7	1·15d.	3d.	9/10	9/4	,,	9/10½	9/3½	,,	9/11½	9/2½
9/8	1·16d.	,,	9/11	9/5	,,	9/11½	9/4½	4¾d.	10/0¾	9/3¼
9/9	1·17d.	,,	10/-	9/6	,,	10/0½	9/5½	,,	10/1¾	9/4¼
9/10	1·18d.	,,	10/1	9/7	,,	10/1½	9/6½	,,	10/2¾	9/5¼
9/11	1·19d.	,,	10/2	9/8	,,	10/2½	9/7½	,,	10/3¾	9/6¼
10/-	1·2d.	,,	10/3	9/9	,,	10/3½	9/8½	,,	10/4¾	9/7¼
10/1	1·21d.	,,	10/4	9/10	3¾d.	10/4¾	9/9¼	,,	10/5¾	9/8¼
10/2	1·22d.	,,	10/5	9/11	,,	10/5¾	9/10¼	5d.	10/7	9/9
10/3	1·23d.	,,	10/6	10/-	,,	10/6¾	9/11¼	,,	10/8	9/10

	4½%	5%			7½%			10%		
INV.	Disct.	Disct.	**ON**	**OFF**	Disct.	**ON**	**OFF**	Disct.	**ON**	**OFF**
5/7	3d.	3¼d.	5/10¼	5/3¾	5d.	6/-	5/2	6¾d.	6/1¾	5/0¼
5/8	,,	3½d.	5/11½	5/4½	,,	6/1	5/3	,,	6/2¾	5/1¼
5/9	,,	,,	6/0½	5/5½	5¼d.	6/2¼	5/3¾	7d.	6/4	5/2
5/10	3¼d.	,,	6/1½	5/6½	,,	6/3¼	5/4¾	,,	6/5	5/3
5/11	,,	,,	6/2½	5/7½	,,	6/4¼	5/5¾	,,	6/6	5/4
6/-	,,	,,	6/3½	5/8½	5½d.	6/5½	5/6½	7¼d.	6/7¼	5/4¾
6/1	,,	3¾d.	6/4¾	5/9¼	,,	6/6½	5/7½	,,	6/8¼	5/5¾
6/2	,,	,,	6/5¾	5/10¼	,,	6/7½	5/8½	7½d.	6/9½	5/6½
6/3	3½d.	,,	6/6¾	5/11¼	5¾d.	6/8¾	5/9¼	,,	6/10½	5/7½
6/4	,,	,,	6/7¾	6/0¼	,,	6/9¾	5/10¼	,,	6/11½	5/8½
6/5	,,	,,	6/8¾	6/1¼	,,	6/10¾	5/11¼	7¾d.	7/0¾	5/9¼
6/6	,,	4d.	6/10	6/2	,,	6/11¾	6/0¼	,,	7/1¾	5/10¼
6/7	,,	,,	6/11	6/3	6d.	7/1	6/1	8d.	7/3	5/11
6/8	,,	,,	7/-	6/4	,,	7/2	6/2	,,	7/4	6/-
6/9	3¾d.	,,	7/1	6/5	,,	7/3	6/3	,,	7/5	6/1
6/10	,,	,,	7/2	6/6	6¼d.	7/4¼	6/3¾	8¼d.	7/6¼	6/1¾
6/11	,,	4¼d.	7/3¼	6/6¾	,,	7/5¼	6/4¾	,,	7/7¼	6/2¾
7/-	,,	,,	7/4¼	6/7¾	,,	7/6¼	6/5¾	8½d.	7/8½	6/3½
7/1	,,	,,	7/5¼	6/8¾	6½d.	7/7½	6/6½	,,	7/9½	6/4½
7/2	,,	,,	7/6¼	6/9¾	,,	7/8½	6/7½	,,	7/10½	6/5½
7/3	4d.	,,	7/7¼	6/10¾	,,	7/9½	6/8½	8¾d.	7/11¾	6/6¼
7/4	,,	4½d.	7/8½	6/11½	,,	7/10½	6/9½	,,	8/0¾	6/7¼
7/5	,,	,,	7/9½	7/0½	6¾d.	7/11¾	6/10¼	9d.	8/2	6/8
7/6	,,	,,	7/10½	7/1½	,,	8/0¾	6/11¼	,,	8/3	6/9
7/7	,,	,,	7/11½	7/2½	,,	8/1¾	7/0¼	,,	8/4	6/10
7/8	4¼d.	,,	8/0½	7/3½	7d.	8/3	7/1	9¼d.	8/5¼	6/10¾
7/9	,,	4¾d.	8/1¾	7/4¼	,,	8/4	7/2	,,	8/6¼	6/11¾
7/10	,,	,,	8/2¾	7/5¼	,,	8/5	7/3	9½d.	8/7½	7/0½
7/11	,,	,,	8/3¾	7/6¼	7¼d.	8/6¼	7/3¾	,,	8/8½	7/1½
8/-	,,	,,	8/4¾	7/7¼	,,	8/7¼	7/4¾	,,	8/9½	7/2½
8/1	,,	,,	8/5¾	7/8¼	,,	8/8¼	7/5¾	9¾d.	8/10¾	7/3¼
8/2	4½d.	5d.	8/7	7/9	,,	8/9¼	7/6¾	,,	8/11¾	7/4¼
8/3	,,	,,	8/8	7/10	7½d.	8/10½	7/7½	10d.	9/1	7/5
8/4	,,	,,	8/9	7/11	,,	8/11½	7/8½	,,	9/2	7/6
8/5	,,	,,	8/10	8/-	,,	9/0½	7/9½	,,	9/3	7/7
8/6	,,	,,	8/11	8/1	7¾d.	9/1¾	7/10¼	10¼d.	9/4¼	7/7¾
8/7	4¾d.	5¼d.	9/0¼	8/1¾	,,	9/2¾	7/11¼	,,	9/5¼	7/8¾
8/8	,,	,,	9/1¼	8/2¾	,,	9/3¾	8/0¼	10½d.	9/6½	7/9½
8/9	,,	,,	9/2¼	8/3¾	8d.	9/5	8/1	,,	9/7½	7/10½
8/10	,,	,,	9/3¼	8/4¾	,,	9/6	8/2	,,	9/8½	7/11½
8/11	,,	,,	9/4¼	8/5¾	,,	9/7	8/3	10¾d.	9/9¾	8/0¼
9/-	,,	5½d.	9/5½	8/6½	,,	9/8	8/4	,,	9/10¾	8/1¼
9/1	5d.	,,	9/6½	8/7½	8¼d.	9/9¼	8/4¾	11d.	10/-	8/2
9/2	,,	,,	9/7½	8/8½	,,	9/10¼	8/5¾	,,	10/1	8/3
9/3	,,	,,	9/8½	8/9½	,,	9/11¼	8/6¾	,,	10/2	8/4
9/4	,,	,,	9/9½	8/10½	8½d.	10/0½	8/7½	11¼d.	10/3¼	8/4¾
9/5	,,	5¾d.	9/10¾	8/11¼	,,	10/1½	8/8½	,,	10/4¼	8/5¾
9/6	5¼d.	,,	9/11¾	9/0¼	,,	10/2½	8/9½	11½d.	10/5½	8/6½
9/7	,,	,,	10/0¾	9/1¼	8¾d.	10/3¾	8/10¼	,,	10/6½	8/7½
9/8	,,	,,	10/1¾	9/2¼	,,	10/4¾	8/11¼	,,	10/7½	8/8½
9/9	,,	,,	10/2¾	9/3¼	,,	10/5¾	9/0¼	11¾d.	10/8¾	8/9¼
9/10	,,	6d.	10/4	9/4	,,	10/6¾	9/1¼	,,	10/9¾	8/10¼
9/11	,,	,,	10/5	9/5	9d.	10/8	9/2	1/-	10/11	8/11
10/-	5½d.	,,	10/6	9/6	,,	10/9	9/3	,,	11/-	9/-
10/1	,,	,,	10/7	9/7	,,	10/10	9/4	,,	11/1	9/1
10/2	,,	,,	10/8	9/8	9¼d.	10/11¼	9/4¾	1/0¼	11/2¼	9/1¾
10/3	,,	6¼d.	10/9¼	9/8¾	,,	11/0¼	9/5¾	,,	11/3¼	9/2¾

INV.	Dec. (1%)	Disct (2½%)	ON	OFF	Disct. (3%)	ON	OFF	Disct. (4%)	ON	OFF
10/4	1·24d.	3d.	10/7	10/1	3¾d.	10/7¾	10/0¼	5d.	10/9	9/11
10/5	1·25d.	3¼d.	10/8¼	10/1¾	,,	10/8¾	10/1¼	,,	10/10	10/-
10/6	1·26d.	,,	10/9¼	10/2¾	,,	10/9¾	10/2¼	,,	10/11	10/1
10/7	1·27d.	,,	10/10¼	10/3¾	,,	10/10¾	10/3¼	,,	11/-	10/2
10/8	1·28d.	,,	10/11¼	10/4¾	,,	10/11¾	10/4¼	,,	11/1	10/3
10/9	1·29d.	,,	11/0¼	10/5¾	,,	11/0¾	10/5¼	5¼d.	11/2¼	10/3¾
10/10	1·30d.	,,	11/1¼	10/6¾	4d.	11/2	10/6	,,	11/3¼	10/4¾
10/11	1·31d.	,,	11/2¼	10/7¾	,,	11/3	10/7	,,	11/4¼	10/5¾
11/-	1·32d.	,,	11/3¼	10/8¾	,,	11/4	10/8	,,	11/5¼	10/6¾
11/1	1·33d.	,,	11/4¼	10/9¾	,,	11/5	10/9	,,	11/6¼	10/7¾
11/2	1·34d.	,,	11/5¼	10/10¾	,,	11/6	10/10	,,	11/7¼	10/8¾
11/3	1·35d.	3½d.	11/6½	10/11½	,,	11/7	10/11	5½d.	11/8½	10/9½
11/4	1·36d.	,,	11/7½	11/0½	,,	11/8	11/-	,,	11/9½	10/10½
11/5	1·37d.	,,	11/8½	11/1½	,,	11/9	11/1	,,	11/10½	10/11½
11/6	1·38d.	,,	11/9½	11/2½	4¼d.	11/10¼	11/1¾	,,	11/11½	11/0½
11/7	1·39d.	,,	11/10½	11/3½	,,	11/11¼	11/2¾	,,	12/0½	11/1½
11/8	1·40d.	,,	11/11½	11/4½	,,	12/0¼	11/3¾	,,	12/1½	11/2½
11/9	1·41d.	,,	12/0½	11/5½	,,	12/1¼	11/4¾	5¾d.	12/2¾	11/3¼
11/10	1·42d.	,,	12/1½	11/6½	,,	12/2¼	11/5¾	,,	12/3¾	11/4¼
11/11	1·43d.	,,	12/2½	11/7½	,,	12/3¼	11/6¾	,,	12/4¾	11/5¼
12/-	1·44d.	,,	12/3½	11/8½	,,	12/4¼	11/7¾	,,	12/5¾	11/6¼
12/1	1·45d.	3¾d.	12/4¾	11/9¼	,,	12/5¼	11/8¾	,,	12/6¾	11/7¼
12/2	1·46d.	,,	12/5¾	11/10¼	4½d.	12/6½	11/9½	,,	12/7¾	11/8¼
12/3	1·47d.	,,	12/6¾	11/11¼	,,	12/7½	11/10½	6d.	12/9	11/9
12/4	1·48d.	,,	12/7¾	12/0¼	,,	12/8½	11/11½	,,	12/10	11/10
12/5	1·49d.	,,	12/8¾	12/1¼	,,	12/9½	12/0½	,,	12/11	11/11
12/6	1·5d.	,,	12/9¾	12/2¼	,,	12/10½	12/1½	,,	13/-	12/-
12/9	1·53d.	,,	13/0¾	12/5¼	,,	13/1½	12/4½	,,	13/3	12/3
13/-	1·56d.	4d.	13/4	12/8	4¾d.	13/4¾	12/7¼	6¼d.	13/6¼	12/5¾
13/3	1·59d.	,,	13/7	12/11	,,	13/7¾	12/10¼	,,	13/9¼	12/8¾
13/6	1·62d.	,,	13/10	13/2	,,	13/10¾	13/1¼	6½d.	14/0½	12/11½
13/9	1·65d.	4¼d.	14/1¼	13/4¾	5d.	14/2	13/4	,,	14/3½	13/2½
14/-	1·68d.	,,	14/4¼	13/7¾	,,	14/5	13/7	6¾d.	14/6¾	13/5¼
14/3	1·71d.	,,	14/7¼	13/10¾	5¼d.	14/8¼	13/9¾	,,	14/9¾	13/8¼
14/6	1·74d.	,,	14/10¼	14/1¾	,,	14/11¼	14/0¾	7d.	15/1	13/11
14/9	1·77d.	4½d.	15/1½	14/4½	,,	15/2¼	14/3¾	,,	15/4	14/2
15/-	1·8d.	,,	15/4½	14/7½	5½d.	15/5½	14/6½	7¼d.	15/7¼	14/4¾
15/3	1·83d.	,,	15/7½	14/10½	,,	15/8½	14/9½	,,	15/10¼	14/7¾
15/6	1·86d.	4¾d.	15/10¾	15/1¼	,,	15/11½	15/0½	7½d.	16/1½	14/10½
15/9	1·89d.	,,	16/1¾	15/4¼	5¾d.	16/2¾	15/3¼	,,	16/4½	15/1½
16/-	1·92d.	,,	16/4¾	15/7¼	,,	16/5¾	15/6¼	7¾d.	16/7¾	15/4¼
16/3	1·95d.	5d.	16/8	15/10	,,	16/8¾	15/9¼	,,	16/10¾	15/7¼
16/6	1·98d.	,,	16/11	16/1	6d.	17/-	16/-	8d.	17/2	15/10
16/9	2·01d.	,,	17/2	16/4	,,	17/3	16/3	,,	17/5	16/1
17/-	2·04d.	,,	17/5	16/7	,,	17/6	16/6	8¼d.	17/8¼	16/3¾
17/3	2·07d.	5¼d.	17/8¼	16/9¾	6¼d.	17/9¼	16/8¾	,,	17/11¼	16/6¾
17/6	2·1d.	,,	17/11¼	17/0¾	,,	18/0¼	16/11¾	8½d.	18/2½	16/9½
17/9	2·13d.	,,	18/2¼	17/3¾	6½d.	18/3½	17/2½	,,	18/5½	17/0½
18/-	2·16d.	5½d.	18/5½	17/6½	,,	18/6½	17/5½	8¾d.	18/8¾	17/3¼
18/3	2·19d.	,,	18/8½	17/9½	,,	18/9½	17/8½	,,	18/11¾	17/6¼
18/6	2·22d.	,,	18/11½	18/0½	6¾d.	19/0¾	17/11¼	9d.	19/3	17/9
18/9	2·25d.	5¾d.	19/2¾	18/3¼	,,	19/3¾	18/2¼	,,	19/6	18/-
19/-	2·28d.	,,	19/5¾	18/6¼	,,	19/6¾	18/5¼	,,	19/9	18/3
19/3	2·31d.	,,	19/8¾	18/9¼	7d.	19/10	18/8	9¼d.	20/0¼	18/5¾
19/6	2·34d.	,,	19/11¾	19/0¼	,,	20/1	18/11	,,	20/3¼	18/8¾
19/9	2·37d.	6d.	20/3	19/3	,,	20/4	19/2	9½d.	20/6½	18/11½
20/-	2·4d.	,,	20/6	19/6	7¼d.	20/7¼	19/4¾	,,	20/9½	19/2½

N^2 4½% - 5% 7½% - 10%

INV.	Disct.	Disct.	ON	OFF	Disct.	ON	OFF	Disct.	ON	OFF
10/4	5½d.	6¼d.	10/10¼	9/9¾	9¼d.	11/1¼	9/6¾	1/0½	11/4½	9/3½
10/5	5¾d.	,,	10/11¼	9/10¾	9½d.	11/2½	9/7½	,,	11/5½	9/4½
10/6	,,	,,	11/0¼	9/11¾	,,	11/3½	9/8½	,,	11/6½	9/5½
10/7	,,	,,	11/1¼	10/0¾	,,	11/4½	9/9½	1/0¾	11/7¾	9/6¼
10/8	,,	6½d.	11/2½	10/1½	,,	11/5½	9/10½	,,	11/8¾	9/7¼
10/9	,,	,,	11/3½	10/2½	9¾d.	11/6¾	9/11¼	1/1	11/10	9/8
10/10	,,	,,	11/4½	10/3½	,,	11/7¾	10/0¼	,,	11/11	9/9
10/11	6d.	,,	11/5½	10/4½	,,	11/8¾	10/1¼	,,	12/-	9/10
11/-	,,	,,	11/6½	10/5½	10d.	11/10	10/2	1/1¼	12/1¼	9/10¾
11/1	,,	6¾d.	11/7¾	10/6¼	,,	11/11	10/3	,,	12/2¼	9/11¾
11/2	,,	,,	11/8¾	10/7¼	,,	12/-	10/4	1/1½	12/3½	10/0½
11/3	,,	,,	11/9¾	10/8¼	10¼d.	12/1¼	10/4¾	,,	12/4½	10/1½
11/4	,,	,,	11/10¾	10/9¼	,,	12/2¼	10/5¾	,,	12/5½	10/2½
11/5	6¼d.	,,	11/11¾	10/10¼	,,	12/3¼	10/6¾	1/1¾	12/6¾	10/3¼
11/6	,,	7d.	12/1	10/11	,,	12/4¼	10/7¾	,,	12/7¾	10/4¼
11/7	,,	,,	12/2	11/-	10½d.	12/5½	10/8½	1/2	12/9	10/5
11/8	,,	,,	12/3	11/1	,,	12/6½	10/9½	,,	12/10	10/6
11/9	,,	,,	12/4	11/2	,,	12/7½	10/10½	,,	12/11	10/7
11/10	6½d.	,,	12/5	11/3	10¾d.	12/8¾	10/11¼	1/2¼	13/0¼	10/7¾
11/11	,,	7¼d.	12/6¼	11/3¾	,,	12/9¾	11/0¼	,,	13/1¼	10/8¾
12/-	,,	,,	12/7¼	11/4¾	,,	12/10¾	11/1¼	1/2½	13/2½	10/9½
12/1	,,	,,	12/8¼	11/5¾	11d.	13/-	11/2	,,	13/3½	10/10½
12/2	,,	,,	12/9¼	11/6¾	,,	13/1	11/3	,,	13/4½	10/11½
12/3	,,	,,	12/10¼	11/7¾	,,	13/2	11/4	1/2¾	13/5¾	11/0¼
12/4	6¾d.	7½d.	12/11½	11/8½	,,	13/3	11/5	,,	13/6¾	11/1¼
12/5	,,	,,	13/0½	11/9½	11¼d.	13/4¼	11/5¾	1/3	13/8	11/2
12/6	,,	,,	13/1½	11/10½	,,	13/5¼	11/6¾	,,	13/9	11/3
12/9	7d.	7¾d.	13/4¾	12/1¼	11½d.	13/8½	11/9½	1/3¼	14/0¼	11/5¾
13/-	,,	,,	13/7¾	12/4¼	11¾d.	13/11¾	12/0¼	1/3½	14/3½	11/8½
13/3	7¼d.	8d.	13/11	12/7	1/-	14/3	12/3	1/4	14/7	11/11
13/6	,,	,,	14/2	12/10	1/0¼	14/6¼	12/5¾	1/4¼	14/10¼	12/1¾
13/9	7½d.	8¼d.	14/5¼	13/0¾	1/0½	14/9½	12/8½	1/4½	15/1½	12/4½
14/-	,,	8½d.	14/8½	13/3½	,,	15/0½	12/11½	1/4¾	15/4¾	12/7¼
14/3	7¾d.	,,	14/11½	13/6½	1/0¾	15/3¾	13/2¼	1/5	15/8	12/10
14/6	,,	8¾d.	15/2¾	13/9¼	1/1	15/7	13/5	1/5½	15/11½	13/0[illegible]
14/9	8d.	,,	15/5¾	14/0¼	1/1¼	15/10¼	13/7¾	1/5¾	16/2¾	13/3¼
15/-	,,	9d.	15/9	14/3	1/1½	16/1½	13/10½	1/6	16/6	13/6
15/3	8¼d.	9¼d.	16/0¼	14/5¾	1/1¾	16/4¾	14/1¼	1/6¼	16/9¼	13/8¾
15/6	,,	,,	16/3¼	14/8¾	1/2	16/8	14/4	1/6½	17/0½	13/11½
15/9	8½d.	9½d.	16/6½	14/11½	1/2¼	16/11¼	14/6¾	1/7	17/4	14/2
16/-	8¾d.	,,	16/9½	15/2½	1/2½	17/2½	14/9½	1/7¼	17/7¼	14/4¾
16/3	8¾d.	9¾d.	17/0¾	15/5¼	1/2¾	17/5¾	15/0¼	1/7½	17/10½	14/7½
16/6	9d.	10d.	17/4	15/8	,,	17/8¾	15/3¼	1/7¾	18/1¾	14/10¼
16/9	,,	,,	17/7	15/11	1/3	18/-	15/6	1/8	18/5	15/1
17/-	9¼d.	10¼d.	17/10¼	16/1¾	1/3¼	18/3¼	15/8¾	1/8½	18/8½	15/3½
17/3	,,	,,	18/1¼	16/4¾	1/3½	18/6½	15/11½	1/8¾	18/11¾	15/6¼
17/6	9½d.	10½d.	18/4½	16/7½	1/3¾	18/9¾	16/2¼	1/9	19/3	15/9
17/9	,,	10¾d.	18/7¾	16/10¼	1/4	19/1	16/5	1/9¼	19/6¼	15/11¾
18/-	9¾d.	,,	18/10¾	17/1¼	1/4¼	19/4¼	16/7¾	1/9½	19/9½	16/2½
18/3	,,	11d.	19/2	17/4	1/4½	19/7½	16/10½	1/10	20/1	16/5
18/6	10d.	,,	19/5	17/7	1/4¾	19/10¾	17/1¼	1/10¼	20/4¼	16/7¾
18/9	10¼d.	11¼d.	19/8¼	17/9¾	1/5	20/2	17/4	1/10½	20/7½	16/10½
19/-	,,	11½d.	19/11½	18/0½	,,	20/5	17/7	1/10¾	20/10¾	17/1¼
19/3	10½d.	,,	20/2½	18/3½	1/5¼	20/8¼	17/9¾	1/11	21/2	17/4
19/6	,,	11¾d.	20/5¾	18/6¼	1/5½	20/11½	18/0½	1/11½	21/5½	17/6½
19/9	10¾d.	,,	20/8¾	18/9¼	1/5¾	21/2¾	18/3¼	1/11¾	21/8¾	17/9¼
20/-	,,	1/-	21/-	19/-	1/6	21/6	18/6	2/-	22/-	18/-

	12½%			15%			17½%		
INV.	Disct.	**ON**	**OFF**	Disct.	**ON**	**OFF**	Disct.	**ON**	**OFF**
1d.	⅛d.	..	..	⅛d.	..	..	⅛d.	..	..
1¼d.	,,	..	..	,,	..	..	,,	..	..
1½d.	,,	..	..	,,	..	..	¼d.	1¾d.	1¼d.
1¾d.	,,	..	..	¼d.	2d.	1½d.	,,	2d.	1½d.
2d.	¼d.	2¼d.	1¾d.	,,	2¼d.	1¾d.	,,	2¼d.	1¾d.
2¼d.	,,	2½d.	2d.	,,	2½d.	2d.	½d.	2¾d.	1¾d.
2½d.	,,	2¾d.	2¼d.	½d.	3d.	2d.	,,	3d.	2d.
2¾d.	,,	3d.	2½d.	,,	3¼d.	2¼d.	,,	3¼d.	2¼d.
3D.	½d.	3½d.	2½d.	,,	3½d.	2½d.	,,	3½d.	2½d.
3¼d.	,,	3¾d.	2¾d.	,,	3¾d.	2¾d.	,,	3¾d.	2¾d.
3½d.	,,	4d.	3d.	,,	4d.	3d.	,,	4d.	3d.
3¾d.	,,	4¼d.	3¼d.	,,	4¼d.	3¼d.	¾d.	4½d.	3d.
4d.	,,	4½d.	3½d.	,,	4½d.	3½d.	,,	4¾d.	3¼d.
4¼d.	,,	4¾d.	3¾d.	¾d.	5d.	3½d.	,,	5d.	3½d.
4½d.	,,	5d.	4d.	,,	5¼d.	3¾d.	,,	5¼d.	3¾d.
4¾d.	,,	5¼d.	4¼d.	,,	5½d.	4d.	,,	5½d.	4d.
5d.	¾d.	5¾d.	4¼d.	,,	5¾d.	4¼d.	1d.	6d.	4d.
5¼d.	,,	6d.	4½d.	,,	6d.	4½d.	,,	6¼d.	4¼d.
5½d.	,,	6¼d.	4¾d.	,,	6¼d.	4¾d.	,,	6½d.	4½d.
5¾d.	,,	6½d.	5d.	,,	6½d.	5d.	,,	6¾d.	4¾d.
6D.	,,	6¾d.	5¼d.	1d.	7d.	5d.	,,	7d.	5d.
6¼d.	,,	7d.	5½d.	,,	7¼d.	5¼d.	,,	7¼d.	5¼d.
6½d.	,,	7¼d.	5¾d.	,,	7½d.	5½d.	1¼d.	7¾d.	5¼d.
6¾d.	,,	7½d.	6d.	,,	7¾d.	5¾d.	,,	8d.	5½d.
7d.	1d.	8d.	6d.	,,	8d.	6d.	,,	8¼d.	5¾d.
7¼d.	,,	8¼d.	6¼d.	,,	8¼d.	6¼d.	,,	8½d.	6d.
7½d.	,,	8½d.	6½d.	1¼d.	8¾d.	6¼d.	,,	8¾d.	6¼d.
7¾d.	,,	8¾d.	6¾d.	,,	9d.	6½d.	,,	9d.	6½d.
8d.	,,	9d.	7d.	,,	9¼d.	6¾d.	1½d.	9½d.	6½d.
8¼d.	,,	9¼d.	7¼d.	,,	9½d.	7d.	,,	9¾d.	6¾d.
8½d.	,,	9½d.	7½d.	,,	9¾d.	7¼d.	,,	10d.	7d.
8¾d.	,,	9¾d.	7¾d.	,,	10d.	7½d.	,,	10¼d.	7¼d.
9D.	1¼d.	10¼d.	7¾d.	,,	10¼d.	7¾d.	,,	10½d.	7½d.
9¼d.	,,	10½d.	8d.	1½d.	10¾d.	7¾d.	,,	10¾d.	7¾d.
9½d.	,,	10¾d.	8¼d.	,,	11d.	8d.	1¾d.	11¼d.	7¾d.
9¾d.	,,	11d.	8½d.	,,	11¼d.	8¼d.	,,	11½d.	8d.
10d.	,,	11¼d.	8¾d.	,,	11½d.	8½d.	,,	11¾d.	8¼d.
10¼d.	,,	11½d.	9d.	,,	11¾d.	8¾d.	,,	1/-	8½d.
10½d.	,,	11¾d.	9¼d.	,,	1/-	9d.	,,	1/0¼	8¾d.
10¾d.	,,	1/-	9½d.	,,	1/0¼	9¼d.	2d.	1/0¾	8¾d.
11d.	1½d.	1/0½	9½d.	1¾d.	1/0¾	9¼d.	,,	1/1	9d.
11¼d.	,,	1/0¾	9¾d.	,,	1/1	9½d.	,,	1/1¼	9¼d.
11½d.	,,	1/1	10d.	,,	1/1¼	9¾d.	,,	1/1½	9½d.
11¾d.	,,	1/1¼	10¼d.	,,	1/1½	10d.	,,	1/1¾	9¾d.
1/-	,,	1/1½	10½d.	,,	1/1¾	10¼d.	,,	1/2	10d.
1/0½	,,	1/2	11d.	2d.	1/2½	10½d.	2¼d.	1/2¾	10¼d.
1/1	1¾d.	1/2¾	11¼d.	,,	1/3	11d.	,,	1/3¼	10¾d.
1/1½	,,	1/3¼	11¾d.	,,	1/3½	11½d.	,,	1/3¾	11¼d.
1/2	,,	1/3¾	1/0¼	,,	1/4	1/-	2½d.	1/4½	11½d.
1/2½	,,	1/4¼	1/0¾	2¼d.	1/4¾	1/0¼	,,	1/5	1/-
1/3	2d.	1/5	1/1	,,	1/5¼	1/0¾	2¾d.	1/5¾	1/0¼
1/3½	,,	1/5½	1/1½	,,	1/5¾	1/1¼	,,	1/6¼	1/0¾
1/4	,,	1/6	1/2	2½d.	1/6½	1/1½	,,	1/6¾	1/1¼
1/4½	,,	1/6½	1/2½	,,	1/7	1/2	3d.	1/7½	1/1½
1/5	2¼d.	1/7¼	1/2¾	,,	1/7½	1/2¼	,,	1/8	1/2
1/5½	,,	1/7¾	1/3¼	2¾d.	1/8¼	1/2¾	,,	1/8½	1/2½
1/6	,,	1/8¼	1/3¾	,,	1/8¾	1/3¼	3¼d.	1/9¼	1/2¾

INV.	12½ % Disct.	12½ % ON	12½ % OFF	15% Disct.	15% ON	15% OFF	17½ % Disct.	17½ % ON	17½ % OFF
1/6½	2¼d.	1/8¾	1/4¼	2¾d.	1/9¼	1/3¾	3¼d.	1/9¾	1/3¼
1/7	2½d.	1/9½	1/4½	,,	1/9¾	1/4¼	,,	1/10¼	1/3¾
1/7½	,,	1/10	1/5	3d.	1/10½	1/4½	3½d.	1/11	1/4
1/8	,,	1/10½	1/5½	,,	1/11	1/5	,,	1/11½	1/4½
1/8½	,,	1/11	1/6	,,	1/11½	1/5½	,,	2/-	1/5
1/9	2¾d.	**1/11¾**	**1/6¼**	3¼d.	**2/0¼**	**1/5¾**	3¾d.	**2/0¾**	**1/5¼**
1/9½	,,	2/0¼	1/6¾	,,	2/0¾	1/6¼	,,	2/1¼	1/5¾
1/10	,,	2/0¾	1/7¼	,,	2/1¼	1/6¾	,,	2/1¾	1/6¼
1/10½	,,	2/1¼	1/7¾	3½d.	2/2	1/7	4d.	2/2½	1/6½
1/11	3d.	2/2	1/8	,,	2/2½	1/7½	,,	2/3	1/7
1/11½	,,	2/2½	1/8½	,,	2/3	1/8	,,	2/3½	1/7½
2/-	,,	**2/3**	**1/9**	,,	**2/3½**	**1/8½**	4¼d.	**2/4¼**	**1/7¾**
2/0½	,,	2/3½	1/9½	3¾d.	2/4¼	1/8¾	,,	2/4¾	1/8¼
2/1	3¼d.	2/4¼	1/9¾	,,	2/4¾	1/9¼	4½d.	2/5½	1/8½
2/1½	,,	2/4¾	1/10¼	,,	2/5¼	1/9¾	,,	2/6	1/9
2/2	,,	2/5¼	1/10¾	4d.	2/6	1/10	,,	2/6½	1/9½
2/3	3½d.	2/6½	1/11½	,,	2/7	1/11	4¾d.	2/7¾	1/10¼
2/4	,,	2/7½	2/0½	4¼d.	2/8¼	1/11¾	5d.	2/9	1/11
2/5	3¾d.	2/8¾	2/1¼	,,	2/9¼	2/0¾	,,	2/10	2/-
2/6	,,	**2/9¾**	**2/2¼**	4½d.	**2/10½**	**2/1½**	5¼d.	**2/11¼**	**2/0¾**
2/7	4d.	2/11	2/3	4¾d.	2/11¾	2/2¼	5½d.	3/0½	2/1½
2/8	,,	3/-	2/4	,,	3/0¾	2/3¼	,,	3/1½	2/2½
2/9	4¼d.	3/1¼	2/4¾	5d.	3/2	2/4	5¾d.	3/2¾	2/3¼
2/10	,,	3/2¼	2/5¾	,,	3/3	2/5	6d.	3/4	2/4
2/11	4½d.	3/3½	2/6½	5¼d.	3/4¼	2/5¾	6¼d.	3/5¼	2/4¾
3/-	,,	**3/4½**	**2/7½**	5½d.	**3/5½**	**2/6½**	,,	**3/6¼**	**2/5¾**
3/1	4¾d.	3/5¾	2/8¼	,,	3/6½	2/7½	6½d.	3/7½	2/6½
3/2	,,	3/6¾	2/9¼	5¾d.	3/7¾	2/8¼	6¾d.	3/8¾	2/7¼
3/3	5d.	3/8	2/10	,,	3/8¾	2/9¼	,,	3/9¾	2/8¼
3/4	,,	3/9	2/11	6d.	3/10	2/10	7d.	3/11	2/9
3/5	5¼d.	3/10¼	2/11¾	6¼d.	3/11¼	2/10¾	7¼d.	4/0¼	2/9¾
3/6	,,	**3/11¼**	**3/0¾**	,,	**4/0¼**	**2/11¾**	,,	**4/1¼**	**2/10¾**
3/7	5½d.	4/0½	3/1½	6½d.	4/1½	3/0½	7½d.	4/2½	2/11½
3/8	,,	4/1½	3/2½	,,	4/2½	3/1½	7¾d.	4/3¾	3/0¼
3/9	5¾d.	4/2¾	3/3¼	6¾d.	4/3¾	3/2¼	8d.	4/5	3/1
3/10	,,	4/3¾	3/4¼	7d.	4/5	3/3	,,	4/6	3/2
3/11	6d.	4/5	3/5	,,	4/6	3/4	8¼d.	4/7¼	3/2¾
4/-	,,	**4/6**	**3/6**	7¼d.	**4/7¼**	**3/4**[illegible]	8½d.	**4/8½**	**3/3½**
4/1	6¼d.	4/7¼	3/6¾	,,	4/8¼	3/5¾	,,	4/9½	3/4½
4/2	,,	4/8¼	3/7¾	7½d.	4/9½	3/6½	8¾d.	4/10¾	3/5¼
4/3	6½d.	4/9½	3/8½	7¾d.	4/10¾	3/7¼	9d.	5/-	3/6
4/4	,,	4/10½	3/9½	,,	4/11¾	3/8¼	,,	5/1	3/7
4/5	6¾d.	4/11¾	3/10¼	8d.	5/1	3/9	9¼d.	5/2¼	3/7¾
4/6	,,	**5/0¾**	**3/11¼**	,,	**5/2**	**3/10**	9½d.	5/3½	3/8½
4/7	7d.	5/2	4/-	8¼d.	5/3¼	3/10¾	9¾d.	5/4¾	3/9¼
4/8	,,	5/3	4/1	8½d.	5/4½	3/11½	,,	5/5¾	3/10¼
4/9	7¼d.	5/4¼	4/1¾	,,	5/5½	4/0½	10d.	5/7	3/11
4/10	,,	5/5¼	4/2¾	8¾d.	5/6¾	4/1¼	10¼d.	5/8¼	3/11¾
4/11	7½d.	5/6½	4/3½	,,	5/7¾	4/2¼	,,	5/9¼	4/0¾
5/-	,,	**5/7½**	**4/4½**	9d.	**5/9**	**4/3**	10½d.	**5/10½**	**4/1½**
5/1	7¾d.	5/8¾	4/5¼	9¼d.	5/10¼	4/3¾	10¾d.	5/11¾	4/2¼
5/2	,,	5/9¾	4/6¼	,,	5/11¼	4/4¾	,,	6/0¾	4/3¼
5/3	8d.	5/11	4/7	9½d.	6/0½	4/5½	11d.	6/2	4/4
5/4	,,	6/-	4/8	,,	6/1½	4/6½	11¼d.	6/3¼	4/4¾
5/5	8¼d.	6/1¼	4/8¾	9¾d.	6/2¾	4/7¼	11½d.	6/4½	4/5½
5/6	,,	**6/2¼**	**4/9¾**	10d.	**6/4**	**4/8**	,,	**6/5½**	

INV.	20% Disct.	20% ON	20% OFF	25% Disct.	25% ON	25% OFF	33⅓% Disct.	33⅓% ON	33⅓% OFF
1d.	⅛d.	..	..	¼d.	1¼d.	¾d.	¼d.	1¼d.	¾d.
1¼d.	¼d.	1½d.	1d.	,,	1½d.	1d.	½d.	1¾d.	¾d.
1½d.	,,	1¾d.	1¼d.	½d.	2d.	1d.	,,	2d.	1d.
1¾d.	,,	2d.	1½d.	,,	2¼d.	1¼d.	,,	2¼d.	1¼d.
2d.	½d.	2½d.	1½d.	,,	2½d.	1½d.	¾d.	2¾d.	1¼d.
2¼d.	,,	2¾d.	1¾d.	,,	2¾d.	1¾d.	,,	3d.	1½d.
2½d.	,,	3d.	2d.	¾d.	3¼d.	1¾d.	,,	3¼d.	1¾d.
2¾d.	,,	3¼d.	2¼d.	,,	3½d.	2d.	1d.	3¾d.	1¾d.
3D.	,,	3½d.	2½d.	,,	3¾d.	2¼d.	,,	4d.	2d.
3¼d.	¾d.	4d.	2½d.	,,	4d.	2½d.	,,	4¼d.	2¼d.
3½d.	,,	4¼d.	2¾d.	1d.	4½d.	2½d.	1¼d.	4¾d.	2¼d.
3¾d.	,,	4½d.	3d.	,,	4¾d.	2¾d.	,,	5d.	2½d.
4d.	,,	4¾d.	3¼d.	,,	5d.	3d.	,,	5¼d.	2¾d.
4¼d.	,,	5d.	3½d.	,,	5¼d.	3¼d.	1½d.	5¾d.	2¾d.
4½d.	1d.	5½d.	3½d.	1¼d.	5¾d.	3¼d.	,,	6d.	3d.
4¾d.	,,	5¾d.	3¾d.	,,	6d.	3½d.	,,	6¼d.	3¼d.
5d.	,,	6d.	4d.	,,	6¼d.	3¾d.	1¾d.	6¾d.	3¼d.
5¼d.	,,	6¼d.	4¼d.	,,	6½d.	4d.	,,	7d.	3½d.
5½d.	,,	6½d.	4½d.	1½d.	7d.	4d.	,,	7¼d.	3¾d.
5¾d.	1¼d.	7d.	4½d.	,,	7¼d.	4¼d.	2d.	7¾d.	3¾d.
6D.	,,	7¼d.	4¾d.	,,	7½d.	4½d.	,,	8d.	4d.
6¼d.	,,	7½d.	5d.	,,	7¾d.	4¾d.	,,	8¼d.	4¼d.
6½d.	,,	7¾d.	5¼d.	1¾d.	8¼d.	4¾d.	2¼d.	8¾d.	4¼d.
6¾d.	,,	8d.	5½d.	,,	8½d.	5d.	,,	9d.	4½d.
7d.	1½d.	8½d.	5½d.	,,	8¾d.	5¼d.	,,	9¼d.	4¾d.
7¼d.	,,	8¾d.	5¾d.	,,	9d.	5½d.	2½d.	9¾d.	4¾d.
7½d.	,,	9d.	6d.	2d.	9½d.	5½d.	,,	10d.	5d.
7¾d.	,,	9¼d.	6¼d.	,,	9¾d.	5¾d.	,,	10¼d.	5¼d.
8d.	,,	9½d.	6½d.	,,	10d.	6d.	2¾d.	10¾d.	5¼d.
8¼d.	1¾d.	10d.	6½d.	,,	10¼d.	6¼d.	,,	11d.	5½d.
8½d.	,,	10¼d.	6¾d.	2¼d.	10¾d.	6¼d.	,,	11¼d.	5¾d.
8¾d.	,,	10½d.	7d.	,,	11d.	6½d.	3d.	11¾d.	5¾d.
9D.	,,	10¾d.	7¼d.	,,	11¼d.	6¾d.	,,	1/-	6d.
9¼d.	,,	11d.	7½d.	,,	11½d.	7d.	,,	1/0¼	6¼d.
9½d.	2d.	11½d.	7½d.	2½d.	1/-	7d.	3¼d.	1/0¾	6¼d.
9¾d.	,,	11¾d.	7¾d.	,,	1/0¼	7¼d.	,,	1/1	6½d.
10d.	,,	1/-	8d.	,,	1/0½	7½d.	,,	1/1¼	6¾d.
10¼d.	,,	1/0¼	8¼d.	,,	1/0¾	7¾d.	3½d.	1/1¾	6¾d.
10½d.	,,	1/0½	8½d.	2¾d.	1/1¼	7¾d.	,,	1/2	7d.
10¾d.	2¼d.	1/1	8½d.	,,	1/1½	8d.	,,	1/2¼	7¼d.
11d.	,,	1/1¼	8¾d.	,,	1/1¾	8¼d.	3¾d.	1/2¾	7¼d.
11¼d.	,,	1/1½	9d.	,,	1/2	8½d.	,,	1/3	7½d.
11½d.	,,	1/1¾	9¼d.	3d.	1/2½	8½d.	,,	1/3¼	7¾d.
11¾d.	,,	1/2	9½d.	,,	1/2¾	8¾d.	4d.	1/3¾	7¾d.
1/-	2½d.	1/2½	9½d.	,,	1/3	9d.	,,	1/4	8d.
1/0½	,,	1/3	10d.	3¼d.	1/3¾	9¼d.	4¼d.	1/4¾	8¼d.
1/1	,,	1/3½	10½d.	,,	1/4¼	9¾d.	,,	1/5¼	8¾d.
1/1½	2¾d.	1/4¼	10¾d.	3½d.	1/5	10d.	4½d.	1/6	9d.
1/2	,,	1/4¾	11¼d.	,,	1/5½	10½d.	4¾d.	1/6¾	9¼d.
1/2½	3d.	1/5½	11½d.	3¾d.	1/6¼	10¾d.	,,	1/7¼	9¾d.
1/3	,,	1/6	1/-	,,	1/6¾	11¼d.	5d.	1/8	10d.
1/3½	,,	1/6½	1/0½	4d.	1/7½	11½d.	5¼d.	1/8¾	10¼d.
1/4	3¼d.	1/7¼	1/0¾	,,	1/8	1/-	,,	1/9¼	10¾d.
1/4½	,,	1/7¾	1/1¼	4¼d.	1/8¾	1/0¼	5½d.	1/10	11d.
1/5	3½d.	1/8½	1/1½	,,	1/9¼	1/0¾	5¾d.	1/10¾	11¼d.
1/5½	,,	1/9	1/2	4½d.	1/10	1/1	,,	1/11¼	11¾d.
1/6	,,	1/9½	1/2½	,,	1/10½	1/1½	6d.	2/-	1/-

INV.	20% Disct.	20% ON	20% OFF	25% Disct.	25% ON	25% OFF	33⅓% Disct.	33⅓% ON	33⅓% OFF
1/6½	3¾d.	1/10¼	1/2¾	4¾d.	1/11¼	1/1¾	6¼d.	2/0¾	1/0¼
1/7	,,	1/10¾	1/3¼	,,	1/11¾	1/2¼	,,	2/1¼	1/0¾
1/7½	4d.	1/11½	1/3½	5d.	2/0½	1/2½	6½d.	2/2	1/1
1/8	,,	2/-	1/4	,,	2/1	1/3	6¾d.	2/2¾	1/1¼
1/8½	,,	2/0½	1/4½	5¼d.	2/1¾	1/3¼	,,	2/3¼	1/1¾
1/9	4¼d.	**2/1¼**	**1/4¾**	,,	**2/2¼**	**1/3¾**	7d.	**2/4**	**1/2**
1/9½	,,	2/1¾	1/5¼	5½d.	2/3	1/4	7¼d.	2/4¾	1/2¼
1/10	4½d.	2/2½	1/5½	,,	2/3½	1/4½	,,	2/5¼	1/2¾
1/10½	,,	2/3	1/6	5¾d.	2/4¼	1/4¾	7½d.	2/6	1/3
1/11	,,	2/3½	1/6½	,,	2/4¾	1/5¼	7¾d.	2/6¾	1/3¼
1/11½	4¾d.	2/4¼	1/6¾	6d.	2/5½	1/5½	,,	2/7¼	1/3¾
2/-	,,	**2/4¾**	**1/7¼**	,,	**2/6**	**1/6**	8d.	**2/8**	**1/4**
2/0½	5d.	2/5½	1/7½	6¼d.	2/6¾	1/6¼	8¼d.	2/8¾	1/4¼
2/1	,,	2/6	1/8	,,	2/7¼	1/6¾	,,	2/9¼	1/4¾
2/1½	,,	2/6½	1/8½	6½d.	2/8	1/7	8½d.	2/10	1/5
2/2	5¼d.	2/7¼	1/8¾	,,	2/8½	1/7½	8¾d.	2/10¾	1/5¼
2/3	5½d.	2/8½	1/9½	6¾d.	2/9¾	1/8¼	9d.	3/-	1/6
2/4	,,	2/9½	1/10½	7d.	2/11	1/9	9¼d.	3/1¼	1/6¾
2/5	5¾d.	2/10¾	1/11¼	7¼d.	3/0¼	1/9¾	9¾d.	3/2¾	1/7¼
2/6	6d.	**3/-**	**2/-**	7½d.	**3/1½**	**1/10½**	10d.	**3/4**	**1/8**
2/7	6¼d.	3/1¼	2/0¾	7¾d.	3/2¾	1/11¼	10¼d.	3/5¼	1/8¾
2/8	6½d.	3/2½	2/1½	8d.	3/4	2/-	10¾d.	3/6¾	1/9¼
2/9	,,	3/3½	2/2½	8¼d.	3/5¼	2/0¾	11d.	3/8	1/10
2/10	6¾d.	3/4¾	2/3¼	8½d.	3/6½	2/1½	11¼d.	3/9¼	1/10¾
2/11	7d.	3/6	2/4	8¾d.	3/7¾	2/2¼	11¾d.	3/10¾	1/11¼
3/-	7¼d.	**3/7½**	**2/4¾**	9d.	**3/9**	**2/3**	1/-	**4/-**	**2/-**
3/1	7½d.	3/8½	2/5½	9¼d.	3/10¼	2/3¾	1/0¼	4/1¼	2/0¾
3/2	,,	3/9½	2/6½	9½d.	3/11½	2/4½	1/0¾	4/2¾	2/1¼
3/3	7¾d.	3/10¾	2/7¼	9¾d.	4/0¾	2/5¼	1/1	4/4	2/2
3/4	8d.	4/-	2/8	10d.	4/2	2/6	1/1¼	4/5¼	2/2¾
3/5	8¼d.	4/1¼	2/8¾	10¼d.	4/3¼	2/6¾	1/1¾	4/6¾	2/3¼
3/6	8½d.	**4/2½**	**2/9½**	10½d.	**4/4½**	**2/7½**	1/2	**4/8**	**2/4**
3/7	,,	4/3½	2/10½	10¾d.	4/5¾	2/8¼	1/2¼	4/9¼	2/4¾
3/8	8¾d.	4/4¾	2/11¼	11d.	4/7	2/9	1/2¾	4/10¾	2/5¼
3/9	9d.	4/6	3/-	11¼d.	4/8¼	2/9¾	1/3	5/-	2/6
3/10	9¼d.	4/7¼	3/0¾	11½d.	4/9½	2/10½	1/3¼	5/1¼	2/6¾
3/11	9½d.	4/8½	3/1½	11¾d.	4/10¾	2/11¼	1/3¾	5/2¾	2/7¼
4/-	,,	**4/9½**	**3/2½**	1/-	**5/-**	**3/-**	1/4	**5/4**	**2/8**
4/1	9¾d.	4/10¾	3/3¼	1/0¼	5/1¼	3/0¾	1/4¼	5/5¼	2/8¾
4/2	10d.	5/-	3/4	1/0½	5/2½	3/1½	1/4¾	5/6¾	2/9¼
4/3	10¼d.	5/1¼	3/4¾	1/0¾	5/3¾	3/2¼	1/5	5/8	2/10
4/4	10½d.	5/2½	3/5½	1/1	5/5	3/3	1/5¼	5/9¼	2/10¾
4/5	,,	5/3½	3/6½	1/1¼	5/6¼	3/3¾	1/5¾	5/10¾	2/11¼
4/6	10¾d.	**5/4¾**	**3/7¼**	1/1½	**5/7½**	**3/4½**	1/6	**6/-**	**3/-**
4/7	11d.	5/6	3/8	1/1¾	5/8¾	3/5¼	1/6¼	6/1¼	3/0¾
4/8	11¼d.	5/7¼	3/8¾	1/2	5/10	3/6	1/6¾	6/2¾	3/1¼
4/9	11½d.	5/8½	3/9½	1/2¼	5/11¼	3/6¾	1/7	6/4	3/2
4/10	,,	5/9½	3/10½	1/2½	6/0½	3/7½	1/7¼	6/5¼	3/2¾
4/11	11¾d.	5/10¾	3/11¼	1/2¾	6/1¾	3/8¼	1/7¾	6/6¾	3/3¼
5/-	1/-	**6/-**	**4/-**	1/3	**6/3**	**3/9**	1/8	**6/8**	**3/4**
5/1	1/0¼	6/1¼	4/0¾	1/3¼	6/4¼	3/9¾	1/8¼	6/9¼	3/4¾
5/2	1/0½	6/2½	4/1½	1/3½	6/5½	3/10½	1/8¾	6/10¾	3/5¼
5/3	,,	6/3½	4/2½	1/3¾	6/6¾	3/11¼	1/9	7/-	3/6
5/4	1/0¾	6/4¾	4/3¼	1/4	6/8	4/-	1/9¼	7/1¼	3/6¾
5/5	1/1	6/6	4/4	1/4¼	6/9¼	4/0¾	1/9¾	7/2¾	3/7¼
5/6	1/1¼	**6/7½**	**4/4¾**	1/4½	**6/10½**	**4/1½**	1/10	**7/4**	**3/8**

12½%   15%   17½%

INV.	Disct.	ON	OFF	Disct.	ON	OFF	Disct.	ON	OFF
5/7	8½d.	6/3½	4/10½	10d.	6/5	4/9	11¾d.	6/6¾	4/7¼
5/8	"	6/4½	4/11½	10¼d.	6/6¼	4/9¾	1/-	6/8	4/8
5/9	8¾d.	6/5¾	5/0¼	"	6/7¼	4/10¾	"	6/9	4/9
5/10	"	6/6¾	5/1¼	10½d.	6/8½	4/11½	1/0¼	6/10¼	4/9¾
5/11	9d.	6/8	5/2	10¾d.	6/9¾	5/0¼	1/0½	6/11½	4/10½
6/-	"	6/9	5/3	"	6/10¾	5/1¼	"	7/0½	4/11½
6/1	9¼d.	6/10¼	5/3¾	11d.	7/-	5/2	1/0¾	7/1¾	5/0¼
6/2	"	6/11¼	5/4¾	"	7/1	5/3	1/1	7/3	5/1
6/3	9½d.	7/0½	5/5½	11¼d.	7/2¼	5/3¾	1/1¼	7/4¼	5/1¾
6/4	"	7/1½	5/6½	11½d.	7/3½	5/4½	"	7/5¼	5/2¾
6/5	9¾d.	7/2¾	5/7¼	"	7/4½	5/5½	1/1½	7/6½	5/3½
6/6	"	7/3¾	5/8¼	11¾d.	7/5¾	5/6¼	1/1¾	7/7¾	5/4¼
6/7	10d.	7/5	5/9	"	7/6¾	5/7¼	"	7/8¾	5/5¼
6/8	"	7/6	5/10	1/-	7/8	5/8	1/2	7/10	5/6
6/9	10¼d.	7/7¼	5/10¾	1/0¼	7/9¼	5/8¾	1/2¼	7/11¼	5/6¾
6/10	"	7/8¼	5/11¾	"	7/10¼	5/9¾	"	8/0¼	5/7¾
6/11	10½d.	7/9½	6/0½	1/0½	7/11½	5/10½	1/2½	8/1½	5/8½
7/-	"	7/10½	6/1½	"	8/0½	5/11½	1/2¾	8/2¾	5/9¼
7/1	10¾d.	7/11¾	6/2¼	1/0¾	8/1¾	6/0¼	1/3	8/4	5/10
7/2	"	8/0¾	6/3¼	1/1	8/3	6/1	"	8/5	5/11
7/3	11d.	8/2	6/4	"	8/4	6/2	1/3¼	8/6¼	5/11¾
7/4	"	8/3	6/5	1/1¼	8/5¼	6/2¾	1/3½	8/7½	6/0½
7/5	11¼d.	8/4¼	6/5¾	"	8/6¼	6/3¾	"	8/8½	6/1½
7/6	"	8/5¼	6/6¾	1/1½	8/7½	6/4½	1/3¾	8/9¾	6/2¼
7/7	11½d.	8/6½	6/7½	1/1¾	8/8¾	6/5¼	1/4	8/11	6/3
7/8	"	8/7½	6/8½	"	8/9¾	6/6¼	"	9/-	6/4
7/9	11¾d.	8/8¾	6/9¼	1/2	8/11	6/7	1/4¼	9/1¼	6/4¾
7/10	"	8/9¾	6/10¼	"	9/-	6/8	1/4½	9/2½	6/5½
7/11	1/-	8/11	6/11	1/2¼	9/1¼	6/8¾	1/4¾	9/3¾	6/6¼
8/-	"	9/-	7/-	1/2½	9/2½	6/9½	"	9/4¾	6/7¼
8/1	1/0¼	9/1¼	7/0¾	"	9/3½	6/10½	1/5	9/6	6/8
8/2	"	9/2¼	7/1¾	1/2¾	9/4¾	6/11¼	1/5¼	9/7¼	6/8¾
8/3	1/0½	9/3½	7/2½	"	9/5¾	7/0¼	"	9/8¼	6/9¾
8/4	"	9/4½	7/3½	1/3	9/7	7/1	1/5½	9/9½	6/10½
8/5	1/0¾	9/5¾	7/4¼	1/3¼	9/8¼	7/1¾	1/5¾	9/10¾	6/11¼
8/6	"	9/6¾	7/5¼	"	9/9¼	7/2¾	"	9/11¾	7/0¼
8/7	1/1	9/8	7/6	1/3½	9/10½	7/3½	1/6	10/1	7/1
8/8	"	9/9	7/7	"	9/11½	7/4½	1/6¼	10/2¼	7/1¾
8/9	1/1¼	9/10¼	7/7¾	1/3¾	10/0¾	7/5¼	1/6½	10/3½	7/2½
8/10	"	9/11¼	7/8¾	1/4	10/2	7/6	"	10/4½	7/3½
8/11	1/1½	10/0½	7/9½	"	10/3	7/7	1/6¾	10/5¾	7/4¼
9/-	"	10/1½	7/10½	1/4¼	10/4¼	7/7¾	1/7	10/7	7/5
9/1	1/1¾	10/2¾	7/11¼	"	10/5¼	7/8¾	"	10/8	7/6
9/2	"	10/3¾	8/0¼	1/4½	10/6½	7/9½	1/7¼	10/9¼	7/6¾
9/3	1/2	10/5	8/1	1/4¾	10/7¾	7/10¼	1/7½	10/10½	7/7½
9/4	"	10/6	8/2	"	10/8¾	7/11¼	"	10/11½	7/8½
9/5	1/2¼	10/7¼	8/2¾	1/5	10/10	8/-	1/7¾	11/0¾	7/9¼
9/6	"	10/8¼	8/3¾	"	10/11	8/1	1/8	11/2	7/10
9/7	1/2½	10/9½	8/4½	1/5¼	11/0¼	8/1¾	1/8¼	11/3¼	7/10¾
9/8	"	10/10½	8/5½	1/5½	11/1½	8/2½	"	11/4¼	7/11¾
9/9	1/2¾	10/11¾	8/6¼	"	11/2½	8/3½	1/8½	11/5½	8/0½
9/10	"	11/0¾	8/7¼	1/5¾	11/3¾	8/4¼	1/8¾	11/6¾	8/1¼
9/11	1/3	11/2	8/8	"	11/4¾	8/5¼	"	11/7¾	8/2¼
10/-	"	11/3	8/9	1/6	11/6	8/6	1/9	11/9	8/3
10/1	1/3¼	11/4¼	8/9¾	1/6¼	11/7¼	8/6¾	1/9¼	11/10¼	8/3¾
10/2	"	11/5¼	8/10¾	"	11/8¼	8/7¾	"	11/11¼	8/4¾
10/3	1/3½	11/6½	8/11½	1/6½	11/9½	8/8½	1/9½	12/0½	8/5½

	20%			25%			33⅓%		
INV.	Disct.	**ON**	**OFF**	Disct.	**ON**	**OFF**	Disct.	**ON**	**OFF**
5/7	1/1½	6/8½	4/5½	1/4¾	6/11¾	4/2¼	1/10¼	7/5¼	3/8¾
5/8	,,	6/9½	4/6½	1/5	7/1	4/3	1/10¾	7/6¾	3/9¼
5/9	1/1¾	6/10¾	4/7¼	1/5¼	7/2¼	4/3¾	1/11	7/8	3/10
5/10	1/2	7/-	4/8	1/5½	7/3½	4/4½	1/11¼	7/9¼	3/10¾
5/11	1/2¼	7/1¼	4/8¾	1/5¾	7/4¾	4/5¼	1/11¾	7/10¾	3/11¼
6/-	1/2½	**7/2½**	**4/9½**	**1/6**	**7/6**	**4/6**	**2/-**	**8/-**	**4/-**
6/1	,,	7/3½	4/10½	1/6¼	7/7¼	4/6¾	2/0¼	8/1¼	4/0¾
6/2	1/2¾	7/4¾	4/11¼	1/6½	7/8½	4/7½	2/0¾	8/2¾	4/1¼
6/3	1/3	7/6	5/-	1/6¾	7/9¾	4/8¼	2/1	8/4	4/2
6/4	1/3¼	7/7¼	5/0¾	1/7	7/11	4/9	2/1¼	8/5¼	4/2¾
6/5	1/3½	7/8½	5/1½	1/7¼	8/0¼	4/9¾	2/1¾	8/6¾	4/3¼
6/6	,,	**7/9½**	**5/2½**	**1/7½**	**8/1½**	**4/10½**	**2/2**	**8/8**	**4/4**
6/7	1/3¾	7/10¾	5/3¼	1/7¾	8/2¾	4/11¼	2/2¼	8/9¼	4/4¾
6/8	1/4	8/-	5/4	1/8	8/4	5/-	2/2¾	8/10¾	4/5¼
6/9	1/4¼	8/1¼	5/4¾	1/8¼	8/5¼	5/0¾	2/3	9/-	4/6
6/10	1/4½	8/2½	5/5½	1/8½	8/6½	5/1½	2/3¼	9/1¼	4/6¾
6/11	,,	8/3½	5/6½	1/8¾	8/7¾	5/2¼	2/3¾	9/2¾	4/7¼
7/-	**1/4¾**	**8/4¾**	**5/7¼**	**1/9**	**8/9**	**5/3**	**2/4**	**9/4**	**4/8**
7/1	1/5	8/6	5/8	1/9¼	8/10¼	5/3¾	2/4¼	9/5¼	4/8¾
7/2	1/5¼	8/7¼	5/8¾	1/9½	8/11½	5/4½	2/4¾	9/6¾	4/9¼
7/3	1/5½	8/8½	5/9½	1/9¾	9/0¾	5/5¼	2/5	9/8	4/10
7/4	,,	8/9½	5/10½	1/10	9/2	5/6	2/5¼	9/9¼	4/10¾
7/5	1/5¾	8/10¾	5/11¼	1/10¼	9/3¼	5/6¾	2/5¾	9/10¾	4/11¼
7/6	**1/6**	**9/-**	**6/-**	**1/10½**	**9/4½**	**5/7½**	**2/6**	**10/-**	**5/-**
7/7	1/6¼	9/1¼	6/0¾	1/10¾	9/5¾	5/8¼	2/6¼	10/1¼	5/0¾
7/8	1/6½	9/2½	6/1½	1/11	9/7	5/9	2/6¾	10/2¾	5/1¼
7/9	,,	9/3½	6/2½	1/11¼	9/8¼	5/9¾	2/7	10/4	5/2
7/10	1/6¾	9/4¾	6/3¼	1/11½	9/9½	5/10½	2/7¼	10/5¼	5/2¾
7/11	1/7	9/6	6/4	1/11¾	9/10¾	5/11¼	2/7¾	10/6¾	5/3¼
8/-	**1/7¼**	**9/7¼**	**6/4¾**	**2/-**	**10/-**	**6/-**	**2/8**	**10/8**	**5/4**
8/1	1/7½	9/8½	6/5½	2/0¼	10/1¼	6/0¾	2/8¼	10/9¼	5/4¾
8/2	,,	9/9½	6/6½	2/0½	10/2½	6/1½	2/8¾	10/10¾	5/5¼
8/3	1/7¾	9/10¾	6/7¼	2/0¾	10/3¾	6/2¼	2/9	11/-	5/6
8/4	1/8	10/-	6/8	2/1	10/5	6/3	2/9¼	11/1¼	5/6¾
8/5	1/8¼	10/1¼	6/8¾	2/1¼	10/6¼	6/3¾	2/9¾	11/2¾	5/7¼
8/6	**1/8½**	**10/2½**	**6/9½**	**2/1½**	**10/7½**	**6/4½**	**2/10**	**11/4**	**5/8**
8/7	,,	10/3½	6/10½	2/1¾	10/8¾	6/5¼	2/10¼	11/5¼	5/8¾
8/8	1/8¾	10/4¾	6/11¼	2/2	10/10	6/6	2/10¾	11/6¾	5/9¼
8/9	1/9	10/6	7/-	2/2¼	10/11¼	6/6¾	2/11	11/8	5/10
8/10	1/9¼	10/7¼	7/0¾	2/2½	11/0½	6/7½	2/11¼	11/9¼	5/10¾
8/11	1/9½	10/8½	7/1½	2/2¾	11/1¾	6/8¼	2/11¾	11/10¾	5/11¼
9/-	,,	**10/9½**	**7/2½**	**2/3**	**11/3**	**6/9**	**3/-**	**12/-**	**6/-**
9/1	1/9¾	10/10¾	7/3¼	2/3¼	11/4¼	6/9¾	3/0¼	12/1¼	6/0¾
9/2	1/10	11/-	7/4	2/3½	11/5½	6/10½	3/0¾	12/2¾	6/1¼
9/3	1/10¼	11/1¼	7/4¾	2/3¾	11/6¾	6/11¼	3/1	12/4	6/2
9/4	1/10½	11/2½	7/5½	2/4	11/8	7/-	3/1¼	12/5¼	6/2¾
9/5	,,	11/3½	7/6½	2/4¼	11/9¼	7/0¾	3/1¾	12/6¾	6/3¼
9/6	**1/10¾**	**11/4¾**	**7/7¼**	**2/4½**	**11/10½**	**7/1½**	**3/2**	**12/8**	**6/4**
9/7	1/11	11/6	7/8	2/4¾	11/11¾	7/2¼	3/2¼	12/9¼	6/4¾
9/8	1/11¼	11/7¼	7/8¾	2/5	12/1	7/3	3/2¾	12/10¾	6/5¼
9/9	1/11½	11/8½	7/9½	2/5¼	12/2¼	7/3¾	3/3	13/-	6/6
9/10	,,	11/9½	7/10½	2/5½	12/3½	7/4½	3/3¼	13/1¼	6/6¾
9/11	1/11¾	11/10¾	7/11¼	2/5¾	12/4¾	7/5¼	3/3¾	13/2¾	6/7¼
10/-	**2/-**	**12/-**	**8/-**	**2/6**	**12/6**	**7/6**	**3/4**	**13/4**	**6/8**
10/1	2/0¼	12/1¼	8/0¾	2/6¼	12/7¼	7/6¾	3/4¼	13/5¼	6/8¾
10/2	2/0½	12/2½	8/1½	2/6½	12/8½	7/7½	3/4¾	13/6¾	6/9¼
10/3	,,	12/3½	8/2¼	2/6¾	12/9¾	7/8¼	3/5	13/8	6/10

	12½ %			15 %			17½ %		
INV.	Disct.	**ON**	**OFF**	Disct.	**ON**	**OFF**	Disct.	**ON**	**OFF**
10/4	1/3½	11/7½	9/0½	1/6½	11/10½	8/9½	1/9¾	12/1¾	8/6¼
10/5	1/3¾	11/8¾	9/1¼	1/6¾	11/11¾	8/10¼	1/10	12/3	8/7
10/6	,,	**11/9¾**	**9/2¼**	**1/7**	**12/1**	**8/11**	,,	**12/4**	**8/8**
10/7	1/4	11/11	9/3	,,	12/2	9/-	1/10¼	12/5¼	8/8¾
10/8	,,	12/-	9/4	1/7¼	12/3¼	9/0¾	1/10½	12/6½	8/9½
10/9	1/4¼	12/1¼	9/4¾	,,	12/4¼	9/1¾	,,	12/7½	8/10½
10/10	,,	12/2¼	9/5¾	1/7½	12/5½	9/2½	1/10¾	12/8¾	8/11¼
10/11	1/4½	12/3½	9/6½	1/7¾	12/6¾	9/3¼	1/11	12/10	9/-
11/-	,,	**12/4½**	**9/7½**	,,	**12/7¾**	**9/4¼**	,,	**12/11**	**9/1**
11/1	1/4¾	12/5¾	9/8¼	1/8	12/9	9/5	1/11¼	13/0¼	9/1¾
11/2	,,	12/6¾	9/9¼	,,	12/10	9/6	1/11½	13/1½	9/2½
11/3	1/5	12/8	9/10	1/8¼	12/11¼	9/6¾	1/11¾	13/2¾	9/3¼
11/4	,,	12/9	9/11	1/8½	13/0½	9/7½	,,	13/3¾	9/4¼
11/5	1/5¼	12/10¼	9/11¾	,,	13/1½	9/8½	2/-	13/5	9/5
11/6	,,	**12/11¼**	**10/0¾**	**1/8¾**	**13/2¾**	**9/9¼**	**2/0¼**	**13/6¼**	**9/5¾**
11/7	1/5½	13/0½	10/1½	,,	13/3¾	9/10¼	,,	13/7¼	9/6¾
11/8	,,	13/1½	10/2½	1/9	13/5	9/11	2/0½	13/8½	9/7½
11/9	1/5¾	13/2¾	10/3¼	1/9¼	13/6¼	9/11¾	2/0¾	13/9¾	9/8¼
11/10	,,	13/3¾	10/4¼	,,	13/7¼	10/0¾	,,	13/10¾	9/9¼
11/11	1/6	13/5	10/5	1/9½	13/8½	10/1½	2/1	14/-	9/10
12/-	,,	**13/6**	**10/6**	,,	**13/9½**	**10/2½**	2/1¼	**14/1¼**	**9/10¾**
12/1	1/6¼	13/7¼	10/6¾	1/9¾	13/10¾	10/3¼	2/1½	14/2½	9/11½
12/2	,,	13/8¼	10/7¾	1/10	14/-	10/4	,,	14/3½	10/0½
12/3	1/6½	13/9½	10/8½	,,	14/1	10/5	2/1¾	14/4¾	10/1¼
12/4	,,	13/10½	10/9½	1/10¼	14/2¼	10/5¾	2/2	14/6	10/2
12/5	1/6¾	13/11¾	10/10¼	,,	14/3¼	10/6¾	,,	14/7	10/3
12/6	,,	14/0¾	10/11¼	1/10½	14/4½	10/7½	2/2¼	14/8¼	10/3¾
12/9	1/7¼	14/4¼	11/1¾	1/11	14/8	10/10	2/2¾	14/11¾	10/6¼
13/-	**1/7½**	**14/7½**	**11/4½**	**1/11½**	**14/11½**	**11/0½**	**2/3¼**	**15/3¼**	**10/8¾**
13/3	1/8	14/11	11/7	1/11¾	15/2¾	11/3¼	2/3¾	15/6¾	10/11¼
13/6	1/8¼	15/2¼	11/9¾	2/0¼	15/6¼	11/5¾	2/4¼	15/10¼	11/1¾
13/9	1/8¾	15/5¾	12/0¼	2/0¾	15/9¾	11/8¼	2/5	16/2	11/4
14/-	**1/9**	**15/9**	**12/3**	**2/1¼**	**16/1¼**	**11/10¾**	**2/5½**	**16/5½**	**11/6½**
14/3	1/9½	16/0½	12/5½	2/1¾	16/4¾	12/1¼	2/6	16/9	11/9
14/6	1/9¾	16/3¾	12/8¼	2/2	16/8	12/4	2/6½	17/0½	11/11½
14/9	1/10¼	16/7¼	12/10¾	2/2½	16/11½	12/6½	2/7	17/4	12/2
15/-	**1/10½**	**16/10½**	**13/1½**	**2/3**	**17/3**	**12/9**	**2/7½**	**17/7½**	**12/4½**
15/3	1/11	17/2	13/4	2/3½	17/6½	12/11½	2/8	17/11	12/7
15/6	1/11¼	17/5¼	13/6¾	2/4	17/10	13/2	2/8½	18/2½	12/9½
15/9	1/11¾	17/8¾	13/9¼	2/4¼	18/1¼	13/4¾	2/9	18/6	13/-
16/-	**2/-**	**18/-**	**14/-**	**2/4¾**	**18/4¾**	**13/7¼**	**2/9½**	**18/9½**	**13/2½**
16/3	2/0½	18/3½	14/2½	2/5¼	18/8¼	13/9¾	2/10¼	19/1¼	13/4¾
16/6	2/0¾	18/6¾	14/5¼	2/5¾	18/11¾	14/0¼	2/10¾	19/4¾	13/7¼
16/9	2/1¼	18/10¼	14/7¾	2/6¼	19/3¼	14/2¾	2/11¼	19/8¼	13/9¾
17/-	**2/1½**	**19/1½**	**14/10½**	**2/6½**	**19/6½**	**14/5½**	**2/11¾**	**19/11¾**	**14/0¼**
17/3	2/2	19/5	15/1	2/7	19/10	14/8	3/0¼	20/3¼	14/2¾
17/6	2/2¼	19/8¼	15/3¾	2/7½	20/1½	14/10½	3/0¾	20/6¾	14/5¼
17/9	2/2¾	19/11¾	15/6¼	2/8	20/5	15/1	3/1¼	20/10¼	14/7¾
18/-	2/3	**20/3**	**15/9**	**2/8½**	**20/8½**	**15/3½**	**3/1¾**	**21/1¾**	**14/10¼**
18/3	2/3½	20/6½	15/11½	2/8¾	20/11¾	15/6¼	3/2¼	21/5¼	15/0¼
18/6	2/3¾	20/9¾	16/2¼	2/9¼	21/3¼	15/8¾	3/2¾	21/8¾	15/3¼
18/9	2/4¼	21/1¼	16/4¾	2/9¾	21/6¾	15/11¼	3/3½	22/0½	15/5½
19/-	**2/4½**	**21/4½**	**16/7½**	2/10¼	**21/10¼**	**16/1¾**	3/4	**22/4**	**15/8**
19/3	2/5	21/8	16/10	2/10¾	22/1¾	16/4¼	3/4½	22/7½	15/10½
19/6	2/5¼	21/11¼	17/0¾	2/11	22/5	16/7	3/5	22/11	16/1
19/9	**2/5¾**	22/2¾	17/3¼	2/11½	22/8½	16/9½	**3/5½**	23/2½	16/3½
20/-	**2/6**	**22/6**	**17/6**	3/-	**23/-**	**17/-**	**3/6**	**23/6**	**16/6**

	20%			25%			33⅓%		
INV.	Disct.	ON	OFF	Disct.	ON	OFF	Disct.	ON	OFF
10/4	2/0¾	12/4¾	8/3¼	2/7	12/11	7/9	3/5¼	13/9¼	6/10¾
10/5	2/1	12/6	8/4	2/7¼	13/0¼	7/9¾	3/5¾	13/10¾	6/11¼
10/6	2/1¼	12/7¼	8/4¾	2/7½	13/1½	7/10½	3/6	14/-	7/-
10/7	2/1½	12/8½	8/5½	2/7¾	13/2¾	7/11¼	3/6¼	14/1¼	7/0¾
10/8	,,	12/9½	8/6½	2/8	13/4	8/-	3/6¾	14/2¾	7/1¼
10/9	2/1¾	12/10¾	8/7¼	2/8¼	13/5¼	8/0¾	3/7	14/4	7/2
10/10	2/2	13/-	8/8	2/8½	13/6½	8/1½	3/7¼	14/5¼	7/2¾
10/11	2/2¼	13/1¼	8/8¾	2/8¾	13/7¾	8/2¼	3/7¾	14/6¾	7/3¼
11/-	2/2½	13/2½	8/9½	2/9	13/9	8/3	3/8	14/8	7/4
11/1	,,	13/3½	8/10½	2/9¼	13/10¼	8/3¾	3/8¼	14/9¼	7/4¾
11/2	2/2¾	13/4¾	8/11¼	2/9½	13/11½	8/4½	3/8¾	14/10¾	7/5¼
11/3	2/3	13/6	9/-	2/9¾	14/0¾	8/5¼	3/9	15/-	7/6
11/4	2/3¼	13/7¼	9/0¾	2/10	14/2	8/6	3/9¼	15/1¼	7/6¾
11/5	2/3½	13/8½	9/1½	2/10¼	14/3¼	8/6¾	3/9¾	15/2¾	7/7¼
11/6	,,	13/9½	9/2½	2/10½	14/4½	8/7½	3/10	15/4	7/8
11/7	2/3¾	13/10¾	9/3¼	2/10¾	14/5¾	8/8¼	3/10¼	15/5¼	7/8¾
11/8	2/4	14/-	9/4	2/11	14/7	8/9	3/10¾	15/6¾	7/9¼
11/9	2/4¼	14/1¼	9/4¾	2/11¼	14/8¼	8/9¾	3/11	15/8	7/10
11/10	2/4½	14/2½	9/5½	2/11½	14/9½	8/10½	3/11¼	15/9¼	7/10¾
11/11	,,	14/3½	9/6½	2/11¾	14/10¾	8/11¼	3/11¾	15/10¾	7/11¼
12/-	2/4¾	14/4¾	9/7¼	3/-	15/-	9/-	4/-	16/-	8/-
12/1	2/5	14/6	9/8	3/0¼	15/1¼	9/0¾	4/0¼	16/1¼	8/0¾
12/2	2/5¼	14/7¼	9/8¾	3/0½	15/2½	9/1½	4/0¾	16/2¾	8/1¼
12/3	2/5½	14/8½	9/9½	3/0¾	15/3¾	9/2¼	4/1	16/4	8/2
12/4	,,	14/9½	9/10½	3/1	15/5	9/3	4/1¼	16/5¼	8/2¾
12/5	2/5¾	14/10¾	9/11¼	3/1¼	15/6¼	9/3¾	4/1¾	16/6¾	8/3¼
12/6	2/6	15/-	10/-	3/1½	15/7½	9/4½	4/2	16/8	8/4
12/9	2/6½	15/3½	10/2½	3/2¼	15/11¼	9/6¾	4/3	17/-	8/6
13/-	2/7¼	15/7¼	10/4¾	3/3	16/3	9/9	4/4	17/4	8/8
13/3	2/7¾	15/10¾	10/7¼	3/3¾	16/6¾	9/11¼	4/5	17/8	8/10
13/6	2/8½	16/2½	10/9½	3/4½	16/10½	10/1½	4/6	18/-	9/-
13/9	2/9	16/6	11/-	3/5¼	17/2¼	10/3¾	4/7	18/4	9/2
14/-	2/9½	16/9½	11/2½	3/6	17/6	10/6	4/8	18/8	9/4
14/3	2/10¼	17/1¼	11/4¾	3/6¾	17/9¾	10/8¼	4/9	19/-	9/6
14/6	2/10¾	17/4¾	11/7¼	3/7½	18/1½	10/10½	4/10	19/4	9/8
14/9	2/11½	17/8½	11/9½	3/8¼	18/5¼	11/0¾	4/11	19/8	9/10
15/-	3/-	18/-	12/-	3/9	18/9	11/3	5/-	20/-	10/-
15/3	3/0½	18/3½	12/2½	3/9¾	19/0¾	11/5¼	5/1	20/4	10/2
15/6	3/1¼	18/7¼	12/4¾	3/10½	19/4½	11/7½	5/2	20/8	10/4
15/9	3/1¾	18/10¾	12/7¼	3/11¼	19/8¼	11/9¾	5/3	21/-	10/6
16/-	3/2½	19/2½	12/9½	4/-	20/-	12/-	5/4	21/4	10/8
16/3	3/3	19/6	13/-	4/0¾	20/3¾	12/2¼	5/5	21/8	10/10
16/6	3/3½	19/9½	13/2½	4/1½	20/7½	12/4½	5/6	22/-	11/-
16/9	3/4¼	20/1¼	13/4¾	4/2¼	20/11¼	12/6¾	5/7	22/4	11/2
17/-	3/4¾	20/4¾	13/7¼	4/3	21/3	12/9	5/8	22/8	11/4
17/3	3/5½	20/8½	13/9½	4/3¾	21/6¾	12/11¼	5/9	23/-	11/6
17/6	3/6	21/-	14/-	4/4½	21/10½	13/1½	5/10	23/4	11/8
17/9	3/6½	21/3½	14/2½	4/5¼	22/2¼	13/3¾	5/11	23/8	11/10
18/-	3/7¼	21/7¼	14/4¾	4/6	22/6	13/6	6/-	24/-	12/-
18/3	3/7¾	21/10¾	14/7¼	4/6¾	22/9¾	13/8¼	6/1	24/4	12/2
18/6	3/8½	22/2½	14/9½	4/7½	23/1½	13/10½	6/2	24/8	12/4
18/9	3/9	22/6	15/-	4/8¼	23/5¼	14/0¾	6/3	25/-	12/6
19/-	3/9½	22/9½	15/2½	4/9	23/9	14/3	6/4	25/4	12/8
19/3	3/10¼	23/1¼	15/4¾	4/9¾	24/0¾	14/5¼	6/5	25/8	12/10
19/6	3/10¾	23/4¾	15/7¼	4/10½	24/4½	14/7½	6/6	26/-	13/-
19/9	3/11½	23/8½	15/9½	4/11¼	24/8¼	14/9¾	6/7	26/4	13/2
20/-	4/-	24/-	16/-	5/-	25/-	15/-	6/8	26/8	13/4

TABLE OF FRACTIONAL PARTS.

The following Tables will be found useful for dividing sums that have to be allocated to different accounts, or for calculating allowances not given in percentages, such as 1-7ths, 1-13ths, 1-25ths, &c.

See the Percentage Tables for the following proportions :—

Half	same as	50%	1-8th same as	12½%	1-40th same as	2½%
1-3rd	,,	33⅓%	1-10th ,,	10%	1-50th ,,	2%
1-4th	,,	25%	1-16th ,,	6¼%	1-80th ,,	1¼%
1-5th	,,	20%	1-20th ,,	5%	1-100th ,,	1
1-6th	,,	16⅔%	1-25th ,,	4%	1-200th ,,	½

Proportions not in Percentage Tables :—

Sum	1-7th	1-9th	1-11th	1-12th	1-13th	1-14th	1-15th	1-17th	1-18th	1-19th
1/-	0s 1¾	0s 1¼	0s 1d	0s 1d	0s 1d	0s 1d	0s 0¾	0s 0¾	0s 0¾	0s 0½
2/-	0 3½	0 2¼	0 2¼	0 2	0 1¾	0 1¾	0 1½	0 1¼	0 1¼	0 1
2/6	0 4¼	0 3¼	0 2¾	0 2½	0 2¼	0 2¼	0 2	0 1¾	0 1¾	0 1½
4/-	0 6¾	0 5¼	0 4½	0 4	0 3¾	0 3½	0 3¼	0 2¾	0 2¾	0 2½
5/-	0 8½	0 6¾	0 5½	0 5	0 4¾	0 4¼	0 4	0 3½	0 3¼	0 3¼
6/-	0 10¼	0 8	0 6½	0 6	0 5½	0 5¼	0 4¾	0 4¼	0 4	0 3¾
7/6	1 0½	0 10	0 8¼	0 7½	0 7	0 6½	0 6	0 5¼	0 5	0 4¾
8/-	1 1¼	0 10¾	0 8¾	0 8	0 7¼	0 6¾	0 6½	0 5¾	0 5½	0 5
10/-	1s 5¼	1s 1¼	0 11d	0 10d	0s 9¼	0s 8¾	0s 8d	0s 7d	0s 6¾	0s 6½
12/-	1 8½	1 4	1 1	1 0	0 11	0 10¼	0 9½	0 8½	0 8	0 7½
12/6	1 9½	1 4¼	1 1¼	1 0½	0 11¼	0 10¾	0 10	0 8¾	0 8¼	0 8
14/-	2 0	1 6¼	1 3¼	1 2	1 1	1 0	0 11¼	0 10	0 9¼	0 9
15/-	2 1¾	1 8	1 4¼	1 3	1 1½	1 0¾	1 0	0 10½	0 10	0 9½
16/-	2 3½	1 9¼	1 5½	1 4	1 2¾	1 1¾	1 0¾	0 11¼	0 10½	0 10
17/6	2 6	1 11¼	1 7	1 5½	1 4¼	1 3	1 2	1 0½	0 11¾	0 11
18/-	2 6¾	2 0	1 7¾	1 6	1 4½	1 3¼	1 2½	1 0¾	1 0	0 11¼
£1	2 10¼	2s 2¼	1s 9½	1s 8d	1s 6½	1s 5¼	1s 4d	1s 2d	1s 1¼	1s 0¾
£2	5 8½	4 5¼	3 7¼	3 4	3 1	2 10¼	2 8	2 4¼	2 2¾	2 1
3	8 6½	6 8	5 5¼	5 0	4 7½	4 3¼	4 0	3 6¼	3 4	3 2
4	11 5¼	8 10½	7 3¼	6 8	6 1¼	5 8½	5 4	4 8¼	4 5¼	4 2¼
5	14 3¼	11 1¼	9 1	8 4	7 8¼	7 1¼	6 8	5 10½	5 6¾	5 3¼
6	17 1¾	13 4	10 11	10 0	9 2¾	8 6¼	8 0	7 0¾	6 8	6 3¾
7	20 0	15 6½	12 8¾	11 8	10 9¼	9 11¼	9 4	8 2¾	7 9¼	7 4½
8	22 10¼	17 9¼	14 6¾	13 4	12 3¾	11 5¼	10 8	9 5	8 10¾	8 5
9	25 8½	20 0	16 4½	15 0	13 10¼	12 10¼	12 0	10 7	10 0	9 5½
£10	28s 6½	22s 2¼	18s 2¼	16s 8d	15s 4½	14s 3¼	13s 4d	11s 9¼	11s 1¼	10s 6¼
£11	31 5¼	24 5¼	20 0	18 4	16 11	15 8¼	14 8	12 11½	12 2¾	11 7
12	34 3¼	26 8	21 9¾	20 0	18 5½	17 1½	16 0	14 1¼	13 4	12 7½
13	37 1¾	28 10¾	23 7¾	21 8	20 0	18 6¾	17 4	15 3½	14 5¼	13 8¼
14	40 0	31 1¼	25 5¼	23 4	21 6¼	20 0	18 8	16 5¾	15 6¾	14 8¾
15	42 10½	33 4	27 3¼	25 0	23 1	21 5¼	20 0	17 7¾	16 8	15 9¼
16	45 8½	35 6¾	29 1	26 8	24 7½	22 10¼	21 4	18 10	17 9¼	16 10
17	48 6¾	37 9¼	30 11	28 4	26 1¾	24 3¼	22 8	20 0	18 10¾	17 10¾
18	51 5¼	40 0	32 8¾	30 0	27 8¼	25 8¼	24 0	21 2	20 0	18 11¼
19	54 3¼	42 2¾	34 6½	31 8	29 2¾	27 1¼	25 4	22 4¼	21 1¼	20 0
£20	57s 1¾	44s 5¼	36s 4¼	33s 4d	30s 9¼	28s 6¼	26s 8d	23s 6½	22s 2¾	21s 0¾
£30	85 8½	66 8	54 6½	50 0	46 1¼	42 10½	40 0	35 3¼	33 4	31 7
40	114 3¼	88 10½	72 8½	66 8	61 6½	57 1¼	53 4	47 0¼	44 5¼	42 1¼
50	142 10½	111 1¼	90 11	83 4	76 11	71 5¼	66 8	58 10	55 6½	52 7¼
60	171 5¼	133 4	109 1	100 0	92 3¼	85 8¼	80 0	70 7	66 8	63 2
70	200 0	155 6½	127 3¼	116 8	107 8¼	100 0	93 4	82 4½	77 9¼	73 8¼
80	228 6¾	177 9¼	145 5½	133 4	123 1	114 3¼	106 8	94 1½	88 10¾	84 2½
90	257 1¾	200 0	163 7¼	150 0	138 5½	128 6½	120 0	105 10½	100 0	94 8½
100	285 8½	222 2¾	181 9¼	166 8	153 10¼	142 10½	133 4	117 7¾	111 1¼	105 3¼
	14⅔%*	11⅛%*	9⅙%*	8⅓%	7⅔%*	7⅟₁₄%*	6⅔%*	5⅞%*	5⁵⁄₉%*	5¼%*

'RAPID' SERIES OF RECKONERS

1. **General Ready Reckoner**, with Discount, Interest, Wages, and other Tables. **1/6**

2. **Discount & Interest Reckoner.** Disct., 44 Rates, $\frac{1}{16}$% to 90%; Interests 1% to 6% (for each day of year at 5%) **1/6**

3. **Cwts. and Lbs. Reckoner.** 1/- to 56/- per Cwt., with every lb., 1 to 112 ; and every Cwt., 1 to 35 **1/6**

4. **'Compact' Paper Reckoner** for Stationers and Printers, with equivalent Sizes and Prices, and Costing Tables **1/6**

5. **Decimal Reckoner.** For Decimal Money; Weights ; or Multiplication or Division to 150 × 100 &c., Special Vol. **1/9**

6. **'Compact' Measuring Reckoner.** Cube or Solid Measure for Timber or Stone . **1/-**

7. **Land and Cattle Reckoner.** Areas × Poles ; Links ; Sq. Yards in Acres, &c. ; Value of Land at per Acre; Weight of Cattle by Measurement . **1/6**

8. **Pocket Pricer ('On Returns')**, giving the profit on cost, but the percentage based on the selling price : (a) $\frac{1}{8}$ths to 2/-, $\frac{1}{8}$ds to 3/-, &c., 5% to 47½% ; (b) 1d. to £500, 1¼% to 60%. Large clear type . **1/6**

10. **Per Ton Reckoner**, by pennies to 91/- per ton. **1/9**

12. **Eason's Thumb Indexed Lightning Calculator** . **1/-**

13. **Steel, Iron, and Metal Reckoner.** Angle, Sheet, Round, Square, Tee, &c. . **1/9**

14. **Total Weight Calculator**, 1 to 500, etc., Articles or Packages each from ¼ lb. to 112 lbs., in Tons, Cwts., Qrs., Lbs. **1/9**

11.	**'Rapid'** 44-Hour Wage Reckoner,		5/- to 60/-		1/6
15.	,, 45-Hour	,,	,,	,,	1/6
16.	,, 46-Hour	,,	,,	5/- to 60/-	1/6
17.	,, 47-Hour	,,	,,	5/- to 64/-	1/6
18.	,, 48-Hour	,,	,,		1/6
19.	,, 49-Hour	,,	,,	5/- to 63/-	1/6
20.	,, 50-Hour	,,	,,	,,	1/6

22. **Harding's Timber Calculator** for volume of Planks **1/6**

24. **'Rapid' Per Dozen Reckoner**, 6d. to 60/- per dozen **1/9**

31. **'Compact' Ready Reckoner.** Special feature every farthing to 10/- . **1/3**

In Paper Covers

23. **Monthly Wages Reckoner** . **1/-**

32. **Foreign Money Supplement** (Rupees Exchange, &c) **1/-**

35. **Tons, Conversion into Lbs.**, every 14 lb to 10 tons **1/-**

36. **Record of Investments** **6d**

37. **Every Number Reckoner**, 1 to 1000, $\frac{1}{8}$ds to 6d. **9d**

— **Live Stock Salesmen's Reckoner**, 19/6 to 76/6 per Cwt. **2/6**

For Books with a greater range of prices and closer intervals, see the 'Express' Reckoner Series :
48 different volumes to suit various trades.
2/- to 3/6 per volume.

If you are in need of a Reckoner for any special purpose, please write to GALL & INGLIS, 12 Newington Road, Edinburgh mentioning what is required.